thermodynamics
and heat power

thermodynamics
and heat power

second edition

irving granet, p.e.
queensborough community college
new york institute of technology

reston publishing company, inc.
 a prentice-hall company
reston, virginia

Library of Congress Cataloging in Publication Data

Granet, Irving.
    Thermodynamics and heat power. 2nd Edition

    Includes bibliographical references and index.
    1. Thermodynamics. 2. Heat engineering. I. Title.
TJ265.G697   1980   621.4'02   79-26158
ISBN 0-8359-7672-6

  Rating of Power-Plant Cycles

  Other Power-Plant Cycles

© 1980 by

Reston Publishing Company, Inc.

A Prentice-Hall Company

Reston, Virginia 22090

10 9 8 7 6 5 4 3 2 1

Printed in the United States of America

preface

In the preface to an earlier introductory text on thermodynamics I noted that, "The subject of Thermodynamics enjoys the unenviable reputation of being one of the most difficult for students to master". Approximately ten years have elapsed since the publication of this earlier text, and in this interval I have been fortunate to have obtained constructive feedback from students, colleagues, and professors who used the book. All of these comments have been carefully considered and incorporated into the present book to obtain a *textbook* suitable for a one-semester course in Thermodynamics and Heat Power. It is hoped that the present text will help the student to master the subject with less difficulty than in the past. For nonmajors, it will provide a completely self-contained coverage, while for those majoring in the field it can serve as the text for a first course.

While this book is completely new, it retains some of the basic proven concepts from the earlier text referred to above as well as from texts that I have written on fluid mechanics and strength of materials. These are as follows:

1 All physical principles are developed as required. For most students who have had an elementary physics course this will serve as a valuable review; for others it will be a logical adjunct development to the main topics.

2 The use of calculus is completely avoided. Instead, the material is developed from first principles. The use of this approach has been tried and proved itself to be a sound learning situation for both student and instructor.

3 The book contains 471 problems of which 132 are illustrative problems that are completely solved as an integral part of the text material. The problems at the end of the chapters are arranged by topic, and answers to even-numbered problems are given in the Appendix. The large number of illustrative problems and answers to even-numbered problems should make the book useful for independent home study courses and as a reference text.

4 It is important for the technically oriented student to see concrete applications of conceptual material. I have accordingly included a large number of illustrations to give the student a better grasp of the physical hardware being studied.

In order to reflect current advances in the science and technology of thermodynamics, material has been included on nuclear power generation, the Wankel rotary combustion engine, and methods of direct energy conversion. For the data on the thermodynamic properties of water, I have used the latest data from the Steam Tables by Keenan, Keyes, Hill, and Moore. Since this material is new and is not generally to be found in other texts, I have extracted portions of these tables with permission of the publisher, John Wiley & Sons, Inc., and included it in the Appendix. Also found in the Appendix is a convenient listing of thermodynamic terms for ready reference. The chapter on heat transfer has been included for completeness for those students who will not take a separate course in heat transfer, as an introduction for a heat transfer course, and for general reference.

I am deeply indebted to my many friends and colleagues at the New York Institute of Technology and Queensborough Community College for the generous time that they have contributed to this effort. The students and instructors who used my earlier text helped to create this book by their constructive suggestions. Professor Stanley M. Brodsky of New York Community College reviewed the completed manuscript, and I am indebted to him for his invaluable critical review. Miss Ruby Ladislav typed the entire manuscript, and her efforts on this book and my earlier books are most gratefully acknowledged.

I find that words cannot express my gratitude to my devoted family for their unselfish support. My wife Arlene and our children, Ellen, Kenny, David, and Jeffrey expressed their love and devotion by their unlimited patience, kindness, and wisdom that enabled me to undertake and complete this book.

Irving Granet

preface
to the second edition

The widespread adoption of the original edition of this text has been most gratifying and has led me to retain most of the arrangement and features of the first edition. During the revision of the text it became necessary to make a decision regarding the adoption of SI units. The generally slow adoption of SI units by the power industry in the United States, as well as the lack of readily available thermodynamic data in the SI system, has dictated the decision to use both the English and SI systems. Equations and problems are developed and presented in both systems, and it is strongly recommended that the student become completely familiar with both systems.

The total number of both Illustrative Problems and exercises for the student has been increased by the addition of 160 problems. These problems are both in SI and English units. The larger number of problems will give the instructor much wider latitude in the selection of assignments. The problems at the ends of the chapters are graded in order of difficulty as well as by topic. As in the original edition, answers are given to even numbered problems in the Appendix.

I am indebted to those users of the book who took the time to make constructive suggestions. I have carefully considered each suggestion and, where feasible, incorporated it in this edition. My colleagues at Queensborough Community College and New York Institute of Technology have been most supportive of me during this undertaking. My wife Arlene's devotion, love, patience, and understanding once again provided the necessary ingredients for the successful completion of this work.

Irving Granet

contents

The following organizations kindly contributed illustrative material.
In alphabetical order they are:

American Chain and Cable Corp.

Babcock and Wilcox Co.

Carrier Corporation

Colt Industries, Fairbanks Morse Power Systems Div.

Combustion Engineering, Inc.

Consolidated Edison Corp.

Curtiss-Wright Corp.

Detroit Stoker Corp.

Fairchild Republic Corp.

Ford Motor Co.

Foster Wheeler Corp.

General Electric Co.

National Pipe Bending Co.

Power

Renwal Co.

Rex Chainbelt Inc., Nordberg Div.

Riley Stoker Corp.

Tubular Exhanger Manufacturers Association

United Aircraft Corp., Pratt & Whitney Div.

Westinghouse Electric Co.

Worthington Corporation

Their contribution and the contribution of many others is gratefully acknowledged.

This book is dedicated to

my beloved wife

Arlene

and my children

Ellen, Kenny, David, and Jeffrey

chapter **1**

fundamental concepts

1.1 INTRODUCTION

Thermodynamics is the study of energy, heat, work, the properties of the media employed, and the processes involved. Since energy can be derived from electrical, chemical, nuclear, or other means, thermodynamics plays an important role in all branches of engineering, physics, chemistry, and the biological sciences.

In defining the word thermodynamics we have used the terms energy and heat and work. It is necessary to examine these terms in detail, and this will be done in subsequent chapters. In this chapter certain fundamental concepts are defined and basic ideas are developed for future use.

1.2 PROPERTIES OF A SYSTEM

In physics, when studying the motion of a rigid body (that is, a body that is not deformed or only slightly deformed by the forces acting on it), extensive use is made of *free-body* diagrams. Briefly, a free-body diagram is an outline of a body (or a portion of a body) showing *all* the external forces acting on it. A free-body diagram is one example of the concept of a system. As a general concept applicable to all situations, we can define a system as a grouping of matter taken in any convenient or arbitrary manner. In addition, a thermodynamic system will invariably have energy transferred from it or to it and can also have energy stored in it. From this definition it will be noted that we are at liberty to choose the grouping, but once having made a choice we must take into account *all* energies involved.

Let us consider a given system and then ask ourselves how we can distinguish changes that occur in the system. It is necessary to have external characteristics which permit us to measure and evaluate system changes. If these external characteristics do not change, we should be able to state that the system has not changed. Some of the external measurements that can be made on a system are temperature, pressure, volume, and position. These observable external characteristics are called *properties*. When all properties of a system are the same at two different times, we can say that we cannot distinguish any difference in the system at these two times. The properties of a system enable us to uncover differences in the system after it has undergone a change. Therefore, the complete description of a system is given by its properties. The condition of the system, that is, its position, energy content, etc., is called *the state of the system*. Thus its properties determine its state. Those properties that depend upon the size and total mass of a system are termed *extensive* properties, that is, they depend upon the extent of the system. An *intensive* property is independent of the size of the system. Pressure and temperature are examples of intensive properties. In addition, there are properties that are known as *specific* properties because they are given per unit mass or per defined mass in the system. Specific properties are intensive properties.

It has already been noted that a given state of a system is reproduced when all its properties are the same. Since a given set of properties determines the state of a system, the state is reproduced regardless of the history or path the system may undergo to achieve the state. For example, consider a weight that is lifted vertically from one position to another. This weight can be brought to the same position by first lifting it vertically part of the way, then moving it horizontally to the right, then lifting it another part of the way, then moving it horizontally to the left, and finally lifting it vertically to the desired point. In this example, the state of the system at the end of the two processes is the same, and the path the system took did not affect its state after the change occurred.

As we shall see in Chapter 2, a consequence of the foregoing is that the change in energy of a system between two given states is the same, regardless of the method of attaining the state. In mathematical terminology, energy is a state function, not a path function.

The properties temperature and pressure are used throughout this text, and it is necessary to have a good understanding of them. The following sections of this chapter deal in detail with these properties.

1.3 TEMPERATURE

The temperature of a system is a measure of the random motion of the molecules of the system. If there are different temperatures within the body (or bodies composing the system), the question arises as to how the temperature at a given location is measured and how this measurement is interpreted. Let us examine this question in detail, since similar questions will also have to be considered when other properties of a system are studied. In air at room pressure and temperature there are approximately 2.7×10^{19} molecules per cubic centimeter. If we divide the cube whose dimensions are one centimeter (1 cm) on a side into smaller cubes, each of whose sides is one thousandth of a centimeter, there will be about 2.7×10^{10} molecules in each of the smaller cubes, still an extraordinarily large number. Although we speak of temperature at a point, we really mean the average temperature of the molecules in the neighborhood of the point.

Let us now consider two volumes of inert gases separated from each other by a third volume of inert gas. By inert we mean that the gases will not react chemically with each other. If the first volume is brought into contact with the second volume and left there until no observable change occurs in any physical property, the two volumes are said to be in *thermal equilibrium*. Should the third volume then be brought in contact with the second and no noticeable change in physical properties is observed, the second and third volumes can also be said to be in thermal equilibrium. For the assumed conditions of this experiment it can be concluded that the three volumes are in thermal equilibrium. Based on this discussion, the three volumes can also be stated to be at the same temperature. This simple experiment can be repeated under the same conditions for solids, liquids, and gases, with the same result every time. The results of all these experiments are summarized and embodied in the *Zeroth Law of Thermodynamics*, which states that two systems having equal temperatures with a third system also have equal temperature with each other. As an alternate definition of the Zeroth Law, we can say that if two bodies are each in thermal equilibrium with a third body, they are in thermal equilibrium with each other. The importance of this apparently obvious statement was recognized after the First Law was given its name, and consequently, it was called the Zeroth Law to denote that it precedes the First Law, just as zero precedes unity. It should be noted that a thermometer measures only its own temperature, and in order that it may be an accurate indication of the temperature of some second system, the thermometer and the second system must be in thermal equilibrium. As a consequence of the Zeroth Law, we can measure the temperatures of two bodies by a third body (a thermometer) without bringing the bodies in contact with each other.

The common scales of temperature are called, respectively, the Fahrenheit and Celsius (centigrade) temperatures and are defined by using the ice point and boiling point of water at atmospheric pressure. In the Celsius temperature scale, the interval between the ice point and the boiling point is divided into 100 equal parts. In addition, as shown in Fig. 1.1, the Celsius ice point is zero and the Fahrenheit ice point is 32. The conversion from one scale to the other is directly derived from Fig. 1.1 and results in the following relations:

$$°C = \tfrac{5}{9}(°F - 32) \qquad\qquad (1.1)$$

$$°F = \tfrac{9}{5}(°C) + 32 \qquad\qquad (1.2)$$

°F	°C	°K	°R	
212	100	373	672	Atmospheric boiling point
32	0	273	492	Ice point
−460	−273	0	0	Absolute zero

Figure 1.1

TABLE 1.1

ELEMENT	MELTING OR BOILING POINT AT 1 ATMOSPHERE	TEMPERATURE	
		°C	°F
Oxygen	Boiling	−182.97	−297.35
Sulfur	Boiling	444.60	832.28
Antimony	Melting	630.50	1166.90
Silver	Melting	960.8	1761.4
Gold	Melting	1063.0	1945.4
Water	Melting	0.	32.
	Boiling	100.	212

The ability to extrapolate to temperatures below the ice point and above the boiling point of water and to interpolate in these regions is provided by the International Scale of Temperature. This agreed-upon standard utilizes the boiling and melting points of different elements and establishes suitable interpolation formulas in the various temperature ranges between these elements. The data for these elements are given in Table 1.1.

ILLUSTRATIVE PROBLEM 1.1

Determine the temperature at which the same value is indicated on both Fahrenheit and Celsius thermometers.

Solution

Using Eq. (1.1) and letting $°C = °F$,

$$°F = \tfrac{5}{9}(°F - 32)$$

$$\tfrac{4}{9}°F = \frac{-160}{9}$$

$$°F = -40$$

Therefore, both Fahrenheit and Celsius temperature scales indicate the same temperature at $-40°$.

By using the results of Illustrative Problem 1.1, it is possible to derive an alternate set of equations to convert from the Fahrenheit to the Celsius temperature scale. When this is done, we obtain

$$°F = \tfrac{9}{5}(40 + °C) - 40 \qquad\qquad (1.3)$$

$$°C = \tfrac{5}{9}(40 + °F) - 40 \qquad\qquad (1.4)$$

The symmetry of Eqs. (1.3) and (1.4) makes them relatively easy to remember and use.

Let us consider the case of a gas that is confined in a cylinder (with a constant cross-sectional area) by a piston that is free to move. If heat is now removed from the system, the piston will move down; but due to its weight it will maintain a constant pressure on the gas. This procedure can be carried out for several gases, and if volume is plotted as a function of temperature, we obtain a family of straight lines that intersect at zero volume (Fig. 1.2a). This unique temperature is known as the absolute zero temperature, and the accepted values on the Fahrenheit and Celsius temperature scales are

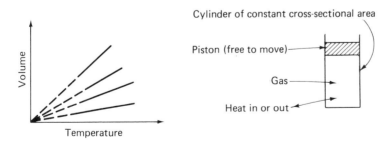

Figure 1.2 Gas thermometer

$-459.69°$ and $-273.16°$, respectively, with the values $-460°$ and $-273°$ used for most engineering calculations. It is also possible to define an absolute temperature scale that is independent of the properties of any substance, and we shall consider this point later in this book.

Thus we define

$$\text{Degrees Rankine} = °R = °F + 460 \qquad (1.5)$$

$$\text{Degrees Kelvin} \ = °K = °C + 273 \qquad (1.6)$$

The relation between degrees Rankine, degrees Fahrenheit, degrees Kelvin, and degrees Celsius is also shown in the table of Fig. 1.1.

As has been noted earlier, the state of a system is uniquely determined by its properties. Thus the accurate measurement of these properties is of great importance from both a theoretical and practical standpoint. Temperatures are measured in many ways, but, in general, all the methods of measuring temperature can be categorized into four classes depending upon the basic physical phenomena used to make the measurement. These classes are as follows:

1 Methods utilizing the expansion of gases, liquids, or solids.

2 Methods utilizing the change in electrical resistance of an element.

3 Methods utilizing the change in electric potential of an element.

4 Methods utilizing the optical changes of a sensor.

The most common device used to measure temperature is the familiar liquid-in-glass thermometer, which consists of a reservoir of liquid and a long glass stem with a fine-line capillary. The operation of this type of thermometer is based upon the coefficient of expansion of the liquid (usually mercury) being greater than the coefficient of expansion of the glass. For accurate measurements, these thermometers are calibrated by either partial, total, or complete immersion in a suitable bath, as shown in Fig. 1.3. If the thermometer is calibrated by one method but is used in a different way, it is necessary to make corrections to the readings for the difference in usage. Advantages of the liquid-in-glass thermometers are low cost, simplicity, good reliability, and long life.

Another device that is used to measure temperature or temperature differences depends upon the expansion of materials and is called the bimetallic element. This element usually consists of two thin flat strips placed side by side and welded together. The composite strip can be used flat or coiled into a helix or spiral. Changes in temperature cause the strip to change its curvature, and the motion produced can be used to move a pointer. The flat bimetallic strip is commonly used in room thermostats, where the motion of one end is used to

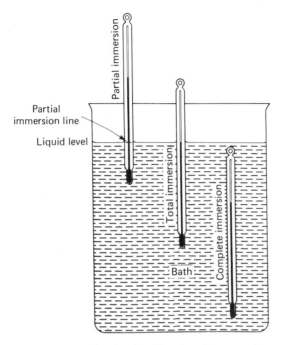

Figure 1.3 Methods of calibrating thermometers

close or open an electrical contact. The action of a bimetallic strip is shown in Fig. 1.4.

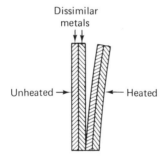

Figure 1.4 Bimetallic strip

Resistance thermometers (Fig. 1.5) are commonly used in industry to measure process temperatures. The basic principle of this type of instrument is that the change in electrical resistance of a sensor due to a change in its temperature is easily measurable. The electrical resistivity of some metals increases very nearly in direct proportion to an increase of temperature. Thus the measured change in resistance of a sensor can be converted to a temperature change. Metals used for the sensors include nickel, copper, and platinum.

Figure 1.5 Industrial resistance thermometer (Courtesy of American Chain and Cable Corp.)

Because of their calibration stability, high temperature coefficient, and moderate cost, nickel resistance units are normally recommended for temperature ranges between $-100°F$ and $+500°F$. The resistance of the sensing element is usually measured by a Wheatstone bridge (shown schematically in Fig. 1.6). When the indicator is nulled to read zero by using the variable resistance r_b,

$$\frac{r_e}{r_b} = \frac{r_1}{r_2} \qquad (1.7)$$

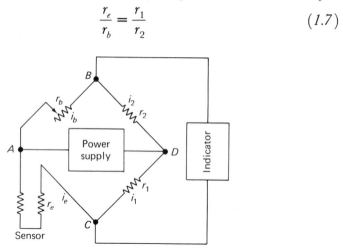

Figure 1.6 Wheatstone bridge

where the various resistances are as shown in Fig. 1.6. Errors in using the Wheatstone bridge make the circuit shown in Fig. 1.6 unsatisfactory for highly accurate work. These errors are due to the contact resistance of the variable resistor, resistance changes in lead wires due to temperature gradients along them, and self-heating of the sensor due to the supply current. Modifications of the basic Wheatstone bridge have been made to compensate for and correct the faults mentioned above. These circuits will be found by the interested student in the references at the end of this chapter.

Thermistors are also included as resistance elements. The name thermistor is derived from *therm*ally sensitive res*istors*, since their resistance varies rapidly with temperature. Thermistors are included in the class of solids known as semiconductors. They have electrical conductivities between those of conductors and insulators. The advantages of the thermistor over the resistance thermometer and the thermocouple (to be discussed later) are as follows:

1 A temperature coefficient of resistance about 10 times that of metals, with a correspondingly greater sensitivity to temperature change.

2 A much higher resistivity than the metals so that small units may have high resistance, virtually eliminating the lead and contact resistance problem.

3 No cold end or lead material compensation is necessary, since the thermistor resistance is a function of its absolute temperature.

For a limited temperature range, the thermistor combines all the best features of resistance thermometers and thermocouples, and has greater sensitivity than either.

When two wires of different materials are joined at their ends and their junctions are at different temperatures, a net thermal electromotive force is generated which induces a net electric current. This is shown schematically in Fig. 1.7a. The thermocouple is used as a thermometer by placing one junction

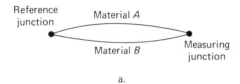

a.

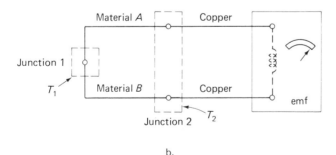

b.

Figure 1.7 Elementary thermocouple circuit*

---

*Figures 1.7b through 1.10 are from *Fundamentals of Temperature, Pressure, and Flow Measurements* by R. P. Benedict, John Wiley & Sons, Inc., New York, 1969, with permission.

in contact with the body whose temperature is to be measured and measuring the voltage produced at the other junction with a millivoltmeter, as shown schematically in Fig. 1.7b. The practical reduction of the thermocouple to use as a temperature-measuring device in industry depends upon three so-called laws:

1 If each section of wire in the circuit is homogeneous, that is, if there is no change in composition or physical properties along its length, then the emf in the circuit depends only on the nature of the metals and the temperatures of the junctions.

2 If both of the junctions involving a particular homogeneous metal are at the same temperature, this metal makes no net contribution to the emf. Thus, if the complete circuit consists of iron, constantan (60 percent copper, 40 percent nickel alloy), and copper, but both of the junctions involving copper are at the same temperature, we can consider the circuit as if it consisted entirely of iron and constantan, with only two junctions.

3 If all junctions of the circuit except one are held at constant temperature, the emf in the circuit will be a function of the temperature of the remaining junction and can be used to measure that temperature. It is customary to prepare tables giving this emf as a function of temperature for the case where the reference junction (or junctions) is held at 0°C (32°F).

Figure 1.7b shows a thermocouple with two *continuous* dissimilar wires from the measuring junction to the reference junction. From the reference junction, copper wires and the potentiometer (or millivoltmeter) complete the

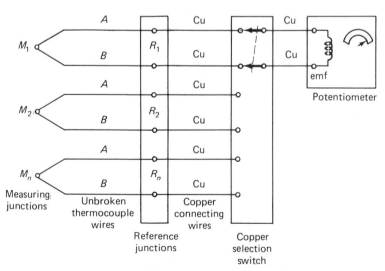

Figure 1.8 Ideal circuit when more than one thermocouple is involved

circuit. For the case of more than one thermocouple to be monitored, a circuit of the type shown in Fig. 1.8 can be used. It is important to note that each thermocouple consists of two continuous wires between the measuring junction and the reference junction. Rather than use a circuit with multiple junctions, it

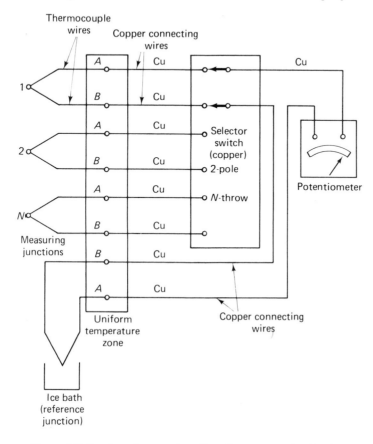

Figure 1.9 Single reference junction–thermocouple circuit

is possible to use the circuit shown in Fig. 1.9, which has a single reference junction. A typical industrial circuit using a potentiometer that is constructed to automatically compensate for the reference junction temperature is shown in Fig. 1.10.

All bodies radiate energy at a rate proportional to the fourth power of their absolute temperature. This is the well-known Stefan–Boltzmann Law (discussed in some detail in Chapter 9). For the moment we will concern ourselves with the optical pyrometer, which provides us with a method of converting this radiation to a temperature measurement. The optical pyrometer, shown schematically in Fig. 1.11, consists of a telescope within which there is mounted a red glass filter and a small light bulb. In practice, the telescope is aimed at the body whose temperature is to be measured. The filament of the

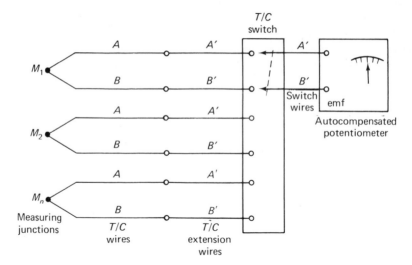

Figure 1.10 Typical industrial thermocouple circuit

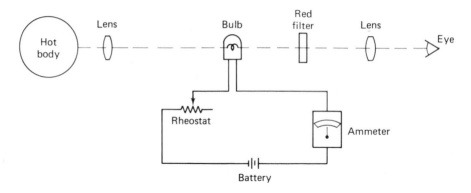

Figure 1.11 Schematic of the optical pyrometer

bulb appears black against the bright background being measured. The current through the bulb is varied by adjusting the rheostat until the brightness of the filament matches the brightness of the body being measured. By prior calibration, the reading of the ammeter is directly convertible to temperature. The advantage of this device is that no part of it is in contact with the body, and the optical pyrometer can be used to measure temperature above the melting points of either resistance thermometers or thermocouples.

A summary of commercially available measuring devices is given in Table 1.2 showing their temperature ranges and characteristics.

TABLE 1.2

SUMMARY OF INFORMATION REGARDING COMMERCIALLY AVAILABLE TEMPERATURE-MEASURING INSTRUMENTS OR SYSTEMS

Kind of instrument	Glass stem (liquid-in-glass)		Bimetal	Filled systems			Thermocouples			
	Mercury	Other liquids		Vapour pressure	Liquid-filled	Gas-filled	Iron/constantan	Chromel/alumel	Copper/constantan	Platinum/platinum-rhodium
Low temp. limit	−38°F(−39°C)	−321°F(−196°C) (pentane)	−100°F(−73°C)	−127°F(−20°K)	−125°F(−87°C)	−452°F(4°K)	about −320°F(−196°C)	about −300°F(−184°C)	−424°F(20°K)	commonly 32°F(0°C)
High temp. limit	1100°F(593°C)	1000°F(538°C)	1000°F(538°C)	600°F(316°C)	1200°F(649°C)	1000°F(538°C)	1400°F(760°C) in oxidizing atm. 1800°F(982°C) in reducing atm. 2000°F(1093°C) spot readings.	2100° to 2300°F(1149° to 1260°C). 2400°F(1316°C) spot readings. (Not to be used in reducing atm.).	660°F(349°C) 930°F(499°C) spot readings.	2600° to 2800°F (1427° to 1538°C) 3216°F(1769°C) spot readings. (Not to be used in reducing atm.).
Remarks	Low price. Reasonable accuracy. Easily broken. Short scale length.		Easier to read than liquid-in-glass. Sometimes damaged by overheating.	Normally has nonlinear scale. Has "cross-ambient" effect. Cheapest of the filled systems.	Can be compensated accurately for ambient temperature variations.	Suitable for wide ranges. Linear scale. Requires large bulb.	*Thermoelectric power, microvolts per degree C* 64 at 760°C — The couple most widely used in industry. Poor reproducibility above 1600°F(871°C).	38 at 1100°C — Chromel is 90 Ni, 10 Cr (chromel P). Alumel is 94 Ni, 3 Mn, 2 Al, 1 Si.	41 at 25°C — Constantan is 57 Cu, 43 Ni	12 at 1200°C (alloy 10% Rh) 14 at 1200°C (alloy 13% Rh) — Expensive

No auxiliary equipment required.

Can give very rapid response, matched only by the radiation and optical pyrometers.

Kind of instrument	Resistance thermometers				Radiation pyrometer	Optical pyrometer	Pyrometric cones	Melting pellets
	Platinum	Copper	Nickel	Thermistors				
Low temp. limit	−300°F(−184°C)	−220°F(−140°C)	−300°F(−184°C)	−76°F(−60°C) (most types)	about room temperature	1400°F(760°C) (normally)	1085°F(585°C)	113°F(45°C)
High temp. limit	1400° to 1800°F (760° to 982°C)	250°F(121°C)	600°F(316°C)	750°F(399°C) (glass coated)	As high as desired	As high as desired	3659°F (2015°C)	2500°F (1371°C)
$(R_{100°C} - R_{0°C})/100\, R_{0°C}$	0.0039	0.0043	0.0066	−0.0098 (one type)	Can operate a recorder and automatic controls.	Cannot operate a recorder or automatic controls.	Indication somewhat affected by heating rate.	
Remarks	May drift at the higher temperatures			High sensitivity. Only fair stability.	Absorbers of radiation, such as windows or dirt, can affect accuracy. Emissivity of source important. Very rapid response.		A single cone or pellet can indicate only its rated temperature, and is normally used only once.	

Give greater accuracy than thermocouples, for the same investment. High sensitivity makes them suitable for narrow-range instruments.

From Temperature, Its Measurement and Control in Science and Industry, edited by Wolfe, ©1955 by Litton Educational Publishing, Inc.; reprinted by permission of Van Nostrand Reinhold Co., New York. Published by Krieger Publishing.

1.4 FORCE AND MASS—UNITS

1.4a The English System

Force is very often defined in elementary physics texts as the push or pull exerted on a body. While this definition serves to satisfy our daily experience, it is not satisfactory when dealing with the motion of bodies that are subjected to resultant forces that are not zero. The following paragraphs of this section will deal with the concept of force in a consistent manner, and we will attempt to clarify the confusion concerning the units of force and mass.

The basis of much of the physical sciences rests on the work of Newton. For the present, two physical laws that are attributed to him will be used:

1 Law of Universal Gravitation.

2 Second Law of Motion.

The first of these, the law of universal gravitation, states simply that the force of attraction experienced by two bodies is proportional to the product of their masses and inversely proportional to the square of the distance (d) separating them. At this point we define the mass of a body as the quantity of matter contained in the body. Thus, if the earth is assumed to be spherical and its mass center is taken to be at its geometrical center, a body on the surface will experience a constant force. This force is given the name *weight*. Since the earth is an oblate spheroid, a body at different locations at the surface will have different weights. Also, the surface of the earth is not smooth, so weight is a function of elevation.

So far it would appear that the foregoing concepts are both clear and relatively simple. In its simplest form it can be stated that the weight of a body, in a given location, is proportional to its mass. By choosing the constant of proportionality to be unity, the mass of an object in pounds at the earth's surface may, for most practical purposes, be assumed to be numerically equal to the weight of the body. The difficulty arises from the fact that force can also be defined by Newton's second law of motion in terms of the fundamental units of length, time, and mass. This relation can be stated as follows:

$$F \propto ma \qquad (1.8)$$

where a is the acceleration of the body. This proportionality can be written more explicitly by defining a force of 1 lb as that force necessary to give a mass of 1 lb an acceleration of 32.17 ft/sec². Equation (1.8) becomes

$$F = \frac{ma}{g_c} \qquad (1.9)$$

where g_c is numerically equal to 32.17. It is in this constant of proportionality, g_c, that the confusion occurs, as well as the ambiguous use of the word pound. Table 1.3 lists some of the most common combinations of units that can be

TABLE 1.3

LENGTH	*TIME*	*MASS*	*FORCE*	g_c
Feet	Second	Pound	Pound	32.17 ft/sec^2 $\times$ pound mass/pound force
Feet	Hour	Pound	Pound	$4.17 \times 10^8 \text{ ft/hr}^2$ $\times$ pound mass/pound force
Feet	Second	Pound	Poundal	$1.0 \text{ ft/sec}^2 \times$ pound mass/poundal
Feet	Second	Slug	Pound	$1.0 \text{ ft/sec}^2 \times$ slug/pound force
Centimeter	Second	Gram	Dyne	$1.0 \text{ cm/sec}^2 \times$ gram/dyne
Metre	Second	Kilogram	Newton	$1.0 \text{ metre/sec}^2 \times$ kilogram/newton
Metre	Second	Kilogram	Kilogram	9.81 metre/sec^2 $\times$ kilogram mass/kilogram force
Metre	Second	Gram	Gram	981 cm/sec^2 $\times$ gram mass/gram force

used. To avoid the obvious confusion that this multitude of units can cause, the definition of pound mass and pound weight, as given in this section, is applied in conjunction with Eq. (1.8) throughout this book. As a consequence of these considerations, weight and mass, at a location in which the local gravitational attraction is expressed as g, can be interrelated in the following manner:

$$W = \frac{mg}{g_c} \qquad\qquad (1.10)$$

We also note that mass can be operationally defined as the inertia a body has in resisting acceleration.

ILLUSTRATIVE PROBLEM 1.2

A mass of 1 lb weighs 1 lb on the earth. How much will it weigh on the moon? Assume that the diameter of the moon is 0.273 when the earth's diameter is taken to be unity, and the mass of the moon is 0.0123 in relation to the earth's mass.

Solution

The force exerted on the mass by the moon will determine its "weight" on the moon. In general, the Law of Universal Gravitation can be written as

$$F = K \frac{m_1 m_2}{d^2}$$

where K is a proportionality constant. Using the subscripts e for earth and m for moon,

$$F_e = \frac{K m_e m}{(r_e)^2}$$

since r_e, the radius of the earth, is the distance separating the mass center of the body m on the earth and the mass center of the earth. Similarly,

$$F_m = \frac{K m_m m}{(r_m)^2}$$

$$\frac{F_e}{F_m} = \left(\frac{m_e}{m_m} \right) \left(\frac{r_m}{r_e} \right)^2 = \frac{1}{0.0123} (0.273)^2 = 6.0$$

Thus a body on earth feels a force (weight) approximately six times the force it would feel on the moon. The solution to the problem is that a mass of 1 lb will weigh approximately $\frac{1}{6}$ lb on the moon.

1.4b The SI System

For the engineer, the greatest confusion has been the units for mass and weight. As we have noted, the literature abounds with units such as slugs, pounds, mass, pound force, poundal, kilogram force, kilogram mass, dyne, and so on. In the SI system, the base unit for *mass* (not weight or force) is the kilogram (kg), which is equal to the mass of the international standard kilogram located at the International Bureau of Weights and Measures. It is used to specify the quantity of matter in a body. The mass of a body never varies, and it is independent of gravitational force.

The SI *derived* unit for force is the newton (N). The unit of force is defined from Newton's Law of Motion: force is equal to mass times acceleration ($F = ma$). Thus, by this definition, one newton applied to a mass of one kilogram gives the mass an acceleration of one metre per second squared ($N = kg \cdot m/s^2$). The newton is used in all combinations of units that include force, for example, pressure or stress (N/m^2), energy ($N \cdot m$), and power

$(N \cdot m/s = W)$. By this procedure, the unit of force is not related to gravity as was the older kilogram-force.

Table 1.4 gives the seven base units of the SI system. Several observations concerning this table should be noted. *The unit of length is the metre (not meter), and the kilogram is a unit of mass, not weight.* Also, symbols are never pluralized, never written with a period, and uppercase and lowercase symbols *must* be used as shown *without exception*.

TABLE 1.4
BASE SI UNITS

QUANTITY	NAME OF BASE SI UNIT	SYMBOL
length	metre	m
mass	kilogram	kg
time	second	s
electric current	ampere	A
thermodynamic temperature	kelvin	K
amount of substance	mole	mol
luminous intensity	candela	cd

Table 1.5 gives the derived units with and without symbols often used in engineering. These derived units are formed by the algebraic combination of base and supplementary units. Note that where the name is derived from a person the first letter of the symbol appears as a capital; for example, newton is N. Otherwise, the convention is to make the symbol lowercase.

Weight has been defined as a measure of gravitational force acting on a material object at a specified location. Thus weight is a force which has both a mass component and an acceleration component (gravity). Gravitational forces vary by about 0.5 percent over the earth's surface. For nonprecision measurements, these variations normally can be ignored. Thus a constant mass has an approximate constant weight on the surface of the earth. The agreed standard value (standard acceleration) of gravity is $9.806\ 650\ m/s^2$. Figure 1.12 illustrates the difference between mass (kilogram) and force (newton.)

The term mass or unit mass should only be used to indicate the quantity of matter in an object, and the old practice of using weight in such cases should be avoided in engineering and scientific practice. However, since the determination of an object's mass will be accomplished by the use of a weighing process, the common usage of the term weight instead of mass is expected to continue, but should be avoided.

Based on the foregoing, Eq. (1.10) can be written in SI units as

$$W = mg \qquad\qquad (1.10a)$$

TABLE 1.5
DERIVED SI UNITS

QUANTITY	NAME	SYMBOL	FORMULA	EXPRESSED IN TERMS OF BASE UNITS
acceleration	acceleration	m/s^2	m/s^2	m/s^2
area	square metre	m^2	m^2	m^2
density	kilogram per cubic metre	—	kg/m^3	$kg \cdot m^{-3}$
energy or work	joule	J	$N \cdot m$	$m^2 \cdot kg \cdot s^{-2}$
force	newton	N	$m \cdot kg \cdot s^{-2}$	$m \cdot kg \cdot s^{-2}$
length	metre	m	m	m
mass	kilogram	kg	kg	kg
moment	newton-metre	$N \cdot m$	$N \cdot m$	$m^2 \cdot kg \cdot s^{-2}$
moment of inertia of area	—	m^4	m^4	m^4
plane angle	radian	rad	rad	rad
power	watt	W	J/s	$m^2 \cdot kg \cdot s^{-3}$
pressure or stress	pascal	Pa	N/m^2	$N \cdot m^{-2}$
rotational frequency	revolutions per second	rev per sec	s^{-1}	s^{-1}
temperature	degree celsius	°C	°C	$1°C = 1 K$
time	second	s	s	s
torque (see moment)	newton-metre	$N \cdot m$	$N \cdot m$	$m^2 \cdot kg \cdot s^{-2}$
velocity (speed)	metre per second	metre per sec	m/s	$m \cdot s^{-1}$
volume	cubic metre	—	m^3	m^3

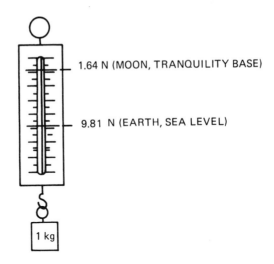

1.64 N (MOON, TRANQUILITY BASE)

9.81 N (EARTH, SEA LEVEL)

1 kg

Figure 1.12 Mass and force

ILLUSTRATIVE PROBLEM 1.3

A body has a mass of 10 kg. If the local gravitational acceleration is 9.5 ms^{-2} determine (a) its weight, and (b) its horizontal acceleration if it is acted upon by a 10 N horizontal force.

Solution

(a) From Eq. (1.10a),

$$W = (10 \text{ kg})\left(9.5 \frac{\text{m}}{\text{s}^2}\right) = 95.0 \frac{\text{kg} \cdot \text{m}}{\text{s}^2} = 95.0 \text{ N}$$

(b) Since $F = ma$, $a = F/m$. Therefore,

$$a = \frac{10 \dfrac{\text{kg} \cdot \text{m}}{\text{s}^2}}{10 \text{ kg}} = 1 \frac{\text{m}}{\text{s}^2}$$

In order for the SI system to be universally understood, it is most important that the symbols for the SI units and the conventions governing their use be strictly adhered to. Care should be taken to use the correct case for symbols, units, and their multiples (for example, K for kelvin, k for kilo, m for milli, M for mega.) As noted earlier, unit names are never capitalized except at the beginning of a sentence. SI unit symbols derived from proper names are written with the first letter in uppercase; all other symbols are written in lowercase, for example, m (metre), s (second), K (kelvin), Wb (weber). Also, unit names form their plurals in the usual manner. Unit symbols are always written in singular form, for example, 350 megapascals or 350 MPa; 50 milligrams or 50 mg. Since the unit symbols are standardized, the symbols should always be used in preference to the unit names. An exception is made when a number written out in words precedes the unit, for example, seven metres, not seven m. Unit symbols are not followed by a period unless they occur at the end of a sentence, and the numerical value associated with a symbol should be separated from that symbol by a space, for example, 1.81 mm, not 1.81mm. The period is only used as a decimal marker. Since the comma is used by some countries as a decimal marker, the SI system does not use the comma. A space is used to separate large numbers in groups of three. Thus 3 807 747 and 0.030 704 254 indicate this type of grouping. Notice that for numerical values less than one the decimal point is preceded by a zero. For a number of four digits, the space can be omitted.

In addition, certain style rules should also be adhered to:

1 When a product is to be indicated, use a space between unit names (for example newton metre).

2 When a quotient is indicated use the word "per" (for example, metre per second).

3 When a product is indicated use the square, cubic, and so on (for example, square metre).

4 In designating the product of units use a centered dot (for example, $N \cdot s$, $kg \cdot m$).

5 For quotients, use a solidus (/) or a negative exponent (for example, m/s or $m \cdot s^{-1}$). The solidus (/) should not be repeated in the same expression unless ambiguity is avoided by parentheses. Thus one should use m/s^2 or $m \cdot s^{-2}$, but not $m/s/s$; also, use $m \cdot kg/(s^3 \cdot A)$ or $m \cdot kg \cdot s^{-3} \cdot A^{-1}$, but not $m \cdot kg/s^3/A$.

One of the most useful features of the older metric system and the current SI system is that multiples and submultiples of units are in terms of factors of 10. Thus the prefixes given in Table 1.6 are used in conjunction with SI units to form names and symbols of multiples of SI units. Certain general rules apply to the use of these prefixes:

1 The prefix becomes part of the name or symbol without separation (for example, kilometre, megagram).

2 Compound prefixes should not be used: use GPa, not kMPa.

3 In calculations, use powers of 10 in place of prefixes.

4 Try to select a prefix so that the numerical value will fall between 0.1 and 1000. This rule may be disregarded when it is better to use the

TABLE 1.6
FACTORS OF 10 FOR SI UNITS

PREFIX	*SYMBOL*		*FACTOR*
tera	T	10^{12}	1 000 000 000 000
giga	G	10^{9}	1 000 000 000
mega	M	10^{6}	1 000 000
kilo	k	10^{3}	1 000
hecto	h	10^{2}	100
deka	da	10^{1}	10
deci	d	10^{-1}	0.1
centi	c	10^{-2}	0.01
milli	m	10^{-3}	0.001
micro	μ	10^{-6}	0.000 001
nano	n	10^{-9}	0.000 000 001
pico	p	10^{-12}	0.000 000 000 001
femto	f	10^{-15}	0.000 000 000 000 001
atto	a	10^{-18}	0.000 000 000 000 000 001

same multiple for all items. It is also recommended that prefixes representing 10 raised to a power which is a multiple of 3 be used (for example, 100 mg, not 10 cg).

5 The prefix is combined with the unit to form a new unit which can be provided with a positive or negative exponent. Therefore, mm^3 is $(10^{-3} m)^3$ or 10^{-9} m^3.

6 Where possible, avoid the use of prefixes in the denominator of compound units. The exception to this rule is the prefix k in the base unit kg (kilogram).

There are certain units outside the SI which may be used together with the SI units and their multiples. These are recognized by the International Committee for Weights and Measures as having to be retained because of their practical importance.

It is almost universally agreed that when a new language is to be learned the student should be completely immersed and made to "think" in the new language. This technique has been proved most effective by the Berlitz language schools and the Ulpan method of language teaching. A classical joke about this is of the American traveling in Europe who was amazed that two-year-old children were able to speak "foreign" languages. In dealing with the SI system, the student should not think in terms of customary units and then perform a mental conversion. It is better to learn to think in terms of the SI system, which will then become a second language. However, there will be times when it may be necessary to convert from customary U.S. units to SI units. In order to facilitate such conversions, Table 1.7 gives some commonly used conversion factors.

TABLE 1.7

CONVERSIONS FROM CONVENTIONAL TO SI UNITS

MULTIPLY	*BY*	*TO OBTAIN*
atmospheres	2.992×10^1	inches mercury (32°F)
atmospheres	1.033×10^4	kilogram/square metre
atmospheres (760 torr)	1.013×10^2	kilopascals
bars	9.869×10^{-1}	atmospheres
bars	1.000×10^2	kilopascals
British thermal units (Btu)	3.927×10^{-4}	horsepower-hours
British thermal units (Btu)	1.056	kilojoules
British thermal units (Btu)	2.928×10^{-4}	kilowatt-hours
British thermal units (Btu)	1.221×10^{-8}	megawatt-days
Btu/hour-square foot	3.153×10^{-4}	Watts/square centimeter
Btu/hour-square foot-°F	5.676×10^{-4}	Watts/square centimeter-degree Celsius
Btu/minute	2.356×10^{-2}	horsepower
Btu/minute	1.757×10^1	Watts
calories	4.190	Joules
cubic feet	2.832×10^{-2}	cubic metres
cubic feet	2.832×10^1	litres
cubic feet/minute	4.720×10^{-4}	cubic metres/second
cubic metres	8.107×10^{-4}	acre-feet
cubic metres	3.531×10^1	cubic feet
cubic metres	2.642×10^2	gallons (US)
cubic metres/second	2.119×10^3	cubic feet/minute
cubic metres/second	1.585×10^4	gallons/minute
degrees Celsius	$(9/5)C + 32$	degrees Fahrenheit
degrees Fahrenheit	$5/9(F - 32)$	degrees Celsius
feet	3.048×10^{-1}	metres
feet of H_2O (39.2°F)	3.048×10^2	kilogram/square metre
feet of H_2O (39.2°F)	4.335×10^{-1}	pounds/square inch
feet/second	3.048×10^{-1}	metres/second
foot-pound (force)	1.356	Joules
foot-pounds (force)/minute	2.260×10^{-2}	Watts

TABLE 1.7(Cont'd)

MULTIPLY	*BY*	*TO OBTAIN*
gallons	3.785×10^{-3}	cubic metres
gallons/minute	6.309×10^{-5}	cubic metres/second
horsepower	4.244×10^{1}	British thermal units/minute
horsepower	7.457×10^{-1}	kilowatts
horsepower-hours	2.547×10^{3}	British thermal units
horsepower-hours	7.457×10^{-1}	kilowatt-hours
inches of H_2O (39.2°F)	2.491×10^{-1}	kilopascals
inches mercury (32°F)	3.342×10^{-2}	atmospheres
inches mercury (32°F)	3.453×10^{2}	kilograms/square metre
inches mercury (32°F)	3.386	kilopascals
inches mercury (32°F)	4.912×10^{-1}	pounds/square inch
Joules	7.376×10^{-1}	foot-pounds (force)
Joules	1.000	Watt-seconds
Joules	2.387×10^{-1}	calories
kilograms	2.205	pounds
kilograms	1.102×10^{-3}	tons (short)
kilograms/cubic metre	6.243×10^{-2}	pounds/cubic foot
kilograms/square metre	9.678×10^{-5}	atmospheres
kilograms/square metre	3.281×10^{-3}	feet of H_2O (at 39.2°F)
kilograms/square metre	2.896×10^{-3}	inches mercury (32°F)
kilograms/square metre	1.422×10^{-3}	pounds/square inch
kilojoules	9.471×10^{-1}	British thermal units
kilopascals	4.015	inches H_2O (at 39.2°F)
kilopascals	1.450×10^{-1}	pounds (force)/square inch
kilopascals	2.953×10^{-1}	inches mercury (32°F)
kilopascals	1.000×10^{-2}	bars
kilopascals	9.869×10^{-3}	atmospheres (760 torr)
kilowatts	1.341	horsepower
kilowatt-hours	3.413×10^{3}	British thermal units
kilowatt-hours	1.341	horsepower-hours
kilowatt-hours	4.167×10^{-5}	megawatt-days
litres	3.531×10^{-2}	cubic feet
megawatt-days	8.189×10^{7}	British thermal units
megawatt-days	2.400×10^{4}	kilowatt-hours
metres	3.281	feet

TABLE 1.7(Cont'd)

MULTIPLY	*BY*	*TO OBTAIN*
Newtons	2.248×10^{-1}	pounds (force)
pounds	4.536×10^{-1}	kilograms
pounds (force)	4.448	Newtons
pounds/cubic feet	1.602×10^{1}	kilograms/cubic meter
pounds/square inch	2.307	feet of H_2O (at 39.2°F)
pounds/square inch	2.036	inches mercury (32°F)
pounds/square inch	7.031×10^{2}	kilograms/square metre
pounds/square inch	6.895	kilopascals
square feet	9.290×10^{-2}	square metres
square metres	2.471×10^{-4}	acres
square metres	1.076×10^{1}	square feet
tonnes	2.205×10^{3}	pounds
tons (short)	9.072×10^{2}	kilograms
Watts	5.688×10^{-2}	Btu/minute
Watts	4.427×10^{1}	foot-pounds (force)/minute
Watt-seconds	1.000	Joules
Watts-square centimeter	3.171×10^{3}	Btu/hour-square foot
Watts/square centimeter-°C	1.762×10^{3}	Btu/hour-square foot-°F

1.5 ELEMENTARY KINETIC THEORY OF GASES

The following derivation, based on elementary kinetic gas theory, is very useful and will serve at a later time to introduce the theory of *ideal* or *perfect* gases.

Imagine a cube, as shown in Fig. 1.13, with sides l. In this volume it will be assumed that there are n identical molecules (particles) each having a mass m. These particles are further assumed to be perfectly elastic spheres each traveling with the same velocity. By perfectly elastic, it is implied that the collision of a molecule with another molecule or the walls of the container causes the molecule to rebound without loss of energy or momentum. The size of the molecule will be taken to be negligibly small compared to dimensions of the system. If the velocity in the x direction is essentially constant over the length l and is denoted by V_x, the molecule shown in Fig. 1.13 will travel a distance equal numerically to V_x in a unit time. In this same time the molecule will collide elastically with the walls (parallel to the y-z plane) a number of

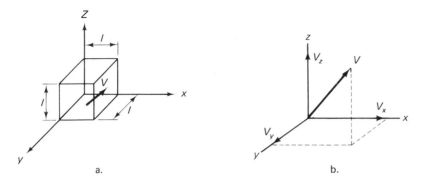

Figure 1.13

times equal to V_x divided by l. This last statement has considered only the x-directed velocity of the molecule. It is also assumed that the molecules do not collide with each other.

At this point it will be necessary to involve the concepts of impulse and momentum for a rigid particle that has only translatory motion. On the basis of Newton's laws of motion for such a particle, it is possible to write Eq. (1.9) as follows:

$$F = \frac{ma}{g_c} = \frac{m(\Delta V)}{g_c(\Delta t)}, \qquad F(\Delta t) = \frac{m\Delta V}{g_c} \qquad (1.11)$$

(Equation 1.11 is written in English units)

The symbol Δt is used to indicate a small interval of time, and ΔV is the change in velocity during this time interval. The term $F(\Delta t)$ is known as the *impulse* imparted to the particle by the force F acting for the time Δt and the term $(m\Delta V/g_c)$ is called the *momentum change* the particle undergoes during this same time interval.

Let us consider the collision of a particle with a wall. As shown in Fig. 1.14, the particle travels in the x direction with a velocity V_x prior to striking the wall. Since the particle has been assumed to be perfectly elastic, it will collide with the wall and rebound with a speed equal to V_x, but it will be

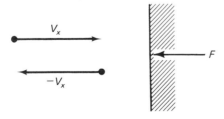

Figure 1.14 Particle collision with wall

traveling in a direction opposite to its initial direction. Thus its velocity will be $-V_x$. The wall is stationary, and as a result of the impact a reactive force F is set up. Since the molecule has a momentum equal to mV_x/g_c just before colliding with the wall and a momentum of $-mV_x/g_c$ after the collision, the change in momentum per molecule will be $2mV_x/g_c$. As stated earlier, the number of collisions with the walls in a unit time will be V_x/l, and we must consider that the n identical particles each undergo the same collision with the walls. The total number of collisions will therefore be nV_x/l.

Multiplying the total number of impacts per unit of time by the momentum change per impact yields the total change of momentum per unit of time for the system:

$$\frac{2mV_x}{g_c}\left[\frac{nV_x}{l}\right] \qquad (1.12)$$

Equation (1.12) also expresses the *force* exerted on the wall. *Pressure* is the normal force exerted per unit surface area. For present purposes it will be reasonable to assume that the force expressed by Eq. (1.12) is distributed uniformly over the y-z planes. Since these consist of two faces, each l^2 in area, the pressure exerted on the y-z plane is

$$\frac{\dfrac{2mV_x}{g_c}\left[\dfrac{nV_x}{l}\right]}{2l^2} = \frac{mnV_x^2}{g_c l^3} \qquad (1.13)$$

However, it was previously assumed that the molecule had the same velocity in each of the three component directions. Therefore, in the unit time interval under consideration there is an equal probability that the particle will hit one of the three sets of parallel faces composing the cube. If this were not so, there would be unequal pressures on the various faces of the cube. Since the volume of the cube (V) equals l^3, Eq. (1.14) follows from Eqs. (1.11) and (1.13) combined:

$$pV = \left(\frac{1}{3}\right)\left(\frac{mnV_x^2}{g_c}\right) \qquad (1.14)$$

or
$$pV = \left(\frac{1}{3}\right)(mnV_x^2) \quad \text{(SI)} \qquad (1.14a)$$

Equation (1.14) is used repeatedly later (in slightly different form) and has special significance. However, for the present, only certain limited conclusions will be deduced from it. It should be remembered that this equation was derived on the basis of certain simplifying and, therefore, restrictive assumptions. In addition to the assumptions stated, it is important to note that the rotations and vibrations of the molecule have been neglected. Also, molecule collisions with other molecules have been ignored. This corresponds to assuming that the dimensions of the unit cube are small compared to the mean free path of the gas particles, that is, the distance molecules travel between molecule–molecule collisions. Although these assumptions and others inherent to this derivation lead to varying degrees of deviation of real gases from Eq. (1.14), it is amazing that this equation can be used with a reasonable degree of accuracy for engineering purposes to describe the behavior of many gases over a wide range of conditions.

On the basis of experimental and theoretical investigations by Joule and others, it can be shown that for ideal gases the pressure of these gases increases equally for equal temperature increments. This is equivalent to stating that the product mV_x^2 is a constant for all gases at a given temperature. As a consequence of this conclusion, Eq. (1.14) yields Avogadro's law, which states that equal volumes of gases at the same temperature and pressure contain the same number of molecules (particles). It is also possible to deduce another concept from Eq. (1.14), specifically, *density*. The product mn found in the numerator of Eq. (1.14) is the total mass of the molecules in the volume under consideration. The total mass divided by the total volume yields the property of *density* (ρ). The reciprocal of density is called *specific volume*. It is the total volume that a unit mass occupies under a given set of conditions. It is denoted by v.

We summarize some of the conclusions of the foregoing analysis: The first three conclusions are limited to gases and the last three are general definitions.

1 Pressure (which is defined as the normal force per unit area) results from the collisions of the molecules with the walls of the container and is a function of the number of impacts per unit time, the mass of the particle, and the velocity of the particle.

2 Avogadro's law states that equal volumes of gases at the same pressure and temperature contain the same number of particles.

3 Temperature can be taken to be a measure of the translational energy of the particles. In a more general sense, it can be said to be a measure of the molecular activity (and internal energy) of the gases.

4 Density is defined as the mass per unit volume (ρ).

5 The reciprocal of density is the volume per unit mass and is called specific volume (v).

6 Specific weight (γ) is defined as the weight per unit volume. Note that this term, which equals $\rho g / g_c$ does not exist in SI as a basic unit.

1.6 PRESSURE

We have seen that, when a gas is confined in a container, molecules of the gas strike the sides of the container, and these collisions with the walls of the container cause the molecules of the gas to exert a force on the walls. When the component of the force that is perpendicular (normal) to the wall is divided by the area of the wall, the resulting normal force per unit area is called the *pressure*. To define the pressure at a point, it is necessary to consider the area in question to be shrinking steadily. Pressure at a point is defined to be the normal force per unit area in the limit as the area goes to zero. Mathematically,

$$p = \left(\frac{\Delta F}{\Delta A} \right)_{\lim(\Delta A \Rightarrow 0)} \qquad (1.15)$$

In common engineering units, pressure is expressed as pounds force per square inch or pounds force per square foot, which are usually abbreviated as psi or psf. In SI units, pressure is expressed in N/m^2, which is known as the pascal (Pa). The *bar* is 10^5 Pa. While these units are most frequently found in the literature, certain others are also used because of the manner in which the pressure measurements are made.

Most mechanical pressure gages, such as the Bourdon gage (Fig. 1.29), measure the pressure above local atmospheric pressure. This pressure is called gage pressure and is measured in units of pounds force per square foot or

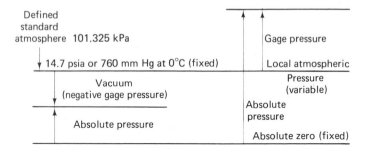

Figure 1.15

pounds force per square inch, that is, psfg or psig. The relation of gage pressure to absolute pressure is shown in Fig. 1.15 and is

$$\text{Absolute pressure} = \text{Atmospheric pressure} + \text{Gage pressure} \qquad (1.16)$$

Absolute pressure is indicated as psia or psfa. It is usual to take the pressure of the atmosphere as being equal to 14.7 psia. However, in Europe 1 "ata" has been defined and is used as 1 kg/cm^2 for convenience, but this unit is not 14.7

psia; it is more nearly 14.2 psia. Care should be exercised when using the unit of pressure that is expressed as ata. In SI the equivalent of 14.696 (14.7) psia is 101.325 kPa. The terms gage and vacuum are not used in SI since all pressures are absolute in this system.

Referring again to Fig. 1.15, it will be noted that pressure below atmospheric pressure is called vacuum. By reference to this figure we obtain the relation between absolute pressure and vacuum as

$$\text{Absolute pressure} = \text{Atmospheric pressure} - \text{Vacuum}$$
$$(1.17)$$

ILLUSTRATIVE PROBLEM 1.4

Assume that a fluid whose specific weight is constant and equal to γ lb/ft^3 is placed in a uniform tube until its height in the tube is h feet above the base of the column. Determine the pressure at the base of the column.

Solution

Consider a disk-shaped element of fluid located a distance x from the base (or reference plane). The height of the column will be measured as positive in the vertical direction, as shown in Fig. 1.16. The height of the disk will be Δx, and

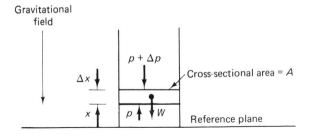

Figure 1.16 Liquid-column analysis

its cross-sectional area will be denoted as A. On the top of the disk there will be assumed to be a pressure $p + \Delta p$, where Δp is a small negative pressure increment. On the bottom of the disk it will be assumed that the pressure is slightly greater than this by an amount Δp. Thus, on the bottom face of the disk the pressure is p. The weight of fluid is the volume of the disk $(\Delta x)A$ multiplied by the specific weight γ. Therefore, acting vertically down, we have the forces $(p + \Delta p)A + (A)(\Delta x\gamma)$, and acting vertically up the force is pA. Equating forces in the vertical direction to obtain the necessary condition of equilibrium yields

$$pA = (p + \Delta p)A + A(\Delta x)\gamma \qquad (1.18)$$

Simplifying Eq. (1.18) gives the result

$$\frac{\Delta p}{\Delta x} = -\gamma = -\frac{\rho g}{g_c} \qquad (1.19)$$

or

$$\frac{\Delta p}{\Delta x} = -\rho g \quad (\text{SI}) \qquad (1.19a)$$

therefore

$$p = \gamma h = \frac{\rho g}{g_c} h \qquad (1.19b)$$

or

$$p = \rho g h \ (\text{SI}) \qquad (1.19c)$$

at the base of the column.

Equation (1.19) can be interpreted by referring to Fig. 1.17, which is a plot of pressure against height. As can be seen, γ is simply the constant negative slope. From Fig. 1.17 we can directly write

$$p = p_a + \gamma h - \gamma x = p_a + \gamma(h - x) \qquad (1.20)$$

or

$$p = p_a + \rho g(h - x) \quad (\text{SI}) \qquad (1.20a)$$

where p_a is the pressure at the free surface on top of the column.

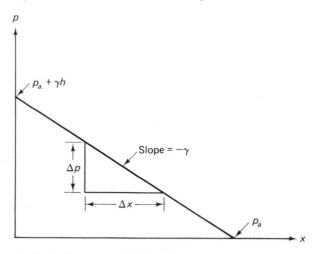

Figure 1.17 The *p-x* relation for a column of liquid

Equation (1.19) or (1.19a) is the fundamental relation between pressure, specific weight, and column height. The negative sign indicates that the pressure decreases as one goes up the column. Note that the pressure in a column can be specified by stating an amount of feet of a fluid of a given specific weight.

The most common fluid used to measure pressure differences, atmospheric pressure, and vacuum pressure is mercury. At approximately room temperature, the specific weight of mercury is very nearly 13.6 g/cm^3. It will usually be assumed that the specific weight of mercury is 13.6 g/cm^3 unless otherwise stated. The effect of temperature on the specific weight of mercury is given in Fig. 1.18.

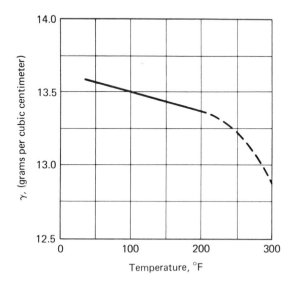

Figure 1.18 Specific weight of mercury

ILLUSTRATIVE PROBLEM 1.5

A tube of glass open at the top has a 1-in. level of mercury in it. Take the specific weight of mercury (Hg) to be 13.6 g/cm^3 and determine the pressure on the base of the column.

Solution

To solve this problem, let us first convert the unit of weight of grams per cubic centimeter to pounds per cubic foot. In 1 lb there are approximately 454 g. Also, there are 2.54 cm in 1 in. Thus 1 g is 1/454 lb, and 1 ft has 12×2.54 cm. To convert one gram per cubic centimeter to pounds per cubic foot we apply the following dimensional reasoning:

$$\frac{g}{cm^3} \times \frac{lb}{g} \times \frac{cm^3}{ft^3} = \frac{lb}{ft^3} = \gamma$$

Continuing,

$$\frac{1\ g}{cm^3} \times \frac{1}{454}\frac{lb}{g} \times (2.54\times12)^3\frac{cm^3}{ft^3} = \frac{62.4\ lb}{ft^3} = \gamma$$

The conversion factor from grams per cubic centimeter to pounds per cubic foot is thus 62.4. The student is strongly urged to check all computations for dimensional consistency when doing problems.

Applying Eq. (1.19),

$$p = \left(\tfrac{1}{12}\ ft\right)(13.6\times62.4)\frac{lb}{ft^3} = \frac{lb}{ft^2}$$

In pounds force per square inch,

$$p\frac{lb}{ft^2} \times \frac{ft^2}{in^2} \times \frac{1}{144} = psi$$

Therefore,

$$p = \frac{1}{12} \times 13.6\times62.4\times \frac{1}{144}\frac{ft^2}{in^2} = 0.491\ psi$$

This is a gage pressure. If the local atmospheric pressure is 14.7 psia,

$$p = 0.491 + 14.7 = 15.19\ psia$$

The value of 0.491 psi/in. Hg is a useful conversion factor.

ILLUSTRATIVE PROBLEM 1.6

The density of mercury is 13 595 kg/m^3. Determine the pressure at the base of a column of mercury that is 25.4 mm high.

Solution

Using Eq. (1.19a),

$$p = -\rho gh = 13\ 595\frac{kg}{m^3} \times 9.806\frac{m}{sec^2} \times 0.0254\ m$$

$$= 3386.1\ Pa$$

Note: 1 psi $\cong$ 6895 Pa. Therefore, $3386.1/6895 = 0.491$ psi, which checks with Illustrative Problem 1.5.

In vacuum work it is common to express the absolute pressure in a vacuum chamber in terms of millimeters of mercury. Thus a vacuum may be expressed as 10^{-5} mm Hg. If this is expressed in pounds force per square inch, it would be equivalent to 0.000000193 psi, with the assumption that the density of mercury (for vacuum work) is 13.6 g/cm^3. Recently, the term *torr* has entered the technical literature. A torr is defined as 1 mm Hg. Thus 10^{-5} torr is the same as 10^{-5} mm Hg. Another unit of pressure used in vacuum work is the micron μ. A micron is defined as one thousandth of 1 mm Hg so that 10^{-3} mm Hg is equal to 1 μ.

ILLUSTRATIVE PROBLEM 1.7

A mercury manometer (vacuum gage) reads 26.5 in. of vacuum when the local barometer reads 30.0 in. Hg at standard temperature. Determine the absolute pressure in psia.

Solution

$$p = (30.0 - 26.5) \text{ in. Hg absolute}$$

and from the preceding problem

$$p = (30 - 26.5)0.491 = 1.72 \text{ psia}$$

If the solution is desired in psfa, it is necessary to convert from square inches to square feet. Since there are 12 in. in 1 ft, there will be 144 in.^{2} in 1 ft^2. Thus the conversion to psfa requires that psia be multiplied by 144. This conversion is often necessary to keep the dimensions of equations consistent.

ILLUSTRATIVE PROBLEM 1.8

A column of fluid is 10 m high. If its density is 2000 kg/m^3, determine the pressure at the base of the column if it is located in a local gravity of 9.6 m/s^2.

Solution

Applying Eq. (1.19c),

$$p = \rho g h = 2000 \frac{\text{kg}}{\text{m}^3} \times 9.6 \frac{\text{m}}{\text{s}^2} \times 10 \text{ m} = 192 \text{ kPa}$$

ILLUSTRATIVE PROBLEM 1.9

Using the data of Illustrative Problem 1.7, determine the absolute pressure in kPa.

Solution

As before, $p = (30 - 26.5) = 3.5$ in. Hg absolute. Using "standard" temperature,

$$3.5 \text{ in.} \times \frac{25.4 \text{ mm/in.}}{1000 \text{ mm/m}} \times (13.6 \times 62.4) \frac{\text{lb}}{\text{ft}^3} \times \frac{1}{2.2 \text{ lb/kg}}$$

$$\times \left[\frac{1}{(12 \times 0.0254)^3} \right] \frac{\text{ft}^3}{\text{m}^3} \times \left(9.806 \frac{\text{m}}{\text{s}^2} \right) = 11.875 \text{ kPa}$$

Note: $11.875 \times 1000/6895 = 1.72$ psia, which checks with Illustrative Problem 1.7.

In performing any measurement it is necessary to have a standard of comparison in order to calibrate the measuring instrument. In the following paragraphs, five pressure standards currently used as the basis for all pressure measurement work will be discussed. Table 1.8 summarizes these standards, the

TABLE 1.8
CHARACTERISTICS OF PRESSURE STANDARDS

TYPE	*RANGE*	*ACCURACY*
Dead-weight piston gage	0.01 to 10,000 psig	0.01 to 0.05% of reading
Manometer	0.01 to 100 psig	0.02 to 0.2% of reading
Micro-manometer	0.0002 to 20 in. H_2O	1% of reading to 0.001 in. H_2O
Barometer	27 to 31 in. Hg	0.001 to 0.03% of reading
McLeod gage	0.01 μ to 1 mm Hg	0.5 to 3% of reading

pressure range in which they are used, and their accuracy.* Figure 1.19 shows the basic pressure measurement concept upon which all pressure standards are based.

---

*The remainder of this section is based upon Appendix B of *Fluid Mechanics for Engineering Technology* by Irving Granet, Prentice-Hall, Inc., Englewood Cliffs, N.J., 1971, reprinted with permission of the publisher.

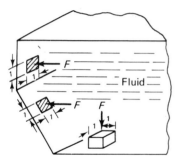

Pressure is the normal force F (lb/in.^{2}, lb/ft.^{2}, dynes/cm^2) exerted on a unit area of a surface bounding a fluid.

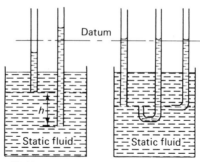

Fluid pressure varies with depth, but it is the same in all directions at a given depth.

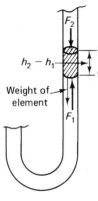

Variation of fluid pressure with elevation is found by balancing the forces on a static-fluid element (F_1 is equal to F_2 plus the weight of the element). For a constant-density fluid, the pressure difference $p_2 - p_1$ is equal to the specific weight γ times $(h_2 - h_1)$.

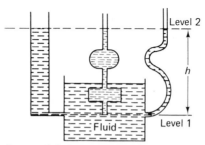

Pressure is independent of the shape and size of the vessel. The pressure difference between level 1 and level 2 is always $p_1 - p_2 = \gamma h$, where γ is the specific weight of the constant-density fluid in the vessel.

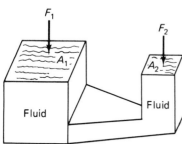

Constant pressure transmission in a confined fluid can be used to multiply force by the relation $p = F_1/A_1 = F_2/A_2$.

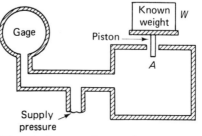

When the known weight is balanced, the gage pressure is $p = W/A$; this is the basic principle of dead-weight testing.

Figure 1.19 Basic pressure-measurement concepts

1.6a Dead-Weight Piston Gage

The dead-weight, free-piston gage consists of an accurately machined piston inserted into a close-fitting cylinder. Masses of known weight are loaded on one end of the free piston, and pressure is applied to the other end until enough force is developed to lift the piston–weight combination. When the piston is floating freely between the cylinder limit stops, the gage is in equilibrium with the unknown system pressure. The dead-weight pressure can then be defined as

$$p_{dw} = \frac{F_e}{A_e} \qquad (1.21)$$

where F_e is the equivalent force of the piston–weight combination, dependent on such factors as local gravity and air buoyancy, and A_e is the equivalent area of the piston–cylinder combination, dependent on such factors as piston–cylinder clearance, pressure level, and temperature.

A fluid film provides the necessary lubrication between the piston and cylinder. In addition, the piston, or less frequently the cylinder, may be rotated or oscillated to reduce friction even further. Because of fluid leakage, system pressure must be continuously trimmed upward to keep the piston–weight combination floating. This is often achieved by decreasing the system volume using a pressure volume apparatus (as shown in Fig. 1.20). As long as the piston is freely balanced, system pressure is defined by Eq. (1.21).

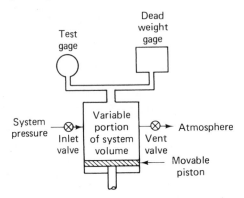

Figure 1.20 Pressure volume regulator to compensate for fluid leakage in a dead-weight gage

Corrections must be applied to the indication of the dead-weight piston gage p_i to obtain the accurate system pressure p_{dw}. The two most important corrections concern air buoyancy and local gravity. The effective area of the dead-weight piston gage is usually taken as the mean of the cylinder and piston areas, but temperature affects this dimension. The effective area increases between 13 and 18 ppm (parts per million)/°F for commonly used materials, and a suitable correction for this effect may also be applied.

1.6b Manometer

We have already shown that the pressure at the base of a column of liquid is simply a function of the height of the column and the specific weight of the liquid. Therefore, the height of a column of liquid of known specific weight can be and is used to measure pressure and pressure differences. Instruments that utilize this principle are known as manometers, and the study of these pressure-measuring devices is known as manometry. By properly arranging a manometer and selecting the fluid judiciously, it is possible to measure extremely small pressures, very large pressures, and pressure differences. A simple manometer is shown in Fig. 1.21, where the right arm is exposed to the

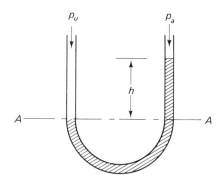

Figure 1.21 U-tube manometer

atmosphere while the left arm is connected to the unknown pressure. As shown, the fluid is depressed in the left arm and raised in the right arm until no unbalanced pressure forces remain. It has already been demonstrated that the pressure at a given level in either arm must be the same so that we can select any level as reference and write a relation for the pressure. Actually, it is much easier amd more convenient to select the interface between the manometer fluid and the unknown fluid as a common reference level. In Fig. 1.21 the pressure at elevation AA is the same in both arms of the manometer. Starting with the open manometer arm (right), we have atmospheric pressure p_a acting on the fluid. As one proceeds down the arm, the pressure increases until we arrive at level AA, where the pressure is $p_a + \gamma h$. This pressure must equal the unknown pressure on the connected arm p_u. Therefore,

$$p_u = p_a + \gamma h \qquad (1.22)$$

or

$$p_u - p_a = \gamma h \qquad (1.23)$$

Temperature and capillary effects must be considered for accurate pressure measurements. To minimize the effect of a variable meniscus, which can be caused by dirt, the method of approaching equilibrium, tube bore, and so on, the tubes are always tapped before reading, and the measured liquid height is always based on readings taken at the center of the meniscus in each leg of the manometer. To reduce the capillary effect itself, the use of large-bore tubes (over $\frac{3}{8}$ in. diameter) is most effective.

To achieve greater accuracy and sensitivity in manometers, several different arrangements have been used. Perhaps the simplest of these is the inclined manometer. Consider a relatively large reservoir of liquid connected to a small-bore tube that makes an angle θ with the horizontal. The pressure or pressure differential to be measured is connected to the large reservoir, while the inclined tube is open ended. Schematically, this is shown in Fig. 1.22. The

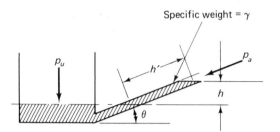

Figure 1.22 Inclined manometer

unknown pressure p_u is given by

$$p_u = p_a + \gamma h \qquad (1.24)$$

or

$$p_u - p_a = \gamma h \qquad (1.25)$$

However, h is $h' \sin \theta$. Thus

$$p_u - p_a = \gamma h' \sin \theta \qquad (1.26)$$

Since θ is fixed, a scale placed along the tube can be calibrated to read directly in units of h of a fluid. Usually, this is done by directly reading inches of water for $p_u - p_a$.

Another method of achieving greater sensitivity and accuracy is to use a manometer with more than one fluid. The manometer shown in Fig. 1.23 can

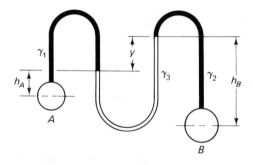

Figure 1.23 Three-fluid manometer

be used for this purpose by properly selecting the manometer fluid. Starting at level A,

$$p_A - h_A \gamma_1 - y\gamma_3 + h_B\gamma_2 = p_B \qquad (1.27)$$

or $$p_A - p_B = (-h_B\gamma_2 + h_A\gamma_1) + y\gamma_3 \qquad (1.28)$$

In the usual case the manometer is connected to different positions on the same pipe, and γ_1 can be taken to be equal to γ_2. Also, $h_B - h_A = y$. Thus

$$p_A - p_B \cong y(\gamma_3 - \gamma_1) \quad \text{or} \quad y(\gamma_3 - \gamma_2) \qquad (1.29)$$

For small differences in $p_A - p_B$, it is apparent that the manometer fluid (γ_3) should have a specific weight very nearly equal to the specific weight of the fluid in the pipes. For large pressure differences, one can use a heavy fluid such as mercury to increase $\gamma_3 - \gamma_2$ and reduce the manometer reading.

A word on the reference pressures employed in manometry is pertinent at this point in the discussion. If atmospheric pressure is used as a reference, the manometer yields gage pressures. Because of the variability of air pressure, gage pressures vary with time, altitude, latitude, and temperature. If, however, a vacuum is used as reference, the manometer yields absolute pressures directly, and it may serve as a barometer. In any case, the absolute pressure is always equal to the sum of the gage and ambient pressures; by ambient pressure we mean the pressure surrounding the gage, which is usually atmospheric pressure.

1.6c Micromanometer

While the manometer is a useful and convenient tool for pressure measurements, it is unfortunately limited when making low-pressure measurements. To extend its usefulness in the low-pressure range, micromanometers have been developed that have extended the useful range of low-pressure manometer measurements to pressures as low as 0.0002 in. H_2O.

One type is the *Prandtl-type* micromanometer in which capillary and meniscus errors are minimized by returning the meniscus of the manometer liquid to a null position before measuring the applied pressure difference. As shown in Fig. 1.24, a reservoir, which forms one side of the manometer, is moved vertically to locate the null position. This position is reached when the meniscus falls within two closely scribed marks on the near-horizontal portion of the micromanometer tube. Either the reservoir or the inclined tube is then moved by a precision lead-screw arrangement to determine the micromanometer liquid displacement (Δh), which corresponds to the applied pressure difference. The Prandtl-type micromanometer is generally accepted as a pressure standard within a calibration uncertainty of 0.001 in. H_2O.

Another method for minimizing capillary and meniscus effects in manometry is to measure liquid displacements with micrometer heads fitted with

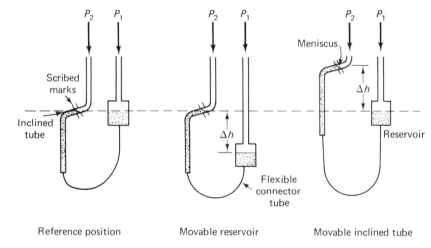

Figure 1.24 Two variations of the Prandtl-type micromanometer

adjustable, sharp index points. Figure 1.25 shows a manometer of this type; the micrometers are located in two connected transparent containers. In some commercial micromanometers, contact with the surface of the manometric liquid may be sensed visually by dimpling the surface with the index point, or even by electrical contact. Micrometer-type micromanometers also serve as pressure standards within a calibration uncertainty of 0.001 in. H_2O.

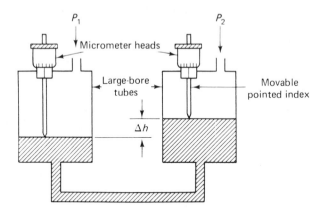

Figure 1.25 Micrometer-type manometer

An extremely sensitive, high-response micromanometer uses air as the working fluid and thus avoids all the capillary and meniscus effects usually encountered in liquid manometry. In this device, shown in Fig. 1.26, the reference pressure is mechanically amplified by centrifugal action in a rotating disk. The disk speed is adjusted until the amplified reference pressure just balances the unknown pressure. This null position is recognized by observing

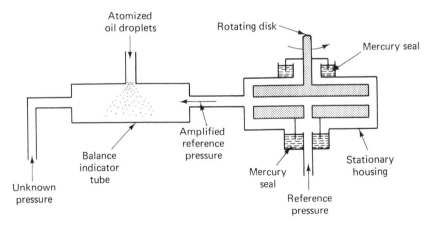

Figure 1.26 Air-type centrifugal micromanometer

the lack of movement of minute oil droplets sprayed into a glass indicator tube. At balance, the air micromanometer yields the applied pressure difference—

$$\Delta p_{\text{micro}} = K p n^2 \qquad (1.30)$$

where p is the reference air density, n is the rotational speed of the disk, and K is a constant that depends on disk radius and annular clearance between the disk and the housing. Measurements of pressure differences as small as 0.0002 in. H$_2$O can be made with this type of micromanometer within an uncertainty of 1 percent.

1.6d Barometers

The reservoir or cistern barometer consists of a vacuum-reference mercury column immersed in a large-diameter, ambient-vented mercury column that serves as a reservoir. The most common cistern barometer in general use is the Fortin type, in which the height of the mercury surface in the cistern can be adjusted. The operation of this instrument can best be explained with reference to Fig. 1.27.

The datum-adjusting screw is turned until the mercury in the cistern makes contact with the ivory index, at which point the mercury surface is aligned with zero on the instrument scale. Next, the indicated height of the mercury column in the glass tube is determined. The lower edge of a sighting ring is lined up with the top of the meniscus in the tube. A scale reading and a vernier reading are taken and combined to yield the indicated mercury height at the barometer temperature.

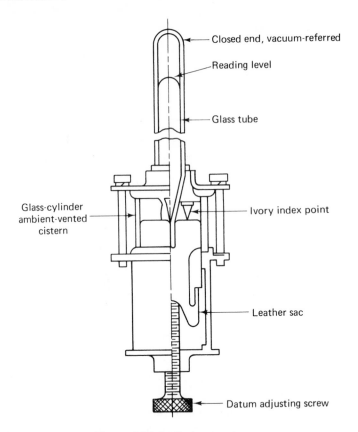

Closed end, vacuum-referred

Reading level

Glass tube

Glass-cylinder ambient-vented cistern

Ivory index point

Leather sac

Datum adjusting screw

Figure 1.27 Fortin barometer

Since atmospheric pressure on the mercury in the cistern is exactly balanced by the weight per unit area of the mercury column in the glass tube,

$$p_{baro} = \gamma_{Hg} h_{to} \qquad (1.31)$$

The referenced specific weight of mercury, γ_{Hg}, depends on such factors as temperature and local gravity; the referenced height of mercury, h_{to}, depends on such factors as thermal expansion of the scale and the mercury.

Other factors may also contribute to the uncertainty of h_{to}. Proper illumination is essential to define the location of the crown of the meniscus. Precision meniscus sighting under optimum viewing conditions can approach ± 0.001 in. With proper lighting, contact between the ivory index and the mercury surface in the cistern can be detected to much better than ± 0.001 in.

To keep the uncertainty in h_{to} within 0.01 percent ($\simeq 0.003$ in. Hg), the mercury temperature must be known within $\pm 1°F$. Scale temperature need not be known to better than $\pm 10°F$ for comparable accuracy. Uncertainties caused by nonequilibrium temperature conditions can be avoided by installing the barometer in a uniform temperature room.

The barometer tube must be vertically aligned for accurate pressure determination. This is accomplished by a separately supported ring encircling the cistern; adjustment screws control the horizontal position.

Depression of the mercury column in commercial barometers is accounted for in the initial calibration setting at the factory. The quality of the barometer is largely determined by the bore of the glass tube. Barometers with a bore of $\frac{1}{4}$ in. are suitable for readings of about 0.01 in. Hg, whereas barometers with a bore of $\frac{1}{2}$ in. are suitable for readings down to 0.002 in. Hg.

1.6e McLeod Gage

The McLeod gage is used in making low-pressure measurements. This instrument (shown in Fig. 1.28) consists of glass tubing arranged so that a sample of gas at unknown pressure can be trapped and then isothermally compressed by a rising mercury column. This amplifies the unknown pressure and allows

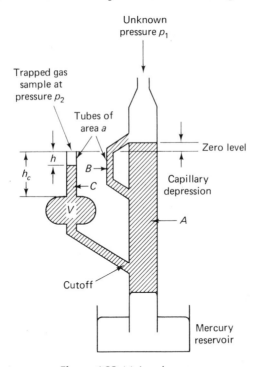

Figure 1.28 McLeod gage

measurement by conventional manometric means. All the mercury is initially contained in the area below the cutoff level. The gage is first exposed to the unknown gas pressure, p_1; the mercury is then raised in tube A beyond the cutoff, trapping a gas sample of initial volume $\overline{V}_1 = \overline{V} + ah_c$. The mercury is continuously forced upward until it reaches the zero level in the reference capillary B. At this time the mercury in the measuring capillary C reaches a level h, where the gas sample is at its final volume, $V_2 = ah$, and at the amplified pressure, $p_2 = p_1 + h$. Then

$$p_1 \overline{V}_1 = p_2 \overline{V}_2 \qquad (1.32)$$

$$p_1 = \frac{ah^2}{\overline{V}_1 - ah} \qquad (1.33)$$

If $ah \ll \overline{V}_1$ as is usually the case,

$$p_1 = \frac{h^2}{\overline{V}_1} \qquad (1.34)$$

The larger the volume ratio ($\overline{V}_1 / \overline{V}_2$), the greater will be the amplified pressure p_2 and manometer reading h. Therefore, it is desirable that measuring tube C have a small bore. Unfortunately, for tube bores under 1 mm, the compression gain is offset by reading uncertainty caused by capillary effects.

Reference tube B is introduced to provide a meaningful zero for the measuring tube. If the zero is fixed, Eq. (1.34) indicates that manometer indication h varies nonlinearly with initial pressure p_1. A McLeod gage with an expanded scale at the lower pressures exhibits a higher sensitivity in this region. The McLeod pressure scale, once established, serves equally well for all the permanent gases (those whose critical pressure is appreciably below room temperature).

There are no corrections to be applied to the McLeod gage reading, but certain precautions should be taken. Moisture traps must be provided to avoid taking any condensable vapors into the gage. Such vapors occupy a larger volume at the initial low pressures than they occupy in the liquid phase at the high reading pressures. Thus the presence of condensable vapors always causes pressure readings to be too low. Capillary effects, while partially counterbalanced by using a reference capillary, can still introduce significant uncertainties, since the angle of contact between mercury and glass can vary ± 30 degrees. Finally, since the McLeod gage does not give continuous readings, steady-state conditions must prevail for the measurements to be useful.

In the earlier portions of this section we discussed five pressure standards that can be used for either calibration or the measurement of pressure in static systems. In this section we shall discuss some common devices that are used for making measurements using an elastic element to convert fluid energy to mechanical energy. Such a device is known as a pressure transducer. Examples of mechanical pressure transducers having elastic elements only are deadweight free-piston gages, manometers, Bourdon gages, bellows, and diaphragm gages.

Electrical transducers have an element that converts their displacement to an electrical signal. Active electrical transducers generate their own voltage or current output as a function of displacement. Passive transducers require an external signal. The piezoelectric pickup is an example of an active electrical transducer. Electric elements employed in passive electrical pressure transducers include strain gages, slide-wire potentiometers, capacitance pickups, linear differential transformers, and variable-reluctance units.

In the Bourdon gage the elastic element is a small-volume tube that is fixed at one end but free at the other end to allow displacement under the deforming action of the pressure difference across the tube walls. In the most common model, shown in Fig. 1.29, a tube with an oval cross section is bent in a circular arc. Under pressure the tube tends to become circular, with a subsequent increase in the radius of the arc. By an almost frictionless linkage, the free end of the tube rotates a pointer over a calibrated scale to give a mechanical indication of pressure.

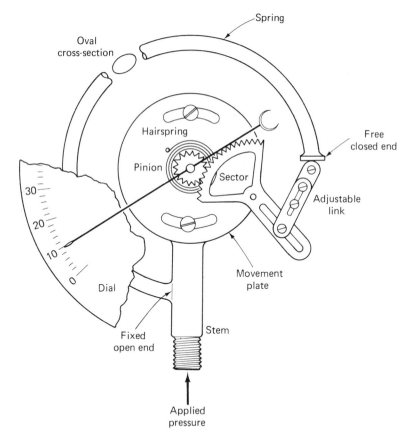

Figure 1.29 Bourdon gage

The reference pressure in the case containing the Bourdon tube is usually atmospheric, so that the pointer indicates gage pressures. Absolute pressures can be measured directly without evacuating the complete gage casing by biasing a sensing Bourdon tube against a reference Bourdon tube, which is evacuated and sealed as shown in Fig. 1.30. Bourdon gages are available for a wide range of absolute gage, and differential pressure measurements within a calibration uncertainty of 0.1 percent of the reading.

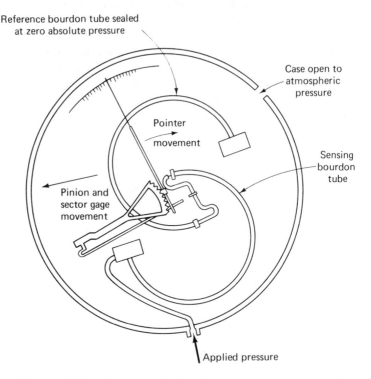

Figure 1.30 Bourdon gage for absolute pressure measurement

Another common elastic element used in pressure transducers is the bellows, shown as a gage element in Fig. 1.31.

In one arrangement, pressure is applied to one side of a bellows and the resulting deflection is partially counterbalanced by a spring. In a differential arrangement, one pressure is applied to the inside of one sealed bellows, and the pressure difference is indicated by a pointer.

A final elastic element to be mentioned because of its widespread use in pressure transducers is the diaphragm. One such arrangement is shown in Fig. 1.32. Such elements may be flat, corrugated, or dished plates; the choice depends on the strength and amount of deflection desired. In high-precision instruments, a pair of diaphragms is used back to back to form an elastic capsule. One pressure is applied to the inside of the capsule; the other pressure is external. The calibration of this differential transducer is relatively independent of pressure magnitude.

Thus far we have discussed a few mechanical pressure transducers. In many applications it is more convenient to use transducer elements that depend

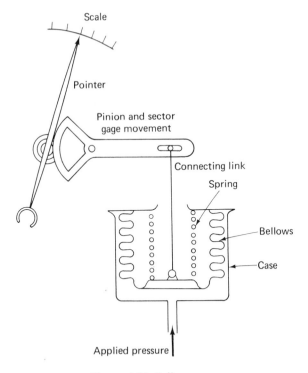

Figure 1.31 Bellows gage

on the change in the electrical parameters of the element as a function of the applied pressure. The only active electrical pressure transducer in common use is the piezoelectric transducer. Sound-pressure instrumentation makes extensive use of piezoelectric pickups in such forms as hollow cylinders and disks. Piezoelectric pressure transducers are also used in measuring rapidly fluctuating or transient pressures. In a recently introduced technique called electrocalibration, the transducer is calibrated by electric field excitation rather than by physical pressure. The most common passive electrical pressure transducers are the variable resistance types.

The strain gage is probably the most widely used pressure transducer element. Strain gages operate on the principle that the electrical resistance of a wire varies with its length under load. In unbonded strain gages, four wires run between electrically insulated pins located on a fixed frame and other pins located on a movable armature, as shown in Fig. 1.33. The wires are installed under tension and form the legs of a bridge circuit. Under pressure the elastic element (usually a diaphragm) displaces the armature, causing two of the wires to elongate while reducing the tension in the remaining two wires. The resistance change causes a bridge imbalance proportional to the applied pressure.

The bonded strain gage takes the form of a fine wire filament set in cloth, paper, or plastic and fastened by a suitable cement to a flexible plate, which

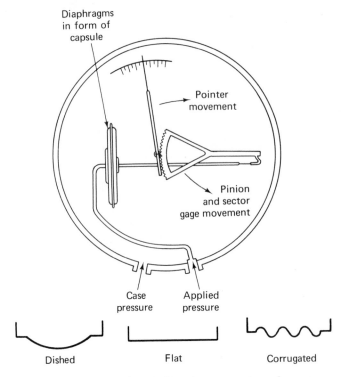

Diaphragms
in form of
capsule

Pointer
movement

Pinion
and sector
gage movement

Case
pressure

Applied
pressure

Dished

Flat

Corrugated

Figure 1.32 Diaphragm-based pressure transducer

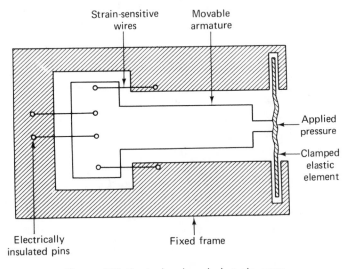

Strain-sensitive
wires

Movable
armature

Applied
pressure

Clamped
elastic
element

Electrically
insulated pins

Fixed frame

Figure 1.33 Typical unbonded strain gage

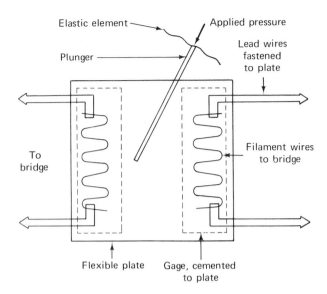

Elastic element ⟶
Applied pressure
Lead wires fastened to plate
Plunger ⟶
To bridge
Filament wires to bridge
Flexible plate
Gage, cemented to plate

Figure 1.34 Typical bonded strain gage

takes the load of the elastic element. This is shown in Fig. 1.34. Two similar strain gage elements are often connected in a bridge circuit to balance unavoidable temperature effects. The nomimal bridge output impedance of most strain gage pressure transducers is 350 ohms (Ω), nominal excitation voltage is 10 V (ac or dc), and natural frequency can be as high as 50 Hz. Transducer resolution is infinite, and the usual calibration uncertainty of such gages is within 1 percent of full scale.

Many other forms of electrical pressure transducers are in use in industry, and a few of these will be discussed briefly. These elements fall under the categories of potentiometer, variable capacitance, linear variable differential transformer (LVDT), and variable reluctance transducers. The potentiometer types are those that operate as variable resistance pressure transducers. In one arrangement, the elastic element is a helical Bourdon tube, while a precision wire-wound potentiometer serves as the electric element. As pressure is applied to the open end of the Bourdon tube, it unwinds, causing the wiper (connected directly to the closed end of the tube) to move over the potentiometer.

In the variable capacitance pressure transducer, the elastic element is usually a metal diaphragm that serves as one plate of a capacitor. Under an applied pressure the diaphragm moves with respect to a fixed plate. By means of a suitable bridge circuit, the variation in capacitance can be measured and related to pressure by calibration.

The electric element in an LVDT is made up of three coils mounted in a common frame to form the device shown in Fig. 1.35. A magnetic core centered in the coils is free to be displaced by a bellows, Bourdon, or diaphragm elastic element. The center coil, the primary winding of the transformer, has an ac excitation voltage impressed across it. The two outside coils form the secondaries of the transformer. When the core is centered, the induced voltages in the two outer coils are equal and 180 degrees out of phase; this represents the zero pressure position. However, when the core is displaced by the action of an applied pressure, the voltage induced in one secondary increases, while that in the other decreases. The output voltage difference varies essentially linearly with pressure for the small core displacements allowed in these transducers. The voltage difference is measured and related to the applied pressure by calibration.

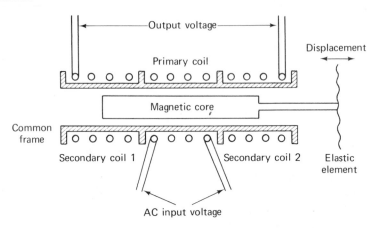

Figure 1.35 Linear variable differential transformer

The last elastic element that will be discussed is the variable reluctance pressure transducer. The basic element of the variable reluctance pressure transducer is a movable magnetic vane in a magnetic field. In one type, the elastic element is a flat magnetic diaphragm located between two magnetic output coils. Displacement of the diaphragm changes the inductance ratio between the output coils and results in an output voltage proportional to pressure.

1.7 CLOSURE

Thermodynamics is a vast study that has engaged the combined efforts of scientists, engineers, physicists, and mathematicians. In this introductory chapter, we have set forth certain concepts regarding systems and properties that we shall build upon in future chapters. Although some of this material may appear to be elementary, it is necessary that it be fully understood before proceeding further. The student is urged to be sure of all the units used in any equation and to be equally sure of the meaning of all terms. Problems at the end of this chapter are included to develop a better level of understanding through the application of the text material. The ability to apply the material studied indicates understanding; regurgitation indicates a good memory.

REFERENCES

1 *Modern College Physics*, 4th Ed., by H. E. White, Van Nostrand Reinhold Co., New York, 1962.

2 *Hydraulics*, 4th Ed., by R. L. Daugherty, McGraw-Hill Book Co., New York, 1937.

3 *Thermodynamics*, 2nd Ed., by G. A. Hawkins, John Wiley & Sons, Inc., New York, 1951.

4 *Principles of Engineering Thermodynamics*, 2nd Ed., by P. J. Kiefer, G. F. Kinney, and M. C. Stuart, John Wiley & Sons, Inc., New York, 1953.

5 *Engineering Thermodynamics* by D. R. Spalding and E. H. Cole, McGraw-Hill Book Co., New York, 1959.

6 *Heat and Thermodynamics*, 4th Ed., by M. W. Zemansky, McGraw-Hill Book Co., New York, 1957.

7 *Engineering Thermodynamics*, by N. C. Ebaugh, Van Nostrand Reinhold Co., New York, 1952.

8 *Concepts of Thermodynamics* by E. F. Obert, McGraw-Hill Book Co., New York, 1960.

9 *Elementary Applied Thermodynamics* by Irving Granet, John Wiley & Sons, Inc., New York, 1965.

10 *Fluid Mechanics for Engineering Technology* by Irving Granet, Prentice-Hall, Inc., Englewood Cliffs, N.J., 1971.

11 *Thermodynamics* by George F. Babits, Allyn & Bacon, Inc., Boston, 1963.

12 *Basic Thermodynamics* by B. G. A. Skrotzki, McGraw-Hill Book Co., New York, 1963.

13 *Thermodynamics*, 6th Ed., by V. M. Faires and C. S. Simmang, Macmillan, Inc., New York, 1978.

14 *Fundamentals of Classical Thermodynamics* by G. J. Van Wylen and R. E. Sonntag, John Wiley & Sons, Inc., New York, 1965.

15 *Fundamentals of Temperature, Pressure and Flow Measurements* by R. P. Benedict, John Wiley & Sons, Inc., New York, 1969.

16 *Temperature Measurement in Engineering* by H. D. Baker, E. A. Ryder, and N. H. Baker, John Wiley & Sons, Inc., New York, 1961.

17 *Temperature—Its Measurement and Control in Industry*, Vol. II, edited by C. M. Herzfeld, Van Nostrand Reinhold Co., New York, 1962.

18 *Temperature, Its Measurement and Control in Science and Industry* edited by Wolfe, © 1955 by Litton Educational Publishing Inc., reprinted by permission of Van Nostrand Reinhold Co., New York, 1955. Published by Krieger Publishing.

19 *University Physics* by F. W. Sears and M. W. Zemansky, Addison-Wesley Publishing Co., Reading, Mass., 1955.

20 *ASME Orientation and Guide for Use of SI (Metric) Units*, 5th Ed., American Society of Mechanical Engineers, New York, 1974.

21 *Applied Mechanics for Engineering Technology* by K. M. Walker, Reston Publishing Co., Reston, Va., 1974.

22 *Statics* by J. L. Merian, 2nd Ed., SI Version, John Wiley & Sons, Inc., New York, 1975.

23 *AISI Metric Practice Guide—SI Units and Conversion Factors for the Steel Industry*, American Iron and Steel Institute, Washington, D.C., 1975.

24 *ASME Text Booklet—SI Units in Strength of Materials*, 1st Ed., The American Society of Mechanical Engineers, New York, 1975.

25 *Engineering Thermodynamics and Applications* by M. D. Burghardt, Harper & Row, Publishers, Inc., New York, 1978.

PROBLEMS

Use $g = 32.17$ ft/sec^2, $g = 9.806$ m/sec^2, and $p_{atm} = 14.696$ psia or 101 325 Pa unless otherwise noted.

1.1 Convert 20°, 40°, and 60°C to equivalent degrees Fahrenheit.

1.2 Change 0°, 10°, and 50°F to equivalent degrees Celsius.

1.3 Convert 500°R, 500°K, and 650°R to degrees Celsius.

1.4 Derive a relation between degrees Rankine and degrees Kelvin, and, based upon the results, show that $(°C + 273)1.8 = °F + 460$.

1.5 An arbitrary temperature scale is proposed in which 20° is assigned to the ice point and 75° is assigned to the boiling point. Derive an equation relating this scale to the Celsius scale.

1.6 For the temperature scale proposed in Problem 1.5, what temperature corresponds to absolute zero?

1.7 A Fahrenheit and Celsius thermometer are used to measure the temperature of a fluid. If the Fahrenheit reading is 1.5 times that of the Celsius reading, what are both readings?

1.8 A new thermometer scale on which the freezing point of water at atmospheric pressure would correspond to a marking of 200 and the boiling point of water at atmospheric pressure would correspond to a marking of minus 400 is proposed. What would the reading of this new thermometer be if a Fahrenheit thermometer placed in the same environment read 80°?

1.9 A skin diver descends to a depth of 60 ft in fresh water. What is the pressure on his body? The specific weight of fresh water can be taken as 62.4 lb/ft^3.

1.10 A skin diver descends to a depth of 25 m in a salt lake where the density is 1026 kg/m^3. What is the pressure on his body at this depth?

1.11 If a Bourdon gage reads 25 psi, what is the absolute pressure in pascals?

1.12 A column of fluid is 1 m high. The fluid has a density of 2500 kg/m^3. What is the pressure at the base of the column?

1.13 A column of fluid is 25 in. high. If the specific weight of the fluid is 60.0 lb/ft^3, what is the pressure in psi at the base of the column?

1.14 Determine the density and specific volume of the contents of a 10 ft^3 tank if the contents weigh 250 lb.

1.15 A tank contains 500 kg of a fluid. If the volume of the tank is 0.5 m^3, what is the density of the fluid and what is the specific volume?

1.16 Convert 14.696 psia to 101 325 kPa.

1.17 A pressure gage indicates 25 psi when the barometer is at a pressure equivalent to 14.5 psia. Compute the absolute pressure in psi and feet of mercury when the specific weight of mercury is 13.0 g/cm^3.

1.18 The same as Problem 1.17. The barometer stands at 750 mm Hg and its specific weight is 13.6 g/cm^3.

1.19 A vacuum gage reads 8 in. Hg when the atmospheric pressure is 29.0 in Hg. If the specific weight of mercury is 13.6 g/cm^3, compute the absolute pressure in psi.

1.20 A vacuum gage reads 10 in. Hg when the atmospheric pressure is 30 in. Hg. Assuming the density of mercury to be 13 595 kg/m^3, determine the pressure in pascals.

1.21 A U-tube mercury manometer, open on one end, is connected to a pressure source. If the difference in the mercury levels in the tube is 6.5 in., determine the unknown pressure in psfa.

1.22 Two sources of pressure M and N are connected by a water–mercury differential gage as shown in Fig. P1.22. What is the difference in pressure between M and N in psi?

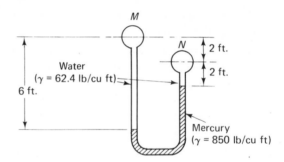

Figure P1.22

1.23 Determine the difference in pressure between A and B if the specific weight of water is 62.4 lb/ft³.

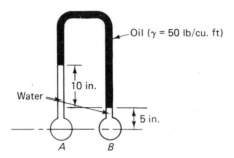

Figure P1.23

1.24 If the liquid in pipe B in Problem 1.23 is carbon tetrachloride, whose specific weight is 99 lb/ft³, determine the pressure difference between A and B.

1.25 In a U-tube manometer, one end is closed, trapping atmospheric air in the column. The other end is connected to a pressure supply of 5 psig. If the level of mercury in the closed end is 2 in. higher than that in the open end, what is the pressure of the trapped air?

1.26 For the arrangement shown in Fig. P1.26, determine $p_A - p_B$.

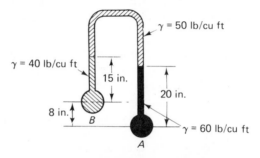

Figure P1.26

1.27 A force of 100 N acts horizontally on a 10 kg body. What is its horizontal acceleration?

1.28 An unbalanced force in pounds equal numerically to the weight of a body in pounds causes the body to accelerate. What is its acceleration?

1.29 A body at mean sea level weighs 100 lb ($g=g_c$). Estimate the weight of this body at an elevation of 7500 ft. Assume the mean diameter of the earth is 12,742 km.

1.30 A mass of 10 kg weighs 980.6 N at sea level. Estimate the weight of this body at the top of a mountain 5 km high. Assume that the mean diameter of the earth is 12 742 km.

1.31 A balance type scale is used to weigh a sample on the moon. If the value of g is one-sixth of earth's gravity and the "standard" weights (earth weights) add up to 20 lb, what is the mass of the body?

1.32 A balance type scale is used to weigh a sample on the moon. If the value of g is one-sixth of earth's gravity and the "standard" weights (earth weights) add up to 100 N, what is the mass of the body?

1.33 Solve Problem 1.31 if a spring balance is used that was calibrated on earth and reads 20 lb.

1.34 Solve Problem 1.32 if a spring balance is used that was calibrated on earth and reads 100 N.

1.35 A mass of 100 kg is hung from a spring in a local gravitational field where $g=9.806$ m/s^2, and the spring is found to deflect 25 mm. If the same mass is taken to a planet where $g=5.412$ m/s^2, how much will the spring deflect if its deflection is directly proportional to the applied force?

1.36 The mass of the planet Mars is 0.1069 relative to earth, and its diameter relative to earth is 0.523. What is the weight of a pound of mass on Mars?

1.37 A body having an unknown mass "weighs" 1 lb on the planet Jupiter. Jupiter has a mass 318.35 times that of earth and its diameter is 10.97 times larger:
a. What will the body weigh on Earth?
b. What is the mass of the body?

1.38 Solve Problem 1.36 for a mass of 10 kg.

1.39 Solve Problem 1.37 for a weight of 10 N on Jupiter.

chapter 2

the first law of thermodynamics

2.1 INTRODUCTION

In Chapter 1 certain concepts were arrived at by considering the motion of gas particles in an enclosure. Briefly, pressure was found to involve the principle of momentum interchange with the container walls, temperature was associated with the motion of the particles, and density was taken to be a measure of the number of particles per unit volume. This simple analysis followed the history of a single particle, and it was subsequently generalized to all the particles in the enclosure. This type of analysis is representative of a microscopic description of the processes occurring within the boundaries of the defined system, since the history of a single particle was followed in detail. Rather than pursue further the microscopic concept of matter, we shall be concerned with the macroscopic, or average, behavior of the particles composing a system. The macroscopic viewpoint essentially assumes that it is possible to describe the average behavior of these particles at a given time and at some subsequent time after changes have occurred to the system. The system changes of concern to us in this study are temperature, pressure, density, work, energy, velocity, and position. The power of the macroscopic approach lies in its ability to describe the changes that have occurred to the system without having to detail all the events of the processes involved.

A system has already been defined as a grouping of matter taken in any convenient or arbitrary manner. However, when dealing with fluids in motion, it is more convenient to utilize the concept of an arbitrary volume in space, known as a *control volume*, that can be bounded by either a real or imaginary surface, known as a *control surface*. By correctly noting all the forces acting on the fluid within the control volume, the energies crossing the control surface, and the mass crossing the control surface, it is possible to derive mathematical expressions that will evaluate the flow of the fluid relative to the control volume. For a system in which fluids are flowing steadily, a monitoring station placed anywhere within the control volume will indicate no change in the fluid properties or energy quantities crossing the control surface with time, even though these quantities can and will vary from position to position within the control volume. As noted by Keenan, "*the first step in the solution of a problem in thermodynamics is the description of a system and its boundaries.*"*

2.2 CONSERVATION OF MASS—THE CONTINUITY EQUATION

As noted in Section 2.1, both energy and mass can enter and leave a control volume and cross the control surface of a system. Since we are considering steady-flow systems, we can express the principle of conservation of mass for these systems as requiring the mass of fluid in the control volume at any time be constant. In turn, this requires that the net mass flowing into the control volume must equal the net mass flowing out of the control volume at any instant of time. To express these concepts in terms of a given system, let us consider the system schematically in Fig. 2.1.

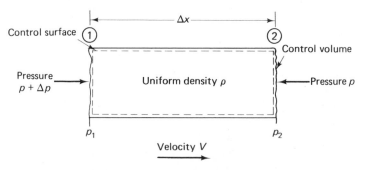

Figure 2.1 Elementary flow system

---

*J. H. Keenan, *Thermodynamics*, John Wiley & Sons, Inc., New York, 1941, p. 14.

Let us assume that at a certain time, fluid starts to enter the control volume by crossing the control surface at ① and that after a small interval of time the flowing fluid fills the pipe for a short distance Δx. If it is further assumed that in this short section of uniform pipe no heat is added or work is exchanged, and that the fluid density stays constant, we can evaluate the amount of fluid that flowed in between ① and ②. The mass contained between these sections is equal to the volume contained between the sections multiplied by the density of the fluid. The volume is $(A)(\Delta x)$, and the density is ρ; therefore, the contained mass is $(\rho A)(\Delta x)$. The distance between stations, Δx, is simply $V\Delta t$, where V is the velocity of the fluid and Δt is the flow time required to fill the pipe between ① and ②. Substituting this for Δx,

$$m = \rho A V (\Delta t) \qquad (2.1a)$$

or
$$\dot{m} = \rho A V = \rho_1 A_1 V_1 = \rho_2 A_2 V_2 \qquad (2.1b)$$

where $\dot{m}$ is the mass rate of flow per unit time, $m/\Delta t$. Also

$$\dot{m} = \frac{A V}{v} \qquad (2.1c)$$

where the specific volume replaces the density, $v = \dfrac{1}{\rho}$.

Equation (2.1) is known as the *continuity equation*, and as written for a pipe or duct we have made the assumption that the flow is normal to the pipe cross section, and the velocity V is either constant across the section or is the average value over the cross section of the pipe. We shall use the continuity equation quite frequently in our study, and it is important to note that it expresses the fact that the mass flow into the control volume must equal the mass flow out of the control volume in steady flow.

ILLUSTRATIVE PROBLEM 2.1

At the entrance to a steady-flow device it is found that the pressure is 100 psia and the density of the fluid is constant and is 62.4 lb/cu ft. If 10,000 cu ft/min of this fluid enters the system and the exit area is 2 sq ft., determine the mass flow rate and the exit velocity. See Fig. 2.2.

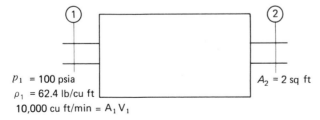

Figure 2.2 Illustrative Problem 2.1

Solution

Let us first calculate the mass flow into the system. From Eq. (2.1b), $\dot{m} = \rho_1 A_1 V_1$. We are told that 10,000 cu ft/min of this fluid enters the system, which is the same as saying $A_1 V_1 = 10{,}000$ cu ft/min. Therefore, $\dot{m} = \rho_1 A_1 V_1 = 62.4 \times 10{,}000 = 624{,}000$ lb/min. Since this mass flow must also leave the system,

$$\dot{m} = \rho_2 A_2 V_2$$

Thus,

$$624{,}000 = 62.4 \times 2 \times V_2 \quad \text{and} \quad V_2 = 5000 \text{ ft/min}$$

ILLUSTRATIVE PROBLEM 2.2

If the fluid entering the system shown in Fig. 2.2 has a density of 1000 kg/m³ and 2000 m³/min enters the system, determine the mass flow rate and the exit velocity if the exit area is 0.5 m². Assume that the density is constant.

Solution

Proceeding as in Illustrative Problem 2.1, $\dot{m} = \rho A V$; $\dot{m} = \rho_1 A_1 V_1$. Therefore,

$$\dot{m} = \left(1000 \frac{\text{kg}}{\text{m}^3}\right) \times 2000 \frac{\text{m}^3}{\text{min}} = 2 \times 10^6 \frac{\text{kg}}{\text{min}} = 33.3 \times 10^3 \text{ kg/s}$$

Since $\dot{m} = \rho_2 A_2 V_2$,

$$2 \times 10^6 = 1000 \frac{\text{kg}}{\text{m}^3} \times 0.5 \text{ m}^2 \times V_2 \quad \text{and} \quad V_2 = 4000 \text{ m/min}$$

ILLUSTRATIVE PROBLEM 2.3

A hose is 1 in. in diameter and has water whose density is 62.4 lb/cu ft flowing steadily in it at a velocity of 100 ft/sec. Determine the mass flow of water in the hose. See Fig. 2.3.

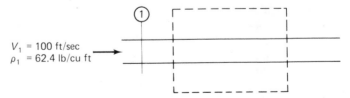

V_1 = 100 ft/sec
ρ_1 = 62.4 lb/cu ft

Figure 2.3 Illustrative Problem 2.3

Solution

From the continuity equation

$$\dot{m} = \rho A V = 62.4 \times \frac{\pi(1)^2}{4 \times 144} \times 100 = 34.0 \text{ lb/sec}$$

Note that the dimension of the area has been used in square feet for dimensional consistency.

Figure 2.4 shows a steam turbine as a flow system. Our present interest is in the flow of steam into and out of the noted boundaries of this system. The actions and interactions within the boundaries of this system will be studied later, but for us at this time the boundaries can be thought of as defining a "black box," and only the fluid (steam) interfaces are considered. The continuity equation is applied to the inlet and outlet steam flow, as in the following example.

ILLUSTRATIVE PROBLEM 2.4

A steam turbine has an inlet steam flow of 50,000 lb/hr of steam whose specific volume is 0.831 cu ft/lb. The inlet diameter is 6 in. At the outlet the pipe diameter is 8 in., and the specific volume of the steam is 1.825 cu ft/lb Determine the velocity at inlet and outlet of the turbine in ft/sec.

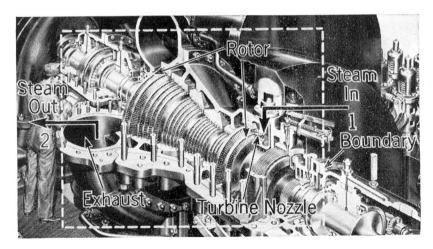

Figure 2.4 Steam turbine flow system (From *Elementary Thermodynamics*, by V. M. Faires, Macmillan, Inc., New York, 1957, p. 27, with permission)

S o l u t i o n

Referring to Fig. 2.4, we have at the inlet $\dot{m}_1 = 50{,}000$ lb/hr and $v_1 = 0.831$ cu ft/lb. Therefore,

$$\dot{m}_1 = \frac{A_1 V_1}{v_1}$$

$$V_1 = \frac{\dot{m}_1 v_1}{A_1} = \frac{50{,}000}{60 \times 60} \times \frac{0.831}{\dfrac{\pi (6)^2}{4 \times 144}} = 58.8 \text{ ft/sec}$$

At the outlet, the value of $\dot{m}_2$ is the same, that is, 50,000 lb/hr. Therefore,

$$V_2 = \frac{\dot{m}_2 v_2}{A_2} = \frac{50{,}000}{60 \times 60} \times \frac{1.825}{\dfrac{\pi (8)^2}{4 \times 144}} = 72.6 \text{ ft/sec}$$

Again note the conversion factors of 144 and 60×60 to obtain the desired units of velocity.

ILLUSTRATIVE PROBLEM 2.5

A steam turbine has an inlet steam flow of 10^4 kg/hr whose specific volume is 0.05 m³/kg. The inlet diameter is 100 mm, and the outlet diameter is 200 mm. If the outlet specific volume is 0.10 m³/kg, determine the inlet and outlet velocities.

S o l u t i o n

$$\dot{m}_1 = \dot{m}_2 = 10^4 \text{ kg/hr}$$

Since $m = AV/v$, $V = \dot{m}v/A$. Therefore,

$$V_1 = \frac{\dot{m}_1 v_1}{A_1} = \frac{10^4 \text{ kg/hr}}{(60 \times 60) \text{ s/hr}} \times \frac{0.05 \dfrac{\text{m}^3}{\text{kg}}}{\dfrac{\pi}{4}(0.1)^2 \text{ m}^2} = 17.68 \text{ m/s}$$

at the outlet,

$$V_2 = \frac{\dot{m}_2 v_2}{A_2} = \frac{10^4 \text{ kg/hr}}{(60 \times 60) \text{ s/hr}} \times \frac{0.10 \dfrac{\text{m}^3}{\text{kg}}}{\dfrac{\pi}{4}(0.2)^2 \text{ m}^2} = 8.84 \text{ m/s}$$

2.3 ENERGY, HEAT, AND WORK

In this book we shall define the work done by a force as the product of the displacement of the body multiplied by the component of the force in the direction of the displacement. Thus in Fig. 2.5 the displacement of the body on the horizontal plane is x, and the component of the force in the direction of the displacement is $(F\cos\theta)$. The work done is $(F\cos\theta)(x)$. The constant force

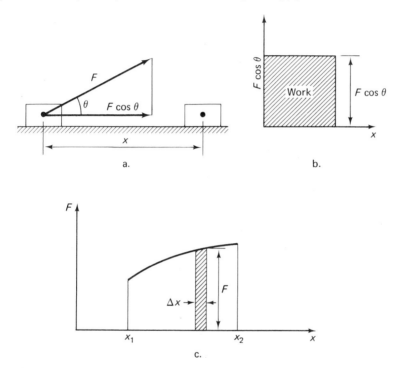

Figure 2.5 Work

$(F\cos\theta)$ is plotted as a function of x in Fig. 2.5b, and it should be noted that the resulting figure is a rectangle. The area of this rectangle (shaded) is equal to the work done, since it is $(F\cos\theta)(x)$. If the force varies so that it is a function of the displacement, it is necessary to consider the variation of force with displacement in order to find the work done. Figure 2.5c shows a general plot of force as a function of displacement. If the displacement is subdivided into many small parts, Δx, and for each of these small parts F is assumed to be very nearly constant, it is apparent that the sum of the small areas $(F)(\Delta x)$ will represent the total work done when the body is displaced from x_1 to x_2. Thus the area under the curve of F as a function of x represents the total work done if F is the force component in the direction of the displacement x.

ILLUSTRATIVE PROBLEM 2.6

A spring is slowly compressed by a varying force F until it reaches an equilibrium position. Assuming that the force on the spring is proportional to the spring displacement, determine the work done on the spring. Assume that the constant of proportionality k is constant and expressed in pounds force per foot of spring deflection or N newtons per metre of spring deflection.

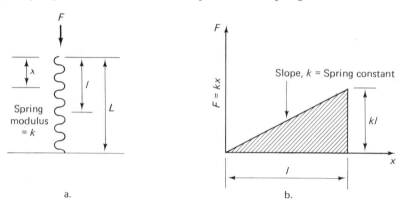

Figure 2.6 Illustrative Problems 2.6 and 2.7

Solution

As shown in Fig. 2.6a, the system consists of a spring and a force F directed along the axis of the spring. A plot of F as a function of x is shown in Fig. 2.6b. It will be noted that the force–displacement relation is a linear one in which the force equals kx at all times. Thus the work done is represented by the shaded triangular area of Fig. 2.6b. Since the base of the triangle is l and the height is kl, the work done is $\frac{1}{2}(l)(kl)$ or $\frac{1}{2}(k)(l^2)$.

ILLUSTRATIVE PROBLEM 2.7

A spring has a spring constant k of 100 lb/in. deflection. How much work is done when the spring is compressed 2 in.?

Solution

Referring to Fig. 2.6 and the results of Illustrative Problem 2.6, we have

$$\text{work} = \tfrac{1}{2}kl^2$$

For this problem

$$\text{work} = \tfrac{1}{2}(100)(2)^2 = 200 \text{ in./lb}$$

ILLUSTRATIVE PROBLEM 2.8

If the spring constant in Illustrative Problem 2.7 is 20 kN/metre, how much work is done when the spring is compressed 75 mm?

Solution

As before,

$$\text{work} = \tfrac{1}{2}kl^2 = \tfrac{1}{2}(20 \times 10^3) \times (0.075)^2 = 56.25 \text{ N·m} = 56.25 \text{ joules}$$

At this point let us define *energy* in terms of work. Energy can be described as the capacity to do work. At first it may appear that this definition is too restrictive when applied to electrical and magnetic systems. Yet in all instances the observed effects on a system can (in principle and ideally) be converted to mechanical work. Since work has been defined as the product of a force multiplied by a displacement, it is not stored in a system. It represents a form of energy that must be crossing the boundaries (real or imaginary) of the system and can properly be placed in the category of energy in transition.

To distinguish between the transfer of energy as work to or from a system, we shall adopt the convention that the work done by a system on its surroundings is positive, and work done by the surroundings on the system is negative. For the student it is best to think of this convention regarding the useful work out of a system as a conventional, desirable quantity and, therefore, positive. Thus in Illustrative Problem 2.6 the spring has work done on it by a force. If we consider the spring as our system, the work is negative; if we consider the system as the external variable force that is compressing the spring, the work is positive. The student will note that the decision whether the work term is positive or negative requires that the system be carefully defined.

The work that a system can perform on its surroundings is not an intrinsic property of the system. The manner in which the process is carried out will determine the effect on the surroundings. As stated earlier, work is a transitory effect and is neither a property of a system nor is it stored in a system. There is one process, however, which does permit the evaluation of the work done, since the path is uniquely defined. This process is frictionless and quasi-static, and we shall find it useful in subsequent discussions. To describe this process, we first define *equilibrium state* in the manner given by Hatsopoulos and Keenan, "A state is an equilibrium state if no finite rate of change can occur without a finite change, temporary or permanent, in the state of the environment."* The term permanent change of state refers to one that is not canceled out before completion of the process. Therefore, the frictionless *quasi-static process* can be

---

*Hatsopoulos and Keenan, "A Single Axiom for Classical Thermodynamics," ASME paper 61-WA-110, 1961.

identified as a succession of equilibrium states. Involved in this definition is the concept of a process carried out infinitely slowly so that it is in equilibrium at all times. The utility of the frictionless quasi-static process lies in our ability to evaluate the work terms involved in it, since its path is uniquely defined. Before considering several mechanical processes, it is first convenient to discuss another form of energy that can cross the boundaries of a system, *heat*.

When a heat interaction occurs in a system, two distinct events are observed. The first is an interchange of energy, and the second is that this interchange would not have taken place if there were no temperature difference between the system and its surroundings. Therefore, we may define *heat* as the energy in transition across the boundaries of a system due to a temperature difference between the system and its surroundings. In this definition of heat, the transfer of mass across the boundaries of the system is excluded. It should be noted that this indicates a similarity between heat and work. Both are energies in transition, and neither is a property of the system in question. Just as in work, heat can transfer quasi-statically to or from a system. The difference in temperature between the system and its surroundings for quasi-static heat transfer can be only an infinitesimal amount at any time. Once again it is necessary to adopt a convention for the energy interchanged by a system with its surroundings. We shall use the convention that heat to a system from its surroundings is positive; heat out of a system is negative. To learn these conventions, it is convenient to consider the conventional situation in which heat is transferred to a system to obtain useful work from the system. This sets the convention that heat into a system is positive and work out of the system is also positive. Positive in this sense means either desirable or conventional from the viewpoint of conventional power cycles. For refrigeration cycles the opposite of this convention will be more useful.

Since work and heat are both forms of energy in transition, it follows that the units of work should be capable of being expressed as heat units, and vice versa. In the English system of units the conversion factor between work and heat is 778.169 ft lb/Btu and is conventionally given the symbol J. We shall use this symbol to designate 778 ft lb/Btu, since this is sufficiently accurate for engineering applications of thermodynamics. In the SI system this conversion factor is not necessary since the joule (N·m) is the basic energy unit.

2.3a Potential Energy

Let us consider the following problem illustrated in Fig. 2.7: a body of mass m is in a locality in which the local gravitational field is constant and equal to g. A force is applied to the body, and the body is raised a distance Z from its initial position. The force is assumed to be only infinitesimally greater than the mass, so that the process is carried out on a frictionless quasi-static basis. In the absence of electrical, magnetic, and other extraneous effects, determine the work done on the body. The solution to this problem is obtained by noting that

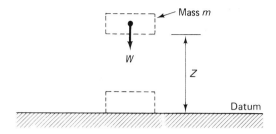

Figure 2.7 Potential energy

the equilibrium of the body requires that a force be applied to it equal to its weight. The weight of the body is given from Chapter 1 as mg/g_c in English Units. In moving through a distance Z, the work done by this force will then equal

$$\text{work} = \frac{mg}{g_c} Z \qquad (2.2a)$$

The work done on the body can be returned to the external environment by simply reversing this frictionless quasi-static process, a feature that is discussed in detail in Chapter 3. Returning to Eq. (2.2a), we conclude that this system has had work done on it equal to $(mg/g_c)(Z)$ and that, in turn, the system has stored in it an amount of energy in excess of the amount it had in its initial position. The energy added to the system in this case is called potential energy. Thus

$$\text{potential energy (P.E.)} = \frac{mg}{g_c} Z \qquad (2.2b)$$

In terms of SI units, Eqs. (2.2a) and (2.2b) become,

$$\text{work} = mgZ \qquad (2.2c)$$
$$\text{potential energy (P.E.)} = mgZ \qquad (2.2d)$$

A feature of importance of potential energy is that a system can be said to possess it only with respect to an arbitrary initial or datum plane.

An interesting application of the concept of potential energy storage is the pumped storage hydroelectric power plant.* The principle of operation can be illustrated using Figs. 2.8a and b. In this system reversible turbine–generator units are used as follows: At those times when excess generating capacity is available from other generating stations, the water can be pumped from the lower to the upper reservoir. When additional generating capacity is required,

---

*See, for example, "Power Systems: The Place of Hydro and Pumped Storage" by J. Tillinghast, *Mechanical Engineering*, July 1969, pp. 24–28.

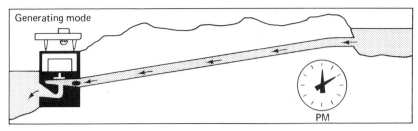

a. Generating Mode

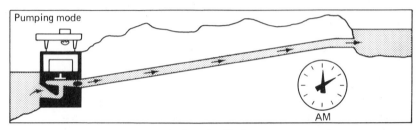

b. Pumping Mode

Figure 2.8 The pumped storage concept

the water is allowed to run downhill, passing through the generating station where it operates the reversible turbine–generator as a turbine to rotate the generator and produce electricity. Thus the pump-storage station helps to smooth out fluctuations in the load demand, resulting in steady, more efficient operation of other stations. In this application the potential energy of the water stored in the upper reservoir provides the energy to the system as needed. Dams also use the potential energy of water to generate electrical power.

ILLUSTRATIVE PROBLEM 2.9

A pumped storage plant uses water pumped to an elevation of 600 feet above the turbogenerators. How much power is generated by a flow of 10,000 gallons/minute. Assume that local gravity is g_c and the density of water is 62.4 lb/cu ft.

Solution

Since local gravity is g_c,

$$\text{P.E.} = \frac{mg}{g_c}(Z) = 1 \times \frac{g}{g_c} \times 600 = 600 \frac{\text{ft lb}}{\text{lb}}$$

The flow is given as 10,000 gallons/min. Since 1 gallon = 231 cu in., $10,000 \times \dfrac{231}{1728} = 1340$ cu ft/min. The total mass flow is $\dot{m} = \rho A V = 62.4 \times 1340$ $= 83,600$ lb/min. The total generating power is the energy stored per pound (P.E.) multiplied by the pounds per minute flowing. Thus $83,600 \times 600 = 50,160,000$ ft lb/min. Finally, since 1 horsepower = 33,000 ft lb/min, $50,160,000/33,000 = 1520$ horsepower.

ILLUSTRATIVE PROBLEM 2.10

A pump delivers 1000 kg/min of water ($\rho = 1000$ kg/m^3) from a well that is 50 m deep. Determine the change in potential energy and the horsepower (hp) required by the pump. Use $g = 9.81$ m/s^2 and neglect kinetic energy changes.

Solution

The change in potential energy is mgZ, where Z is 50 m, using the bottom of the well as the datum. Therefore,

$$\text{P.E.} = mgZ = 1000 \text{ kg/min} \times 9.81 \,\frac{\text{m}}{\text{sec}^2} \times 50 \text{ m} \times \frac{1}{60 \text{ sec/min}}$$

$$\text{P.E.} = 8175 \,\frac{\text{N} \cdot \text{m}}{\text{s}} = 8175 \,\frac{\text{J}}{\text{s}} = 8175 \text{ W}$$

Since 1 hp = 746 W,

$$\frac{8175}{746} \,\frac{\text{W}}{\text{W/hp}} = 10.96 \text{ hp}$$

2.3b Kinetic Energy

Let us consider another situation in which a body of mass m is at rest on a frictionless plane (Fig. 2.9). If the force F is applied to the mass, it will be accelerated in the direction of the force. After moving through a distance Δx, the velocity of the body will have increased from V_1 to V_2. The only effect of the work done on the body will be to increase its velocity.

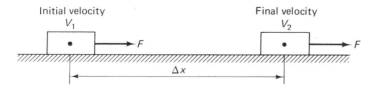

Figure 2.9 Kinetic energy

To solve this situation, we shall apply the impulse–momentum relation used in Chapter 1. Thus, in English units,

$$F\Delta t = \frac{m\Delta V}{g_c} \qquad (2.3)$$

where Δt is the time interval during which the force is applied and ΔV is the change in velocity during this time interval. The distance traveled during this time, Δx, equals the average velocity during the time interval multiplied by the time interval. Mathematically,

$$\Delta x = \bar{V}(\Delta t) \qquad (2.4)$$

where $\bar{V}$ is the average velocity.

If the value of Δt from Eq. (2.4) is substituted into Eq. (2.3),

$$\frac{F\Delta x}{\bar{V}} = \frac{m\Delta V}{g_c} \qquad (2.4a)$$

or

$$F\Delta x = \frac{m\bar{V}\Delta V}{g_c} \qquad (2.4b)$$

The change in velocity ΔV is equal to $V_2 - V_1$, and the average velocity $\bar{V}$ is equal to $\frac{1}{2}(V_1 + V_2)$. These relations can be placed into Eq. (2.4b) to obtain

$$F\Delta x = \frac{m}{g_c}\left(\frac{V_1 + V_2}{2}\right)(V_2 - V_1) \qquad (2.5)$$

and

$$F\Delta x = \frac{mV_2^2}{2g_c} - \frac{mV_1^2}{2g_c} \qquad (2.6)$$

It will be noted that the left side of Eq. (2.6) is the work done on the system by the force F. The terms on the right side of the equation are called the kinetic energy (K.E.) of the body at the beginning and end of the process. Thus Eq. (2.6) expresses the energy possessed by a body of mass m having a velocity V relative to a stationary reference. It is usual to consider the earth as being the reference.

In SI units, Eq. (2.6) becomes

$$F\Delta x = \frac{mV_2^2}{2} - \frac{mV_1^2}{2} \qquad (2.6a)$$

ILLUSTRATIVE PROBLEM 2.11

A mass of 10 lb is slowed from a velocity of 88 ft/sec to 10 ft/sec. What is the change in the kinetic energy of the system if the body is considered to be the system?

Solution

The kinetic energy of the body before it is slowed down is

$$\text{K.E.} = \frac{mV^2}{2g_c} = \frac{10 \times (88)^2}{2 \times 32.2} = 1202.5 \text{ ft lb}$$

After slowing down,

$$\text{K.E.} = \frac{mV^2}{2g_c} = \frac{10 \times (10)^2}{2 \times 32.2} = 15.5 \text{ ft lb}$$

The change in kinetic energy $\Delta(\text{K.E.})$ is, therefore,

$$\Delta\text{K.E.} = 1202.5 - 15.5 = 1187 \text{ ft lb}$$

ILLUSTRATIVE PROBLEM 2.12

A car having a mass of 1500 kg is slowed from 50 km/hr to 30 km/hr. What is the change in its kinetic energy if $g = 9.81$ m/s²?

Solution

The car's initial kinetic energy is $mV^2/2$. Therefore,

$$\text{K.E.} = 1500 \text{ kg} \times \left(\frac{50 \times 1000 \text{ m/hr}}{3600 \text{ s/hr}}\right)^2 = 289.35 \text{ kJ}$$

After slowing down,

$$\text{K.E.} = \frac{mV^2}{2} = 1500 \text{ kg} \times \left(\frac{30 \times 1000 \text{ m/hr}}{3600 \text{ s/hr}}\right)^2 = 104.17 \text{ kJ}$$

The change in kinetic energy is therefore,

$$\Delta\text{K.E.} = 289.35 - 104.17 = 185.18 \text{ kJ}$$

Note that g did not enter the problem in this system of units.

2.3c Internal Energy

To this point we have considered the energy in a system that arises from the work done on the system. However, it was noted in Chapter 1 and earlier in this chapter that a body possesses energy by virtue of the motion of the molecules of the body. In addition, it possesses energy due to the internal attractive and repulsive forces between particles. These forces give rise to the storage of energy internally as potential energy. The energy from all such sources is called the internal energy of the body and is designated by the symbol U. Per unit mass (m), the specific internal energy is denoted by the symbol u, where $mu = U$. From a practical standpoint, the measurement of the absolute internal energy of a system in a given state presents an insurmountable problem and is not essential to our study of thermodynamics. We are concerned with changes in internal energy, and the arbitrary datum for the zero of internal energy will not enter into these problems.

Just as it is possible to distinguish the various forms of energy, such as work and heat, in a mechanical system, it is equally possible to distinguish the various forms of energy associated with electrical, chemical, and other systems. For the purposes of this book, these forms of energy, work, and heat are not considered. The student is cautioned that if a system includes any forms of energy other than mechanical these items must be included. For example, the energy that is dissipated in a resistor as heat when a current flows through it must be taken into account when all the energies of an electrical system are being considered.

2.4 THE FIRST LAW OF THERMODYNAMICS

The first law of thermodynamics can be expressed in the following equivalent statements:

1 The first law of thermodynamics is essentially the statement of the principle of the conservation of energy for thermodynamical systems. As such, it may be expressed by stating that the variation of energy of a system during any transformation is equal to the amount of energy that the system receives from its environment (Fermi, p. 11).

2 Energy can be neither created nor destroyed but only converted from one form to another (Obert, p. 59).

3 If a system is caused to change from an initial state to a final state by adiabatic means only, the work done is the same for all adiabatic paths connecting the two states (Zemansky, p. 59).

In statement 3, by Zemansky, the term adiabatic is used. In general, we define an *adiabatic* transformation of a system as a process the system is caused to undergo, with no energy interchange as heat occurring during the process.

4 If an adiabatic process of a system occurs in such a way that there are no effects external to the system except the change between specified levels of a number of standard weights, the number of standard weights is fixed by the end states of the system and is independent of the details of the process (Keenan and Hatsopoulos).

For the purposes of this book, the concept of the conservation of energy, explicitly stated in the Fermi and Obert definitions, is essentially the first law of thermodynamics. By combining them we have for the statement of the **first law of thermodynamics** that *energy can neither be created nor destroyed but only converted from one form to another.* Since we shall not concern ourselves with nuclear reactions at this time, it will not be necessary to invoke the interconvertibility of energy and mass in our present study.

2.5 THE NONFLOW SYSTEM

The statements made in Section 2.4 about the first law of thermodynamics are, in essence, equivalent to each other in that they express the concept of energy conservation. To explore some of the implications and applications of the first law, let us examine the *nonflow* or *closed system*. This system will have boundaries across which both heat and work can penetrate, but no mass will be permitted to cross them. An example is a piston-and-cylinder arrangement in which the piston compresses the working fluid in the cylinder and heat may cross the boundary (say, by cooling of the cylinder) at the same time. This system is shown schematically in Fig. 2.10. For convenience, it is assumed that there is a

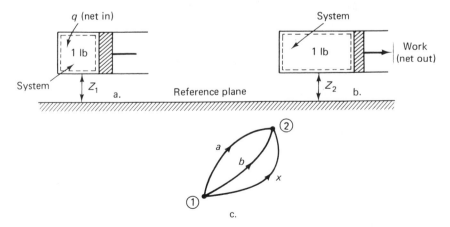

Figure 2.10

unit mass in the cylinder. Assuming also that there are no (or negligible) changes in elevation during the process and that there is no directed (net) velocity of the working fluid, we may properly neglect energy terms relating to potential and kinetic energy. Writing the first law in words which state that the energy in state *a* plus or minus any additions or depletions from the system must equal the energy in state *b* yields the following:

$$u_1 + q - W = u_2 \qquad (2.7)$$

By rearranging,

$$u_2 - u_1 = q - W \qquad (2.8a)$$

where both q and W are used to denote the net heat and net work, respectively, entering or leaving the system per unit mass of fluid.

It is interesting and instructive to note that the piston–cylinder arrangement is treated as a nonflow process by the selection of the boundaries of the

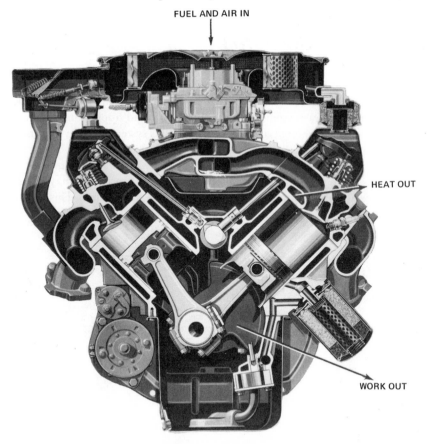

FUEL AND AIR IN

HEAT OUT

WORK OUT

Figure 2.11 A 429-cubic-inch displacement V-8 engine (Courtesy of Ford Motor Corp.)

system, as shown by the dashed lines in Fig. 2.10a and b. However, when the piston and cylinder are part of an internal combustion engine, such as shown in Fig. 2.11, the selection of the system boundary at the exterior of the engine as shown leads us to a steady-flow system where fuel and air enter while heat and work cross the boundary. This concept will be treated in further detail when we concern ourselves with power cycles in Chapter 7.

Equation (2.8a) is useful in establishing that internal energy is a property of a system and is not dependent on the path taken to place the system in a given configuration. This is true even though both q and W are path functions; that is, their values depend on the method of placing a system in a given configuration. For proof of the fact that internal energy is a property, the following reasoning is used*: Consider a system initially at state 1 that is caused to undergo a change to a second state 2 via path a. From Eq. (2.8a) and Fig. 2.10c, we have

$$u_2 - u_1 = q_a - W_a \qquad\qquad (2.8b)$$

where the subscript a is used to denote path a. If path b is now followed between the same points 1 and 2, Eq. (2.8a) becomes

$$u_2 - u_1 = q_b - W_b \qquad\qquad (2.8c)$$

This procedure can be carried out for any path (x), and it must follow that when Eq. (2.8a) is applied

$$u_2 - u_1 = q_x - W_x \qquad\qquad (2.8d)$$

Since the left sides of Eqs. (2.8b), (2.8c), and (2.8d) are equal, it follows that the right sides of these equations

$$q_x - W_x = q_a - W_a = q_b - W_b \qquad\qquad (2.9a)$$

are also equal, and that $u_2 - u_1$ is fixed only by the end states of the system and is independent of the process. It can, therefore, be concluded that internal energy is a property. As such it is a state function and independent of the path of any process. There is one point about which the student should make careful note. The proof of the fact that internal energy is a property is extremely important. In the calculus an area can be obtained by integration. This process can be performed for those functions (paths) that can be evaluated as being continuous and dependent only on the end states. Such a function is said to be mathematically exact, and it is possible to perform all operations of the calculus on it. Opposed to this concept is the function whose value between two end states is determined, not by the end states, but by the path taken to achieve the

---

*This material is a modification of the proof in *Thermodynamics* by J. H. Keenan, John Wiley & Sons, Inc., New York, 1941, p. 12 and following.

end state. For example, the work done in moving a given block from one position on a plane to another position on the plane will depend on the amount of work done against friction. If the table is rough, more work is required to go from the initial to the final position than if the table were smooth. Mathematically, such a function is said to be inexact, and, in general, it is not possible to evaluate this function directly by the methods of the calculus unless the path is defined. *Work and heat are inexact (path functions), whereas internal energy has just been shown to be exact (a function of the end states only).*

ILLUSTRATIVE PROBLEM 2.13

If a nonflow constant volume process has 10 Btu/lb added to the system, what is the change in internal energy per pound of working fluid?

Solution

For a constant-volume process we can consider that the piston in Fig. 2.10 has not moved. Alternately, we can consider that a tank having a fixed volume has heat added to it. Under these conditions the mechanical work done on or by the system must be zero. The application of Eq. (2.8a) to this system yields

$$u_2 - u_1 = q$$

and it must be concluded that all the energy crossing the boundary as heat has been converted to internal energy of the working fluid. Therefore,

$$u_2 - u_1 = 10 \text{ Btu/lb}$$

ILLUSTRATIVE PROBLEM 2.14

The working fluid in a nonflow system undergoes an adiabatic change. Determine the work done in this process.

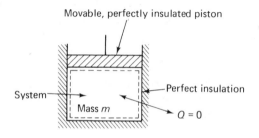

Figure 2.12 Illustrative Problem 2.14

Solution

An adiabatic process has been defined to be one during which no energy interchange as heat crosses the boundary of a system. As shown in Fig. 2.12 this is the same as considering the system boundaries to be perfectly insulated. Notice, however, that the piston can and does move. Application of Eq. (2.8a) to this situation yields

$$u_2 - u_1 = - W$$

Thus the energy interchange as work to or from the system per unit mass of working substance equals the change in internal energy of the working fluid per unit mass of fluid. The negative sign is taken to mean that work into the system (negative work by convention) will cause an increase in the internal energy of the working fluid and that work out of the system (positive work) will cause a decrease in the internal energy of the working fluid.

Let us now consider the case of the piston and cylinder arrangement shown in Fig. 2.13. We assume that the piston is in equilibrium with the contents and initially a distance l above the end of the cylinder. The piston will now be permitted to compress the contents of the cylinder frictionlessly and quasi-statically. After the piston has moved a distance Δl, a very small change in distance, the pressure in the cylinder will have increased from its initial value of p to a value of $p + \Delta p$, where Δp indicates a very small change in pressure. Since this process was specified to be quasi-static, it is possible to evaluate the work as the product of the average force multiplied by the displacement. The average force is $\frac{1}{2}[pA + (p + \Delta p)A]$, and the displacement is Δl. Thus

$$W(\text{per unit mass}) = \left[\frac{p + (p + \Delta p)}{2} \right](A\Delta l) \qquad (2.9b)$$

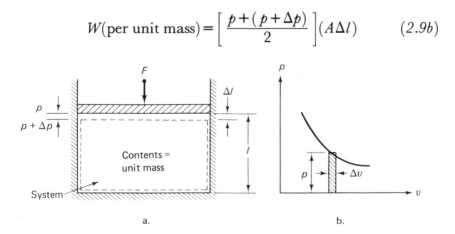

Figure 2.13 Quasi-static nonflow compression process

However, the product of $A\Delta l$ is the small change in volume that the piston has swept out. Replacing $A\Delta l$ by Δv and saying that the product of two very small numbers $(\Delta v\Delta p)$ is indeed so small as to be negligible

$$W = p\Delta v \quad \text{(per unit mass of working fluid)} \qquad (2.9c)$$

Equation (2.9c) can be interpreted by referring to Fig. 2.13b. It will be noted that the term $p\Delta v$ represents a small element of area, and that the total work can be evaluated by summing all the $p\Delta v$ terms. Therefore, we can conclude that the work done in a quasi-static, frictionless, nonflow process is the area under the pv curve. Using Eq. (2.9c), with Eq. (2.8a) permits us to arrive at the following useful relation:

$$u_2 - u_1 = q - p\Delta v \qquad (2.10)$$

Equation (2.10) is written per unit mass of working fluid, and the student is cautioned to understand the reasoning behind this equation fully so that he will not misapply it.

Either Eq. (2.8a) or Eq. (2.10) is called the *nonflow energy equation* and expresses the first law as applied to a nonflow process. Equation (2.10) is more restrictive and in the strictest sense is applicable only to frictionless, quasi-static, nonflow processes.

ILLUSTRATIVE PROBLEM 2.15

Solve Illustrative Problem 2.13 by the direct application of Eq. (2.10).

Solution

$$u_2 - u_1 = q - p\Delta v$$

But $v_2 - v_1$ (or Δv) is zero. Therefore,

$$u_2 - u_\mathrm{i} = q \quad \text{(as before)}$$

There is one nonflow process that will be found to be quite important in our subsequent discussion, the quasi-static *nonflow constant pressure* process. Using Eq. (2.10), we will now derive an expression relating heat, work, and internal energy for this process. Refer to the situation illustrated in Fig. 2.10 where heat and work can cross the system boundary. Transposing terms in Eq. (2.10) yields

$$u_2 - u_1 + p\Delta v = q \qquad (2.10a)$$

However, p, the pressure, has been defined to be constant. Therefore,

$$u_2 - u_1 + p(v_2 - v_1) = q \qquad (2.10b)$$

The condition of constant pressure permits us to write $p = p_1 = p_2$. Thus

$$u_2 - u_1 + p_2 v_2 - p_1 v_1 = q \qquad (2.10c)$$

Equation (2.10c) is consistent in terms of SI units. If the internal energy is in Btu per pound, pressure is in pounds per square foot, and specific volume is in cubic feet per pound, we can regroup terms and place them into consistent thermal units of Btu per pound as follows:

$$\left(u_2 + \frac{p_2 v_2}{J}\right) - \left(u_1 + \frac{p_1 v_1}{J}\right) = q \qquad (2.10d)$$

The composite term $u + pv/J$ is a property that we will find to have a great deal of utility when flow processes are considered. At present we will simply define h to be enthalpy expressed in Btu/lb and to be given by

$$h = u + \frac{pv}{J} \qquad (2.11)$$

The conversion factor J is carried along as a reminder to the student of the necessity to use consistent units in the English system at all times. Returning to Eq. (2.10d), we now have the following energy equation for the nonflow quasi-static constant-pressure process:

$$q = h_2 - h_1 = \Delta h \qquad (2.10e)$$

So far, three nonflow, quasi-static processes have been considered. To summarize the energy equations for these processes,

1 *Constant-volume process:*

$$q = u_2 - u_1 = \Delta u \qquad (2.12)$$

2 *Adiabatic process:*

$$-W = u_2 - u_1 = \Delta u \qquad (2.13)$$

3 *Constant-pressure process:*

$$q = h_2 - h_1 = \Delta h \qquad (2.10e)$$

4 *Work of a quasi-static nonflow process:*

$$W = p\Delta v \qquad (2.9c)$$

5 *Enthalpy is defined as*

$$h = u + \frac{pv}{J} \qquad\qquad (2.11)$$

or
$$h_2 - h_1 = \left(u_2 + \frac{p_2 v_2}{J}\right) - \left(u_1 + \frac{p_1 v_1}{J}\right) \qquad (2.14)$$

In all the foregoing it has been assumed that the mass of fluid was unity. The equations derived can be used for any mass simply by multiplying each term in the energy equation by m, the mass involved. The enthalpy definition used in this book will include the conversion factor J for convenience and consistency, especially when using English units.

ILLUSTRATIVE PROBLEM 2.16

A rigid container contains 10 lb of water. (a) If 100 Btu are added to the water, what is its change in internal energy per pound of water? (b) If the 100 Btu are added by the mechanical friction of a paddle wheel stirring the water, what is the change in internal energy of the water? Discuss both processes. Refer to Fig. 2.14.

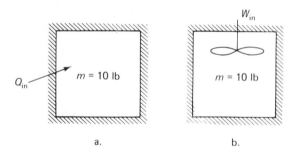

Figure 2.14 Illustrative Problem 2.16

Solution

(a) The nonflow energy equation applied to this process yields $q = u_2 - u_1$. Per pound of working substance, $q = 100/10$, or 10 Btu/lb. Therefore, $u_2 - u_1 = 10$ Btu/lb. (b) In this process energy crosses the boundary of the system by means of frictional work. As far as the system is concerned, we note only that energy has crossed its boundaries. The similarity of the terms work and heat lies in the fact that both are energy in transition. Thus for the present problem the contents of the tank will not distinguish between the energy if it is added as heat or the energy added as frictional work. As for part a, $u_2 - u_1 = 10$ Btu/lb.

ILLUSTRATIVE PROBLEM 2.17

A process is carried out in a nonflow quasi-static manner so that the pressure–volume relationship of the fluid is given by

$$pv = \text{constant}$$

where p is the pressure and v is the specific volume of the fluid. Determine the work done on the fluid if it undergoes a process in which its specific volume goes from v_1 to v_2.

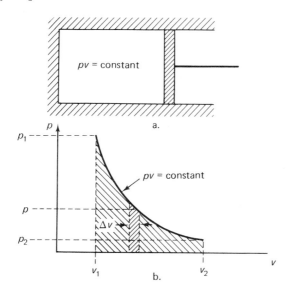

Figure 2.15 Illustrative Problem 2.17

Solution

In order to solve this problem, it is necessary to sum all values of $p\Delta v$ over the entire range of the problem. As shown in Fig. 2.15b, this corresponds to obtaining the area under the pv curve between the limits of v_2 and v_1. Therefore,

$$W = \sum p\Delta v$$

where the symbol $\sum$ means the sum of all such values. To carry out this summation, we must first express p as a function of v. From the given p,v relation, $p = \text{constant}/v$, where the constant is $pv = p_1v_1 = p_2v_2$. When this is substituted in the $p\Delta v$ expression, we obtain

$$W = \text{constant} \sum \frac{\Delta v}{v}$$

where the total work is the sum of these terms. The summation referred to can best be illustrated by plotting $1/v$ as a function of v. The shaded area of Fig. 2.16 is simply $\Delta v/v$. Thus the total work per pound of fluid is the area under this curve between v_1 and v_2 multiplied by a constant. Using the methods of the calculus, we find the summation to be numerically equal to $\ln(v_2/v_1)$. Note that $\ln x = \log_e x = 2.3026 \log_{10} x$. Since the constant was either $p_1 v_1$ or $p_2 v_2$,

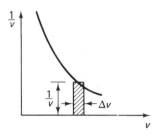

Figure 2.16 Evaluation of $\Sigma \dfrac{\Delta v}{v}$

$$W = p_1 v_1 \ln \frac{v_2}{v_1} \frac{\text{ft lb}}{\text{lb}} \quad \text{or} \quad \frac{\text{N·m}}{\text{kg}}$$

or
$$W = p_2 v_2 \ln \frac{v_2}{v_1} \frac{\text{ft lb}}{\text{lb}} \quad \text{or} \quad \frac{\text{N·m}}{\text{kg}}$$

We shall have occasion to perform this type of summation in connection with other situations, and the procedure should be understood at this time for ease of application in the future.

ILLUSTRATIVE PROBLEM 2.18

For the process described in Illustrative Problem 2.17, the initial pressure is found to be 100 psia and the initial specific volume, 2 cu ft/lb. If the final specific volume is 1 cu ft/lb, how much work was done on the fluid per pound of fluid?

Solution

From Illustrative Problem 2.17, $W = p_1 v_1 \ln(v_2/v_1)$. For the proper units it is necessary that pressure be expressed as psfa when the volume is in cubic feet. Thus 100 psia = 100 (144) psfa and $v_1 = 2$ cu ft/lb.

$$W = (100 \times 144 \times 2)\left(\ln \tfrac{1}{2}\right)$$

This is best evaluated by noting that $\ln \tfrac{1}{2} = \ln 1 - \ln 2$. The $\ln 2$ is 0.693 and the $\ln 1$ is zero. Therefore,

$$W = -100 \times 144 \times 2 \times 0.693 = -19{,}963 \text{ ft lb/lb}$$

In thermal units

$$W = \frac{-19{,}963 \text{ ft lb/lb mass}}{778 \text{ ft lb/Btu}} = -25.7 \text{ Btu/lb}$$

The minus sign in the answer indicates work into the system. As an exercise, it is left to the student to solve this problem by graphically evaluating the area under the pressure–volume curve.

ILLUSTRATIVE PROBLEM 2.19

For the process $pv = $ constant, a gas compression is carried out from an initial pressure of 200 kPa to a final pressure of 800 kPa. If the initial specific volume is 0.1 m^3/kg, determine the work done per kilogram of gas.

Solution

Since $p_1 v_1 = p_2 v_2$,

$$v_2 = \frac{p_1 v_1}{p_2} = \frac{200}{800} \times 0.1 = 0.025 \text{ m}^3/\text{kg}$$

and

$$W = p_1 v_1 \ln \frac{v_2}{v_1}$$

$$= 200 \times 0.1 \times \ln \frac{0.025}{0.100} = -27.7 \text{ kJ/kg} \quad \text{(into the system)}$$

2.6 THE STEADY FLOW SYSTEM

In the steady flow system, both mass and energy are permitted to cross the boundaries of the system, but by denoting the process to be steady we limit ourselves to those systems that are not time dependent. In Section 2.2 we developed the continuity equation that expresses the fact that the amounts of fluid flowing into and out of the system are equal to each other or, in other words, the mass of fluid in the system remains constant.

When a fluid is caused to flow in a system, it is necessary that somewhere in the system work must have been supplied. At this time, let us evaluate the net work required to push the fluid into and out of the system. Consider the system shown in Fig. 2.17, where a fluid is flowing steadily across the system boundaries as shown. At the inlet section ①, the pressure is p_1, the area is A_1,

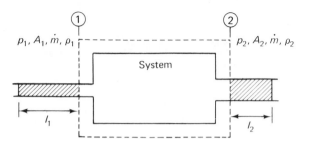

Figure 2.17 Steady flow system—flow work

the mass flow rate is $\dot{m}$, and the fluid density is ρ_1 (or its reciprocal specific volume, $1/v_1$); at the outlet section ②, the pressure is p_2, the area is A_2, the mass flow rate is still $\dot{m}$, and the fluid density is ρ_2 (or its reciprocal specific volume $1/v_2$). Let us now consider a plug of fluid of length l_1 entering the system such that the amount of fluid contained in the plug is numerically $\dot{m}$. The force acting on the inlet cross-sectional area A_1 is $p_1 A_1$. To push the plug into the system, it is necessary for this force to move the plug a distance equal to l_1. In so doing the work done will be $p_1 A_1 l_1$. However, $A_1 l_1$ is the volume of the plug containing a mass m. Using this we find the work, W, to be

$$W = p_1 A_1 l_1 = m(p_1 v_1) \quad \text{(ft lb) or (N·m)} \qquad (2.15)$$

The work per unit mass is

$$W = p_1 v_1 \quad \text{(ft lb/lb) or (N·m/kg)} \qquad (2.15a)$$

If we now consider the outlet section, using the same reasoning we have

$$W = m(p_2 v_2) \quad \text{(ft lb) or (N·m)} \qquad (2.15b)$$

$$\text{or} \qquad W = p_2 v_2 \quad \text{(ft lb/lb) or (N·m/kg)} \qquad (2.15c)$$

Each of the pv terms is known as the flow work. The net flow work becomes

$$\text{net flow work} = p_2 v_2 - p_1 v_1 \quad \text{(ft lb/lb) or (N·m/kg)} \qquad (2.16)$$

or in thermal units

$$\text{net flow work (Btu/lb)} = \frac{p_2 v_2}{J} - \frac{p_1 v_1}{J} \qquad (2.16a)$$

$$\text{or} \qquad \text{net flow work} = p_2 v_2 - p_1 v_1 \quad \text{(N·m/kg)} \qquad (2.16b)$$

Equation (2.16) is interpreted to mean that the difference in the pv terms represents the amount of work that is done on a system to introduce a unit mass into it minus the work done on its environment as it leaves the system. However, a word of caution is necessary at this time. Any fluid in any system has both properties, pressure and specific volume, and, therefore, the product pv can always be evaluated. *The product pv only represents flow work in the steady flow system.* Thus, even though we have already seen that the term pv/J appears in the nonflow constant pressure process, it cannot and does not represent flow work since the system is by definition stationary. Flow work only exists to cause fluid to cross the boundaries of a flow system.

In the foregoing derivations, certain assumptions were made, and these are repeated here for emphasis. The term steady, when applied to a flow situation, means that the condition at any section of the system is independent of time. Even though the velocity, specific volume, and temperature of the fluid can vary in any arbitrary manner across the stream, they are not permitted to vary with time. The mass entering the system per unit time must equal the mass leaving the system in the same period of time; otherwise, the system would either store or be depleted of fluid.

ILLUSTRATIVE PROBLEM 2.20

At the entrance to a steady flow device it is found that the pressure is 100 psia and the density of the fluid is 62.4 cu ft/lb. At the exit the pressure is 50 psia and the corresponding density is 30 cu ft/lb. Determine the flow work term at the entrance and exit of the device.

Solution

Refer to Fig. 2.17. At the entrance

$$\frac{pv}{J} = \frac{100 \times 144(1/62.4)}{778} = 0.297 \text{ Btu/lb}$$

At the exit

$$\frac{pv}{J} = \frac{50 \times 144(1/30)}{778} = 0.308 \text{ Btu/lb}$$

ILLUSTRATIVE PROBLEM 2.21

Determine the flow work at the entrance and exit of a steady flow device in which the entrance pressure is 200 kPa and the density of the fluid is 1000 kg/m^3. At the exit the pressure is 100 kPa and the density is 250 kg/m^3.

Solution

At entrance

$$pv = (200 \times 1000) \frac{N}{m^2} \times \frac{1}{1000 \text{ kg/m}^3} = 200 \frac{N \cdot m}{kg}$$

at exit

$$pv = (100 \times 1000) \frac{N}{m^2} \times \frac{1}{250 \text{ kg/m}^3} = 400 \frac{N \cdot m}{kg}$$

Since 1 N·m/kg is 1 joule/kg, the answers are in J/kg.

Figure 2.18 shows a steady flow system in which it is assumed that each form of energy can enter and leave the system. At entrance, $\dot{m}$ lb of fluid per second enter and the same amount leaves at the exit. At the entrance the fluid has a pressure of p_1, a specific volume of v_1, an internal energy of u_1, and a velocity of V_1. At the exit we have similar quantities expressed as p_2, v_2, and V_2. The fluid enters and leaves at different elevations, and work and heat cross the boundary in both directions.

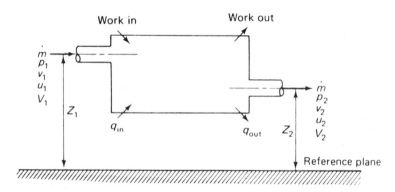

Figure 2.18 Steady-flow system

In applying the first law to a system in which both mass and energy can cross the boundaries, it is necessary to adhere to the mathematical conventions chosen for positive and negative quantities of energy. It is also imperative that all pertinent energy terms be included in any analysis. To summarize the work of this chapter for steady-flow systems, Table 2.1 identifies six energy terms that apply to various situations.

We express the first law for the system shown in Fig. 2.18 by stating that all the energy entering the system must equal all the energy leaving the system. This energy balance is set up in Table 2.2.

TABLE 2.1
ENERGY TERMS

ITEM	*VALUE* (Btu / unit mass)	*VALUE0* (joules / unit mass)
Potential energy	$\dfrac{Zg}{Jg_c}$	Zg
Kinetic energy	$\dfrac{V^2}{2g_aJ}$	$\dfrac{V^2}{2}$
Internal energy	u	u
Flow work	$\dfrac{pv}{J}$	pv
Work	$\dfrac{W}{J}$	W
Heat	q	q

TABLE 2.2
ENERGY BALANCE

	ENERGY IN (Btu / lb)	*ENERGY IN* (SI)	*ENERGY OUT* (Btu / lb)	*ENERGY OUT* (SI)
Potential energy	$\dfrac{Z_1 g}{Jg_c}$	$Z_1 g$	$\dfrac{Z_2 g}{Jg_c}$	$Z_2 g$
Kinetic energy	$\dfrac{V_1^2}{2g_cJ}$	$\dfrac{V_1^2}{2}$	$\dfrac{V_2^2}{2g_cJ}$	$\dfrac{V_2^2}{2}$
Internal energy	u_1	u_1	u_2	u_2
Flow work	$\dfrac{p_1 v_1}{J}$	$p_1 v_1$	$\dfrac{p_2 v_2}{J}$	$p_2 v_2$
Work	$\dfrac{W_{in}}{J}$	W_{in}	$\dfrac{W_{out}}{J}$	W_{out}
Heat	q_{in}	q_{in}	q_{out}	q_{out}

By equating all the terms in Table 2.2 in English units,

$$\frac{Z_1}{J}\left(\frac{g}{g_c}\right) + \frac{V_1^2}{2g_cJ} + u_1 + \frac{p_1 v_1}{J} + \frac{W_{in}}{J} + q_{in}$$

$$= \frac{Z_2}{J}\left(\frac{g}{g_c}\right) + \frac{V_2^2}{2g_cJ} + u_2 + \frac{p_2 v_2}{J} + \frac{W_{out}}{J} + q_{out} \qquad (2.17)$$

In SI units,

$$Z_1 g + \frac{V_1^2}{2} + u_1 + p_1 v_1 + W_{in} + q_{in} = Z_2 g + \frac{V_2^2}{2} + u_2 + p_2 v_2 + W_{out} + q_{out}$$

$$(2.17a)$$

Equation (2.17) is quite general and expresses the first law for this system. It is sometimes called the *steady flow energy* or the *general energy equation*. We note that it is also quite proper to call it the *energy equation* applied to a steady flow system.

If at this point we note that both the heat and the work terms can be combined to form individual terms of net heat and net work, and being careful of the mathematical signs of these net terms, we can write for English units,

$$\frac{Z_1}{J}\left(\frac{g}{g_c}\right) + \frac{V_1^2}{2g_c J} + u_1 + \frac{p_1 v_1}{J} + q = \frac{Z_2}{J}\left(\frac{g}{g_c}\right) + \frac{V_2^2}{2g_c J} + u_2 + \frac{p_2 v_2}{J} + \frac{W}{J}$$

$$(2.18)$$

In SI units,

$$Z_1 g + \frac{V_1^2}{2} + u_1 + p_1 v_1 + q = Z_2 g + \frac{V_2^2}{2} + p_2 v_2 + W \quad (2.18a)$$

In Eq. (2.18) all terms are written as Btu/lb, and q and W represent *net values* per unit mass of working fluid. If we now note further that the grouping of terms $u + pv/J$ appears on both sides of Eq. (2.18) and that this combined term is a property that we have already called enthalpy, we have, from the definition of the term enthalpy,

$$h = u + \frac{pv}{J} \qquad (2.11)$$

(or $h = u + pv$ in SI units). Using Eqs. (2.11) and (2.18) yields, for English units,

$$\frac{Z_1}{J}\left(\frac{g}{g_c}\right) + \frac{V_1^2}{2g_c J} + h_1 + q = \frac{Z_2}{J}\left(\frac{g}{g_c}\right) + \frac{V_2^2}{2g_c J} + h_2 + \frac{W}{J}$$

$$(2.19)$$

By regrouping the terms in Eq. (2.19),

$$q - \frac{W}{J} = (h_2 - h_1) + \left(\frac{Z_2 - Z_1}{J}\right)\left(\frac{g}{g_c}\right) + \left(\frac{V_2^2 - V_1^2}{2g_c J}\right) \quad (2.20)$$

In terms of SI units,

$$q - W = h_2 - h_1 + g(Z_2 - Z_1) + \frac{V_2^2 - V_1^2}{2} \qquad (2.20a)$$

The student should note that Eqs. (2.17) through (2.20) are essentially the same. To apply these equations intelligently, it is important that each of the terms be completely understood. Although they are not difficult, the student may encounter trouble at this point because of a lack of understanding of these energy equations and the basis for each of the terms in them.

Before illustrating the use of these energy equations, let us consider the following situation. A fluid is flowing steadily in a device in which it undergoes a compression. Let us further assume that this process is frictionless and quasi-static. Its work term can be written as the sum of the work done on the fluid plus the flow work. Kinetic and potential energy terms are assumed to be negligible. Thus the work for this process becomes

$$W = p_1 v_1 - p_2 v_2 - p \Delta v \qquad (2.21)$$

Let us now plot a pv diagram for the fluid, as shown in Fig. 2.19. As is shown in Fig. 2.19a the term $p\Delta v$ is the area under the curve between the limits 1 and 2. Subtracting $p_1 v_1$ and adding $p_2 v_2$ (graphically) results in $v\Delta p$ and is shown on Fig. 2.19b. Mathematically,

$$- v\Delta p = p_2 v_2 - p_1 v_1 + p\Delta v \qquad (2.22)$$

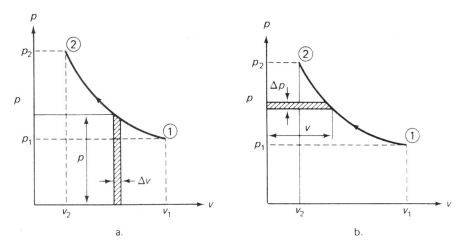

Figure 2.19 The pv diagram

It will be recalled that for the quasi-static, frictionless nonflow system, $p\Delta v$ evaluated the work done on the working fluid. For the flow system, flow work of an amount of $p_1 v_1$ enters the system and flow work of an amount of $p_2 v_2$ leaves the system. We can therefore interpret the meaning of the areas on Fig.

2.19 or the terms of Eq. (2.22) as follows: The work of the quasi-static frictionless flow system (neglecting the kinetic and potential energy terms) is the algebraic sum of the work to induct the fluid into the system plus the work of compression (or expansion), less the flow work to deliver the fluid to the downstream exit. It is sometimes convenient to think of $p\Delta v$ as the work of *compression* (or expansion) and $v\Delta p$ as the work of the *compressor* (or expander). It is extremely important to note that both $p\Delta v$ and $v\Delta p$ evaluate work only for a quasi-static process or system. For systems that are real, they do not evaluate work. However, for a large class of systems they approximate the work terms, and their use is justified both from this approximation and the relative ease with which they can be evaluated.

2.6a The Bernoulli Equation

In fluid mechanics use is sometimes made of the Bernoulli equation. Because of the frequent misapplication of this equation, a brief discussion of it will now be undertaken. Let us consider a system in which the flow is steady, there is no change in internal energy, no work is done on or by the system, no energy as heat crosses the boundaries of the system, and the fluid is incompressible. We further assume that all processes are ideal in the sense that they are frictionless. For this system the energy equation reduces to the following in mechanical units of foot pounds per pound:

$$Z_1\left(\frac{g}{g_c}\right) + \frac{V_1^2}{2g_c} + p_1 v_1 = Z_2\left(\frac{g}{g_c}\right) + \frac{V_2^2}{2g_c} + p_2 v_2 \qquad (2.23)$$

or in SI units

$$Z_1 g + \frac{V_1^2}{2} + p_1 v_1 = Z_2 g + \frac{V_2^2}{2} + p_2 v_2 \qquad (2.23a)$$

Equation (2.23) is the usual form of the Bernoulli equation found in elementary physics and fluid mechanics texts. Each term can represent a height, since the dimension of foot pounds per pound corresponds numerically (and dimensionally) to a height. Hence the term *head* is frequently used to denote each of the terms in Eq. (2.23). From the derivation of this equation we note that its use is restricted to situations in which the flow is steady, there is no friction, no shaft work is done on or by the fluid, the flow is incompressible, and there is no change in internal energy during the process. These restrictions are severe, and only under the simplest situations can we hope to apply the Bernoulli equation successfully. It becomes even more difficult to justify the procedure of adding heat and work terms to this equation while maintaining all the other restrictions. The student is cautioned against use of this equation without a thorough understanding of its restrictions. In every case it is preferable to write the complete and correct form of the energy equation first and then to make those assumptions that can be justified for each problem.

2.6b Specific Heat

The term *specific heat* is defined as the ratio of energy as *heat* transferred during a particular process per unit mass of fluid involved, divided by the corresponding change of temperature of the fluid that occurs during this process. Since heat can be transferred to or from a fluid, and since algebraic signs have been adopted for the direction of heat transfer, it is entirely possible for a process to have a negative specific heat. The student should not confuse the specific heat of a process with the specific heat property.

This definition of specific heat is important for two processes because they serve to define a new property of a fluid. These processes are the constant pressure process (flow or nonflow) and the constant volume process. It will be recalled from the earlier work of this chapter that the constant pressure nonflow process is characterized by the energy equation that $q = h_2 - h_1 = \Delta h$. For the steady-flow process without change in elevation, in the absence of external work, and with negligible changes in kinetic energy, the steady flow energy equation leads to the same result. Thus for *any constant pressure process* (flow or nonflow with the conditions noted) the specific heat is defined as

$$c_p = \left(\frac{q}{\Delta T}\right)_p = \left(\frac{\Delta h}{\Delta T}\right)_p \qquad (2.24)*$$

or

$$(c_p \Delta T = \Delta h)_p \qquad (2.24a)$$

where the subscript p indicates a constant-pressure process.

For the constant-volume process (which can only be a nonflow process) $q = u_2 - u_1 = \Delta u$. Therefore,

$$c_v = \left(\frac{q}{\Delta T}\right)_v = \left(\frac{\Delta u}{\Delta T}\right)_v \qquad (2.25)*$$

or

$$(c_v \Delta T = \Delta u)_v \qquad (2.25a)$$

where the subscript v indicates a constant-volume process.

These specific heats are the properties of the fluid and depend only on the state of the fluid. A further discussion of specific heats is given in Chapter 5 where the internal energy and enthalpy of the ideal gas are functions of temperature only, making the definition of Eqs. (2.24) and (2.25) general for the ideal gas and not restricted to only constant-pressure or constant-volume processes.

---

*Equations (2.24) and (2.25) are more correctly written mathematically as

$$c_p \equiv \left(\frac{\partial h}{\partial t}\right)_p \quad \text{and} \quad c_v \equiv \left(\frac{\partial u}{\partial t}\right)_v.$$

For a further discussion, see the references at the end of the chapter.

ILLUSTRATIVE PROBLEM 2.22

A gas initially at $100°F$ and having $c_p = 0.22$ Btu/lb °F and $c_v = 0.17$ Btu/lb °F is placed within a cylinder. If 800 Btu is added to 10 lb of the gas in a nonflow constant-pressure process, determine the final gas temperature. Also determine the work done on or by the gas. Refer to Fig. 2.20.

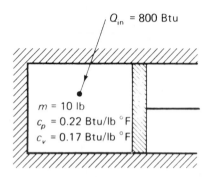

Q_{in} = 800 Btu

m = 10 lb
c_p = 0.22 Btu/lb °F
c_v = 0.17 Btu/lb °F

Figure 2.20 Illustrative Problem 2.22

Solution

For the nonflow constant-pressure process $q = \Delta h = h_2 - h_1$. But Eq. (2.24) allows us to evaluate Δh in terms of temperature and the specific heat at constant pressure. Thus

$$q = h_2 - h_1 = c_p(T_2 - T_1)$$

Using the data given and using q on a unit mass basis,

$$q = \frac{800}{10} = 0.22(T_2 - T_1)$$

and $T_2 - T_1 = 363.6°F$. Since the initial temperature is $100°F$, the final temperature is $363.6°F + 100 = 463.6°F$.

To obtain the work, we apply Eq. (2.8) to the nonflow process,

$$q - W = u_2 - u_1$$

The term $u_2 - u_1$ can be evaluated in terms of temperature and the specific heat at constant volume from Eq. (2.25). Using this we obtain

$$-W = (u_2 - u_1) - q = c_v(T_2 - T_1) - q$$

Using q on a unit mass basis, and noting that $T_2 - T_1 = 363.6°F$,

$$-W = 0.17(363.6) - \frac{800}{10}$$

$$-W = 61.8 - 80 = -18.2 \text{ Btu/lb}$$

or
$$W = 18.2 \text{ Btu/lb}$$

Thus 18.2 Btu/lb or 182 Btu as work is taken out of the system due to work done by the gas since there is 10 lb in the system.

2.7 APPLICATIONS OF THE FIRST LAW OF THERMODYNAMICS

At this point in our study we will apply the first law to several steady flow situations that we will have applications for in later sections of this book. For the present we will restrict ourselves to five steady flow processes:

1 The steam or gas turbine
2 Pipe flow
3 The boiler
4 The flow in nozzles
5 The throttling process

2.7a The Turbine

As our first illustration of the applicability of the first law to steady flow processes, let us consider the steam turbine shown in Fig. 2.21. In this device, steam enters and expands in fixed nozzles to a high velocity. The high velocity steam is then directed over the turbine blades where it does work on the turbine wheel. The steam then exhausts from the turbine. The purpose of this machine is to obtain shaft work, and certain features about it should be noted. The first is that the shaft of the turbine is horizontal; second, as the steam expands, its specific volume increases (Chapter 4), and to keep the exit velocity nearly equal to the entering velocity, the exit pipe area is proportionally greater than the inlet pipe area; the turbine is suitably insulated to minimize heat losses to the surroundings and also to eliminate the possibility of injuring operating personnel working in the vicinity of the hot turbine casing.

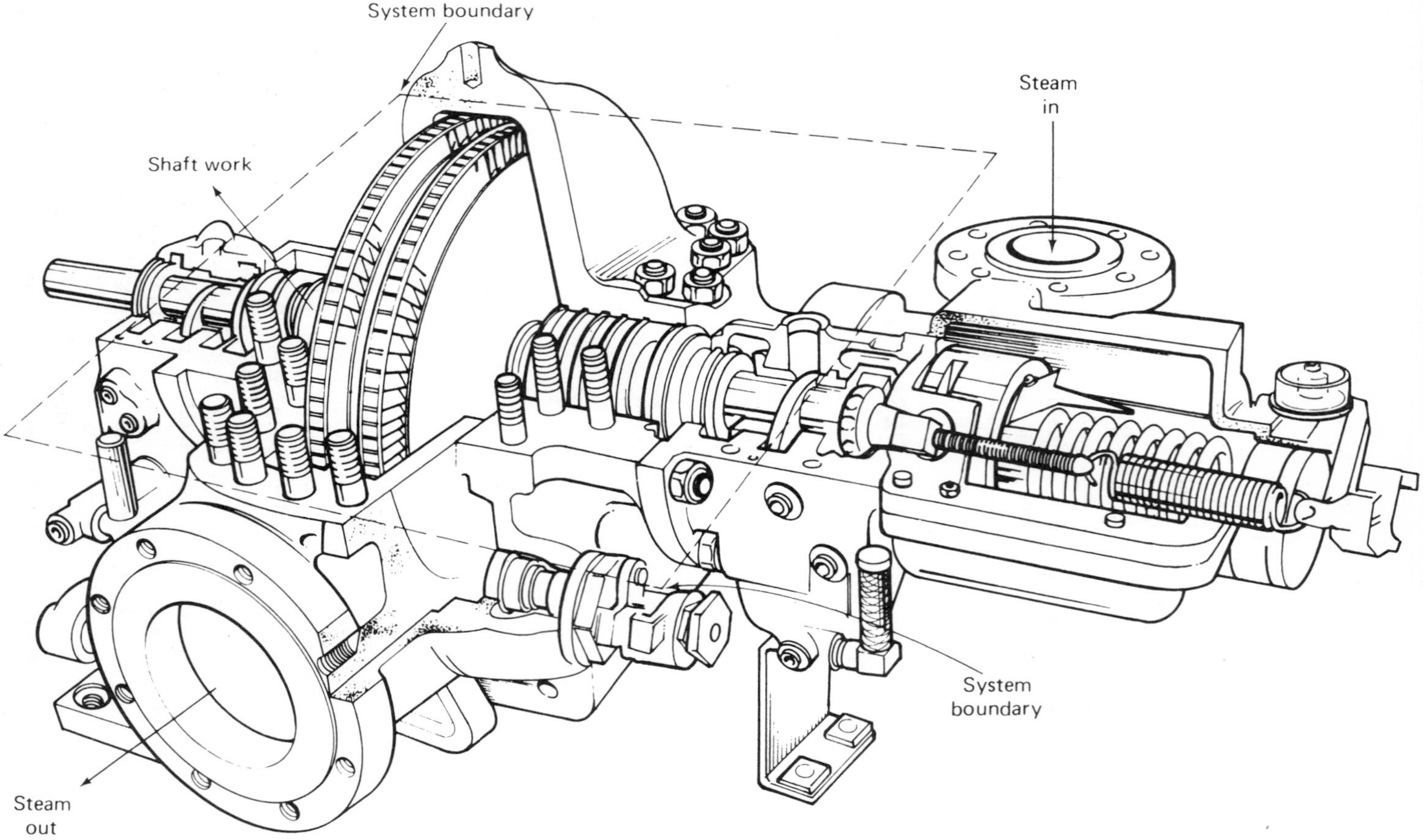

Figure 2.21 Single-stage turbine (Courtesy of Worthington Corporation)

Steam in

System boundary

System boundary

Shaft work

Steam out

With the foregoing in mind, let us now apply the first law to the turbine (either steam or gas) shown schematically in Fig. 2.22. The first law is given by

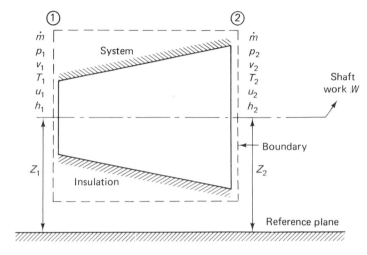

Figure 2.22 Schematic of a turbine

Eq. (2.20) as

$$q - \frac{W}{J} = h_2 - h_1 + \left(\frac{Z_2 - Z_1}{J}\right)\left(\frac{g}{g_c}\right) + \left(\frac{V_2^2 - V_1^2}{2g_c J}\right) \quad (2.20)$$

or

$$q - W = h_2 - h_1 + g(Z_2 - Z_1) + \left(\frac{V_2^2 - V_1^2}{2}\right) \quad (2.20a)$$

Since the shaft of the machine is horizontal, $[(Z_2 - Z_1)/J](g/g_c)$ can be taken to be zero; that is,

$$\left(\frac{Z_2 - Z_1}{J}\right)\frac{g}{g_c}^{\,0}$$

where $\nearrow^{0}$ is taken to mean goes to zero. Also as noted, the inlet and outlet velocities are kept nearly equal leading us to conclude that the kinetic energy difference term goes to zero:

$$\left(\frac{V_2^2 - V_1^2}{2g_c J}\right)^{0}$$

Finally, the insulation of the turbine would effectively prevent heat losses to the surroundings:

Equation (2.20), as applied to this device, becomes,

$$\frac{W}{J} = h_1 - h_2$$

or from equation (2.20a),

$$W = h_1 - h_2$$

All the assumptions made for the steam turbine are equally applicable to the gas turbine shown in Fig. 2.23. In this industrial unit the turbine also drives the compressor. Exhaust gases leave at the right of the figure via an exhaust elbow. This unit will be discussed in detail in Chapter 7 as a prime mover in a power producing cycle.

Figure 2.23 Industrial gas turbine (Courtesy of Pratt and Whitney Div. of United Aircraft Corp.)

ILLUSTRATIVE PROBLEM 2.23

A turbine (gas) receives air at 150 psia and 1000°R and discharges to a pressure of 15 psia. The actual temperature at discharge is 600°R. If c_p of the gas can be taken to be constant over this temperature range and equal to 0.24

Btu/lb °F, determine the work output of the turbine per pound of working fluid. At inlet conditions the specific volume is 2.47 cu ft/lb, and at outlet it is 14.8 cu ft/lb. The data are also shown in Fig. 2.24.

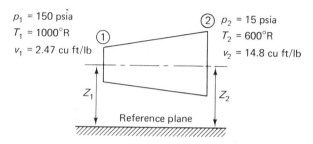

Figure 2.24 Illustrative Problem 2.23

Solution

We have already discussed the turbine in detail and arrived at the conclusion that the first law yields

$$\frac{W}{J} = h_1 - h_2$$

Equation (2.24) enables us to obtain $h_1 - h_2$, since for the gas

$$h_1 - h_2 = c_p(T_1 - T_2)$$

Therefore,

$$\frac{W}{J} = h_1 - h_2 = c_p(T_1 - T_2) = 0.24(1000 - 600)$$

and

$$\frac{W}{J} = 96 \text{ Btu/lb}$$

Note that the specific volume and pressure given do not enter the solution of the problem. However, a pressure differential is required to cause the gas to flow.

ILLUSTRATIVE PROBLEM 2.24

Even though the turbine of Illustrative Problem 2.23 may be well insulated, there will be some heat loss. If the heat loss is found by experiment to be equal to 1.1 Btu/lb of gas, determine the work output of the turbine per pound of gas.

Solution

We must return to the point in our discussion where we took q ⁰ and not make this assumption. Doing this gives us

$$q - \frac{W}{J} = h_2 - h_1$$

or

$$\frac{W}{J} = q + (h_1 - h_2)$$

Since q is out of the system, it is a negative quantity, and $h_1 - h_2$ is the same as for Illustrative Problem 2.23. Thus

$$\frac{W}{J} = -1.1 + 96.0 = 94.9 \text{ Btu/lb}$$

In other words, a heat loss decreases the work output of the turbine.

ILLUSTRATIVE PROBLEM 2.25

A steam turbine operates with an inlet pressure of 50 bars and an inlet temperature of 500°C. At these conditions, $v = 68.57 \text{ cm}^3/\text{g}$, $u = 3091.0 \text{ J/g}$, and $h = 3433.8 \text{ J/g}$. At the outlet the pressure is 1 bar, the specific volume is 1694.0 cm^3/g, $u = 2506.1 \text{ J/g}$, and $h = 2675.5 \text{ J/g}$. Determine the work output per kilogram.

Solution

Refer to Illustrative Problem 2.23 and also note that the units used in this problem correspond to those given in *Steam Tables—International Edition*.* The bar is a unit of pressure corresponding to 10^5 Pa. Proceeding,

$$W = h_1 - h_2$$
$$= 3433.8 - 2675.5 = 758.3 \text{ J/g}$$

or

$$W = 758.3 \text{ kJ/kg}$$

Notice that while u and v were not used in this problem, we could check the consistency of data using $h = u + pv$. As a check at the outlet,

$$h = 2675.5 = 2506.1 + \frac{10^5 \times 1694.0}{10^6} = 2675.5$$

which checks.

---

*By J. H. Keenan, F. G. Keyes, P. G. Hill, and J. G. Moore, John Wiley & Sons, Inc., New York, 1969.

2.7b Pipe Flow

As our next illustration of the first law, we will apply the law to the flow of fluids in pipes. Figure 2.25 shows a large chemical processing plant, and from the figure the amount and complexity of the piping in installations of this type is self-evident.

Figure 2.25 A large chemical processing plant (Courtesy of Foster Wheeler Corp.)

ILLUSTRATIVE PROBLEM 2.26

A gas flows in a pipe, whose pressure and temperature at one section are 100 psia and 950°F. At a second section of the pipe the pressure is 76 psia and the temperature is 580°F. The specific volume of the inlet gas is 4.0 cu ft/lb and at the second section it is 3.86 cu ft/lb. Assume that the specific heat at constant volume is 0.32 Btu/lb °F. If no shaft work is done and if the velocities are small, determine the magnitude and direction of the heat transfer. Assume the pipe to be horizontal and neglect velocity terms. The data are also shown in Fig. 2.26.

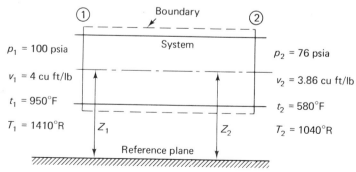

Figure 2.26 Illustrative Problem 2.26

Solution

We first write out the equation of the first law and then apply it to this process.

$$\left(\frac{Z_1}{J}\right)\frac{g}{g_c} + \frac{V_1^2}{2g_cJ} + u_1 + \frac{p_1v_1}{J} + q$$

$$= \left(\frac{Z_2}{J}\right)\frac{g}{g_c} + \frac{V_2^2}{2g_cJ} + u_2 + \frac{p_2v_2}{J} + \frac{W}{J}$$

Since the pipe is horizontal and velocity terms are to be neglected,

$$\left(\frac{Z_1-Z_2}{J}\right)\left(\frac{g}{g_c}\right)^{\!0}, \qquad \left(\frac{V_2^2-V_1^2}{2g_cJ}\right)^{\!0}$$

Also, $\dfrac{W}{J}^{\,0}$ since no work crosses the boundaries of the system. The energy equation is reduced to

$$u_1 + \frac{p_1v_1}{J} + q = u_2 + \frac{p_2v_2}{J}$$

However, Eq. (2.25) permits us to express the internal energy change for the gas in terms of the temperature change as

$$u_2 - u_1 = c_v(T_2 - T_1) \quad \text{for constant } c_v$$

Therefore,

$$q = c_v(T_2 - T_1) + \frac{p_2v_2}{J} - \frac{p_1v_1}{J}$$

By inserting numerical quantities

$$q = 0.32(1040 - 1410) + \frac{76 \times 144 \times 3.86}{778} - \frac{100(144)(4)}{778}$$

$$= -118.4 + 54.3 - 74.0 = -138.1 \text{ Btu/lb}$$

Thus 138.1 Btu/lb is transferred *from* the gas.

ILLUSTRATIVE PROBLEM 2.27

If the pipe referred to in Illustrative Problem 2.26 was a vertical run of pipe such that section 2 was 100 ft above section 1, determine the direction and magnitude of the heat transfer.

S o l u t i o n

Using the reference plane of Fig. 2.26 to coincide with the elevation of the pipe at section 1 makes $Z_1 = 0$. The energy equation becomes

$$u_1 + \frac{p_1 v_1}{J} + q = u_2 + \frac{p_2 v_2}{J} + \left(\frac{Z_2}{J}\right)\left(\frac{g}{g_c}\right)$$

and

$$q = u_2 - u_1 + \frac{p_2 v_2}{J} - \frac{p_1 v_1}{J} + \frac{Z_2}{J}\left(\frac{g}{g_c}\right)$$

Using $u_2 - u_1 = c_v(T_2 - T_1)$ and $Z_2 = 100$ ft,

$$q = 0.32(1040 - 1410) + \frac{76 \times 144 \times 3.86}{778} - \frac{100(144)(4)}{778} + \frac{100}{778}\left(\frac{g}{g_c}\right)$$

Letting $g/g_c = 1$,

$$q = -118.4 + 54.3 - 74.0 + 0.13 = -138.0 \text{ Btu/lb}$$

For this problem, neglecting the elevation term leads to an insignificant error.

2.7c The Boiler

The next application of the first law will be to the boiler or steam generator. The basic purpose of the steam generator is the turning of water into steam by the application of heat. Figure 2.27a shows a large steam generating unit, which, as can be seen, consists of a combination of many elements. In this unit pulverized coal is burned in the furnace with air that has been preheated in the air heater. In addition to generating superheated steam, this unit reheats steam from the high pressure turbine exhaust and returns it to the low pressure turbine. The energy input to this system comes from the fuel, air, and feed water, and the useful output is steam. Figure 2.27b shows an energy diagram for this unit with numbers corresponding to the ones shown on Fig. 2.27a. Since the purpose of the unit is to generate steam, the energy in the stack gas, unburned fuel, and heat transfer to the surroundings all represent losses which decrease the useful steam output. Again, we shall return to the steam generator in Chapter 7, where it is studied in some detail. For the present, the following problem will serve to illustrate the application of the first law to this unit.

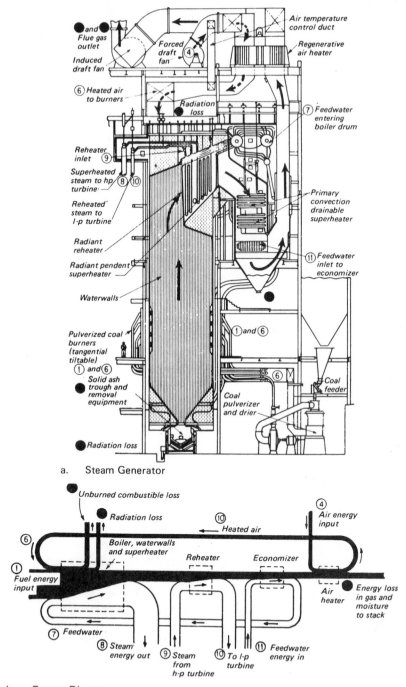

a.   Steam Generator

b.   Energy Diagram

Figure 2.27 Modern steam generator (Reprinted with permission from *Power*, special report "Steam Generation," copyright by McGraw-Hill, Inc., June 1964)

ILLUSTRATIVE PROBLEM 2.28

A steam boiler is required to produce 10,000 lb/hr of superheated steam at 1000°F and 1000 psia ($h = 1505.9$ Btu/lb) from feed water supplied at 1000 psia and 100°F ($h = 70.68$ Btu/lb). How much energy has been added to the water to convert it to steam at these conditions? The data are shown in Fig. 2.28.

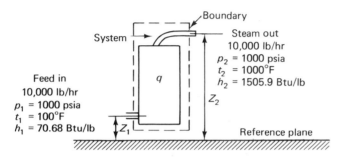

Figure 2.28 Illustrative Problem 2.28

Solution

As indicated in Fig. 2.28, we can consider this system as a single unit with feed water entering and steam leaving. If well designed, this unit will be thoroughly insulated and heat losses will be reduced to a negligible amount; no work is added to the fluid during the time it is passing through the unit, and kinetic energy differences will be assumed to be negligibly small. In large units the inlet and outlet may be as much as 100 ft apart. However, 100/778 is 0.129 Btu/lb, which is quite small compared to the 1000 Btu/lb or more involved in this problem. On this basis, differences in elevation will also be considered negligible. Once again, the energy equation is

$$\left(\frac{Z_1}{J}\right)\left(\frac{g}{g_c}\right) + \frac{V_1^2}{2g_cJ} + u_1 + \frac{p_1v_1}{J} + q = \left(\frac{Z_2}{J}\right)\left(\frac{g}{g_c}\right) + \frac{V_2^2}{2g_cJ} + u_2 + \frac{p_2v_2}{J} + \frac{W}{J}$$

and for this problem

$$\cancel{\left(\frac{Z_1 - Z_2}{J}\right)\left(\frac{g}{g_c}\right)}^{0}, \qquad \cancel{\left(\frac{V_2^2 - V_1^2}{2g_cJ}\right)}^{0}$$

Therefore,

$$u_1 + \frac{p_1v_1}{J} + q = u_2 + \frac{p_2v_2}{J}$$

or since

$$h = u + \frac{pv}{J}$$

$$q = h_2 - h_1 \qquad \text{(this is the net value since we assumed no heat losses)}$$

Using the data given,

$$q = (1505.9 - 70.68) = 1435.2 \text{ Btu/lb}$$

For 10,000 lb/hr,

$$10{,}000 \times 1435.2 = 14.35 \times 10^8 \text{ Btu/hr}$$

are required.

2.7d Nozzle

A nozzle is a static device that is used to convert the energy of a fluid into kinetic energy. Basically, the fluid enters the nozzle at a high pressure and leaves at a lower pressure. In the process of expanding, velocity is gained as the fluid progresses through the nozzle. No work is done on or by the fluid in its passage through the nozzle.

ILLUSTRATIVE PROBLEM 2.29

Steam is expanded in a nozzle from an initial enthalpy of 1220 Btu/lb to a final enthalpy of 1100 Btu/lb. (a) If the initial velocity of the steam is negligible, what is the final velocity? (b) If the initial velocity is 1000 ft/sec, what is the final velocity? See Fig. 2.29.

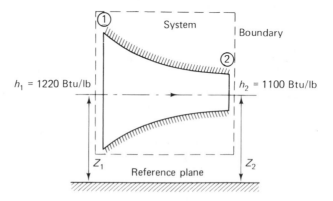

Figure 2.29 Illustrative Problem 2.29

Solution

The energy equation for a steady-flow device is

$$\left(\frac{Z_1}{J}\right)\left(\frac{g}{g_c}\right) + \frac{V_1^2}{2g_cJ} + u_1 + \frac{p_1v_1}{J} + q = \left(\frac{Z_2}{J}\right)\left(\frac{g}{g_c}\right) + \frac{V_2^2}{2g_cJ} + u_2 + \frac{p_2v_2}{J} + \frac{W}{J}$$

For this device, differences in elevation are negligible; no work is done on or by the fluid, friction is negligible, and due to the speed of the fluid flowing and the short length of the nozzle heat transfer to or from the surroundings is also negligible. Under these circumstances

$$\left(\frac{Z_2 - Z_1}{J}\right)\left(\frac{g}{g_c}\right)^{\!\!0}, \qquad q^{\,0}, \qquad \left(\frac{W}{J}\right)^{\!\!0}$$

Therefore,

$$u_1 + \frac{p_1v_1}{J} + \frac{V_1^2}{2g_cJ} = u_2 + \frac{p_2v_2}{J} + \frac{V_2^2}{2g_cJ}$$

or

$$h_1 - h_2 = \frac{V_2^2 - V_1^2}{2g_cJ}$$

(a) For negligible entering velocity

$$h_1 - h_2 = \frac{V_2^2}{2g_cJ}$$

and

$$V_2 = \sqrt{2g_cJ(h_1 - h_2)}$$

Substituting the data of the problem,

$$V_2 = \sqrt{2 \times 32.2 \times 778 \times (1220 - 1100)} = 2452 \text{ ft/sec}$$

(b) If the initial velocity is appreciable,

$$h_1 - h_2 + \frac{V_1^2}{2g_cJ} = \frac{V_2^2}{2g_cJ}$$

Again inserting numerical values

$$1220 - 1100 + \frac{(1000)^2}{2 \times 32.2 \times 778} = \frac{V_2^2}{2 \times 32.2 \times 778}$$

$$120 + 20 = \frac{V_2^2}{2 \times 32.2 \times 778}$$

$$V_2 = 2648 \text{ ft/sec}$$

Note that in this part of the problem the entering velocity was nearly 40 percent of the final velocity, yet neglecting the entering velocity makes only a $7\frac{1}{2}$ percent error in the answer. It is quite common to neglect the entering velocity in many of these problems.

ILLUSTRATIVE PROBLEM 2.30

Assume steam enters a nozzle with an enthalpy of 3450 J/g and leaves with an enthalpy of 2800 J/g. If the initial velocity of the steam is negligible, what is the final velocity?

Solution

Refer to Illustrative Problem 2.29 and note that in SI units

$$\frac{V_2^2}{2} = h_1 - h_2$$

and

$$V_2 = \sqrt{2(h_1 - h_2)}$$

Substituting,

$$V_2 = \sqrt{2 \times 1000(3450 - 2800)} = 1140.2 \text{ m/s}$$

2.7e The Throttling Process

The last device that we shall consider at this time is the case of an obstruction placed in a pipe (deliberately or due to the presence of a valve). One deliberate local obstruction that is often placed in a pipe is an orifice that is used to meter the quantity of fluid flowing. When used in this manner, the orifice usually consists of a thin plate inserted into a pipe and clamped between flanges. The hole in the orifice plate is concentric with the pipe, and static pressure taps are provided upstream and downstream of the orifice. Due to the presence of the orifice, the flow is locally constricted, and a measurable drop in static pressure occurs across the orifice. Static taps placed as shown in Fig. 2.30 are usually

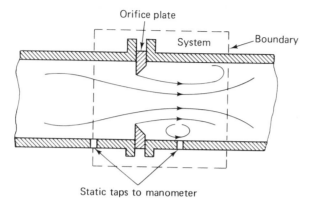

Figure 2.30 Orifice as a meter

used to measure the flow. The advantages of this device are its relatively small size, the ease of installation in a pipe, and the fact that standard installations can be used without the need for calibration. However, the orifice meter behaves in the same manner as a partly open valve and causes a relatively high pressure drop. This effect leads to the descriptive term of *throttling* for partly open valves, orifices, or other obstructions in pipes. In effect, the full flow is throttled back to some lesser flow by the obstruction.

ILLUSTRATIVE PROBLEM 2.31

A fluid is flowing in a pipe. At some section of the pipe there is an obstruction that causes an appreciable local pressure loss. Derive the energy equation for this process after flow has become uniform in the downstream section of the pipe. As noted earlier, this process is known as a throttling process and is characteristic of valves and orifices placed in pipe lines. Refer to Fig. 2.31.

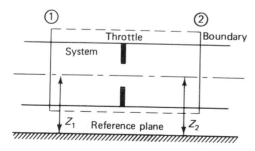

Figure 2.31 Illustrative Problem 2.31

Solution

For the conditions of this problem we can take differences in elevation to be negligible, differences in kinetic energy terms will be relatively small, and no work or heat crosses the system boundary. The complete energy equation is

$$\left(\frac{Z_1}{J}\right)\left(\frac{g}{g_c}\right) + \frac{V_1^2}{2g_c J} + u_1 + \frac{p_1 v_1}{J} + q = \left(\frac{Z_2}{J}\right)\left(\frac{g}{g_c}\right) + \frac{V_2^2}{2g_c J} + u_2 + \frac{p_2 v_2}{J} + \frac{W}{J}$$

and, with the assumptions made for this process,

$$u_1 + \frac{p_1 v_1}{J} = u_2 + \frac{p_2 v_2}{J}$$

or
$$h_1 = h_2$$

In words, a throttling process is carried out at constant enthalpy. One assumption should be verified; that is, the kinetic energy differences at inlet and outlet are indeed negligible. This can easily be done by using the constant enthalpy condition and using the final properties of the fluid and the cross-sectional area of the duct to determine an approximate final velocity. The throttling process is discussed again in Chapter 4.

2.8 CLOSURE

In this chapter several novel concepts have been presented, and it has been my experience that most students find difficulty (at first) in fully understanding all of them. More than the usual student effort may be required to master this portion of the subject, but the effort is worth the investment since a large portion of the remainder of this book utilizes the concepts of this chapter. In addition, I have indicated in the illustrative problems and strongly suggest to the student that the following procedure be used to analyze all problems.

1 Read, visualize, and understand the problem.
2 Draw a schematic sketch of the problem and indicate all known quantities.
3 Write out the full energy equation.
4 On the basis of the statement of the problem or knowledge of the device in question, determine those terms that can be omitted or neglected.

5 Solve the problem by performing the necessary algebraic and arithmetic steps. Check dimensional consistency.

6 Using the solution as a first approximation, check the validity of the assumptions made in step 4.

There are no shortcuts to an understanding of thermodynamics, and the student will find that the procedure outlined above will prove to be invaluable.

REFERENCES

1 *College Physics*, 3rd. Ed., by F. W. Sears and M. W. Zemansky, Addison-Wesley Publishing Co., Reading, Mass., 1960.

2 *Modern College Physics*, 4th Ed., by H. E. White, Van Nostrand Reinhold Co., New York, 1962.

3 *Heat and Thermodynamics*, 4th Ed., by M. W. Zemansky, McGraw-Hill Book Co., New York, 1957.

4 *Thermodynamics* by Enrico Fermi, Dover Publications, New York, 1956.

5 "A Single Axiom for Classical Thermodynamics" by G. N. Hatsopoulos and J. H. Keenan, ASME paper 61-WA-110, 1961.

6 *Concepts of Thermodynamics* by E. F. Obert, McGraw-Hill Book Co., New York, 1960.

7 *Fundamentals of Thermodynamics* by R. A. Kenyon and H. Schenck, Jr., Ronald Press, New York, 1962.

8 *Thermodynamics* by H. B. Callen, John Wiley & Sons, Inc., New York, 1960.

9 *Principles of Engineering Thermodynamics*, 2nd Ed., by P. J. Kiefer, G. F. Kinney, and M. C. Stuart, John Wiley & Sons, Inc., New York, 1954.

10 *Thermodynamics* by J. H. Keenan, John Wiley & Sons, Inc., New York, 1941.

11 *Engineering Thermodynamics* by D. B. Spalding and E. H. Cole, McGraw-Hill Book Co., New York, 1959.

12 *Elementary Applied Thermodynamics* by I. Granet, John Wiley & Sons, Inc., New York, 1965.

13 *Thermodynamics*, 2nd Ed., by G. A. Hawkins, John Wiley & Sons, Inc., New York, 1960.

14 *Thermodynamics*, 2nd Ed., by F. P. Durham, Prentice-Hall, Inc., Englewood Cliffs, N.J., 1959.

15 *Fluid Mechanics for Engineering Technology* by I. Granet, Prentice-Hall Inc., Englewood Cliffs, N.J., 1971.

16 *Elementary Thermodynamics*, 3rd Ed., by V. M. Faires, Macmillan, Inc., New York, 1957.

17 "The Place of Hydro- and Pumped Storage" by J. Tillinghast, *Mechanical Engineering*, July 1969, pp. 24–28.

18 *Engineering Thermodynamics with Applications* by M. D. Burghardt, Harper & Row, Publishers, Inc., New York, 1978.

PROBLEMS

Unless otherwise indicated, use $g_c = 32.17$ ft/s^2 and 9.806 m/s^2 for g.

2.1 A body of mass 10 lb is placed 10 ft above an arbitrary plane. If the local gravitational field is equivalent to an acceleration of 16.1 ft/sec^2, how much work (ft lb) was done lifting the body above the plane?

2.2 A body of mass of 10 kg is placed 3 m above a plane. How much work was done to lift the body above the plane?

2.3 A body has a mass of 5 kg. If its velocity is 10 m/s, what is its kinetic energy?

2.4 From what height would the body in Problem 2.3 have to fall in order to attain this velocity?

2.5 A body weighing 10 lb is lifted 100 ft. What is its change in potential energy? What velocity will it possess after falling the 100 ft?

2.6 A body weighing 10 lb ($g = g_c$) is moving with a velocity of 50 ft/sec. From what height would it have to fall to achieve this velocity? What is its kinetic energy?

2.7 A body weighing 100 N is lifted 3 m. What will its velocity be after a free fall of 3 m?

2.8 Water flows over the top of a dam and falls freely until it reaches the bottom some 600 ft below. What is the velocity of the water just before it hits the bottom? What is its kinetic energy per pound at this point?

2.9 A spring is compressed 5 in. from its equilibrium position. If the spring modulus k is 10 lb/in. of deflection, how much work was done in foot pounds to deflect the spring?

2.10 A spring is deflected by a weight a distance of 100 mm. If the modulus of the spring is 100 N/m, what is the mass that was placed on the spring?

2.11 A 5-lb mass ($g = g_c$) falls 25 ft until it impacts on a spring. If the spring modulus k is 25 lb/ft of deflection, how far will the spring be deflected? Assume that all the energy of the falling body just goes to compress the spring.

2.12 A 10 kg mass falls 3 m until it impacts a spring. If the spring modulus k is 1000 N/m, how far will the spring be deflected if all the energy of the falling body goes into compressing the spring?

2.13 In a constant pressure process, steam at 100 psia is presented to the piston of a pump and causes it to travel 3 in. If the cross-sectional area of the piston is 5 sq in., how much work was done by the steam on the piston?

2.14 A gas expands according to the equation $pv = 100$, where p is the pressure in pounds per square foot absolute and v is the specific volume in cubic feet per pound. If the pressure of the gas drops from 100 to 50 psfa, how much work was done by the gas?

2.15 A pressure of 5 bars is presented to the piston of a pump and causes it to travel 100 mm. The cross-sectional area of the piston is 1000 mm². How much work is done by the steam on the piston if the steam pressure is constant?

2.16 A gas expands according to the equation $pv = 1000$, where p is the pressure in kPa and v is the specific volume in m³/kg. If the gas pressure drops from 10 bars to 5 bars, how much work was done by the gas?

2.17 A nonflow process is carried out when 1000 Btu are added to 10 lb of hydrogen at constant volume. What is the change in specific internal energy? How much work is done by the gas?

2.18 If a nonflow process is carried out so that 30 Btu/lb of work is removed from the process while 100 Btu/lb is added as heat, determine the change (increase or decrease) in the internal energy of the fluid.

2.19 If 10 kg of a gas is heated by the addition of 5 kJ in a nonflow process, what is the change in its specific internal energy if the process is carried out at constant volume?

2.20 If a nonflow process is carried out so that 30 kJ/kg of work is removed while 75 kJ/kg is added as heat, determine the change in internal energy of the fluid.

2.21 In a constant pressure nonflow process 10 lb of gas has 500 Btu added to it. During the process the internal energy decreases by 25 Btu/lb. How much work was done by the gas per pound of gas?

2.22 A constant pressure nonflow process is carried out at a pressure of 200 kPa. If 50 kJ of heat is removed while the volume changes from 0.2 m³ to 0.1 m³, what is the change in internal energy of the working fluid? Assume 0.5 kg of fluid.

2.23 A nonflow process is carried out adiabatically. If 55 kJ of work is removed from 4 kg of fluid, what is the change in the total internal energy and the specific internal energy of the fluid?

2.24 A nonflow process is carried out adiabatically. What is the change in internal energy of the fluid if 55,000 ft lb of work is removed from 8 lb of fluid in this process?

2.25 During a certain nonflow process 100 Btu/lb is added as heat to the working fluid, while 25,000 ft lb/lb is extracted as work. Determine the change in internal energy of the fluid.

2.26 Heat is supplied to a gas in a rigid container. If the container has 0.6 lb of gas in it and 100 Btu is added, determine the change in temperature of the gas and the change in its internal energy. c_v for this gas is 0.35 Btu/lb °F.

2.27 If 100 kJ/kg of heat is added to 10 kg of a fluid while 25 kJ/kg is extracted as work, determine the change in the internal energy of the fluid for a nonflow process.

2.28 Heat is supplied to a gas that is contained in a rigid container. If 0.2 kg of gas has 100 kJ added to it, determine the change in temperature of the gas and the change in its internal energy. Use $c_v = 0.7186$ kJ/kg·K and $c_p = 1.0062$ kJ/kg·K.

2.29 If c_p and c_v of air are, respectively, 1.0062 and 0.7186 kJ/kg·K, and 1 MJ is added to 10 kg in a nonflow constant-pressure process, what is the final temperature of the gas, and how much work is done by the gas? Assume that the initial temperature of the gas is 50°C.

2.30 The c_p and c_v of air are 0.24 and 0.17 Btu/lb°F, respectively. If 1000 Btu is added to 20 lb of air in a nonflow constant-pressure process, what is the final temperature? How much work is done by the gas? The initial temperature is 100°F.

2.31 Air is adiabatically compressed in a nonflow process from a pressure and temperature of 14.7 psia and 70°F to 200 psia and 350°F. If c_v of the air is 0.171 Btu/lb°F, determine the change in internal energy of the air and the work done.

2.32 A nonflow cylinder–piston apparatus contains 0.5 lb of a gas. If 10 Btu is supplied as work to compress the gas as its temperature increases from 70°F to 150°F, determine the energy interchange as heat. c_v for the gas can be taken as 0.22 Btu/lb°F.

2.33 Ten cubic feet of fluid per second flows in a pipe 1 in. in diameter. If the fluid is water whose density is 62.4 lb/ft³, determine the weight rate of flow in pounds per hour.

2.34 A gallon is a volume measure of 231 in³. Determine the velocity in a pipe 2 in. in diameter when water flows at the rate of 20 gal/min in the pipe.

2.35 When a fluid of constant density flows in a pipe, show that for a given mass flow the velocity is inversely proportional to the square of the pipe diameter.

2.36 Water having a density of 1000 kg/m³ flows in a pipe that has an internal diameter of 50 mm. If 0.5 m³/s flows in the pipe, determine the mass flow rate in kilograms per hour.

2.37 What is the velocity of the water flowing in Problem 2.36?

2.38 Show that the kinetic energy of a fluid flowing in a pipe varies inversely as the fourth power of the pipe diameter.

2.39 A water turbine operates from a water supply that is 100 ft above the turbine inlet. It discharges to the atmosphere through a 6-in.-diameter pipe with a velocity of 25 ft/sec. If the reservoir is infinite in size, determine the work out of the turbine if the density of water is 62.4 lb/cu ft.

2.40 A water pump is placed at the bottom of a well. If it is to pump 10 cu ft/sec to the surface, 100 ft away, through a 4-in. inside diameter pipe, determine the power required in foot pounds per second if the density of water is 62.4 lb/cu ft.

2.41 Air is compressed until its final volume is half its initial volume. The initial pressure is 100 psia and the final pressure is 35 psia. If the initial specific volume is 1 cu ft/lb, determine the difference in the pv/J term in Btu/lb. Is this difference "flow work" for this process?

2.42 Determine the work of a turbine if 2000 kg/min of water is compressed from 100 kPa to 1 MPA. The water density can be taken to be 1000 kg/m^3, and its temperature does not change. The inlet to the pump is 100 mm in diameter and the outlet is 150 mm in diameter. The inlet is 50 m below the outlet.

2.43 A steady flow device is operated with an entering pressure of 50 psia and a specific volume of 0.8 cu ft/lb. At the exit of the device the pressure is 15 psia and the specific volume is 3.2 cu ft/lb. Determine the change in flow work in this device.

2.44 If a fluid flows past a section of pipe with a pressure of 100 kPa and having a specific volume of 10^{-3} m^3/kg, determine its flow work.

2.45 At the entrance to a steady flow device the pressure is 350 kPa and the specific volume is 0.04 m^3/kg. At the outlet the pressure is 1 Mpa and the specific volume is 0.02 m^3/kg. Determine the flow work change in this device.

2.46 The enthalpy of a substance is found to be 1000 Btu/lb at 1000°F above an arbitrary datum of 0°F. If c_v is a constant and equal to 0.5 Btu/lb°F, determine the difference in the pv/J terms at zero and 1000°F. Does this difference represent flow work?

2.47 Determine the specific heat of an adiabatic process. Is this the specific heat at constant volume or the specific heat at constant pressure?

2.48 In a certain steady flow process the working fluid is cooled until 100 Btu/lb has been extracted. During this process 100 ft lb/lb of fluid is added as work. If the working substance undergoes a change in temperature from 100° to 50°F, what is the specific heat of the process?

2.49 Two kilograms of a gas receives 200 kJ at constant volume. If the temperature of the gas increases by 100°C, determine the c_v of the process.

2.50 A closed system receives 1 kJ as heat, and its temperature rise is 10 K. If 20 kg is in the system, what is the specific heat of the process?

2.51 A constant pressure nonflow system receives heat at a constant pressure of 350 kPa. The internal energy of the system increases by 180 kJ while the temperature increases by 170°C, and the work done is 75 kJ. Determine c_p and the change in volume if there is 1.5 kg in the cylinder.

2.52 A steam turbine is supplied with steam at 700°F and 500 psia. The steam is expanded adiabatically until the final condition is saturated vapor at 300°F. If the properties of steam at the initial and final states are as given here, determine the work output of the turbine per pound of steam.

500 psia and 700°F		300°F (saturated vapor)	
h	1356.7 Btu/lb	h	1180.2 Btu/lb
v	1.3040 cu ft/lb	v	6.472 cu ft/lb

2.53 A fluid at 1 MPa has a specific volume of 0.2 m^3/kg and an entering velocity of 200 m/s. The heat loss is 10 kJ/kg and the fluid does 180 kJ/kg of work. The fluid leaves the device with a pressure of 200 kPa, a specific volume of 1 m^3/kg, and a velocity of 600 m/s. What is the change in the internal energy of the fluid?

2.54 A steam turbine operates adiabatically with inlet and outlet conditions as given below. Determine the work out of the turbine. State all assumptions.

At 50 bars and 500°C	At 1 bar (saturated vapor)
$h = 3433.8$ J/g	$h = 2675.5$ J/g
$v = 68.57$ cm^3/g	$v = 1694.0$ cm^3/g

2.55 A steam turbine receives steam at 110 ft/sec velocity and 1525 Btu/lb enthalpy. The steam leaves at 810 ft/sec and 1300 Btu/lb enthalpy. What is the work out in Btu per pound?

2.56 A turbine is operated with an enthalpy at entrance of 1340 Btu/lb and an exit enthalpy of 1285 Btu/lb. If the entrance velocity to the turbine is 150 fps and the exit velocity is 500 fps, determine the work out of the turbine.

2.57 Solve Problem 2.56 if there is a heat loss of 5.5 Btu/lb of fluid by heat transfer from the turbine casing.

2.58 A gas turbine has gas entering it at 1100°F and leaving at 800°F. If the specific heat $c_p = 0.265$ Btu/lb°F, determine the work out of the turbine. Neglect losses and velocity effects.

2.59 Solve Problem 2.58 if the entering velocity is 100 fps and the leaving velocity is 300 fps, and if there is a heat loss of 4.8 Btu/lb from the turbine.

2.60 Gas enters a turbine at 600°C and leaves at 350°C. If the specific heats of the gas are $c_p = 0.8452$ kJ/kg·K and $c_v = 0.6561$ kJ/kg·K, determine the work out of the turbine. State all assumptions.

2.61 Air expands through a nozzle from 1000 psia and 500°F to 600 psia and 0°F. If c_p of air can be taken to be constant and equal to 0.24 Btu/lb°F, what is the final velocity? Assume that the initial velocity is zero.

2.62 Steam expands in a nozzle from an initial enthalpy of 1300 Btu/lb to a final enthalpy of 980 Btu/lb. Determine the final velocity if the entering velocity and heat losses are negligible.

2.63 Solve Problem 2.62 if the initial velocity is 1100 fps.

2.64 Air expands in a nozzle from 7 MPa and 250°C to 3.5 MPa and 50°C. If $c_p = 1.0062$ kJ/kg·K and $c_v = 0.7186$ kJ/kg·K, determine the work out of the turbine. State all assumptions.

2.65 Steam is generated in a boiler. If the initial water enters the boiler as saturated water at 1000 psia ($h = 542.4$ Btu/lb) and leaves as superheated steam at 950 psia and 1000°F ($h = 1507.4$ Btu/lb), how much heat is added to the steam to generate 1 lb of steam at these conditions?

2.66 A gas turbine receives an air–fuel mixture having an enthalpy of 550 Btu/lb of gas. If 10 Btu/lb is lost by heat transfer from the turbine, and the enthalpy of the leaving gas is 50 Btu/lb, how much work can be obtained from the turbine?

2.67 Water flows in a heat exchanger, and heat is transferred from the water to heat air. At the inlet the pressure of the water is 100 psia and at the outlet it is 80 psia. The initial specific volume is 0.017736 cu ft/lb, and the final specific volume is 0.01757 cu ft/lb. The initial enthalpy is 298.61 Btu/lb, the initial internal energy is 298.28 Btu/lb, the final enthalpy is 282.21 Btu/lb, and the final internal energy is 281.95 Btu/lb. Determine the heat transferred from the water. State all assumptions.

2.68 Air flows in steady flow in a pipeline whose internal diameter is constant. At a particular section of the pipe the pressure, temperature, and velocity are 150 psia, 500°R, and 30 ft/sec. The specific volume corresponding to these conditions is 1.24 cu ft/lb. At a section farther downstream the pressure is 300 psia, the velocity is 60 ft/sec, and the temperature is 1500°R. Determine the specific volume of the air at the downstream section and also the magnitude and direction of the heat transfer in Btu per pound. Assume that c_p is 0.24 Btu/lb°F, c_v is 0.171 Btu/lb°F, and that both are constant.

2.69 Dry saturated steam at 200 psia flows adiabatically in a pipe. At the outlet of the pipe the pressure is 100 psia and the temperature is 400°F. The initial specific volume of the steam is 2.289 cu ft/lb, and its internal energy is 1114.6 Btu/lb. The final enthalpy is 1227.5 Btu/lb, and the final specific volume is 4.934 cu ft/lb. How much energy per pound was transferred? Was this into or out of the system? Was this heat or work?

chapter 3

the second law of thermodynamics

3.1 INTRODUCTION

Thus far we have considered various forms of energy (including energy in transition as both work and heat) without regard to any limitations on these quantities. It has been assumed that work and heat are mutually interchangeable forms of energy, and it may have appeared to the student that the distinction made between these quantities was arbitrary and possibly not necessary. In this chapter the interconvertibility of these quantities is explored with the object of determining any possible limitations and to express these limitations quantitatively, if they exist. As an example of the point in question, consider the motion of a block sliding along a rough horizontal plane. For motion to proceed along the plane, it is necessary that work be done on the body. All this work subsequently appears as heat at the interface between the block and the plane. There is no question that work has been converted into heat, but can the heat generated in this process be converted into an equivalent amount of work? Let us assume (incorrectly) that this heat can be converted into work without any losses in the process. We know that the energy as heat resides in the motion of the individual molecules of the body. By increasing the molecular motion within the body, we have, in a general sense, done work, but it is also possible to distinguish that this form of work is not the same as the external work put into the process. The original transitional energy as work has been converted into heat, and this heat can be expressed as molecular work, but this form of energy will not be available to return the body to its original state. From this simple example we note that work can be converted into heat, but that the conversion of heat into useful work may not always be possible. Even though the first law states that energy is conserved, it does not furnish the necessary information to enable us to determine whether energy has become unavailable.

It is now necessary to define certain terms. The first of these is the concept of a heat engine. As defined by Keenan,

> *A heat engine may be defined as a continuously operating system across whose boundaries flow only heat and work. It may be used to deliver work to external devices, or it may receive work from external devices and cause heat to flow from a low level of temperature to a high level of temperature. This latter type of heat engine is known as a refrigerator.**

In essence, this definition of a heat engine can be taken to be the definition of a thermodynamic cycle, which we shall understand to be a series of thermodynamic processes during which the working fluid can be made to undergo changes involving only heat and work interchanges and is then returned to its original state.

The purpose of the conventional engineering thermodynamic cycle is, of course, to convert heat into work. In an air-conditioning or refrigeration cycle, work is used to remove heat from an area in which it is undesirable. Other special cycles exist but are not treated in this text. Associated with the concept of a cycle is the term efficiency. Since the usual purpose of a cycle is to produce useful work, the *thermal efficiency* of a cycle is defined as the ratio of the *net work* of the cycle to the *heat added* to the cycle; that is,

$$\eta = \frac{\text{net work output} \times 100}{\text{heat added}} \qquad (3.1)$$

Note that the heat term is the heat added and is not the net heat of the cycle. For power-producing cycles, the heat is usually added from some high-temperature source. Using the notation that Q_{in} is the heat added to the cycle and that Q_r is the heat rejected by the cycle, the first law applied to the cycle will yield $W/J = Q_{in} - Q_r$. Therefore,

$$\eta = \left(\frac{Q_{in} - Q_r}{Q_{in}} \right) 100 = \left(1 - \frac{Q_r}{Q_{in}} \right) 100 \qquad (3.2)$$

---

*Thermodynamics by J. H. Keenan, John Wiley & Sons, Inc., New York, 1941, p. 58.

For cycles whose purpose is not the production of useful work, other standards of comparison have been devised and are in use.

An examination of Eq. (3.2) leads us to the conclusion that minimizing the heat rejection of a cycle leads to the maximum conversion of heat to work. This leads us to two questions, (a) must there be a rejection of heat from a cycle and, if so, (b) what is the best mode of cycle operation to minimize the heat rejected in order to obtain maximum thermal efficiency. These questions will be partially answered in this chapter, and we shall return to them when we study practical engine cycles.

3.2 REVERSIBILITY—THE SECOND LAW OF THERMODYNAMICS

In Section 3.1 the illustration of a block sliding along a horizontal plane was used to introduce the concept that heat and work are not always mutually convertible without losses. This same body moving along the plane will also serve to answer the following question; by reversing each step of the process that caused the body to move along the plane, is it possible to restore the body to its original state, and at the same time will the surroundings also be restored to the condition that existed before the start of the original process? To answer this question, let us once again consider the forward motion of the body along the plane. We have stated that as the block moves heat is generated at the interface between the block and the plane. This energy is transferred to the body and the plane and will tend to raise the temperature of the body and its surroundings. When the block reaches the end of the plane, let us reverse the force system acting on the body and attempt to restore it to its original position. As the body moves back along the path, heat will again be generated at the interface between the body and the plane. Obviously, the heat generated on the return path is *in addition* to the heat generated at the interface during the forward motion of the body. To the casual observer who viewed the block before the beginning of motion and then viewed it some time after motion had ceased, it would appear that the body had not moved and that the body, as well as the surroundings, had been restored to its original state. This is not true. A net transfer of energy has taken place to the surroundings, and they are not in their original state. Even though the net effect has been an infinitesimal change in the temperature of the surroundings, it is a real effect that precludes us from saying that the system *and its surroundings* have been restored to their original state. We also notice that each step of the forward motion of the body was not identically reversed because of this effect on the surroundings. The heat generated during the forward motion of the block was not returned to the system as work during the return motion. On the contrary, more heat was generated during the return motion, and even if both the plane and the body were perfectly insulated from their surroundings, none of the heat generated would have been returned to the system as work.

The process we have considered is illustrative of an irreversible process. To formalize the concepts of reversibility and irreversibility, the following definition of a reversible process is used:

> *A reversible process is any process performed so that the system and all its surroundings can be restored to their initial states by performing the process in reverse.*

All processes of a reversible cycle must, therefore, also be reversible. The student should note that the concept of the frictionless quasi-static process introduced in Chapter 2 basically implies that such a process is reversible.

The second law of thermodynamics is an expression of empirical fact that all forms of energy are not necessarily equivalent in their ability to perform useful work. There are many statements and corollaries of the second law that can be found in the literature on thermodynamics. For the present, the statement (or axiom) of Clausius and the axiom of Planck will serve to express the second law fully.*

The Clausius Axiom: *Heat cannot, of itself, pass from a lower to a higher temperature.*

The Planck Axiom: *It is impossible to construct an engine that will work in a complete cycle and produce no effect except the raising of a weight and the cooling of a heat reservoir.*

One of the many consequences of the second law of thermodynamics is the conclusion that all natural processes are irreversible. It has already been shown that the presence of friction will cause a process to be irreversible. Some processes that are irreversible are the following:

1 *Any process* in which work is transformed into internal energy via the agency of friction or inelastic action.

2 *Any process* in which inelastic molecular action occurs.

3 *Any process* that transfers heat from one portion of a system to another by virtue of a finite temperature difference.

4 *Any process* that causes temperature differences between parts of the same system.

5 *Any process* involving combustion or chemical reactions.

6 *Any process* that is not performed quasi-statically. Thus to be reversible a process must proceed at an infinitesimally slow rate.

---

* Concepts of Thermodynamics by E. F. Obert, McGraw-Hill Book Co., New York, 1960, pp. 120, 121.

It is important for the student to fully understand where the irreversibilities occur in the listed processes. Also, by observing the effects on the environment, other irreversible processes will become apparent.

The next question we ask is under what conditions will a process be reversible? The answer is that in reality no process is reversible. However, as an abstract ideal the reversible process is extremely useful, and this ideal can be achieved only if the process is frictionless and quasi-static, and then only for an isothermal or adiabatic process. The quasi-static process is always in thermodynamic equilibrium and is carried out with infinite slowness so that at any step in the process it can be reversed and all steps retraced. Also, when such a process is specified to be either isothermal or adiabatic, temperature differences within the system or in parts of the system are precluded. In order to be general, we must exclude other irreversible effects such as magnetic hysteresis and electrical currents.

3.3 THE CARNOT CYCLE

The material discussed so far in this chapter has served to define a cycle, its efficiency, and the concept of a reversible process. It would appear quite natural at this point to combine all these concepts and to discuss reversible cycles and their efficiency. Historically, these concepts were first enunciated by Nicolas Leonard Sadi Carnot in 1824, and the reversible thermodynamic cycle that he proposed now bears his name. It is interesting to note that Carnot did his work approximately 150 years ago. In this short span of man's history, scientific thermodynamics has become a reality.

As noted in the preceding section, the two frictionless quasi-static processes that are reversible are the isothermal (constant temperature) and adiabatic (no energy as heat crosses the boundary). Carnot proposed a reversible cycle composed of two reversible isothermal processes and two reversible adiabatic processes, and on the basis of this cycle he was able to reach certain general conclusions. Let us consider the cycle that has been named for him by describing each step of the cycle. Figure 3.1 (solid line) is a schematic of a direct engine cycle. For the Carnot cycle, we define the following sequence of events:

1 Heat is taken from an infinite reservoir (source) at T_1 isothermally and reversibly. Basically, this is equivalent to a quasi-static reception of heat into the cycle without temperature differences.

2 The energy received from step 1 is permitted to produce work by expanding reversibly and adiabatically in an ideal frictionless engine. During this step net work is produced, but no energy as heat is

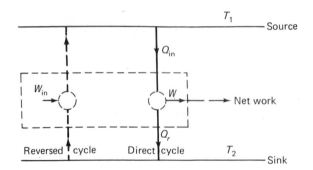

Figure 3.1 Elements of Carnot cycle

permitted to cross the boundaries of the system, even though the pressure and temperature of the working fluid may have changed.

3 At this point in the cycle the working fluid is at temperature T_2, and we shall want to return it to its starting point. To do this we first reject heat at constant temperature (T_2) reversibly and isothermally to an infinite sink.

4 The final step in the cycle is to cause the working fluid to be adiabatically and reversibly compressed to its initial state.

For a noncondensing gas the steps of the cycle are portrayed on pressure–volume coordinates in Fig. 3.2.

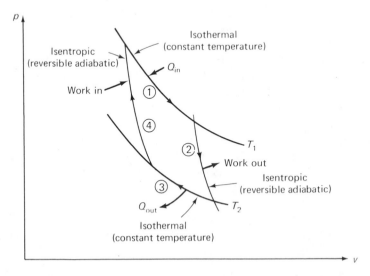

Figure 3.2 Carnot cycle on *p–v* coordinates: noncondensible gas

The Carnot cycle just described is a reversible cycle, and it is therefore possible to reverse each step in turn and thus reverse the cycle. Such a reversed cycle would effectively take work as an input and pump heat from T_2 to T_1. The reversed cycle is known as a *heat pump* and is discussed further in Chapter 8. It should be noted that the Carnot cycle is not unique, and it is not the only reversible cycle that can be devised. Actually, many reversible cycles have been proposed as prototypes of real cycles. The power of the Carnot cycle is that the following general conclusions can be deduced from it:

1 *No engine operating between fixed source (T_1) and sink (T_2) temperatures and continuously delivering work can be more efficient than a reversible engine operating between these same temperature limits.*

To prove this proposition, let us take two reversible engine cycles and let the output of the first engine cycle be used to operate the second cycle in reverse. Schematically, this arrangement is shown in Fig. 3.3. For the direct cycle, Q_{in} at T_1 serves to produce a net work output, and Q_r is the rejected heat to the sink at T_2. The net work serves as the input to the second cycle. Let us now assume that the second (reversed) engine is more efficient than the first

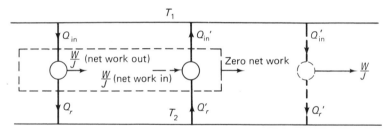

Figure 3.3 Proof of Carnot principle 1

engine operating directly, and we will denote the energy quantities for the reversed cycle as Q'_r and Q'_{in}, respectively. Since the second engine cycle is reversible, it is shown in Fig. 3.3 acting as if it were a direct cycle by the dotted schematic. In each of these cycles W/J is, by assumption, the same. By applying Eq. (3.1) to both cycles, we have

$$\frac{(W/J)}{Q'_{in}} > \frac{W/J}{Q_{in}} \qquad (3.3)$$

since the efficiency of the second cycle was assumed to be greater than that of the first cycle. Thus $Q'_{in} < Q_{in}$. Since the net work is constant and equal to $Q_{in} - Q_r$ for the first (direct engine) and $Q'_{in} - Q'_r$ for the reversed (more efficient engine), it follows that $Q'_r < Q_r$. The conclusion is that such an arrangement in which both cycles are combined takes net heat out of the reservoir at temperature T_2 and delivers this heat to the reservoir at the higher temperature T_1, but no net work is put into the combined cycle. This directly violates the Clausius axiom of the second law of thermodynamics, which states that heat cannot *of itself* pass from a lower to a higher temperature, and we may reject the assumption that the second reversible engine can be more efficient than a reversible engine operating between the same temperature limits. Thus Carnot principle 1 is proved.

   2 *The efficiency of all reversible cycles operating between the same temperature limits is the same.*

The proof of Carnot principle 2 is essentially the same as that used for Carnot principle 1 and is not given in detail. The student should note that this principle, combined with the first, proves that the reversible cycle and its associated processes indeed serve to establish the index of performance for heat engine cycles.

   3 *The thermal efficiency of a reversible engine is a function solely of the upper and lower temperatures of the cycle and is not a function of the working substances used in the cycle.*

This third principle is somewhat different in its viewpoint, and part of the mathematical reasoning is quite abstract. We can argue this point qualitatively in the following manner. Let us assume that the efficiency of a reversible engine is a function of the working substance used in the cycle. By using two reversible cycles, as for principle 1, we can place a different working fluid in each of the cycles. One reversible cycle would be more efficient than the other, and by the identical reasoning used in principle 1 we would arrive at a violation of the Clausius axiom. Thus the efficiency of a reversible engine cycle cannot be a function of the working substance used in the cycle. By continuing this line of reasoning, we are also directed to the conclusion that the efficiency of a reversible engine is a function only of the upper and lower temperatures used in the cycle.

To establish the temperature function, we can resort to reasoning similar to that used by Fermi and Dodge. Consider the three heat reservoirs shown in Fig. 3.4 and maintained at temperatures t_1, t_2, and t_3, respectively, on some

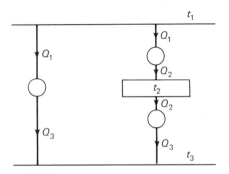

Figure 3.4 Derivation of the absolute temperature

arbitrary absolute temperature scale. Assume that three Carnot heat engines operate between these temperatures. Since the efficiency of the cycle is assumed to be some function of the temperature limits of the cycle, it follows from Eq. (3.2) that for each engine Q_r/Q_{in} is also a function of t_1 and t_2 for the respective temperatures and heat quantities associated with each engine. Therefore,

$$\frac{Q_1}{Q_2} = \phi_1(t_1, t_2) \qquad (3.4a)$$

$$\frac{Q_2}{Q_3} = \phi_2(t_2, t_3) \qquad (3.4b)$$

$$\frac{Q_1}{Q_3} = \phi_3(t_1, t_3) \qquad (3.4c)$$

The symbol ϕ is interpreted to mean "a function of"; thus from Eq. (3.4a) Q_1/Q_2 is a function of t_1 and t_2. Dividing Eq. (3.4c) into Eq. (3.4b) and comparing with Eq. (3.4a) yields

$$\frac{Q_1}{Q_2} = \phi_1(t_1, t_2) = \frac{\phi_3(t_1, t_3)}{\phi_2(t_2, t_3)} \qquad (3.5)$$

The left side of Eq. (3.5) indicates that ϕ_3/ϕ_2 is only a function of t_1 and t_2. Thus the function of t_3 must cancel out of Eq. (3.5), and we obtain

$$\frac{Q_1}{Q_2} = \phi_1(t_1, t_2) = \frac{\phi_3(t_1)}{\phi_2(t_2)} \qquad (3.6a)$$

At this point it becomes impossible to determine the function in Eq. (3.6a) analytically, for it is entirely arbitrary. For convenience, the absolute thermodynamic temperature scale defined by Eq. (3.6a) has been made equal to the absolute temperature scale defined by the ideal gas (see Chapters 1 and 5). Thus the temperature functions given by Eq. (3.6a) become simply the corresponding absolute temperatures. Using the notation of capital T for absolute temperature,

$$\frac{Q_1}{Q_2} = \frac{T_1}{T_2} \qquad (3.6b)$$

If Eq. (3.6b) is inverted,

$$\frac{Q_2}{Q_1} = \frac{T_2}{T_1} \qquad (3.6c)$$

Subtracting unity from each side of Eq. (3.6c) gives us

$$\frac{Q_2}{Q_1} - 1 = \frac{T_2}{T_1} - 1 \qquad (3.7)$$

Simplifying Eq. (3.7),

$$\left(\frac{Q_1 - Q_2}{Q_1} \right) = \left(\frac{T_1 - T_2}{T_1} \right) = \left(1 - \frac{T_2}{T_1} \right) \qquad (3.7a)$$

In terms of the preceding notation,

$$\eta = 100 \left(\frac{Q_{in} - Q_r}{Q_{in}} \right) = \left(\frac{T_1 - T_2}{T_1} \right) 100 = \left(1 - \frac{T_2}{T_1} \right) 100 \quad (3.7b)$$

The student should note that the relations of Eq. (3.7) apply only to reversible cycles.

From Eq. (3.7) we conclude the following:

1 The efficiency of a reversible-engine cycle is a function only of the upper and lower temperatures of the cycle.

2 Increasing the upper temperature while the lower temperature is kept constant increases the efficiency of the cycle.

3 Decreasing the temperature at which heat is rejected while keeping the upper temperature of the cycle constant increases the efficiency of the cycle.

The temperature scale that is defined by Eq. (3.7) is called the absolute thermodynamic temperature scale, since it does not depend on the working substance. By defining it in this manner, it becomes identical to the temperature scale defined for the ideal gas (Chapters 1 and 5).

ILLUSTRATIVE PROBLEM 3.1

A reversible engine operates between 1000° and 80°F. (a) What is the efficiency of the engine? (b) If the upper temperature is increased to 2000°F while the lower temperature is kept constant, what is the efficiency of the engine? (c) If the lower temperature of the cycle is increased to 160°F while the upper temperature is kept at 1000°F, what is the efficiency of the cycle?

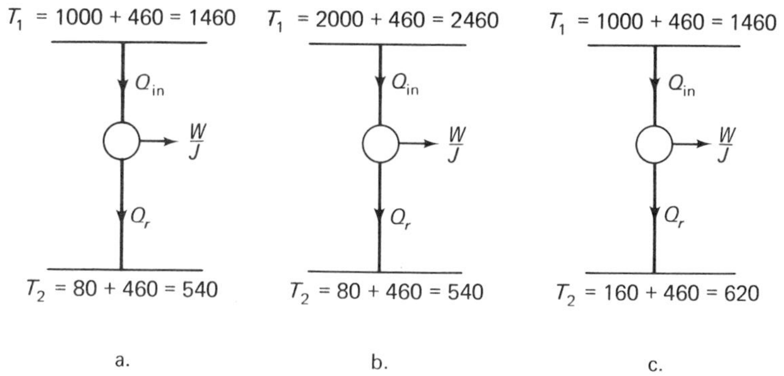

$T_1 = 1000 + 460 = 1460$ $T_1 = 2000 + 460 = 2460$ $T_1 = 1000 + 460 = 1460$

$T_2 = 80 + 460 = 540$ $T_2 = 80 + 460 = 540$ $T_2 = 160 + 460 = 620$

a.   b.   c.

Figure 3.5 Illustrative Problem 3.1

Solution

Referring to Fig. 3.5 and converting all temperatures to absolute temperatures,

(a) $\dfrac{T_1 - T_2}{T_1} = \dfrac{1460 - 540}{1460} = 0.63 = 63\%$

(b) $\dfrac{T_1 - T_2}{T_1} = \dfrac{2460 - 540}{2460} = 0.78 = 78\%$

(c) $\dfrac{T_1 - T_2}{T_1} = \dfrac{1460 - 620}{1460} = 0.575 = 57.5\%$

ILLUSTRATIVE PROBLEM 3.2

Assume that 100 units of heat enter the reversible engine in Illustrative Problem 3.1. If the cycle is reversed, determine the amount of work into the cycle and the heat removed from the reservoir at T_2.

Solution

The quantities of energy in the reversed cycle must equal those of the direct cycle. Several approaches are possible in solving this problem. We can use the efficiency obtained in Illustrative Problem 3.1. Therefore,

$$\frac{(W/J)}{Q_{in}} = 0.63 \quad \text{and} \quad \frac{W}{J} = 100(0.63) = 63 \text{ units out}$$

$$Q_{in} - Q_r = \frac{W}{J}$$

Therefore, $100 - 63 = 37 = Q_r$.

For the reversed cycle we have only to note that Q_r (or 37 units) is taken into the system from the low-temperature reservoir, 63 units of work enter the system, and 100 units are returned to the high-temperature reservoir.

ILLUSTRATIVE PROBLEM 3.3

A Carnot engine operates between a source temperature of 1000°F and a sink temperature of 100°F. If the engine is to have an output of 50 hp, determine the heat supplied, the efficiency of the engine, and the heat rejected. Refer to Fig. 3.6.

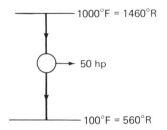

Figure 3.6 Illustrative Problem 3.3

Solution

$$50 \text{ hp} = \frac{50 \times 33,000}{778} = 2120.8 \text{ Btu/min as output}$$

since 1 horsepower is equivalent to 33,000 ft lb/min.

$$\eta = \left(1 - \frac{T_2}{T_1}\right)100 = \left(1 - \frac{560}{1460}\right)100 = 61.6\%$$

$$= \frac{W/J}{Q_{in}} = \frac{2120.8}{Q_{in}}$$

$$Q_{in} = \frac{2120.8}{0.616} = 3443 \text{ Btu/min}$$

$$Q_r = 3443(1 - 0.616) = 1322 \text{ Btu/min}$$

ILLUSTRATIVE PROBLEM 3.4

A Carnot engine operates between a source temperature of 700°C and a sink temperature of 20°C. Assuming that the engine will have an output of 65 hp, determine the heat supplied, the efficiency of the engine and the heat rejected.

Solution

We can also refer to Fig. 3.6, noting that $T_1 = 700 + 273 = 973$ K and $T_2 = 20 + 273 = 293$ K. The efficiency of the Carnot engine is

$$\eta = \left(\frac{T_1 - T_2}{T_1} \right) 100 = \left(\frac{973 - 293}{973} \right) 100 = 69.9\%$$

The work output of the engine is $65 \times 746 = 48.49$ kJ. Since efficiency is work out/heat in,

$$\text{heat in} = Q_{in} = \frac{48.49}{0.699} = 69.37 \text{ kJ}$$

$$\text{heat rejected} = Q_{in} - \text{work out} = 69.37 - 48.49 = 20.88 \text{ kJ}$$

As a check,

$$Q_r = Q_{in}(1 - \eta) = 69.37(1 - 0.699) = 20.88 \text{ kJ}$$

3.4 ENTROPY

If we refer to the working fluid and the changes that occur to it (for any reversible cycle operating between the same temperature limits), we have established that

$$\frac{Q_{in}}{T_1} = \frac{Q_r}{T_2}$$

In other words, the heat reception or rejection for the fluid in *any* reversible cycle divided by the temperature at which the heat is interchanged is a constant. The specific reversible paths that constitute the cycle do not change the value of these quantities. If the value of these quantities was a function of the specific reversible paths chosen, we could readily show that a violation of the second law would result.

The uniqueness of these ratios leads us to the conclusion that they may represent state functions of the fluid, and as such we may define them for a reversible process as properties. In fact, it is correct to make this assumption. To generalize the foregoing conclusion, we define the quantity S as referring to this new property and call it *entropy*. On a unit mass basis, the specific entropy is s.

The defining equation for entropy is given by Eq. (3.8).

$$\Delta S = \left(\frac{Q}{T} \right) \quad \text{reversible process}$$

$$\Delta s = \left(\frac{q}{T} \right) \quad \text{reversible process} \qquad (3.8)$$

To show that entropy is a property of the state and not a function of the path chosen, let us consider the following situation: a reversible cycle operates between states a and b as indicated by the path $a,1,b,2,a$ in Fig. 3.7. Let us also indicate a second possible return path, $b,3,a$. For the first path $(a,1,b,2,a)$,

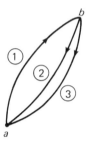

Figure 3.7 Proof that entropy is a property

$$\Delta S_{1,2} = \left[\frac{Q}{T} \right]_{a,b}^{\text{path 1}} + \left[\frac{Q}{T} \right]_{b,a}^{\text{path 2}} \qquad (3.9)$$

where the symbol $[\quad]_{a,b}^{\text{path 1}}$ indicates the sum of the Q/T items from a to b via path 1 and $[\quad]_{b,a}^{\text{path 2}}$ denotes the same from b to a via path 2. For path $b,3,a$, as the return path,

$$\Delta S_{1,3} = \left[\frac{Q}{T} \right]_{a,b}^{\text{path 1}} + \left[\frac{Q}{T} \right]_{b,a}^{\text{path 3}} \qquad (3.10)$$

All the processes in these two cycles are reversible, which permits us to write the foregoing relations for known paths. Let us once again repeat that the two frictionless quasi-static processes that are reversible are the adiabatic and isothermal. For the reversible isothermal process Q is not a function of T, and the reversible adiabatic process requires Q to be zero. Thus, if a cycle is composed of these reversible processes, ΔS of the cycle is zero. We may generalize this statement for all reversible cycles and say that the summation of ΔS around the reversible cycle must equal zero. Using this fact and equating Eqs. (3.9) and (3.10) yields

$$\left[\frac{Q}{T} \right]_{b,a}^{\text{path 2}} = \left[\frac{Q}{T} \right]_{b,a}^{\text{path 3}} \qquad (3.11)$$

Thus we can conclude that the function $(Q/T)_{\text{reversible}}$ represents a property that is only a function of the state of the fluid and is independent of the reversible path taken to reach the particular state. The importance of this statement is not just in the proof of the fact that entropy is a state function; it is important also in that it provides us with the means of calculating the change in entropy for any process. All that is necessary is a knowledge of the initial and final states of the process, since we can always (at least, in principle) consider a reversible process between the same initial and final states. It must be emphasized that (Q/T) can be used only to evaluate the entropy change for a reversible process.

Since entropy is a state function, we may use it to portray graphically any equilibrium state of a fluid. Let us plot on temperature–entropy coordinates the reversible processes constituting the Carnot cycle. For convenience we use a unit mass of working fluid, and the entropy coordinate becomes the specific entropy s. Let us consider each step of the cycle and interpret each step with the aid of Fig. 3.8.

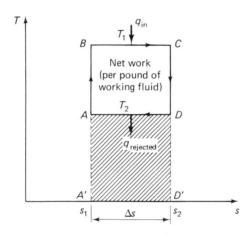

Figure 3.8 Direct Carnot cycle

Energy as heat enters the cycle at the constant upper temperature T_1 with an increase in entropy from B to C. This is represented by the horizontal line BC. Since $\Delta s = q_{\text{in}}/T_1$, $q_{\text{in}} = T_1 \Delta s$, which is equivalent to the area under the line BC or area $A'BCD'$. The fluid is then expanded via a reversible adiabatic process, which cannot give rise to an increase in entropy since no heat enters or leaves the system during its course. The reversible adiabatic process is therefore carried out at constant entropy. Because of this fact, it is called an *isentropic* process. A reversible adiabatic process is isentropic, but not all isentropic processes are reversible adiabatic processes. Therefore, the expansion of this step is the vertical line CD. The next step in the cycle is the isothermal rejection of heat represented by the horizontal line DA. Since $\Delta s = q_r/T_2$, $T_2(\Delta s) = q_r$, the heat rejected by the cycle is represented by area $A'ADD'$, which is the area under the line DA. The final step in the cycle is the isentropic (reversible adiabatic) compression along path AB to return the cycle to its starting point. Since the area $A'BCD'$ is the heat into the cycle and area $A'ADD'$ is the heat rejected, the net work of the cycle is the area $ABCD$, or the area enclosed by the paths of the cycle on Ts coordinates. It should be noted that we have considered 1 lb of working fluid, since s is the specific entropy.

ILLUSTRATIVE PROBLEM 3.5

To vaporize 1 lb of saturated water into saturated steam at 200 psia, 843.7 Btu is required. If the temperature of this process is constant and equal to 381.86°F, what is the change in entropy for the process?

Solution

For the reversible isothermal process we can write $\Delta s = q/T$. Thus

$$\Delta s = \frac{843.7}{(381.86 + 460)} \quad \text{or} \quad \Delta s = 1.002$$

ILLUSTRATIVE PROBLEM 3.6

If the process described in Illustrative Problem 3.5 is the heat reception portion of a Carnot cycle, what is the efficiency of the cycle if the lowest temperature of the cycle is 50°F? How much work is done per pound of fluid? How much energy is rejected?

Solution

$$\eta = 100\left(\frac{T_1 - T_2}{T_1}\right) = 100\left(1 - \frac{T_2}{T_1}\right) = 100\left(1 - \frac{460 + 50}{460 + 381.86}\right)$$

$$= 100(1 - 0.606) = 39.4\%$$

$$\frac{W}{J} = q_{in}\eta = (0.394)(843.7) = 332.4 \text{ Btu/lb}$$

$$q_r = q_{in} - \frac{W}{J} = 843.7 - 332.4 = 511.3 \text{ Btu/lb}$$

As an alternate solution and referring to Fig. 3.8, we can write the following:

$$q_{in} = T_1 \Delta s \qquad\qquad (3.12a)$$

$$q_r = T_2 \Delta s \qquad\qquad (3.12b)$$

$$\frac{W}{J} = q_{in} - q_r = (T_1 - T_2)\Delta s \qquad\qquad (3.12c)$$

$$q_r = T_2 \Delta s = (460 + 50)(1.002) = 511 \text{ Btu/lb}$$

$$\frac{W}{J} = q_{in} - q_r = 843.7 - 511 = 332.7 \text{ Btu/lb}$$

$$\eta = \frac{W/J}{q_{in}} \times 100 = \frac{332.7}{843.7} \times 100 = 39.4\%$$

ILLUSTRATIVE PROBLEM 3.7

A pressure of 200 psia corresponds closely to 13.8 bars. Using 13.8 bars, determine the change in entropy for the vaporization of 1 kg of saturated water to saturated steam. The *Steam Tables* give the heat required as 1962.3 J/g and the temperature as 194.4°C.

Solution

As in Illustrative Problem 3.6, we consider the vaporization process to be isothermal. Therefore,

$$\Delta s = \frac{1962.3}{194.4 + 273} = 4.1983 \frac{J}{g \cdot K}$$

Using 273.16 to obtain temperature in degrees Kelvin yields a value very close to that given in the *Steam Tables*, that is, 4.1969 versus 4.1965.

It has already been noted that the cycle efficiency can be improved by raising the upper temperature of the cycle or lowering its lowest temperature. From Eq. (3.12b) it is noted that the heat rejected during this cycle is equal to the change in entropy during the heat rejection process multiplied by the temperature at which the heat is rejected. In a general sense the entropy change of the process becomes a measure of the amount of heat that becomes unavailable (rejected) during the cycle. For an irreversible process, we have already indicated that some energy becomes unavailable because of friction during the process. If it is assumed that the irreversible process can be restored to its original state by the input of additional work to the system via a reversible path, it can be shown that the increase in entropy during the irreversible process can be used to evaluate the least amount of work necessary to restore the system to its original state. Thus a greater entropy change requires more work to restore the system. In this sense entropy is also a measure of the unavailability of energy that occurs in an irreversible process.

ILLUSTRATIVE PROBLEM 3.8

One hundred Btu enters a system at 1000°F. How much of this energy is unavailable with respect to a receiver at 50°F? Also, how much of this energy is unavailable with respect to a receiver at 0°F?

Solution

Let us assume that a Carnot engine cycle operates between the two temperatures in each case.

$$\Delta S = \frac{Q_{in}}{T_1} = \frac{100}{1460} = 0.0685, \qquad Q_r = T_2 \Delta S$$

Therefore,

(1) $Q_r = (50 + 460)(0.0685) = 34.9$ Btu for the receiver at 50°F

(2) $Q_r = (0 + 460)(0.0685) = 31.5$ Btu for the receiver at 0°F

Note that ΔS for the process is independent of the receiver temperature.

ILLUSTRATIVE PROBLEM 3.9

If 1 kJ enters a system at 500°C, how much of this energy is unavailable with respect to a receiver at 20°C and also to a receiver at 0°C.

Solution

$$\Delta S = \frac{Q_{in}}{T_1} = \frac{1000}{500 + 273} = 1.2937$$

$$Q_r = T_2 \Delta S_1$$

Therefore,

(1) $Q_r = (273 + 20)(1.2937) = 379.05$ J for the receiver at 20°C

(2) $Q_r = (273 + 0)(1.2937) = 353.18$ J for the receiver at 0°C

Any process can be considered to have a characteristic specific heat associated with it. Therefore, the heat transfer during such a process can be written as

$$q = c\Delta T \qquad (3.13)$$

whether it is reversible or irreversible.

Using Eq. (3.13) and the definition of entropy given in Eq. (3.8), $s_2 - s_1$ = summation of $c\Delta T/T$ for a reversible process between its temperature limits. This relation can be used to evaluate the change in entropy for a process taking place between temperatures T_1 and T_2, and it will correctly evaluate the change in entropy for any process between the prescribed limits as long as we restrict it to apply to the system and not to the surroundings. Thus, for a constant c, it can be shown that the summation of $c\Delta T/T$ between the limits of T_1 and T_2 yields

$$s_2 - s_1 = c \ln \frac{T_2}{T_1} \qquad (3.14)$$

where the symbol ln is the natural logarithm to the base e. In terms of the common logarithmic base 10,

$$\ln x = \log_e x = 2.3026 \log_{10} x \qquad (3.15)$$

ILLUSTRATIVE PROBLEM 3.10

If 1 lb of water at 500°F is adiabatically mixed with 1 lb of water at 100°F, determine the change in entropy. Assume that the specific heat of the hot and cold streams can be considered constant and equal to unity. Also the specific heat of the mixture can be taken to be unity. Refer to Fig. 3.9.

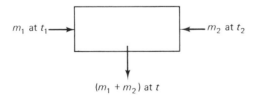

m_1 at t_1 → ← m_2 at t_2

$(m_1 + m_2)$ at t

Figure 3.9 Illustrative Problem 3.10

Solution

To solve this problem, it is necessary first to establish the equilibrium temperature of the final mixture. We apply the first law energy balance to the diagram, $m_1 c_1 t_1 + m_2 c_2 t_2 = (m_1 + m_2)c_{\text{mix}}t$, where t is the resulting mixture temperature.

Therefore,

$$(1)(1)500 + (1)(1)100 = (1+1)(1)t \quad \text{and} \quad t = 300°F$$

For this problem the hot stream is cooled from 500°F to 300°F. Since we may state that heat Q was removed during this process, Δs would be expected to be negative. By applying Eq. (3.14),

$$\Delta s = 1 \ln\left(\frac{300 + 460}{500 + 460} \right) = \ln \frac{760}{960} = -\ln \frac{960}{760} = -\ln 1.263$$
$$= -0.233 \text{ Btu/lb}$$

The cold stream is heated from 100° to 300°F; therefore,

$$\Delta s = 1 \ln \frac{760}{560} = \ln 1.357 = 0.305 \text{ Btu/lb }°F$$

The net change is $0.305 - 0.233 = +0.072$ Btu/lb°F. An alternate solution to this problem is found by assuming an arbitrary temperature lower than any other temperature in the system. The change in entropy of each fluid is determined with respect to this arbitrary temperature, and the net change in entropy is the algebraic sum of the values found in this manner. An illustration of the procedure is found in Chapter 6, as well as in Illustrative Problem 3.11.

ILLUSTRATIVE PROBLEM 3.11

Solve Illustrative Problem 3.10 using 0°F as a reference temperature for entropy.

Solution

As a first step, we calculate the final mixture temperature as was done in Illustrative Problem 3.10 and find it to be 300°F. Next, let us calculate the initial entropy of each fluid above the 0°F base.

For the "hot" fluid,

$$\Delta s = c \ln \frac{T_2}{T_1} = 1 \ln\left(\frac{500 + 460}{0 + 460} \right)$$
$$= 1 \ln 2.087 = 0.736 \text{ Btu/lb }°F$$

For the "cold" fluid,

$$s = c \ln \frac{T_2}{T_1} = 1 \ln\left(\frac{100 + 460}{0 + 460} \right)$$
$$= 1 \ln 1.217 = 0.196 \text{ Btu/lb }°F$$

At the final mixture temperature of 300°F, the entropy of each stream above 0°F is,

For the "hot" fluid,

$$s = c \ln \frac{T_2}{T_1} = c \ln\left(\frac{300 + 460}{0 + 460} \right)$$

$$= 1 \ln 1.652 = 0.502 \text{ Btu/lb °F}$$

For the "cold" fluid,

$$s = c \ln \frac{T_2}{T_1} = c \ln\left(\frac{300 + 460}{0 + 460} \right)$$

$$= 1 \ln 1.652 = 0.502 \text{ Btu/lb °F}$$

The change in entropy of the "hot" fluid is $0.502 - 0.736 = -0.234$ Btu/lb °F. The change in entropy of the "cold" fluid is $0.502 - 0.196 = 0.306$ Btu/lb °F.

$$\text{total change} = 0.306 - 0.234 = 0.072 \text{ Btu/lb °F}$$

The advantage of this alternate procedure is that by using a convenient, arbitrary datum below the lowest temperature in the system we avoid negative logarithms. Either method is correct, and the choice of one over the other is purely personal preference.

The fact that entropy is a property leads us to inquire whether there are possible relations between entropy and other properties of a fluid. If they exist, they should prove to be very valuable, since it would then be possible to compute one from the other without having to resort to experiment. Let us recall the energy equation applied to the reversible nonflow process.

$$q = \Delta u + \frac{p \Delta v}{J} \qquad (3.16)$$

Since the process is assumed to be reversible, we may replace q by $T\Delta s$. Thus

$$T\Delta s = \Delta u + \frac{p \Delta v}{J} \qquad (3.17)$$

In Eq. (3.17), $T\Delta s$ evaluates the energy only as heat if the process is reversible, and similarly $p\Delta v/J$ evaluates only the work of a reversible process. However, each term of this equation consists of properties of the fluid that are not functions of the path. Thus, by applying the energy equation and the second law to a reversible nonflow process, we have been able to arrive at an equation involving only property terms that is therefore completely general.

The only restriction on this equation occurs when the various terms are interpreted as either heat or work.

By referring to the reversible steady-flow process, we can arrive at another relationship between the properties. Alternately, the same result can be obtained as follows: by definition

$$h_2 - h_1 = (u_2 - u_1) + \frac{p_2 v_2 - p_1 v_1}{J} \tag{3.18}$$

or

$$\Delta h = \Delta u + \frac{\Delta(pv)}{J} \tag{3.19}$$

The change in the product pv/J equals

$$\frac{(p + \Delta p)(v + \Delta v) - pv}{J} \tag{3.20}$$

Carrying out the multiplication of the terms of Eq. (3.20) yields

$$\frac{\Delta(pv)}{J} = (\Delta p)v + (\Delta v)p + (\Delta p)(\Delta v) \tag{3.21}$$

The product $(\Delta p)(\Delta v)$ is the product of two small terms and can be considered negligible. Thus

$$\frac{\Delta(pv)}{J} = \frac{(\Delta p)v + p(\Delta v)}{J} \tag{3.22}$$

Replacing $\Delta(pv)/J$ in Eq. (3.19) with its equivalent from Eq. (3.22) yields

$$\Delta h = \Delta u + \frac{(\Delta p)v + (\Delta v)p}{J} \tag{3.23}$$

By the substitution of Eq. (3.23) into Eq. (3.17) and rearranging, we have the desired result:

$$T\Delta s = \Delta h - \frac{v(\Delta p)}{J} \tag{3.24}$$

We can thus relate entropy to enthalpy by means of Eq. (3.24). Once again, each term in this equation is a property, but the interpretation of such terms as $T\Delta s$ as a heat quantity or $v\Delta p$ as a work quantity can be valid only for a reversible process.

The student should note that Eqs. (3.16) through (3.24) can be written in terms of SI units simply by omitting the conversion factor J wherever it appears. The final result would be

$$T\Delta s = \Delta h - v(\Delta p) \tag{3.24a}$$

It has been established that entropy is a property and can be evaluated by considering reversible paths connecting the given end states of a process. Let us consider the situation in which two processes start out from a given state. The first one is carried out reversibly until a second state is reached. The second process is carried out irreversibly until the same pressure as the first process has stopped at is reached. These processes operate between a fixed source at T_1 and a fixed sink at T_2 as part of a Carnot cycle. For the reversible process

$$\frac{Q_{in}}{T_1} = \frac{Q_r}{T_2}$$

For the irreversible process, less net work is produced, with the consequence that more energy must be rejected as heat. Thus Q_r/T_2 for the irreversible process can at best equal the equivalent ratio of the reversible process or, as is the case in all instances, it must be greater. Using this qualitative argument we can arrive at another important consequence of the second law:

*The entropy of an isolated system increases or in the limit remains the same.**

This principle of the increase of entropy also serves as a criterion of irreversibility. Thus, if we find during a process that the entropy of an isolated system increases, we must conclude that the process is irreversible. Another consequence of the principle of the increase of entropy is that, at a given internal energy, that state having the greatest entropy will be the most probable state that the system will assume. At this most probable state the system is said to be in stable equilibrium.

The foregoing can be summarized by the following simple equation:

$$\Delta S \gtreqless 0 \text{ for isolated systems} \qquad (3.25)$$

which is interpreted to state that, for any reversible change in an isolated system, the total entropy remains unchanged, and for any irreversible change the total entropy increases.

3.5 CLOSURE

In Chapters 1 and 2 we introduced and discussed the properties pressure, temperature, specific volume, density, internal energy, enthalpy, and specific weight, as well as the term energy. Basically, all these terms (with the possible

---

* *Thermodynamics* by J. H. Keenan, John Wiley & Sons, Inc., New York, 1941.

exception of enthalpy) are terms that are found in the general vocabulary or terms that the student is exposed to in his physics and chemistry courses. The property that we have introduced in this chapter and called entropy has often been a problem in that it is a new term that is not familiar, and the student does not have a physical "feel" for it. When treated as an abstract or philosophical entity, entropy can and does present many facets and difficulties when first introduced to the student. For the present it is strongly recommended that entropy be treated simply as another property such as pressure and temperature, and the material of this chapter should be considered as defining this property. As progress is made in later chapters of this book, the utility of this property will become more apparent and the student will be as comfortable using it as he is when using the property of enthalpy on internal energy.

Van Wylen and Sonntag raise the following questions, and their response to these questions is worthy of note at this point:

> *The final point to be made is that the Second Law of Thermodynamics and the principle of the increase of entropy have philosophical implications. Does the Second Law of Thermodynamics apply to the universe as a whole? Are there processes unknown to us that occur somewhere in the universe, such as "continual creation," that have a decrease in entropy associated with them, and thus offset the continual increase in entropy that is associated with the natural processes that are known to us? If the Second Law is valid for the universe (we, of course, do not know if the universe can be considered as an isolated system) how did it get in the state of low entropy? On the other end of the scale, if all processes known to us have an increase in entropy associated with them, what is the future of the natural world as we know it?*

Quite obviously it is impossible to give conclusive answers to these questions on the basis of the Second Law of Thermodynamics alone. However, the authors see the Second Law of Thermodynamics as man's description of the prior and continuing work of a creator, who also holds the answer to the future destiny of man and the universe.*

REFERENCES

1 *Thermodynamics* by E. Fermi, Dover Publications, New York, 1956.

2 *Heat and Thermodynamics*, 4th Ed., by M. W. Zemansky, McGraw-Hill Book Co., New York, 1957.

3 *Concepts of Thermodynamics* by E. F. Obert, McGraw-Hill Book Co., New York, 1960.

*Fundamentals of Classical Thermodynamics by G. J. Van Wylen and R. E. Sonntag, John Wiley & Sons, Inc., New York, 1965.

4 *Principles of Engineering Thermodynamics*, 2nd Ed., by P. J. Kiefer, G. F. Kinney, and M. C. Stuart, John Wiley & Sons, Inc., New York, 1954.

5 *Thermodynamics* by J. H. Keenan, John Wiley & Sons, Inc., New York, 1941.

6 *Elementary Applied Thermodynamics* by Irving Granet, John Wiley & Sons, Inc., New York, 1965.

7 *Engineering Thermodynamics* by D. B. Spaulding and E. H. Cole, McGraw-Hill Book Co., New York, 1959.

8 *Chemical Engineering Thermodynamics* by B. F. Dodge, McGraw-Hill Book Co., New York, 1944.

9 *Fundamentals of Classical Thermodynamics* by G. J. Van Wylen and R. E. Sonntag, John Wiley & Sons, Inc., New York, 1965.

PROBLEMS

3.1 An engine cycle is operated to produce 12.5 Btu/min as work. If 100 Btu/min enters the cycle, determine the heat rejected and the efficiency of the cycle.

3.2 A Carnot cycle is operated between 1000°F and 500°F. If the upper temperature is increased to 1100°F, what is the efficiency of the cycle? If the lower temperature is decreased to 400°F, what is the efficiency of the cycle? From this conclude whether by equal temperature change it is more desirable to raise T_1 or to lower T_2 to obtain the greatest increase in cycle efficiency.

3.3 An engine produces 10 kJ as work while 80 kJ enters the engine cycle as heat. Determine the energy rejected and the thermal efficiency of the cycle.

3.4 A Carnot cycle operates between 900° and 100°C. Determine the efficiency of the cycle, the heat rejected, and the useful work output if 100 kJ enters the cycle as heat.

3.5 An inventor claims to have an engine that has a thermal efficiency of 90 percent. Comment on his claim.

3.6 Is it possible for a reversible engine cycle to produce 100 hp if it receives 5000 Btu/sec at 1000°F and rejects heat at 500°F?

3.7 A reversible engine operates between 900°F and 200°F. What is the maximum efficiency of this cycle? If the rating of this engine is 1 hp, determine the heat rejected per minute.

3.8 If the cycle in Problem 3.7 is reversed, how much heat is rejected to the upper temperature reservoir?

3.9 A reversible engine operates between 750° and 80°C. Determine the maximum efficiency of the cycle and the heat rejected if the engine is rated at 1 hp.

3.10 If the cycle in Problem 3.9 is reversed, how much heat is rejected to the upper temperature reservoir?

3.11 A Carnot engine operates between a source temperature of 900°F and a sink temperature of 100°F. If the engine produces 100,000 ft lb of work, determine its thermal efficiency, the heat supplied, and the heat rejected.

3.12 A Carnot engine receives 1000 Btu at 1000°F and operates with a sink temperature of 150°F. Determine the efficiency, work out, and heat rejected by this engine.

3.13 A Carnot engine operates between an upper temperature of 700°C and a lower temperature of 30°C. If the engine can produce 150 kJ of work, determine its thermal efficiency, the heat supplied, and the heat rejected.

3.14 A Carnot engine develops 30 hp while rejecting 100 MJ/hr to a receiver at 20°C. Determine the upper temperature of the cycle and its efficiency.

3.15 A Carnot engine develops 20 hp while rejecting 70,000 Btu/hr to a receiver at 80°F. Determine the efficiency of the engine and the source temperature.

3.16 A reversed Carnot engine operates between 150° and 60°F; 100 Btu/min is extracted from the cold body. Determine the horsepower required to operate the engine.

3.17 A reversed Carnot engine operates with an efficiency of 30 percent and removes 1000 Btu from the cold sink. Compute the heat rejected to the hotter source.

3.18 A reversed Carnot engine operates between 80° and 20°C; 100 kJ/min is extracted from the cold body. Determine the horsepower required to operate the engine.

3.19 A reversed Carnot engine operates with an efficiency of 30 percent, removing 1 MJ from the cold sink. Calculate the heat rejected to the hotter source.

3.20 A reversed Carnot cycle operates between temperatures of 100° and 0°F. If the motor input is 5 hp, determine the heat removed from the cold sink.

3.21 A reversed Carnot cycle is used to heat a room. If 9000 Btu/hr is required, how much energy must be put in electrically if the room is to be at 70°F and a deep well at 40°F is used as the source of working fluid for the cycle?

3.22 A reversed Carnot engine operates between 40° and 5°C. If the motor input is 4 hp, determine the heat removed from the cold sink.

3.23 A reversed Carnot engine is used to heat a room. If 10 kW is required to replace heat losses from the room, how much energy must be put into the motor if the room is to be kept at 22°C and a deep well at 4°C is used as the source of the working fluid of the cycle?

3.24 A reversed Carnot engine is used to cool a large room in the summer. The room is to be kept at 24°C when the outside temperature is 35°C. It is estimated that 150 kJ/min is the heat transfer from the outside to the room. Calculate the power required to operate the engine.

3.25 A Carnot engine receives 5800 Btu/min at a temperature of 400°F. If the engine develops 50 hp, what is the receiver temperature? What is the change in entropy during the heat input portion of the cycle?

3.26 The Steam Table shows that at 100°F, the heat of vaporization, h_{fg}, is 1037.0 Btu/lb. Determine the change in entropy, s_{fg}, and compare the calculated value to the value given for s_{fg} in the Steam Tables. (*Note:* The Steam Table uses -459.67°F as absolute zero.)

3.27 A steam power plant can operate at 1400°F when the water used in the condenser is at 40°F. Calculate the maximum efficiency that this plant can have.

3.28 To change a pound of saturated water to saturated steam at 32°F, 1075.4 Btu/lb is required. Determine the change in entropy for this process.

3.29 Water is heated from 32° to 212°F. If the specific heat of this process is taken to be constant and equal to unity, what is the change in entropy for this process per pound of water?

3.30 If the process described in Problem 3.29 is reversed, what is the change in entropy per pound of water?

3.31 One kilogram of air is heated at constant volume from 100° to 400°C. If c_v is 0.7186 kJ/kg·K, determine the change in entropy of the air.

3.32 If the process described in Problem 3.31 is carried out at constant pressure with $c_p = 1.0062$ kJ/kg·K, determine the change in entropy of the process.

3.33 A Carnot engine has an entropy change during the isothermal heat addition portion of the cycle of 0.15 Btu/lb°F when it operates between temperatures of 1500° and 500°F. How much work does this engine deliver per pound of working fluid?

3.34 One pound of air is heated at constant volume. If the value of $c_v = 0.171$ Btu/lb°F and is constant, determine the entropy change when the air is heated from 200° to 800°F.

3.35 If the process in Problem 3.34 is carried out at constant pressure and $c_p = 0.24$ Btu/lb °F, determine the entropy change.

3.36 Five pounds of water at 200°F is mixed with 2 lb at 100°F. What is the total change in entropy for this process? Assume that all specific heats are constant and equal to unity. Work this problem by considering each stream separately.

3.37 A process is carried out at constant volume. It is found that the change in entropy for the process is 0.05 Btu/lb°F. If c_v is constant and equal to

0.171 Btu/lb°F, and the upper temperature of the process is 250°F, determine the initial temperature of the process.

3.38 A process is carried out at constant volume. It is found that the entropy change is 1 kJ/kg·K. If c_v is constant and equal to 0.7186 kJ/kg·K, and the lower temperature of the cycle is 20°C, determine the upper temperature.

3.39 An *isentropic* process is carried out with the working fluid expanding from 700° to 100°F. The specific heat at constant pressure is 0.24 Btu/lb°F. During the process the internal energy changes by 102.6 Btu/lb. Determine the change in entropy for this process.

3.40 A constant temperature process is carried out with a concurrent change in entropy of 0.1 Btu/lb°F at 600°F. Determine the unavailable portion of the energy received with respect to a receiver at 50°F, and at 100°F.

3.41 During a constant pressure process it is found that the change in entropy is equal to $\frac{1}{2}c_p$. If c_p is constant and the initial temperature is 450°F, determine the final temperature for the process.

chapter 4

properties of liquids and gases

4.1 INTRODUCTION

In Chapter 1, a brief introductory study of the properties of a gas was presented. In this chapter the properties of liquids and gases are investigated in some detail, since the state of a system can be described in terms of its properties. Based on the observable properties of pressure, temperature, and volume, it is possible to derive other properties which can also suffice to describe the state of a system. The relationship between the pressure, volume, and temperature of a system, when expressed mathematically, is called the equation of state for the substance in question. A state is an equilibrium state if no finite rate of change of state can occur without a finite change, temporary or permanent, in the state of the environment. The ideal gas relation derived in Chapter 1 and used extensively throughout Chapter 5 is an example of such an equation of state.

A phase of a substance can be defined as that part of a pure substance which consists of a single homogeneous aggregate of matter. The three common phases that are usually spoken of are solid, liquid, and gaseous. When dealing with the gaseous phase, a distinction is made between a gas and a vapor that is somewhat artificial but in common usage. The term *vapor* is applied to the gaseous phase that is in contact with saturated liquid or is not far removed from the saturated state, and the term *gas* is used for the vapor that is either at very low pressure or far removed from the saturated state.

4.2 LIQUIDS AND VAPORS

The distinction between vapor and liquid is usually made (in an elementary manner) by stating that both will take up the shape of their containers, but that the liquid will present a free surface if it does not completely fill its container. The vapor (or gas) will always fill its container.

With the foregoing in mind, let us consider the following system: a container is filled with water, and movable frictionless piston is placed on the container, as shown in Fig 4.1. As heat is added to the system, the temperature

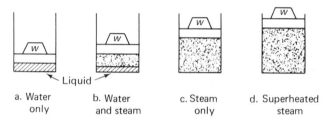

a. Water only   b. Water and steam   c. Steam only   d. Superheated steam

Figure 4.1 Heating water and steam at constant pressure

of the system will increase. Notice that the pressure on the system is being kept constant by the weight of the piston. The continued addition of heat will cause the temperature of the system to increase until the pressure of the vapor generated exactly balances the pressure of the atmosphere plus the pressure due to the weight of the piston. At this point the vapor and liquid are said to be *saturated*. As more heat is added, the liquid which was at saturation will start to vaporize. The two-phase mixture of vapor and liquid has only one degree of freedom, and as long as liquid is present vaporization will continue at constant temperature. As long as liquid is present the mixture is said to be *wet*, and both the liquid and vapor are saturated. After all the liquid is vaporized, only the vapor is present, and the further addition of heat will cause the temperature of the vapor to increase at constant system pressure. This state is called the *superheat state*, and the vapor is said to be *superheated*. If this process is carried out at various pressures, a singular curve of temperature of saturation as a function of pressure will be generated. Such a curve is called a *vapor pressure* or *saturation curve* for the substance.

For a constant rate of heat input, it is possible to plot a curve of temperature as a function of time or heat added at a given system pressure, say 100 psia. This curve is shown as a solid line in Fig. 4.2. If the rate of heating is kept constant and the identical system is again made to undergo this process, but with a system pressure of 1000 psia, the dotted curve of Fig. 4.2 will represent the heat-added temperature history of the system. The decreased slope at 1000 psia during the heating portion indicates an increased specific heat of the liquid (water) due to the increased pressure. At the end of the heating portion the liquid is saturated at a higher temperature. The water is subsequently vaporized at constant temperature, and the length of the horizontal portions of the curves is proportional to the heat necessary to vaporize the fluid at constant pressure (the latent heat of vaporization). At 1000 psia the figure shows that less heat is required to vaporize a unit mass of fluid than at 100 psia. After all the water is vaporized, the specific heat of the vapor at the higher pressure is higher.

From curves such as those of Fig. 4.2 it is possible to derive many of the useful thermodynamic functions, for example, the specific heat of the liquid

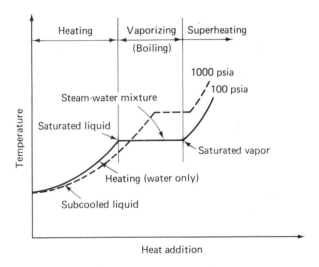

Figure 4.2 Heating of water

and vapor as functions of pressure and temperature, the latent heat of vaporization as a function of pressure and temperature, and the saturation curve. Based on certain general thermodynamic relations, known as the *Maxwell relations*, it is possible to derive enthalpy, internal energy, entropy, and other thermodynamic functions from these data. For these methods of computation and for the mathematical derivation of the Maxwell relations, the interested student is referred to the references at the end of this chapter. It should also be noted that it is possible to determine the thermodynamic properties of a substance indirectly by measurement of its specific heat, density, or other properties. Again, the application of the Maxwell relations permits the other thermodynamic properties to be evaluated. A complete discussion of the methods used to establish the thermodynamic properties of steam is given in the Steam Tables.

One feature, however, that is unique is known as the *critical point*. If the liquid in a closed container does not fill the container entirely and it is heated, the vapor and liquid will be in contact at all times. At some point, a pressure and temperature will be reached at which it becomes impossible to distinguish between the vapor and liquid phases. At this point the specific volume of the liquid and vapor are equal, and the temperature and pressure corresponding to it are known, respectively, as the critical temperature and the critical pressure. At the critical point the properties of the liquid and gas phases are identical.

4.3 THERMODYNAMIC PROPERTIES OF STEAM

Water has been used as a thermodynamic working fluid for many centuries and has been the subject of extensive research to establish its thermodynamic properties in the last two centuries. Figure 4.3 shows a modern *once-through* steam generator in which water that is subcooled (that is, the pressure is greater

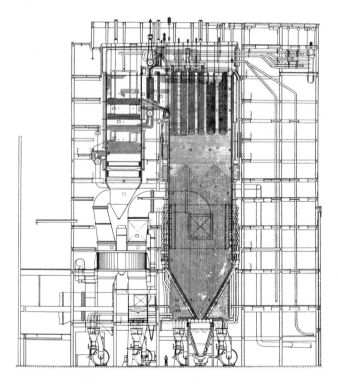

Figure 4.3 Once-through steam generator (Courtesy of Combustion Engineering, Inc.)

than the saturation pressure corresponding to its temperature) enters at one end of a continuous tube, and superheated steam is discharged at the other end of the tube. In the design shown in Fig. 4.3 the water–steam flow is through the furnace walls, primary horizontal superheater, and, finally, the first and second sections of secondary (pendant) superheater. The water–steam flow is through a multitude of tubes that discharge into a common header at the outlet. A unit such as this can handle pressures above or below the critical pressure.

The need to know the thermodynamic properties of water from the subcooled liquid state to state above the critical point is obvious if units such as that shown in Fig. 4.3 are to be properly designed. The research on the thermodynamic properties of water has been carried out throughout the world, and as a result of this research extensive tables of the properties of water have been published.* There are nine tables of thermodynamic properties in the *Steam Tables* (as this work is commonly called) that cover the properties of ice, water, and steam. These tables include the transport properties, viscosity, and thermal conductivity. The triple point, that is, the state in which the solid, liquid, and vapor are in equilibrium, is used as the reference state for zero internal energy and zero entropy. The use of this reference state gives rise to negative values of internal energy, enthalpy, and entropy of the liquid state at 32°F. The fact that these properties are negative should not cause any difficulty since we are invariably interested in differences in properties.

Tables 1 and 2 of the *Steam Tables* are for the saturated state. Table 1 presents the data with temperature as the independent variable; Table 2 presents essentially the same data with pressure as the independent variable. All the tabulated data are arranged to facilitate linear interpolation between values. The nomenclature used in the *Steam Tables* is as follows:

	ENGLISH UNITS	*METRIC UNITS*
t = temperature	°F	degrees Celsius (°C)
p = absolute pressure	psia or in. Hg	bars (10^5 Pa)
v = specific volume	ft³/lb	cm³/g
h = enthalpy	Btu/lb	J/g
s = entropy	Btu/lb °F	J/g·K
u = internal energy	Btu/lb	J/g
Subscripts		
f = a property of the saturated liquid		
g = a property of the saturated vapor		
fg = a property change due to evaporation		

Steam Tables—Thermodynamic Properties of Water Including Vapor, Liquid, and Solid Phases by J. H. Keenan, F. G. Keyes, P. G. Hill, and J. G. Moore, John Wiley & Sons, Inc., New York, 1969. These tables are in English units. A separate volume bearing the same title with the additional parenthetical phrase (*International Edition—Metric Units*) has also been published by the same authors.

TABLE 1

SATURATION TEMPERATURES

Temp °F	Press Lbf Sq. In.	SPECIFIC VOLUME		INTERNAL ENERGY			ENTHALPY			ENTROPY		
		Sat. Liquid	Sat. Vapor	Sat. Liquid	Evap.	Sat. Vapor	Sat. Liquid	Evap.	Sat. Vapor	Sat. Liquid	Evap.	Sat. Vapor
t	p	v_f	v_g	u_f	u_{fg}	u_g	h_f	h_{fg}	h_g	s_f	s_{fg}	s_g
90	0.6988	0.016099	467.7	58.07	982.2	1040.2	58.07	1042.7	1100.7	0.11165	1.8966	2.0083
91	0.7211	0.016102	454.0	59.06	981.5	1040.6	59.07	1042.1	1101.2	0.11346	1.8922	2.0056
92	0.7439	0.016105	440.9	60.06	980.8	1040.9	60.06	1041.5	1101.6	0.11527	1.8877	2.0030
93	0.7674	0.016108	428.2	61.06	980.2	1041.2	61.06	1041.0	1102.0	0.11708	1.8833	2.0003
94	0.8914	0.016111	415.9	62.06	979.5	1041.5	62.06	1040.4	1102.4	0.11888	1.8788	1.9977
95	0.8162	0.016114	404.0	63.06	978.8	1041.9	63.06	1039.8	1102.9	0.12068	1.8744	1.9951
96	0.8416	0.016117	392.4	64.05	978.1	1042.2	64.06	1039.2	1103.3	0.12248	1.8700	1.9925
97	0.8677	0.016121	381.3	65.05	977.5	1042.5	65.05	1038.7	1103.7	0.12427	1.8657	1.9899
98	0.8945	0.016124	370.5	66.05	976.8	1042.8	66.05	1038.1	1104.2	0.12606	1.8613	1.9874
99	0.9220	0.016127	360.1	67.05	976.1	1043.2	67.05	1037.5	1104.6	0.12785	1.8569	1.9848

Figure 4.4 Extract from saturation table*

*Figures 4.4, 4.5, 4.7, and 4.8 are extracted from *Steam Tables* by J. H. Keenan, F. G. Keyes, P. G. Hill, and J. G. Moore, John Wiley & Sons, Inc., 1969, with permission. More detailed values are found in the Appendix. The "a" tables are from the *International Edition—Metric Units*.

TABLE 1

SATURATION: TEMPERATURES

| Sat. °C | Bars | SPECIFIC VOLUME | | INTERNAL ENERGY | | | ENTHALPY | | | ENTROPY | | |
| | | Sat. Liquid | Sat. Vapor | Liquid | Sat. Evap. | Sat. Vapor | Liquid | Sat. Evap. | Vapor | Liquid | Evap. | Vapor |
t	p	v_f	v_g	u_f	u_{fg}	u_g	h_f	h_{fg}	h_g	s_f	s_{fg}	s_g
30	.04246	1.0043	32 894	125.78	2290.8	2416.6	125.79	2430.5	2556.3	.4369	8.0164	8.4533
31	.04496	1.0046	31 165	129.96	2288.0	2418.0	12.997	2428.1	2558.1	.4507	7.9822	8.4329
32	.04759	1.0050	29 540	134.14	2285.2	2419.3	134.15	2425.7	2559.9	.4644	7.9483	8.4127
33	.05034	1.0053	28 011	138.32	2282.4	2420.7	138.33	2423.4	2561.7	.4781	7.9146	8.3927
34	.05324	1.0056	26 571	142.50	2279.5	2422.0	142.50	2421.0	2563.5	.4917	7.8811	8.3728
35	.05628	1.0060	25 216	146.67	2276.7	2423.4	146.68	2418.6	2565.3	.5053	7.8478	8.3531
36	.05947	1.0063	23 940	150.85	2273.9	2424.7	150.86	2416.2	2567.1	.5188	7.8147	8.3336
37	.06281	1.0067	22 737	155.03	2271.1	2426.1	155.03	2413.9	2568.9	.5323	7.7819	8.3142
38	.06632	1.0071	21 602	159.20	2268.2	2427.4	159.21	2411.5	2570.7	.5458	7.7492	8.2950
39	.06999	1.0074	20 533	163.38	2265.4	2428.8	163.39	2409.1	2572.5	.5592	7.7167	8.2759

Figure 4.4a Extract from saturation table (metric)

TABLE 2

SATURATION PRESSURES

Press. Lbf. Sq. In.	Temp °F	SPECIFIC VOLUME		INTERNAL ENERGY			ENTHALPY			ENTROPY		
		Sat. Liquid	Sat. Vapor	Sat. Liquid	Evap.	Sat. Vapor	Sat. Liquid	Evap.	Sat. Vapor	Sat. Liquid	Evap.	Sat. Liquid
p	t	v_f	v_g	u_f	u_{fg}	u_g	h_f	h_{fg}	h_g	s_f	s_{fg}	s_g
115	338.12	0.017850	3.884	308.95	798.8	1107.7	309.33	881.0	1190.4	0.48786	1.1042	1.5921
116	338.77	0.017858	3.852	309.62	798.2	1107.8	310.01	880.5	1190.5	0.48870	1.1027	1.5914
117	339.41	0.017865	3.821	310.29	797.6	1107.9	310.68	880.0	1190.7	0.48954	1.1012	1.5907
118	340.04	0.017872	3.790	310.96	797.1	1108.1	311.34	879.5	1190.8	0.49037	1.0996	1.5900
119	340.68	0.017879	3.760	311.62	796.6	1108.2	312.01	879.0	1191.0	0.49119	1.0981	1.5893
120	341.30	0.017886	3.730	312.27	796.0	1108.3	312.67	878.5	1191.1	0.49201	1.0966	1.5886
121	341.93	0.017894	3.701	312.92	795.5	1108.4	313.32	877.9	1191.3	0.49282	1.0951	1.5880
122	342.55	0.017901	3.672	313.57	794.9	1108.5	313.97	877.4	1191.4	0.49363	1.0937	1.5873
123	343.17	0.017908	3.644	314.21	794.4	1108.6	314.62	876.9	1191.6	0.49443	1.0922	1.5866
124	343.78	0.017915	3.616	314.85	793.9	1108.7	315.26	876.4	1191.7	0.49523	1.0907	1.5860

Figure 4.5 Extract from saturation table

TABLE 2

SATURATION PRESSURES

Press. Bars	Temp °C	SPECIFIC VOLUME		INTERNAL ENERGY			ENTHALPY			ENTROPY		
		Sat. Liquid	Sat. Vapor	Sat. Liquid	Evap.	Sat. Vapor	Sat. Liquid	Evap.	Sat. Vapor	Sat. Liquid	Evap.	Sat. Vapor
p	t	v_f	v_g	u_f	u_{fg}	u_g	h_f	h_{fg}	h_g	s_f	s_{fg}	s_g
10.0	179.91	1.1273	194.44	761.68	1822.0	2583.6	762.81	2015.3	2778.1	2.1387	4.4478	6.5865
10.2	180.77	1.1284	190.80	765.47	1818.8	2584.2	766.63	2012.2	2778.9	2.1471	4.4326	6.5796
10.4	181.62	1.1296	187.30	769.21	1815.6	2584.8	770.38	2009.2	2779.6	2.1553	4.4177	6.5729
10.6	182.46	1.1308	183.92	772.89	1812.5	2585.4	774.08	2006.2	2780.3	2.1634	4.4030	6.5664
10.8	183.28	1.1319	180.67	776.52	1809.4	2585.9	777.74	2003.3	2781.0	2.1713	4.3886	6.5599
11.0	184.09	1.1330	177.53	780.09	1806.3	2586.4	781.34	2000.4	2781.7	2.1792	4.3744	6.5536
11.2	184.89	1.1342	174.49	783.62	1803.3	2586.9	784.89	1997.5	2782.4	2.1869	4.3605	6.5473
11.4	185.68	1.1353	171.56	787.11	1800.3	2587.4	788.40	1994.6	2783.0	2.1945	4.3467	6.5412
11.6	186.46	1.1364	168.73	790.56	1797.4	2587.9	791.86	1991.8	2783.6	2.2020	4.3332	6.5351
11.8	187.23	1.1375	165.99	793.94	1794.4	2588.4	795.28	1989.0	2784.2	2.2093	4.3199	6.5292

Figure 4.5a Extract from saturation table (metric)

It should be noted that all the tabulated properties are specific properties and are tabulated per unit mass. Table 1, the temperature table, goes to the critical temperature of 705.44°F, and Table 2 tabulates data up to the corresponding critical pressure of 3203.6 psia. Portions of these tables are shown in Figs. 4.4 (4.4a for metric units) and 4.5 (4.5a for metric units). The metric table goes to 374.136°C and 220.9 bars.

Note that the change in property going from saturated liquid to saturated vapor (the *fg* subscript) is given for internal energy, enthalpy, and entropy, but not for specific volume. The relation for the saturation state properties, that is, *f*, *g*, and *fg*, is given by

$$h_g = h_f + h_{fg}$$
$$v_g = v_f + v_{fg}$$
$$s_g = s_f + s_{fg}$$
$$u_g = u_f + u_{fg} \qquad (4.1)$$

and, in addition, the definition of enthalpy in terms of internal energy, pressure, and specific volume must also be satisfied. Thus

$$h = \left(u + \frac{pv}{J} \right) \qquad (4.2)$$

or in SI units
$$h = (u + pv) \qquad (4.2a)$$

The following examples will serve to illustrate the use of Tables 1 and 2.

ILLUSTRATIVE PROBLEM 4.1

Determine the enthalpy of saturated steam at 90°F using the tabulated properties of pressure, specific volume, and internal energy in Table 1. Compare the result with the tabulated value of *h*.

Solution

From Table 1 (Fig. 4.4),

$$p = 0.6988 \text{ psia}$$

$$v_g = 467.7 \text{ cu ft/lb}$$

$$u_g = 1040.2 \text{ Btu/lb}$$

Since
$$h = u + \frac{pv}{J}, \qquad h_g = u_g + \frac{pv_g}{J}$$

Therefore,

$$h_g = 1040.2 + \frac{0.6988 \times 144 \times 467.7}{778} = 1100.7 \text{ Btu/lb}$$

This value is in agreement with 1100.7 Btu/lb for h_g from Table 1.

ILLUSTRATIVE PROBLEM 4.2

Determine the enthalpy of saturated steam at 30°C using the tabulated properties of pressure, specific volume, and internal energy in Table 1. Compare the result with the tabulated value of h_g.

Solution

From Table 1 (Fig. 4.4a),

$$p = 0.04246 \text{ bars} = 4.246 \text{ kPa}$$

$$v_g = 32\ 894 \text{ cm}^3/\text{g} = 32.894 \text{ m}^3/\text{kg}$$

$$u_g = 2416.6 \text{ J/g} = 2416.6 \text{ kJ/kg}$$

Since $h = u + pv$,

$$h_g = u_g + pv_g,$$

$$h_g = 2416.6 + 4.246 \times 32.894 = 2556.27 \text{ J/g or kJ/kg}$$

The tabulated value of h_g from Table 1 is 2556.3 J/g.

ILLUSTRATIVE PROBLEM 4.3

Determine the enthalpy, entropy, specific volume, and internal energy of saturated steam at 118 psia. Assume that the values for 115 psia and 120 psia are available and perform the necessary interpolations. Compare the results with the tabulated values for 118 psia.

Solution

The necessary interpolations are best done in tabular form as shown below:

p	h_g
115	1190.4
118	1190.8
120	1191.1

Table 2 $(h_g)_{118} = 1190.8$

p	v_g
115	3.884
118	3.792
120	3.730

Table 2 $(v_g)_{118} = 3.790$

$\frac{3}{5}(1191.1 - 1190.4) = 0.42$
$(h_g)_{118} = 1190.4 + 0.42 = 1190.8$ Btu/lb

$\frac{3}{5}(3.884 - 3.730) = 0.09$
$(v_g)_{118} = 3.884 - 0.09 = 3.792$ cu ft/lb

p	s_g
115	1.5921
118	1.5900
120	1.5886

Table 2 $(s_g)_{118} = 1.5900$

p	u_g
115	1107.7
118	1108.06
120	1108.3

Table 2 $(u_g)_{118} = 1108.1$

$\frac{3}{5}(1.5921 - 1.5886) = 0.0021$
$(s_g)_{118} = 1.5921 - 0.0021 = 1.5900$

$\frac{3}{5}(1108.3 - 1107.7) = 0.36$
$(u_g)_{118} = 1107.7 + 0.36 = 1108.06$

It will be seen that the results of this problem and the tabulated values are essentially in exact agreement, and that linear interpolation is satisfactory in these tables.

ILLUSTRATIVE PROBLEM 4.4

Determine h_{fg} for saturated steam at 115 psia using the pressure, volumes, and internal energy data given in Table 2 (Fig. 4.5).

Solution

By definition,

$$h_g = u_g + \frac{pv_g}{J}$$

$$h_f = u_f + \frac{pv_f}{J}$$

and

$$h_{fg} = h_g - h_f = (u_g - u_f) + \frac{p(v_g - v_f)}{J} = u_{fg} + \frac{p(v_g - v_f)}{J}$$

From Table 2 at 115 psia,

$$u_{fg} = 798.8 \text{ Btu/lb}$$
$$v_g = 3.884 \text{ cu ft/lb}$$
$$v_f = 0.017850 \text{ cu ft/lb}$$

Note that if the table had v_{fg} we could have read it directly, since $v_g - v_f = v_{fg}$. Proceeding

$$h_{fg} = 798.8 + \frac{115 \times 144(3.884 - 0.017850)}{778}$$
$$= 798.8 + 82.3 = 881.1 \text{ Btu/lb}$$

The tabulated value is 881.0 Btu/lb and the agreement is satisfactory.

ILLUSTRATIVE PROBLEM 4.5

Determine h_{fg} for saturated steam at 10 bars using the pressure, volumes, and internal energy data given in Table 2 (Fig. 4.5a).

Solution

Refer to Illustrative Problem 4.4. From Table 2 at 10 bars,

$$u_{fg} = 1822.0 \text{ J/g} = 1822.0 \text{ kJ/kg}$$
$$v_g = 194.44 \text{ cm}^3/\text{g} = 0.19444 \text{ m}^3/\text{kg}$$
$$v_f = 1.1273 \text{ cm}^3/\text{g} = 0.0011273 \text{ m}^3/\text{kg}$$
$$p = 10 \text{ bars} = 10^3 \text{ kPa}$$

Since $v_{fg} = v_g - v_f$

$$v_{fg} = 0.19444 - 0.0011273 = 0.1933127 \text{ m}^3/\text{kg}$$
$$h_{fg} = u_{fg} + p(v_{fg}) = 1822.0 + (1000)(0.1933127) = 2015.3 \text{ J/g}$$

The tabulated value is 2015.3 J/g, which is in exact agreement with the value calculated.

ILLUSTRATIVE PROBLEM 4.6

Determine h_{fg} at 115 psia by considering this process to be a reversible constant-temperature process where $T\Delta s = \Delta h$.

Solution

For constant-temperature reversible vaporization, $h_{fg} = (\Delta h) = T(\Delta s) = Ts_{fg}$. Therefore, $(338.12 + 460)1.1042 = 881.3$ Btu/lb, which is also in good agreement with the tabular values.

Between the saturated liquid and the saturated vapor there exists a mixture of vapor plus liquid (the *wet* region). To denote the state of a liquid–vapor mixture, it is necessary to introduce a term describing the relative quantities of liquid and vapor in the mixture. The quality of a mixture (x) is defined as the ratio of the mass of vapor to the mass of the mixture. Thus in 1 lb of mixture there must be $(1 - x)$ lb of liquid. Another term is used to describe the wet region; this term is *percent moisture*. A mixture whose quality is 80 percent has 20 percent moisture by weight and is simply said to have 20 percent moisture.

Consider a mixture weighing 1 lb and having a quality x. In this mixture there is x lb of vapor and $(1 - x)$ lb of liquid. The enthalpy of this mixture per pound of mixture is the sum of the enthalpies of the components. Therefore, the enthalpy of the liquid portion of the mixture

$$h_\ell = (1 - x)h_f$$

and the enthalpy of the vapor portion is

$$h_v = xh_g$$

The sum of these terms is the enthalpy of the mixture h_x:

$$h_x = (1 - x)h_f + xh_g \qquad (4.3a)$$

By the same reasoning, the entropy, internal energy, and specific volume of the wet mixture are given as

$$s_x = (1 - x)s_f + xs_g \qquad (4.3b)$$

$$u_x = (1 - x)u_f + xu_g \qquad (4.3c)$$

$$v_x = (1 - x)v_f + xv_g \qquad (4.3d)$$

It is sometimes more convenient to express Eq. (4.3) in terms of the property change during vaporization. By noting that the *fg* property is equal to the g value minus the f value, it is possible to rewrite Eq. (4.3) as follows:

$$h_x = h_f + xh_{fg} \qquad (4.4a)$$

$$s_x = s_f + xs_{fg} \qquad (4.4b)$$

$$u_x = u_f + xu_{fg} \qquad (4.4c)$$

$$v_s = v_f + xv_{fg} \qquad (4.4d)$$

The relationship between these quantities can be demonstrated by referring to Fig. 4.6, which is a Ts diagram for water. The saturation curve is indicated, and a point below the saturation curve is in the wet region. The Ts diagram is further discussed later in this chapter, but for the present it should be noted that the expressions for entropy in Eqs. (4.3) and (4.4) can be directly determined from Fig. 4.6.

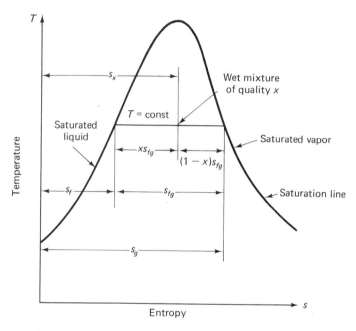

Figure 4.6 Ts diagram showing relation of properties and quality (From *Thermodynamics*, 2nd Ed., by F. P. Durham, Prentice-Hall, Inc., 1959, p. 43, with permission.)

ILLUSTRATIVE PROBLEM 4.7

A wet steam mixture at 120 psia is found to have a quality of 80 percent. Determine its entropy, enthalpy, internal energy, and specific volume.

Solution

Using Table 2 and a quality of 80 percent ($x = 0.8$), we have

$$s_x = s_f + xs_{fg} = 0.49201 + 0.8(1.0966) = 1.3693$$
$$h_x = h_f + xh_{fg} = 312.67 + 0.8(878.5) = 1015.47 \text{ Btu/lb}$$
$$u_x = u_f + xu_{fg} = 312.27 + 0.8(796.0) = 949.07 \text{ Btu/lb}$$
$$v_x = v_f + xv_{fg} = 0.017886 + 0.8(3.730 - 0.017886) = 2.988 \text{ cu ft/lb}$$

As a check on the solution obtained,

$$u_x = h_x - \frac{p_x v_x}{J}$$

$$u_x = 1015.47 - \frac{120 \times 144 \times 2.988}{778}$$

$$u_x = 949.10 \text{ Btu/lb}$$

which agrees with the 949.07 Btu/lb.

ILLUSTRATIVE PROBLEM 4.8

A wet mixture at 10 bars is found to have a quality of 85 percent. Determine its entropy, enthalpy, internal energy, and specific volume.

Solution

Using $x = 0.85$,

$$s_x = s_f + xs_{fg} = 2.1387 + 0.85(4.4487) = 5.9201 \text{ J/g·K}$$
$$h_x = h_f + xh_{fg} = 762.81 + 0.85(2015.3) = 2475.82 \text{ J/g}$$
$$u_x = u_f + xu_{fg} = 761.68 + 0.85(1822.0) = 2310.38 \text{ J/g}$$
$$v_x = v_f + xv_{fg} = 1.1273 + 0.85(194.44 - 1.1273) = 165.44 \text{ cm}^3/\text{g}$$

As a check,

$$u_x = h_x - p_x v_x = 2475.82 - 10(100)\frac{(165.44)}{1000} = 2310.38 \text{ J/g}$$

Again, the agreement is exact.

ILLUSTRATIVE PROBLEM 4.9

A mixture of wet steam at 90°F is found to have an enthalpy of 900 Btu/lb. What is its quality?

Solution

For the wet mixture, $h_x = h_f + xh_{fg}$. Solving for x,

$$x = \frac{h_x - h_f}{h_{fg}}$$

Using the data from Table 1 (Fig. 4.4), we have

$$x = \frac{900 - 58.07}{1042.7} = 0.808 = 80.8\%$$

ILLUSTRATIVE PROBLEM 4.10

A mixture of wet steam at 30°C is found to have an enthalpy of 2000.0 J/g. Determine its quality.

Solution

Since $\quad h_x = h_f + xh_{fg}$,

$$x = \frac{h_x - h_f}{h_{fg}} = \frac{2000.0 - 125.79}{2430.5} = 0.771 \text{ or } 77.1\%$$

Table 3 of the *Steam Tables* gives the properties of the superheated vapor and it occupies 89 pages in the main table. The beginning of this table is for water vapor at low pressure, which can be treated as an ideal gas. For the present we will not be concerned with this section of Table 3. The main portion of the table extends to pressures of 15,000 psia and 2400°F. In the metric tables the values go to 1000 bars and 1300°C. For the superheated region it is necessary to specify two variables, such as pressure and temperature or enthalpy and pressure, in order to specify the state of the vapor. Table 3 is organized using pressure and temperature as independent variables, and it lists values of specific volume, internal energy, enthalpy, and entropy corresponding to specified values of temperature and pressure. Referring to Fig. 4.7 (Fig. 4.7a gives metric units), which is an extract from Table 3, it will be noted that the topmost line

TABLE 3

VAPOR

p (t Sat.)	320 (423.39)				325 (424.84)				330 (426.27)			
t	v	u	h	s	v	u	h	s	v	u	h	s
Sat.	1.4493	1118.6	1204.4	1.5058	1.4274	1118.6	1204.5	1.5044	1.4061	1118.7	2204.6	1.5031
410	1.4110	1110.8	1194.4	1.4944	1.3852	1110.0	1193.3	1.4917	1.3602	1109.2	1192.2	1.4890
420	1.4398	1116.6	1201.9	1.5030	1.4139	1115.9	1200.9	1.5004	1.3887	1118.1	1199.9	1.4978
430	1.4677	1122.2	1209.2	1.5112	1.4416	1121.5	1208.2	1.5087	1.4163	1120.8	1207.3	1.5061
440	1.4949	1127.7	1216.2	1.5191	1.4686	1127.0	1215.4	1.5166	1.4430	1126.4	1214.5	1.5142
450	1.5213	1133.0	1223.1	1.5267	1.4948	1132.4	1222.3	1.5243	1.4691	1131.8	1221.5	1.5219
460	1.5472	1138.1	1229.8	1.5340	1.5205	1137.6	1229.0	1.5316	1.4945	1137.0	1228.2	1.5293
470	1.5726	1143.2	1236.3	1.5411	1.5456	1142.6	1235.6	1.5387	1.5194	1142.1	1234.9	1.5364
480	1.5975	1148.1	1242.7	1.5479	1.5702	1147.6	1242.0	1.5456	1.5438	1147.1	1241.4	1.5434
490	1.6219	1152.9	1249.0	1.5545	1.5944	1152.4	1248.3	1.5523	1.5678	1152.0	1247.7	1.5501

p (t Sat.)	335 (427.68)				340 (429.07)				345 (430.45)			
t	v	u	h	s	v	u	h	s	v	u	h	s
Sat.	1.3854	1118.8	1204.7	1.5017	1.3653	1118.9	1204.8	1.5004	1.3457	1118.9	1204.9	1.4991
410	1.3360	1108.3	1191.2	1.4863	1.3124	1107.5	1190.1	1.4837	1.2894	1106.6	1189.0	1.4810
420	1.3643	1114.3	1198.9	1.4952	1.3406	1113.6	1197.9	1.4926	1.3175	1112.8	1196.9	1.4901
430	1.3917	1120.1	1206.4	1.5036	1.3678	1119.4	1205.5	1.5012	1.3445	1118.7	1204.5	1.4987
440	1.4182	1125.7	1213.6	1.5117	1.3941	1125.0	1212.8	1.5093	1.3707	1124.4	1211.9	1.5069
450	1.4441	1131.1	1220.7	1.5195	1.4198	1130.5	1219.8	1.5171	1.3962	1129.9	1219.0	1.5148
460	1.4693	1136.4	1227.5	1.5270	1.4448	1135.8	1226.7	1.5247	1.4210	1135.2	1226.0	1.5224
470	1.4940	1141.5	1234.2	1.5342	1.4693	1141.0	1233.4	1.5319	1.4453	1140.4	1232.7	1.5297
480	1.5182	1146.6	1240.7	1.5412	1.4933	1146.0	1240.0	1.5389	1.4691	1145.5	1239.3	1.5368
490	1.5419	1151.5	1247.1	1.5479	1.5168	1151.0	1246.4	1.5458	1.4924	1150.5	1245.8	1.5436

Figure 4.7 Extract from superheat table

TABLE 3
VAPOR

p (t Sat.) t	20.0 (212.42) v	u	h	s	20.5 (213.67) v	u	h	s	21.0 (214.90) v	u	h	s
Sat.	99.63	2600.3	2799.5	6.3409	97.25	2600.7	2800.0	6.3318	94.98	2601.0	2800.5	6.3229
200	95.27	2570.6	2761.1	6.2608	92.52	2567.6	2757.3	6.2427				
205	97.06	2582.8	2777.0	6.2941	94.29	2580.1	2773.4	6.2765	91.65	2577.2	2769.7	6.2591
210	98.80	2594.7	2792.3	6.3259	96.01	2592.1	2788.9	6.3089	93.35	2589.5	2785.5	6.2920
215	100.50	2606.2	2807.2	6.3566	97.69	2603.7	2804.0	6.3399	95.01	2601.3	2800.8	6.3235
220	102.15	2617.4	2821.7	6.3861	99.32	2615.1	2818.7	6.3699	96.62	2612.8	2815.7	6.3538
225	103.77	2628.3	2835.8	6.4147	100.92	2626.1	2833.0	6.3987	98.20	2623.9	2830.2	6.3831
230	105.36	2638.9	2849.6	6.4423	102.48	2636.9	2847.0	6.4267	99.74	2634.9	2844.3	6.4113
235	106.91	2649.4	2863.2	6.4691	104.02	2647.5	2860.7	6.4538	101.25	2645.5	2858.2	6.4387
240	108.45	2659.6	2876.5	6.4952	105.52	2657.8	2874.1	6.4801	102.74	2656.0	2871.7	6.4653
245	109.95	2669.7	2889.6	6.5205	107.01	2668.0	2887.3	6.5057	104.20	2666.2	2885.0	6.4911

p (t Sat.) t	21.5 (216.10) v	u	h	s	22.0 (217.29) v	u	h	s	22.5 (218.45) v	u	h	s
Sat.	92.81	2601.4	2800.9	6.3141	90.73	2601.7	2801.3	6.3056	88.75	2602.0	2801.7	6.2972
200												
205	89.12	2574.4	2766.0	6.2419	86.71	2571.5	2762.2	6.2248				
210	90.81	2586.8	2782.0	6.2753	88.38	2584.1	2778.5	6.2587	86.06	2581.3	2774.9	6.2423
215	92.45	2598.8	2797.6	6.3073	90.01	2596.3	2794.3	6.2912	87.66	2593.7	2790.9	6.2753
220	94.05	2610.4	2812.6	6.3380	91.58	2608.1	2809.5	6.3223	89.23	2605.7	2806.4	6.3068
225	95.60	2621.7	2827.3	6.3676	93.12	2619.5	2824.4	6.3523	90.75	2617.3	2821.5	6.3372
230	97.13	2632.8	2841.6	6.3962	94.63	2630.7	2838.9	6.3812	92.23	2628.6	2836.1	6.3664
235	98.62	2643.6	2855.6	6.4238	96.10	2641.6	2853.0	6.4092	93.69	2639.6	2850.4	6.3947
240	100.08	2654.1	2869.3	6.4506	97.54	2652.2	2866.8	6.4362	95.11	2650.4	2864.4	6.4220
245	101.52	2664.5	2882.7	6.4767	98.96	2662.7	2880.4	6.4626	96.51	2660.9	2878.1	6.4486

Figure 4.7a Extract from superheat table (metric)

lists the different pressures in psia and in parentheses displays the saturation temperature corresponding to the pressure. The second horizontal line down lists column headings. All values are specific values, and the temperature is listed in °F. The third horizontal line shown lists saturation (Sat.) values corresponding to the pressure listed on the first line of the table. These values are for convenience so that it is not necessary to turn back to Tables 1 and 2 for saturation properties. The vertical column at the leftmost and rightmost parts of the table gives temperature in °F in bold letters. The desired thermodynamic properties at a given temperature are read horizontally underneath the appropriate pressure heading. It will be noted that at the upper part of the table values are given in italics for certain temperatures, with a horizontal line separating the main portion of the table from the italicized values. The values in italics (above the horizontal dividing line) are for vapor temperature *below* the saturation temperature corresponding to the pressure listed. These states are metastable states (they are not equilibrium states), and we will not deal with them at all in our study. They should be ignored at this time by the student.

The metric tables are arranged in the same manner as the English tables. Pressures are in bars (100 kPa), temperatures are in degrees Celsius (°C), and the unit mass is the gram (g). The energy unit is the joule (J), and the volume unit is the cubic centimeter (cm^3; 10^{-6} m^3). Figure 4.7a is an extract from the superheat table.

ILLUSTRATIVE PROBLEM 4.11

Determine the specific volume, internal energy, enthalpy, and entropy of superheated steam at 330 psia and 450°F.

Solution

The values of temperature and pressure are listed in Table 3 (Fig. 4.7) and can be read directly.

$$v = 1.4691 \text{ cu ft/lb}$$
$$u = 1131.8 \text{ Btu/lb}$$
$$h = 1221.5 \text{ Btu/lb}$$
$$s = 1.5219 \text{ Btu/lb°R}$$

ILLUSTRATIVE PROBLEM 4.12

Determine the specific volume, internal energy, enthalpy, and entropy of superheated steam at 20 bars and 240°C.

Solution

Reading directly from Figure 4.7a,

$$v = 108.45 \text{ cm}^3/\text{g}$$

$$u = 2659.6 \text{ J/g}$$

$$h = 2876.5 \text{ J/g}$$

$$s = 6.4952 \text{ J/g} \cdot \text{K}$$

ILLUSTRATIVE PROBLEM 4.13

Determine the specific volume, internal energy, enthalpy, and entropy of superheated steam at 330 psia and 455°F.

Solution

Since the data in Fig. 4.7 do not give the properties at this temperature, it is necessary to interpolate between 450° and 460°F. Thus at 330 psia

t	v
460	1.4945
455	1.4818
450	1.4691

t	u
460	1137.0
455	1134.4
450	1131.8

t	h
460	1228.2
455	1224.8
450	1221.5

$$v_{455} = 1.4691 + \tfrac{1}{2} \quad\quad u_{455} = 1131.8 + \tfrac{1}{2} \quad\quad h_{455} = 1221.5 + \tfrac{1}{2}$$
$$(1.4945 - 1.4691) \quad\quad (1137.0 - 1131.8) \quad\quad (1228.2 - 1.221.5)$$

t	s
460	1.5293
455	1.5256
450	1.5219

$$s_{455} = 1.5219 + \tfrac{1}{2}$$
$$(1.5293 - 1.5219)$$

Thus

$$v = 1.4818 \text{ cu ft}/\text{lb}$$
$$u = 1134.4 \text{ Btu}/\text{lb}$$
$$h = 1224.8 \text{ Btu}/\text{lb}$$
$$s = 1.5256 \text{ Btu}/\text{lb}°\text{R}$$

ILLUSTRATIVE PROBLEM 4.14

Determine the specific volume and enthalpy of superheated steam at 465°F and 337 psia.

Solution

It will be noted from Fig. 4.7 that neither the temperature nor the pressure values of the problem are tabulated in Table 3. Thus it becomes necessary to interpolate around both the listed temperature and pressure for the desired properties. We will first obtain the properties at 337 psia and 460°F and then 337 psia and 470°F. Proceeding with the calculation:

At 460°F

p	v
340	1.4448
337	1.4595
335	1.4693

p	h
340	1226.7
337	1227.2
335	1227.5

$$v_{337} = 1.4693 - \tfrac{2}{5}(1.4693 - 1.4448) \qquad h_{337} = 1227.5 - \tfrac{2}{5}(1227.5 - 1226.7)$$

At 470°F

p	v
340	1.4693
337	1.4841
335	1.4940

p	h
340	1233.4
337	1233.9
335	1234.2

$$v_{337} = 1.4940 - \tfrac{2}{5}(1.4940 - 1.4693) \qquad h_{337} = 1234.2 - \tfrac{2}{5}(1234.2 - 1233.4)$$

Therefore, *at 337 psia*

t	v
470	1.4841
465	1.4718
460	1.4595

t	h
470	1233.9
465	1230.7
460	1227.5

$$v_{465} = 1.4595 + \tfrac{1}{2}(1.4841 - 1.4595) \qquad h_{465} = 1227.5 + \tfrac{1}{2}(1233.9 - 1227.5)$$

The desired values of specific volume and enthalpy at 465°F and 337 psia are 1.4718 cu ft/lb and 1230.7 Btu/lb.

A great deal of effort is involved in these interpolations, and it is at once obvious that if these properties could be plotted as functions of pressure and temperature much of this work could be eliminated. Such charts are illustrated in later sections of this chapter.

An extract from Table 4 of the *Steam Tables* entitled *Liquid* is shown in Fig. 4.8 (Fig. 4.8a gives metric units). The state of the liquid is the subcooled state in which the pressure on the liquid exceeds the saturation pressure corresponding to the temperature of the liquid. In this region the tabulated properties of specific volume, internal energy, enthalpy, and entropy are exhibited as functions of pressure and temperature similar to the format used for the superheated vapor. It will be noted from Fig. 4.8 that italicized values are shown for certain values of pressure and temperature. Once again these are metastable states, since they correspond to temperatures of the liquid above the saturation temperature, and are not to be used within the scope of this text.

A useful first approximation is often made for the enthalpy of the subcooled liquid by assuming it to be essentially incompressible. Then

$$h - h_f \cong \frac{(p - p_f)v_f}{J} \qquad (4.5)$$

where p_f and v_f are the values of pressure and specific volume corresponding to the saturation condition at the temperature of the fluid. In other words, the change in enthalpy is approximately equal to $(\Delta p)v$, the work done on the fluid during a process carried out at nearly constant volume. In SI units,

$$h - h_f \cong (p - p_f)v_f \qquad (4.5a)$$

TABLE 4
LIQUID

p (t Sat.) t	0 v	0 u	0 h	0 s	500 (467.13) v	500 u	500 h	500 s	1000 (544.75) v	1000 u	1000 h	1000 s
Sat.					0.019748	447.70	449.53	0.64904	0.021591	538.39	542.38	0.74320
32	0.016022	−0.01	−0.01	0.00003	0.015994	0.00	1.49	0.00000	0.015967	0.03	2.99	0.00005
50	0.016024	18.06	18.06	0.0360	0.015998	18.02	19.50	0.03599	0.015972	17.99	20.94	0.03592
100	0.016130	68.05	68.05	0.12963	0.016106	67.87	69.36	0.12932	0.016082	67.70	70.68	0.12901
150	0.016343	117.95	117.95	0.21504	0.016318	117.66	119.17	0.21457	0.016293	117.38	120.40	0.21410
200	0.016635	168.05	168.05	0.29402	0.016608	167.65	169.19	0.29341	0.016580	167.26	170.32	0.29281
250	0.017003	218.52	218.52	0.36777	0.016972	217.99	219.56	0.36702	0.016941	217.47	220.61	0.36628
300	0.017453	269.61	269.61	0.43732	0.017416	268.92	270.53	0.43641	0.017379	268.24	271.46	0.43552
350	0.018000	321.59	321.59	0.50359	0.017954	320.71	322.37	0.50249	0.017909	319.83	323.15	0.50140
400	0.018668	374.85	374.85	0.56740	0.018608	373.68	375.40	0.56604	0.018550	372.55	375.98	0.56472
450	0.019503	429.96	429.96	0.62970	0.019420	428.40	430.19	0.62798	0.019340	426.89	430.47	0.62632
500	0.02060	488.1	488.1	0.6919	0.02048	485.9	487.8	0.6896	0.02036	483.8	487.5	0.6874
510	0.02087	500.3	500.3	0.7046	0.02073	497.9	499.8	0.7021	0.02060	495.6	499.4	0.6997
520	0.02116	512.7	512.7	0.7173	0.02100	510.1	512.0	0.7146	0.02086	507.6	511.5	0.7121
530	0.02148	525.5	525.5	0.7303	0.02130	522.6	524.5	0.7273	0.02114	519.9	523.8	0.7245
540	0.02182	538.6	538.6	0.7434	0.02162	535.3	537.3	0.7402	0.02144	532.4	536.3	0.7372
550	0.02221	552.1	552.1	0.7569	0.02198	548.4	550.5	0.7532	0.02177	545.1	549.2	0.7499
560	0.02265	566.1	566.1	0.7707	0.02237	562.0	564.0	0.7666	0.02213	558.3	562.4	0.7630
570	0.02315	580.8	580.8	0.7851	0.02281	576.0	578.1	0.7804	0.02253	571.8	576.0	0.7763
580					0.02332	590.8	592.9	0.7946	0.02298	585.9	590.1	0.7899
590					0.02392	606.4	608.6	0.8096	0.02349	600.6	604.9	0.8041
600									0.02409	616.2	620.6	0.8189
610									0.02462	632.9	637.5	0.8345

Figure 4.8 Extract from subcooled table

TABLE 4

LIQUID

p (t Sat.)	0				25 (223.99)				50 (263.99)			
t	v	u	h	s	v	u	h	s	v	u	h	s
Sat.					1.1973	959.1	962.1	2.5546	1.2859	1147.8	1154.2	2.9202
0	1.0002	−.03	−.03	−.0001	.9990	−.00	2.50	−.0000	.9977	.04	5.04	.0001
20	1.0018	83.95	83.95	.2966	1.0006	83.80	86.30	.2961	.9995	83.65	88.65	.2956
40	1.0078	167.56	167.56	.5725	1.0067	167.25	169.77	.5715	1.0056	166.95	171.97	.5705
60	1.0172	251.12	251.12	.8312	1.0160	250.67	253.21	.8298	1.0149	250.23	255.30	.8285
80	1.0291	334.87	334.87	1.0753	1.0280	334.29	336.86	1.0737	1.0268	333.72	338.85	1.0720
100	1.0436	418.96	418.96	1.3069	1.0423	418.24	420.85	1.3050	1.0410	417.52	422.72	1.3030
120	1.0604	503.57	503.57	1.5278	1.0590	502.68	505.33	1.5255	1.0576	501.80	507.09	1.5233
140	1.0800	588.89	588.89	1.7395	1.0784	587.82	590.52	1.7369	1.0768	586.76	592.15	1.7343
160	1.1024	675.19	675.19	1.9434	1.1006	673.90	676.65	1.9404	1.0988	672.62	678.12	1.9375
180	1.1283	762.72	762.72	2.1410	1.1261	761.16	763.97	2.1375	1.1240	759.63	765.25	2.1341
200	1.1581	851.8	851.8	2.3334	1.1555	849.9	852.8	2.3294	1.1530	848.1	853.9	2.3255
210	1.1749	897.1	897.1	2.4281	1.1720	895.0	898.0	2.4238	1.1691	893.0	898.8	2.4195
220	1.1930	943.0	943.0	2.5221	1.1898	940.7	943.7	2.5174	1.1866	938.4	944.4	2.5128
230	1.2129	989.6	989.6	2.6157	1.2092	987.0	990.1	2.6105	1.2056	984.5	990.6	2.6055
240	1.2347	1037.1	1037.1	2.7091	1.2305	1034.2	1037.2	2.7034	1.2264	1031.4	1037.5	2.6979
250	1.2590	1085.6	1085.6	2.8027	1.2540	1082.3	1085.4	2.7964	1.2493	1079.1	1085.3	2.7902
260	1.2862	1135.4	1135.4	2.8970	1.2804	1131.6	1134.8	2.8898	1.2749	1127.9	1134.3	2.8830
270	1.3173	1186.8	1186.8	2.9926	1.3102	1182.4	1185.7	2.9844	1.3036	1178.2	1184.3	2.9766
280	1.3535	1240.4	1240.4	3.0904	1.3447	1235.1	1238.5	3.0808	1.3365	1230.2	1236.8	3.0717
290	1.3971	1297.0	1297.0	3.1918	1.3855	1290.5	1294.0	3.1801	1.3750	1284.4	1291.3	3.1693
300	1.4520	1358.1	1358.1	3.2992	1.4357	1349.6	1353.2	3.2843	1.4214	1341.9	1349.0	3.2708
310									1.4803	1404.1	1411.5	3.3789

Figure 4.8a Extract from subcooled table (metric)

ILLUSTRATIVE PROBLEM 4.15

Determine the enthalpy, specific volume, internal energy, and entropy of subcooled water at 300°F and 1000 psia.

Solution

From Table 4 (Fig. 4.8), we find the values are directly tabulated. Therefore,

$$v = 0.017379 \text{ cu ft/lb}$$
$$u = 268.24 \text{ Btu/lb}$$
$$h = 271.46 \text{ Btu/lb}$$
$$s = 0.43552 \text{ Btu/lb°R}$$

ILLUSTRATIVE PROBLEM 4.16

Determine the enthalpy of the subcooled water in Illustrative Problem 4.15 using the approximation of Eq. (4.5) and compare the result obtained with the tabulated value.

Solution

It is necessary to obtain the saturation values corresponding to 300°F. This is done by reading Table A.1, which gives us $p_f = 66.98$ psia, $v_f = 0.017448$ cu ft/lb, and $h_f = 269.73$ Btu/lb. From Eq. (4.5),

$$h = h_f + \frac{(p - p_f)v_f}{J}$$

$$= 269.73 + \frac{(1000 - 66.98)0.017448 \times 144}{778}$$

$$= 272.74 \text{ Btu/lb}$$

The difference between this value and the value found in Illustrative Problem 4.15 expressed as a percentage is

$$\text{percent of error} = \left(\frac{272.74 - 271.46}{271.46} \right)100 = 0.47\%$$

For this pressure and temperature the approximation expressed by Eq. (4.5) is obviously within the accuracy required in most engineering calculations.

4.4 THERMODYNAMIC DIAGRAMS

Tables of thermodynamic properties provide accurate data for various substances. However, diagrams and charts based on the data of these tables are both useful and desirable. One most important fact must be borne in mind. Thermodynamic data such as those given by the *Steam Tables* are equilibrium data, and charts plotted from these data can represent only the equilibrium states. The path of a process which is not an equilibrium path cannot be drawn on these charts.

Figure 4.9 shows a *Ts* diagram for steam showing the liquid and vapor phases. In the wet region (below the saturation curve) lines of constant

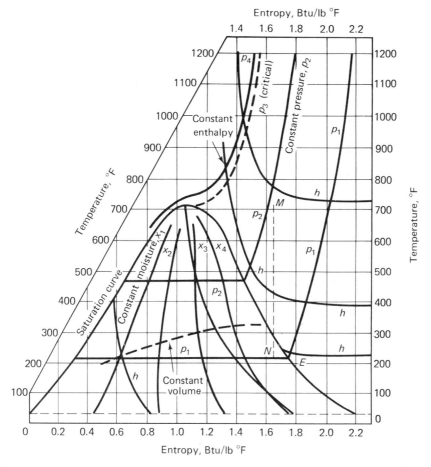

Figure 4.9 Outline of a temperature entropy diagram for steam (From B. F. Dodge, *Chemical Engineering Thermodynamics*, McGraw-Hill Book Co., New York, 1944)

temperature and lines of constant pressure are horizontal lines. For convenience, lines of constant moisture (constant x) and lines of constant volume are also shown in the wet region. In the superheat region above the saturation curve, lines of constant pressure start at the saturation curve, rise steeply, and are almost vertical. Lines of constant enthalpy are nearly horizontal away from the saturation curve. Near the saturation curve and especially near the critical point there is a marked change in curvature of the constant enthalpy lines, which approach the vertical as the critical pressure is approached. On the large

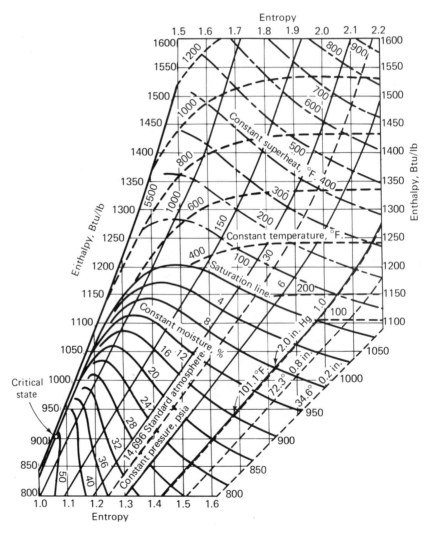

Figure 4.10 Outline of *hs* diagram for steam (From B. F. Dodge, *Chemical Engineering Thermodynamics*, McGraw-Hill Book Co., New York, 1944)

Ts diagram that is found in the *Steam Tables*, curves of constant superheat are also shown in the superheat region. A curve of constant superheat corresponds to a curve plotted parallel to the saturation curve and a fixed number of degrees above the saturation curve. Thus the term "200 degrees of superheat" means superheated steam whose temperature corresponds to saturation temperature plus 200°F. While the *Ts* chart is useful in portraying processes, it is not as useful nor as widely used as the *hs* diagram (or Mollier chart as the *hs* diagram is usually called).

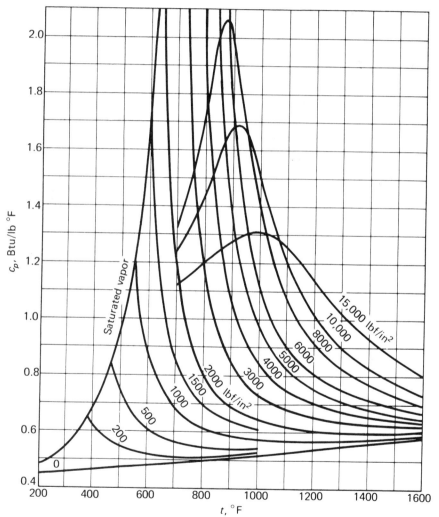

Figure 4.11 Specific heat of steam at constant pressure*

*Figures 4.11, 4.12, and 4.13 are from the *Steam Tables* by J. H. Keenan, F. G. Keyes, P. G. Hill, and J. G. Moore, John Wiley & Sons, Inc. New York, 1969, with permission.

The Mollier chart is a plot on *hs* coordinates of the thermodynamic properties of a substance. Figure 4.10 shows the outline of a portion of the Mollier chart for steam. Below the saturation line, lines of constant pressure (which are also lines of constant temperature) and lines of constant moisture are shown. Above the saturation line, curves of constant temperature, constant pressure, and constant superheat are shown. As noted for the *Ts* diagram, the curves of constant superheat correspond to curves plotted parallel to the saturation curve and a fixed number of degrees above the saturation curve. As we shall see, the Mollier Chart is particularly suited to obtaining properties, in describing flow, or describing constant-pressure processes. If a process is not

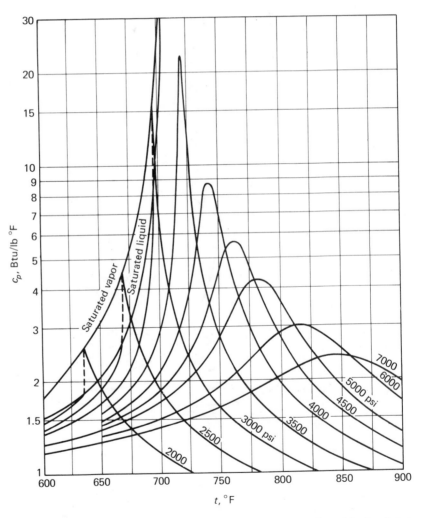

Figure 4.12 Specific heat at constant pressure near the critical point

reversible, then only its end states can be shown on a thermodynamic diagram such as the *Ts* diagram or Mollier chart. A Mollier chart similar to the one in the *Steam Tables* is found in the Appendix.

In addition to the *Ts* and *hs* charts, other diagrams of thermodynamic properties also have utility. Figure 4.11 shows the specific heat of steam at constant pressure as a function of temperature and pressure. It can be proved by theoretical reasoning that the specific heats at the critical point are infinite, and it will be seen from Fig. 4.11 that in the regions of the critical temperature there is a sharp rise in specific-heat values.

The wide fluctuations in the region of the critical point are more evident from Fig. 4.12, which also shows the specific heat at constant pressure for a saturated liquid. At the critical point, the saturated vapor and saturated liquid are indistinguishable, and both curves merge to infinity.

The effect of pressure on the specific heat at constant pressure for a liquid (water) is shown in Fig. 4.13. It should be noted that the specific heat at constant pressure and at a given temperature decreases with increasing pressure. At a given pressure it increases with temperature.

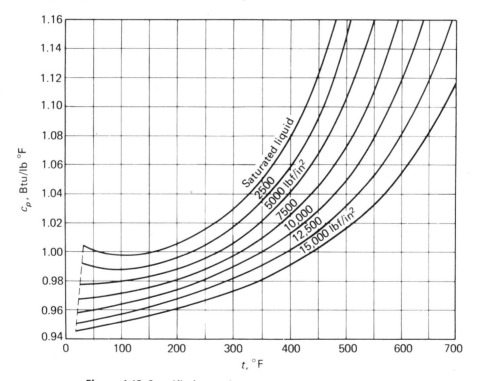

Figure 4.13 Specific heat of water at constant pressure

It should be noted that Figs. 4.9 through 4.13 exist in metric units in the *International Edition* of the *Steam Tables*.

ILLUSTRATIVE PROBLEM 4.17

Determine the enthalpy of saturated steam at 90°F using the Mollier chart. Compare the result with Illustrative Problem 4.1.

Solution

On the chart in the Appendix it is necessary to estimate the 90°F point on the saturation line. From the chart or the table in the upper left of the chart, we note that 90°F is between 1.4 and 1.5 in. of mercury. Estimating the intersection of this value with the saturation curve yields $h_g = 1100$ Btu/lb. This is in good agreement with Illustrative Problem 4.1.

ILLUSTRATIVE PROBLEM 4.18

Determine the enthalpy of a wet steam mixture at 120 psia having a quality of 80 percent by using the Mollier chart. Compare the results with Illustrative Problem 4.7.

Solution

The Mollier chart has lines of constant moisture in the wet region which correspond to $(1 - x)$. Therefore, we read at 20 percent moisture (80 percent quality) and 120 psia an enthalpy of 1015 Btu/lb, which also agrees well with the calculated value in Illustrative Problem 4.7.

ILLUSTRATIVE PROBLEM 4.19

Using the Mollier chart, determine the quality of a wet steam mixture having an enthalpy of 900 Btu/lb and a temperature of 90°F. Compare the result with Illustrative Problem 4.9.

Solution

Entering the Mollier chart at 900 Btu/lb and estimating 90°F (near the 1.5 in. Hg dashed line) yields a constant moisture percent of 19.2 percent. The quality is therefore $(1 - 0.192)100 = 80.8$ percent. We again show good agreement with the calculated value.

ILLUSTRATIVE PROBLEM 4.20

Determine the enthalpy of steam at 330 psia and 450°F using the Mollier chart. Compare the results with Illustrative Problem 4.11.

Solution

From the chart, $h = 1220$ Btu/lb, compared to 1221.5 Btu/lb found in Illustrative Problem 4.11.

ILLUSTRATIVE PROBLEM 4.21

Determine the enthalpy of steam at 465°F and 337 psia. Compare the results with Illustrative Problem 4.14.

Solution

Since neither pressure nor temperature is shown directly, it is necessary to estimate to obtain the desired value. Reading the chart in this manner, we obtain $h = 1231$ Btu/lb. In Illustrative Problem 4.14 we obtained $h = 1230.7$ Btu/lb. The agreement is good and the savings in laborious interpolations is considerable.

Use of the Mollier chart does not permit us to obtain the specific volume or internal energy directly. Special charts by F. O. Ellenwood et al. are available which plot enthalpy as ordinate and specific volume as abscissa. These charts are particularly useful in steam turbine computations.

4.5 PROCESSES

Thus far we have concerned ourselves with the properties of a substance in a given state. These properties are useful in actual processes to describe the path of the fluid or to establish the end states, once the process has been specified. Some of the processes of interest are the throttling process (pipe flow and flow measurement), the constant-volume process (accumulator), reversible and irreversible compressions and expansions (pumps and turbines), and the constant-pressure process (heaters and boilers). For each of these processes it is necessary to know the energy equation for the path and one of the end states.

4.5a Throttling

The throttling process, as has already been noted in Chapter 2, is found to occur when an obstruction occurs in a pipe that locally disturbs the flow. This process is an irreversible adiabatic process whose path equation we have seen to be a constant enthalpy path. Figure 4.14 shows this process on both Ts and hs coordinates. The end states, 1 and 2, are known, and the path is shown as a dashed line on both diagrams since it is an irreversible path. As will be noted from the diagram, steam that is initially wet will become drier, and, depending upon the initial and final states, it will become superheated after throttling. The final pressure is always less than the initial pressure.

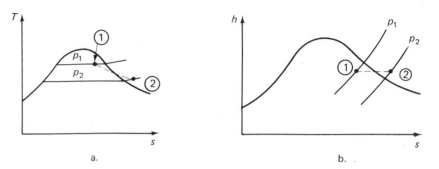

Figure 4.14 Throttling process

The superheating of initially wet steam in a throttling process provides the basis for a device known as a throttling calorimeter that is used to determine the quality of wet steam flowing in a pipe. Figure 4.15 is a diagram of the throttling calorimeter showing its installation in a vertical run of pipe. The steam enters the sampling tube and is expanded in the orifice to the main body of the calorimeter. The initial pressure in the pipe is monitored by a pressure gage, and the final temperature and pressure after expansion are monitored by a thermometer and manometer. To eliminate the velocity terms in the energy equation, the unit is sized so that the entry flow area and the flow area at the point of temperature measurement are made approximately equal. For reliable operation of the calorimeter, the final state should have a superheat of at least 10°F. The calculations for the throttling process are greatly simplified by use of the Mollier chart, as will be seen from Illustrative Problem 4.22.

ILLUSTRATIVE PROBLEM 4.22

Steam flows in a pipe at 150 psia. If a throttling calorimeter installed in the pipe has a thermometer reading of 250°F, and the calorimeter pressure is essentially 14.7 psia, determine the moisture in the steam flowing in the pipe.

Solution

As already noted, $h_1 = h_2$ for this process. On the Mollier chart h_2 is found to be 1170 Btu/lb at 14.7 psia and 250°F. Proceeding to the left on the chart, the constant-enthalpy value of 1170 Btu/lb to 150 psia yields a moisture of 3 percent or a quality of 97 percent.

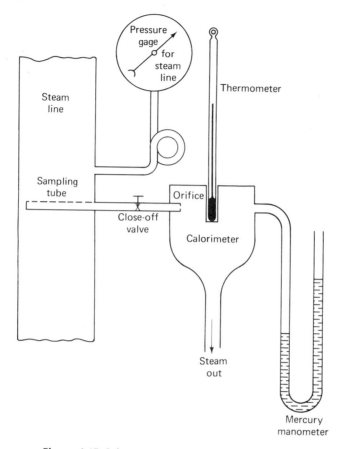

Figure 4.15 Schematic of a throttling calorimeter

If we use the tables to obtain the solution to this problem, we would first obtain h_2 from the superheated vapor tables as 1168.8 Btu/lb. Since $h_x = h_f + x h_{fg}$, we obtain x as

$$x = \frac{h_x - h_f}{h_{fg}} \qquad \text{where } h_f \text{ and } h_{fg} \text{ are values at 150 psia}$$

$$= \frac{1168.8 - 330.75}{864.2} = 0.97$$

Very often it is necessary to perform multiple interpolations if the tables are used, and the Mollier chart yields results within the required accuracy for most engineering problems with a considerable savings of time.

4.5b Constant Volume Process (Isometric Process)

The constant volume process is a nonflow process that we can consider to occur when a fluid is heated in a closed tank. Figure 4.16 shows a constant volume process in which wet steam (1) is heated at constant volume in a closed tank and goes to the superheated state at (2). The energy equation for this process

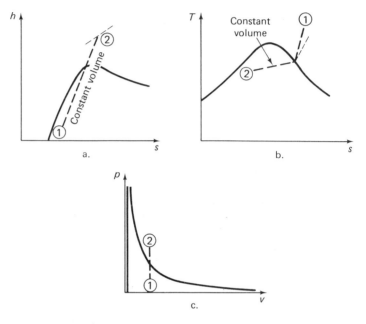

Figure 4.16 Constant volume process

has already been derived as $q = u_2 - u_1$. Since the Mollier chart does not have lines of constant volume, it is not suited for calculations of this process. The Ts chart does not have lines of constant internal energy, and it is not too useful in calculations involving the constant volume process. A heat exchanger utilizing U-bend removable elements is shown in Fig. 4.17. This unit can be used to heat

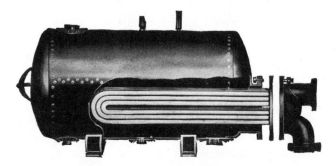

Figure 4.17 Tank type heat exchanger (Courtesy of National Pipe Bending Co.)

stored materials or to provide pressurization of a system, as well as to heat process fluids in chemical plants.

ILLUSTRATIVE PROBLEM 4.23

A closed tank contains 1 lb of saturated liquid at 150°F. If the tank is heated until it is filled with saturated steam, determine the final pressure of the steam and the heat added. The tank has a volume of 10 cu ft.

Solution

Since the tank volume is 10 cu. ft, the final specific volume of the steam is 10 cu ft/lb. Interpolations in Table 2 yield a final pressure of 42 psia. The heat added is simply the difference in internal energy between the two states.

$$q = u_2 - u_1 = (1093.0 - 117.95) = 975.05 \text{ Btu/lb added}$$

ILLUSTRATIVE PROBLEM 4.24

A closed tank has a volume of 60 ft^3. It contains 15 ft^3 of steam and 45 ft^3 of water at 14.7 psia. Heat is added until the pressure increases to 800 psia. Determine the heat added.

Solution

We note that the mass of fluid in the tank is constant, and that the heat added will be the change in internal energy of the contents of the tank between the two states. The initial mass in the tank is found as follows:

$$m_f = \frac{V_f}{v_f} = \frac{45}{0.016715} = 2686.57$$

$$m_g = \frac{V_g}{v_g} = \frac{15}{26.80} = \frac{0.56}{2687.13 \text{ lb}}$$

The initial internal energy is the sum of the internal energy of the liquid plus the vapor:

$$U_g = m_g U_g = 0.56 \times 1077.6 = 603.5$$

$$U_f = m_f u_f = 2689.57 \times 180.1 = \underline{484391.6}$$

$$\text{Total internal energy} = 484{,}995.1 \text{ Btu}$$

Since the mass in the tank is constant, the final specific volume must equal the initial specific volume, or

$$v_x = \frac{60}{2687.13} = 0.022329 \text{ cu ft/lb}$$

But $v_x = v_f + x v_{fg}$. Therefore,

$$x = \frac{v_x - v_f}{v_{fg}} = \frac{0.022329 - 0.02087}{0.5691 - 0.02087} = 0.0026613$$

The final amount of vapor is

$$0.0026613 \times 2687.13 = 7.15 \text{ lb}$$

The final amount of liquid is

$$2687.13 - 7.15 = 2679.98 \text{ lb}$$

The final internal energy is found as before:

$$U_g = m_g u_g = \quad 7.15 \times 1115.0 = \qquad 7972$$

$$U_f = m_f u_f = 2679.98 \times 506.6 = \underline{1,357,678}$$

$$1,365,650 \text{ Btu}$$

The difference is

$$1,365,650 - 484995 = 880,655 \text{ Btu}$$

Per unit mass, the heat added is

$$\frac{880,655}{2687.13} = 327.73 \text{ Btu/lb}$$

The small quantity of vapor mass necessitates the unusual accuracy needed to solve this problem.

4.5c Adiabatic Processes

The adiabatic process is one of the most important processes that we shall consider, since most compressions and expansions can be idealized as adiabatic processes. Ideally, these processes would be carried out isentropically or approach isentropic conditions. Figure 4.18 shows the *hs* diagram for two differing types of expansions and two differing types of compressions. The solid lines on

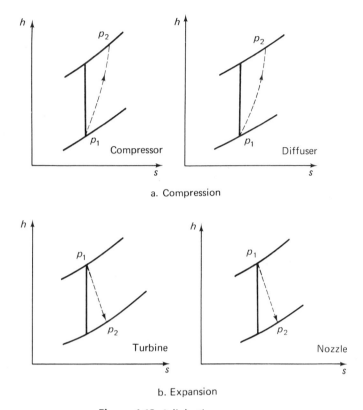

a. Compression

b. Expansion

Figure 4.18 Adiabatic processes

this figure represent isentropic (reversible adiabatic) paths, while the dashed lines are used to represent irreversible processes. All the processes shown in Fig. 4.18 are steady-flow processes. Figures 4.19 and 4.20 show a vertical multiple plunger compressor and a single-stage turbine, respectively, as typical of some of the equipment used industrially.

ILLUSTRATIVE PROBLEM 4.25

Steam is expanded isentropically without change in elevation and with negligible kinetic energy differences between the inlet and outlet section of a turbine. If the initial pressure is 800 psia and the initial temperature is 600°F, determine the change in enthalpy if the end-state pressure is 200 psia.

Solution

As shown in Fig. 4.18b, the process described in this problem is a vertical line on the Mollier chart. For 800 psia and 600°F, the Mollier chart yields

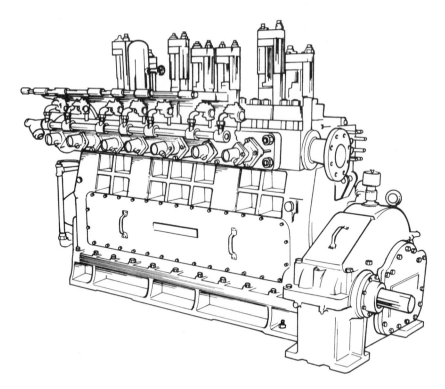

Figure 4.19 A 300-horsepower vertical multiple plunger pump capable of a maximum discharge of 600 gallons/minute and a maximum discharge pressure of 2400 psig (Courtesy of Worthington Corp.)

$h_1 = 1270$ Btu/lb and $s_1 = 1.485$. Proceeding vertically down the chart at constant s to 200 psia yields a final enthalpy $h_2 = 1148$ Btu/lb. The change in enthalpy for the process is $1270 - 1148 = 122$ Btu/lb.

We may also solve this problem using the *Steam Tables* in Appendix 3. Thus the enthalpy at 800 psia and 600°F is 1270.4 Btu/lb, and its entropy is 1.4861 Btu/lb°R. Since the process is isentropic, the final entropy at 200 psia must be 1.4861. From the saturation table, the entropy of saturated steam at 200 psia is 1.5464, which indicates the final steam condition must be wet, since the entropy of the final steam is less than the entropy of saturation. Using the wet steam relation,

$$s_x = s_f + x s_{fg}, \qquad 1.4861 = 0.5440 + x(1.0025)$$

$$x = \frac{1.4861 - 0.544}{1.0022} = 0.94$$

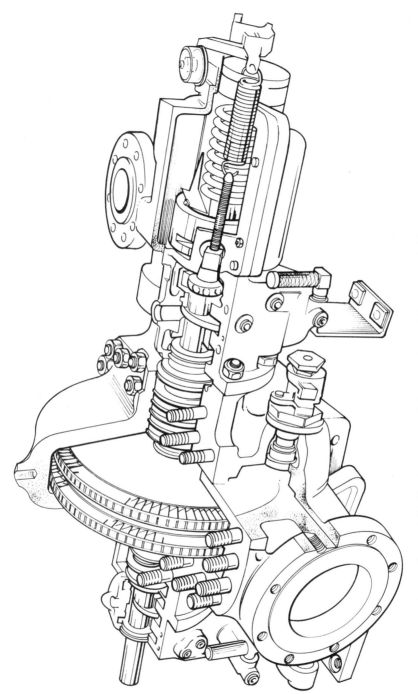

Figure 4.20 Single stage turbine used to drive pumps, blowers, compressors, generators, fans, and so on, provides a compact, economical, and reliable plant accessory (Courtesy of Worthington Corp.)

The final enthalpy is, therefore,

$$h_x = h_f + x h_{fg} = 355.6 + 0.94(843.7) = 1148.7 \text{ Btu/lb}$$

The change in enthalpy is $1270.4 - 1148.7 = 121.7$ Btu/lb. Note the agreement with the Mollier chart solution and the effort saved by use of the chart.

ILLUSTRATIVE PROBLEM 4.26

If the process described in Illustrative Problem 4.25 is carried out adiabatically but not reversibly between the same initial conditions and the same final pressure, determine the final state of the steam if only 80 percent of the isentropic enthalpy difference is realized.

Solution

Again referring to Fig. 4.19, it will be seen that the final temperature and enthalpy will both be higher than for the isentropic case. The change in enthalpy is $0.8 \times 122 = 97.6$ Btu/lb. Therefore, the final enthalpy is $1270 - 97.6 = 1172.4$ Btu/lb, and the final pressure is 200 psia. The Mollier chart indicates the final state to be in the wet region, with a 3.1 percent moisture content and an entropy of 1.514 Btu/lb°R.

4.5d Constant Pressure Process (Isobaric Process)

The constant pressure process is an idealization that can be used to describe the addition of heat to the working fluid in a boiler or the combustion process in a gas turbine. Figure 4.21 shows the pv, Ts, and hs diagrams for a vapor undergoing an irreversible constant pressure process. The paths are shown as dashed lines to denote that the process is irreversible. A large industrial gas turbine is shown in Fig. 4.22 with both compressor and turbine blading clearly visible and a portion of the combustion section also visible. A large exhaust

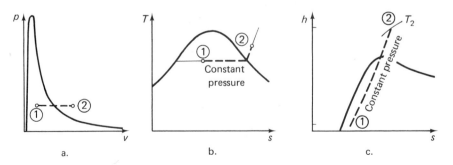

Figure 4.21 Constant pressure process

Figure 4.22 Large industrial gas turbine unit (Courtesy of Pratt & Whitney Division of United Aircraft Corp.)

duct is provided for exhausting the hot gases from the unit. Both the heat addition portions and heat rejection portion of the gas turbine cycle are considered as constant-pressure flow processes.

Since the exhaust temperature of a gas turbine is relatively high, the exhaust gases can also be used as a heat source. Figure 4.23 shows a combined cycle unit in which the exhaust of the gas turbine is used to generate steam for a steam turbine generator. Supplemental oil or gas firing keeps steam pressure and temperature at required level. Since a substantial number of Btu's are recovered from gas-turbine exhaust, this unit operates at relatively high efficiency. This combination of gas turbine and heat recovery steam generator is responsible for much of the current interest in on-site generating systems for commercial buildings and small industrial plants.

ILLUSTRATIVE PROBLEM 4.27

Steam that is initially saturated is superheated in a boiler at constant pressure. Determine the final state if the initial pressure is 500 psia and the final temperature is 800°F. How much heat per pound of steam was added?

Solution

From the saturation table, 500 psia corresponds to a temperature of 467.13°F, and the saturated vapor has an enthalpy of 1205.3 Btu/lb. At 500 psia and 800°F, the superheated vapor has an enthalpy of 1412.1 Btu/lb. Since this process is a steady flow process at constant pressure, the energy equation becomes $q = h_2 - h_1$, assuming that differences in the kinetic energy and potential energy terms are negligible. Therefore, $q = 1412.1 - 1205.3 = 206.8$ Btu/lb added.

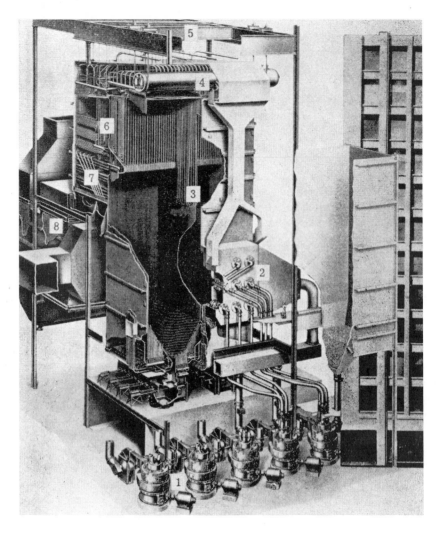

Figure 4.23 Combined cycle steam generator (Courtesy of Pratt & Whitney Division of United Aircraft Corp.)

4.5e Constant Temperature Process (Isothermal Process)

At the exhaust of a steam turbine, the steam is usually wet. This steam is subsequently condensed in a unit appropriately known as a condenser. Since the steam is initially wet, this process is carried out essentially at constant temperature (isothermally). This process is also one of constant pressure in the wet region.

Figure 4.24 shows the isothermal process on various diagrams, and Fig. 4.25 shows a schematic of a shell and tube condenser, indicating the steam flow and cooling water paths.

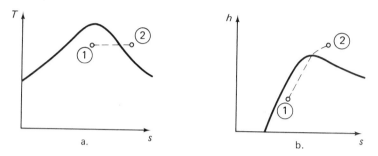

Figure 4.24 Isothermal process

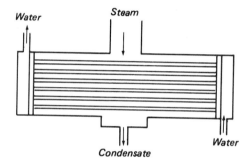

Figure 4.25 Shell and tube condenser

ILLUSTRATIVE PROBLEM 4.28

Steam is initially wet, having a moisture content of 3 percent at 1 psia. If it is condensed to saturated liquid, how much heat is removed?

Solution

From the saturation table at 1 psia, $h_f = 69.74$ Btu/lb, $h_{fg} = 1036.0$ Btu/lb, and $h_g = 1105.8$ Btu/lb. Since the condensation process is carried out at constant pressure, the energy equation is $q = \Delta h$. The initial enthalpy is

$$h_x = h_f + x h_{fg} = 69.74 + 0.97(1036.0) = 1074.66 \text{ Btu/lb}$$

The final enthalpy is $h_f = 69.74$. The enthalpy difference (Δh) is $1074.66 - 69.74 = 1004.92$ Btu/lb removed during the condensation process.

A summary of all the foregoing processes on the Mollier diagram is shown in Fig. 4.26. The dashed paths are used to indicate that these are not equilibrium paths, and as such they cannot really be drawn on an equilibrium diagram.

For the irreversible expansion between the same pressure limits, the final enthalpy (and temperature) is higher than that for the same process performed reversibly. The constant-pressure process is also one of constant temperature in the wet region. Finally, throttling is the irreversible constant-enthalpy process shown in Fig. 4.26.

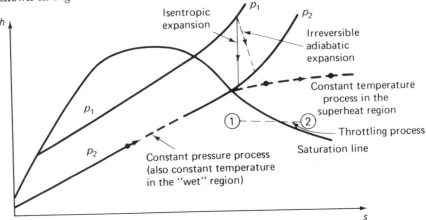

Figure 4.26 Processes on a Mollier diagram

4.6 CLOSURE

This chapter has been devoted primarily to the properties of water, since the most detailed and complete information is known about these properties. This information exists in the *Steam Tables* in extensive tabulations and as charts. It is important for the student to become familiar with these tables and charts for the work required in subsequent chapters of this book as well as for future professional applications. It is unfortunate that there are great amounts of arithmetic computation associated with the application of the data in the *Steam Tables*. These can be both time consuming and frustrating. However, facility in using and understanding this material will be quite rewarding.

One word of caution is appropriate at this time. *Always* write the energy equation of a process *before* attempting to solve a problem. This procedure will lead to a better understanding of the problem, as well as elimination of a great deal of unnecessary numerical calculations that often lead to incorrect solutions to problems.

REFERENCES

1 *Thermodynamics* by E. Fermi, Dover Publications, New York, 1956.

2 *Chemical Engineering Thermodynamics* by B. F. Dodge, McGraw-Hill Book Co., New York, 1944.

3 *Basic Thermodynamics* by B. G. A. Skrotzki, McGraw-Hill Book Co., New York, 1963.

4 *Thermodynamics*, 6th Ed., by V. M. Faires and C. M. Simmang, Macmillan, Inc., New York, 1978.

5 *Thermal Engineering* by C. C. Dillio and E. P. Nye, International Textbook Co., Scranton, Pa., 1959.

6 *Fundamentals of Classical Thermodynamics* by G. J. Van Wylen and R. E. Sonntag, John Wiley & Sons, Inc., New York, 1965.

7 *Steam Tables—Thermodynamic Properties of Water Including Vapor, Liquid, and Solid Phases* by J. H. Keenan, F. G. Keyes, P. G. Hill, and J. G. Moore, John Wiley & Sons, Inc., New York, 1969.

8 *Concepts of Thermodynamics* by E. F. Obert, McGraw-Hill Book Co., New York, 1960.

9 *Thermodynamics*, 2nd Ed., by F. P. Durham, Prentice-Hall, Inc., Englewood Cliffs, N.J., 1959.

10 *Elementary Applied Thermodynamics* by Irving Granet, John Wiley & Sons, Inc., New York, 1965.

11 *Thermodynamics*, 2nd Ed., by G. A. Hawkins, John Wiley & Sons, Inc., New York, 1951.

12 *Engineering Thermodynamics with Applications* by M. D. Burghardt, Harper & Row, Publishers, New York, 1978.

PROBLEMS

Wherever appropriate, sketch processes on a *Ts* or *hs* diagram. Also use the tables and Mollier chart in the Appendix for all problems.

4.1 Determine the enthalpy, entropy, specific volume, and internal energy of saturated steam at 100 psia and at 1000 psia.

4.2 Determine the enthalpy, entropy, specific volume, and internal energy of saturated steam at 10 bars and 11 bars.

4.3 Determine the enthalpy, entropy, specific volume, and internal energy of saturated water at 10 bars and 11 bars.

4.4 Determine the pressure, specific volume, and enthalpy of saturated water at 350°F and 500°F.

4.5 Determine the pressure, specific volume, and entropy of saturated water at 35°C.

4.6 Determine the enthalpy, entropy, specific volume, and internal energy of wet steam at 100 psia if it has 5 percent moisture.

4.7 Determine the enthalpy, specific volume, entropy, and internal energy of wet steam at 11.2 bars if the quality is 90 percent.

4.8 Steam at 200 psia has an enthalpy of 1050 Btu/lb. Determine its quality.

4.9 If the enthalpy of steam at 10 bars is 1400 kJ/kg, what is its quality?

4.10 Steam at 150 psia has a quality of 97 percent. What is the specific volume of this wet mixture?

4.11 The internal energy of wet steam is 2000 kJ/kg. If the pressure is 11.8 bars, what is the quality of the mixture?

4.12 Saturated steam has an enthalpy of 2782.0 kJ/kg. What is its pressure?

4.13 If the enthalpy of saturated water is 100 Btu/lb, determine its pressure, temperature, and specific volume.

4.14 A 20 ft³ drum contains saturated steam at 400°F. What is the pressure in the drum and what is the mass of vapor in the drum?

4.15 Solve Problem 4.14 if the drum contains saturated water.

4.16 A steam drum has a volume of 70 cu ft. If 70 percent of the volume is occupied by the vapor and the contents of the drum are at 500 psia, determine the weight of liquid and vapor in the drum.

4.17 Ten pounds of a steam–water mixture occupies a steam drum. If the quality of the mixture is 65 percent, what is the volume of the drum? The pressure is 100 psia.

4.18 A steam drum has a volume of 7 m³. If the quality is 80 percent and the drum is at 11 bars, determine the weight of liquid and vapor in the drum.

4.19 Steam at 500 psia has a specific volume of 0.800 cu ft/lb. Determine its enthalpy and temperature.

4.20 Steam at 300 psia is at 600°F. Determine its specific volume.

4.21 Steam at 200 psia is at 610°F. Determine its enthalpy.

4.22 Steam is at 22 bars and 227°C. Determine its enthalpy.

4.23 Determine the internal energy of steam at 190 psia and 910°F.

4.24 What is the internal energy of steam at 21.7 bars and 225°C?

4.25 Determine the enthalpy, specific volume, internal energy, and entropy of subcooled water at 500°F and 4000 psia.

4.26 Determine the enthalpy of subcooled water at 500°F and 4000 psia using Eq. (4.5). Compare your result with Problem 4.25.

4.27 Steam at 245°C has a specific volume of 100 cm³/g. Determine its pressure.

4.28 Steam at 500 psia has a specific volume of 1.7500 cu ft/lb. Determine its temperature and enthalpy.

4.29 One pound of saturated water at 200°F is converted to saturated steam at 100 psia. Determine the enthalpy difference between these two states.

4.30 If saturated steam at 500 psia is superheated to a temperature of 1000°F, determine the change in enthalpy between these two states. Assume the final pressure of the steam to be 500 psia.

4.31 If the final pressure of the steam in Problem 4.30 is 450 psia, determine the difference in enthalpy between the two states given.

4.32 Steam flowing in a pipe is throttled by a partly open valve. The initial steam conditions are 600 psia and 800°F. Determine the final temperature if the final pressure of the steam is 100 psia.

4.33 Wet steam at a pressure of 200 psia and a quality of 90 percent is throttled to a final pressure of 80 psia. What is the temperature and quality of the final condition? Use the *Steam Tables* to obtain your solution.

4.34 Solve Problem 4.33 using the Mollier chart.

4.35 After throttling, it is found that the pressure and temperature of steam are 30 psia and 300°F, respectively. If the pressure before throttling is 400 psia, what is the quality of the initial mixture? Use the *Steam Tables*.

4.36 Solve Problem 4.35 using the Mollier chart.

4.37 Superheated steam is expanded isentropically from 900 psia and 700°F to saturated vapor. Determine the difference in enthalpy for this expansion. Use the *Steam Tables*.

4.38 Solve Problem 4.37 using the Mollier chart.

4.39 One pound of steam is expanded isentropically from 500 psia and 800°F to 10 psia. Use the Mollier chart to determine the final enthalpy.

4.40 Solve Problem 4.39 using the *Steam Tables*.

4.41 Steam expands isentropically from 300 psia and 620°F to saturation. Determine the final enthalpy using the Mollier chart.

4.42 Solve Problem 4.41 using the Steam Tables.

4.43 Steam is used for heating a room. Assuming that the required heating load is 10,000 Btu/hr and the steam enters at 20 psia and 250°F and is condensed, how many pounds of steam per hour are required? Assume that pressure losses are negligible and that the liquid is just saturated.

4.44 Calculate the "average" specific heat at constant pressure for superheated steam between 400° and 1000°F if the pressure is 200 psia. The definition of average for this case is $\Delta h / \Delta T$. Compare this result with Fig. 4.11 and discuss.

4.45 Steam expands isentropically in a turbine from 500 psia and 1000°F to 14.7 psia. Determine the difference in enthalpy between the initial and final conditions.

4.46 If the expansion in Problem 4.45 is not carried out isentropically but is expanded irreversibly to the same final pressure and has 40° of superheat, determine the difference in enthalpy between the initial and final conditions. Use the Mollier chart.

4.47 One pound of superheated steam at 200 psia and 800°F expands irreversibly and adiabatically to 14.7 psia and 250°F. Determine the change in enthalpy between the initial and final states.

4.48 Wet steam leaves the exhaust of a turbine and is subsequently condensed. Assuming the wet steam to be at 0.5 psia with 15 percent moisture, determine the heat extracted in the condenser if the condensation process takes the mixture to saturated liquid.

4.49 Heat is added to steam in a closed cylinder. If a movable piston is placed on one end of the cylinder, it is possible (in principle) to carry out the process at constant pressure. If the initial steam is at 250°F and is saturated, how much heat is added if the final temperature is 500°F?

4.50 Saturated steam at 500°F expands isothermally to 100 psia. Determine the change in enthalpy between the initial and final states.

4.51 Saturated water enters a boiler at 500 psia. It is vaporized and superheated to a final condition of 500 psia and 1000°F. From this state it enters a turbine where it is expanded isentropically to 1 in. Hg. What fraction of the energy required to produce the steam is obtained from the turbine if the turbine is 100 percent efficient?

4.52 How much heat must be added to 1 lb of saturated steam at 500 psia in a closed tank to convert it to superheated steam at 1000 psia and 800°F?

4.53 Saturated steam fills a 100-cu ft container at 100 psia. If the container is cooled until the contents are at 50 psia, what is the quality of the final mixture?

4.54 A boiler drum is filled with water and heated until it contains a steam–water mixture at 100 psia. At this time there is 10,000 lb of water in the drum and 5 lb of vapor. If the contents of the drum are now heated until the pressure is 200 psia, how much heat was added?

chapter 5

the
ideal gas

5.1 INTRODUCTION

In Chapter 1 we derived a simple equation for the pressure–volume relation of a gas, based on elementary considerations. Since many oversimplifications were involved in this derivation, it could not be reasonably expected that the result obtained in this manner would even closely approach the behavior of a real gas. Surprisingly, it has been found that the equation can be used to represent the behavior of a large class of actual gases with an accuracy usually sufficient for engineering applications. In any case, this equation can be used to predict qualitatively the behavior of most gases, and the results so obtained can be employed as a guide for design or performance purposes.

Figures 5.1 and 5.2, respectively, show a modern high-performance automotive engine and an aircraft gas turbine. Based upon certain idealizations, which will be investigated in some detail in Chapter 7, it is possible to analyze the performance of these engines to obtain meaningful design criteria using the simplified equation of state.

The expressions *ideal gas* and *perfect gas* appear in many texts on thermodynamics, and unfortunately some confusion has developed regarding the exact definition of these terms. For clarity and consistency, these terms will be given identical meanings and defined as gases having equations of state that correspond to Eq. (5.8).

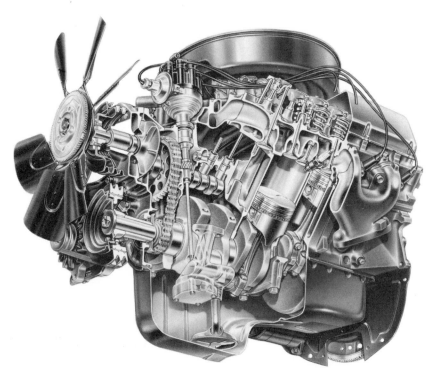

Figure 5.1 A 429 cubic inch displacement, eight-cylinder high performance automotive engine (Courtesy of Ford Motor Co.)

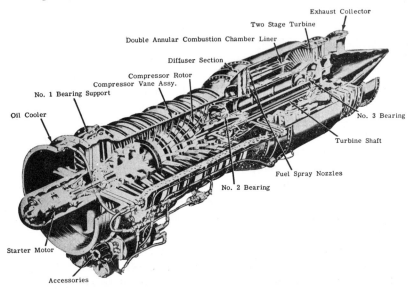

Exhaust Collector

Two Stage Turbine

Double Annular Combustion Chamber Liner

Diffuser Section

Compressor Rotor

Compressor Vane Assy.

No. 1 Bearing Support

Oil Cooler

No. 3 Bearing

Turbine Shaft

Fuel Spray Nozzles

No. 2 Bearing

Starter Motor

Accessories

Figure 5.2 Gas turbine used for aircraft propulsion (Courtesy of Pratt & Whitney Division of United Aircraft Corp.)

5.2 BASIC CONSIDERATIONS

The first observations concerning the equation of state of a gas were made by Robert Boyle in the middle of the 17th century. He observed experimentally that the volume of a given quantity of gas varies inversely with absolute pressure if the temperature of the gas is held constant. Figure 5.3 shows a plot

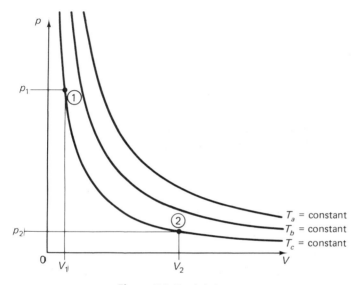

Figure 5.3 Boyle's law

of pressure and volume at constant temperature for a gas. If we consider the gas to be at temperature T_c and that it expands from state ① to state ②, we can write Boyle's law as

$$\frac{p_1}{p_2} = \frac{V_2}{V_1} \quad \text{or} \quad p_1 V_1 = p_2 V_2 \qquad (5.1)$$

Since $T = $ constant, we can also write Eq. (5.1) as

$$pV = C \qquad (5.1a)$$

where C represents a constant for a given temperature. A family of curves for different temperatures is shown in Fig. 5.3. Each of these curves is an equilateral hyperbola since they are of the form $xy = C$.

ILLUSTRATIVE PROBLEM 5.1

A gas occupies a volume of 100 cu ft and is at a pressure of 100 psia. If the pressure is reduced to 30 psia, what volume will the gas occupy? Assume that the gas temperature is kept constant.

Solution

For a constant-temperature process,

$$p_1 V_1 = p_2 V_2$$

Therefore,

$$V_2 = \frac{p_1}{p_2}(V_1)$$

and

$$V_2 = \frac{100}{30}(100) = 333 \text{ cu ft}$$

ILLUSTRATIVE PROBLEM 5.2

A gas occupies a volume of 2 m³ at a pressure of 1 MPa. If the pressure is increased to 8 MPa, what volume will the gas occupy if the gas temperature is kept constant.

Solution

For the constant-temperature process, we again have

$$p_1 V_1 = p_2 V_2$$

and

$$V_2 = \frac{p_1}{p_2}(V_1) = \frac{10^6}{8 \times 10^6}(2) = 0.25 \text{ m}^3$$

Approximately 100 years after Boyle's law was discovered, a second law was found which subsequently has been called Charles' law. We can obtain this law by considering two separate but related experiments. First, let us consider the case shown in Fig. 5.4a. In this figure a fixed mass of gas is contained in a rigid container to which heat can be added or removed, all the while maintaining

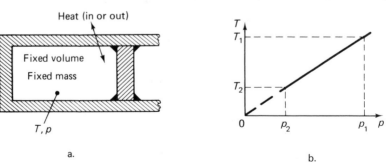

Figure 5.4 Charles' law: Experiment 1

the volume constant. A plot of absolute temperature against absolute pressure of the gas in this container will yield a straight line curve such as shown in Fig. 5.4b. The dashed extension of this plot will go through absolute zero pressure and temperature.

We may state the results of this experiment to be that the absolute temperature of a fixed volume of gas varies linearly with its absolute pressure. Referring to Fig. 5.4b, we can express this as

$$\frac{p_1}{p_2} = \frac{T_1}{T_2} \qquad\qquad (5.2)$$

or

$$\frac{p_1}{T_1} = \frac{p_2}{T_2} = \text{constant} \qquad\qquad (5.2a)$$

Equation (5.2a) is the equation of a straight line going through the origin. Although all gases deviate somewhat from Charles' law and Boyle's law, both reasonably express the behavior of real gases at moderate temperatures and pressures.

Let us now perform the second experiment, which is shown in Fig. 5.5. In this experiment, a weight is placed on the movable piston so that the pressure

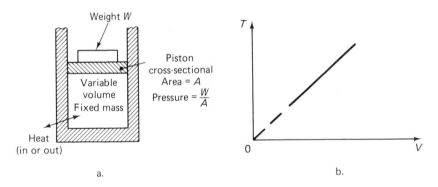

Figure 5.5 Charles' law: Experiment 2

on the gas is kept constant. The piston is free to move, which gives us a variable volume for the mass of gas in the cylinder. If heat is added, this piston moves up, increasing the gas volume; if heat is removed, the piston moves down, decreasing the gas volume. A plot of absolute temperature against volume is found to be a straight line, which, when extended, goes through the origin. As a result of this second experiment, we can state that the volume of a given mass of gas varies directly with its absolute temperature when the pressure is kept constant. Mathematically,

$$\frac{V_1}{V_2} = \frac{T_1}{T_2} \qquad\qquad (5.3)$$

or
$$\frac{T_1}{V_1} = \frac{T_2}{V_2} = \text{constant} \tag{5.3a}$$

Equation (5.3a) is also the equation of a straight line going through the origin.

ILLUSTRATIVE PROBLEM 5.3

A given mass of gas occupies 150 cu ft at 32°F. If heat is added while the gas pressure is kept constant, determine the volume the gas occupies when its temperature is 100°F.

Solution

For the conditions given, $T_1 = 32 + 460 = 492°R$ and $T_2 = 100 + 460 = 560°R$. Thus, for a constant-pressure process,

$$\frac{V_1}{V_2} = \frac{T_1}{T_2} \quad \text{or} \quad V_2 = V_1 \left(\frac{T_2}{T_1} \right) = \frac{150(560)}{492} = 170.7 \text{ cu ft}$$

ILLUSTRATIVE PROBLEM 5.4

If, after the process performed in Illustrative Problem 5.3, the gas is contained at constant volume and its absolute temperature is increased by 25 percent, what percent increase in its absolute pressure will occur?

Solution

If, for this process, $T_2 = 1.25 \, T_1$,

$$\frac{T_2}{T_1} = 1.25$$

Therefore,

$$\frac{p_1}{p_2} = \frac{T_1}{T_2} \quad \text{or} \quad \frac{p_2}{p_1} = \frac{T_2}{T_1}$$

Thus, $p_2/p_1 = T_2/T_1 = 1.25$, and the absolute gas pressure increases by 25 percent.

ILLUSTRATIVE PROBLEM 5.5

A gas is cooled at constant pressure from 100° to 0°C. If the initial volume is 4 m^3, what will its final volume be?

Solution

$$V_2 = V_1\left(\frac{T_2}{T_1}\right) = 4\left(\frac{0+273}{100+273}\right) = 2.93 \text{ m}^3$$

By combining Boyle's law and Charles' law into a single relation, we can obtain a general gas law. We can do this by considering a gas which goes from one state, state ①, to a second state, state ②. To go from state ① to state ② we shall first assume that the pressure is increased from state ① to the pressure of state ② by heating at constant volume. The gas is then cooled at constant pressure (the pressure at ②) until its volume reaches the volume of state ②.

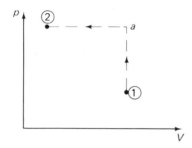

Figure 5.6 General gas law derivation

These events are portrayed in Fig. 5.6. From this figure we can write for the constant-volume path 1–a,

$$\frac{p_a}{p_1} = \frac{T_a}{T_1} \qquad (5.4)$$

and for path a–2, the constant-pressure path,

$$\frac{T_a}{T_2} = \frac{V_a}{V_2} \qquad (5.5)$$

Solving for T_a from Eq. (5.4) and substituting into Eq. (5.5) yields

$$\frac{p_a T_1}{p_1} = \frac{T_2 V_a}{V_2} \qquad (5.6)$$

But $p_a = p_2$ and $V_a = V_1$. Using this and rearranging gives us

$$\frac{p_1 V_1}{T_1} = \frac{p_2 V_2}{T_2} \qquad (5.7)$$

Since we selected points ① and ② arbitrarily, it follows that the term pV/T

must be a constant for a given gas. For convenience it is easier to express this constant on the basis of a unit mass of gas. Denoting the constant per unit mass by the symbol R, we have

$$pV = mRT \qquad (5.8)$$

It will be recalled from Chapter 1 that we identified the velocity term in the equation derived on the basis of elementary kinetic theory as being proportional to the temperature of the gas (the random motion of the gas molecules). Using this, we can also obtain the equation of state of a gas as Eq. (5.8).

In English engineering units, p is the pressure in pounds per square foot absolute, V is the total volume of the gas in cubic feet, T is the absolute temperature in degrees Rankine, m is the mass of gas in pounds, and R is a constant of proportionality in consistent units. If Eq. (5.8) is divided by the mass m, it becomes

$$pv = RT \qquad (5.9)$$

in which p, R, and T correspond to the terms in Eq. (5.8) and v represents specific volume. In SI units, p is in kilopascals, T is in degrees Kelvin, m is in kilograms when R is in kilojoules per kilomole degrees Kelvin and v is in cubic metres per kilogram.

R for actual gases is not a constant and varies from gas to gas. However, it has been found experimentally that most gases at very low pressure or with high degrees of superheat exhibit nearly constant values of R. As further indicated in Table 5.1, the product of molecular weight (MW) and R for most gases is nearly constant and in usual English engineering units equals 1545.3 ft lb/lb-mole °R. For any other combination of pressure, volume, and temperature units, it is a relatively straightforward calculation to derive R. Some values of this constant in other systems are listed in Table 5.2. For the purposes of this book, a value of $(MW) \times (R)$ of 1545 ft lb/lb-mole °R is used. In SI units the value of this product is 8.314 kJ/kg·mole·K.

TABLE 5.1

GAS	GAS MW (APPROX)	PRODUCT MW × R
Air	29	1545
Ammonia (NH_3)	17	1520
Carbon dioxide (CO_2)	44	1532
Carbon monoxide (CO)	28	1545
Hydrogen (H_2)	2	1535
Nitrogen (N_2)	28	1537
Oxygen (O_2)	32	1543

From Thermodynamics, 2nd Ed., by G. A. Hawkins, John Wiley & Sons, Inc., New York, 1951.

TABLE 5.2

MOLECULAR WEIGHT $\times$ R
1545.3 ft lb/lb-mole, °R
0.082 liter-atm/g-mole, K
8.3143×10^7 erg/g-mole, K
8.314 joules/g-mole, K
1.986 Btu/lb-mole, °R
1.986 cal/g-mole, K

The pound-mole or, more briefly, mole is simply the molecular weight of a substance expressed in pounds. Thus 28 lb of nitrogen (N_2) is 1 lb mole of nitrogen. Similarly, the kg·mole is the molecular weight in kilograms.

ILLUSTRATIVE PROBLEM 5.6

Nitrogen at 200 psig is used to fill a container of 120 cu in. The filling process is very slow, and the contents of the tank attain the room temperature of 73°F. How much gas is there in the container?

Solution

Let us first put each of the given variables into a consistent set of units:

$$p = (200 + 14.7)(144) \text{ psfa}$$

$$T = (460 + 73)°R$$

$$V = \frac{120}{1728} \text{ cu ft}$$

$$R = \frac{1545}{28} \quad \text{(Since the molecular weight of nitrogen is 28)}$$

Applying Eq. (5.9), $pv = RT$, $v = RT/p$,

$$v = \frac{(1545/28)(460 + 73)}{(200 + 14.7)(144)}$$

$$= 0.951 \text{ cu ft/lb}$$

The total weight of gas is the total volume divided by the specific volume. Thus

$$\frac{(120/1728) \text{ cu ft}}{0.951 \text{ cu ft/lb}} = 0.073 \text{ lb}$$

The same result is obtained by direct use of Eq. (5.8), $pV = mRT$; $m = pV/RT$.

$$m = \frac{(200 + 14.7)(144)(120/1728)}{(1545/28)(460 + 73)} = 0.073 \text{ lb}$$

ILLUSTRATIVE PROBLEM 5.7

If the gas in Illustrative Problem 5.6 is now heated until the temperature is 200°F, what is the pressure?

Solution

Apply Eq. (5.8) and note that the volume is constant.

$$\frac{p_1 V_1}{T_1} = \frac{p_2 V_2}{T_2} \quad \text{and} \quad p_2 = p_1\left(\frac{T_2}{T_1}\right) \quad \text{since} \quad V_1 = V_2$$

Therefore,

$$p_2 = (200 + 14.7)\frac{(460 + 200)}{(460 + 73)} = 266 \text{ psia}$$

ILLUSTRATIVE PROBLEM 5.8

Carbon dioxide (MW = 44) occupies a tank at 100°C. If the volume of the tank is 0.5 m³ and the pressure is 500 kPa, determine the mass of gas in the tank.

Solution

For CO_2,

$$R = \frac{8.314}{44} = 0.1890$$

Applying Eq. (5.8), $pV = mRT$,

$$m = \frac{pV}{RT} = \frac{(500)(0.5)}{0.1890(273 + 100)} = 3.546 \text{ kg}$$

It is sometimes convenient to express the volume of a gas in terms of the volume that one mole of gas will occupy at a given temperature and pressure. We can readily obtain this value by considering Eq. (5.9). Let us multiply both sides of this equation by MW, the molecular weight of a given gas. Thus

$$(\text{MW})pv = (\text{MW})RT \qquad (5.10)$$

Since $R = 1545/\mathrm{MW}$,

$$p(v)(\mathrm{MW}) = 1545\,T \qquad (5.11)$$

The molecular weight of a gas has the units of lb/lb mole or kg/kg mole. Thus the product of $v(\mathrm{MW})$ is (cu ft/lb) (lb/lb mole) or cu ft/lb mole or m^3/kg mole or the molar volume. Using V_{molar} to express this volume, we have,

$$V_{\mathrm{molar}} = \frac{1545\,T}{p} \quad \text{or} \quad \frac{8.314\,T}{p} \qquad (5.12)$$

It is apparent from Eq. (5.12) that for a given pressure and temperature a mole of *any* gas will occupy the *same volume*. Quite often the term *standard state* appears in the engineering and scientific literature, and some confusion exists as to its specific meaning. This is due to the lack of general agreement on the definition of temperature and pressure at this state. The most common standard state in use is 32°F and 14.7 psia. For this state it will be found that 1 lb mole occupies 358 cu ft or 22.4 liters/g-mole. The use of the term standard state should be avoided unless the conditions of this state are specified.

ILLUSTRATIVE PROBLEM 5.9

What volume does 0.073/28 lb moles of nitrogen occupy at 200 psig and 73°F?

Solution

This problem is the inverse problem of Illustrative Problem 5.6. We can obtain the solution by noting from Eq. (5.12) that the molar volume increases with increased temperature and decreases with increased pressure. Thus

$$\left(\frac{0.073}{28} \right)(358)\left(\frac{460 + 73}{460 + 32} \right) \times \frac{14.7}{(200 + 14.7)} = 0.0692 \text{ cu ft}$$

From Illustrative Problem 5.6, the volume is $120/1728 = 0.0694$ cu ft.

5.3 THE SPECIFIC HEAT

In the general case of a fluid involved in a thermodynamic process, both heat and work energy interchanges are involved, and concurrently there is a temperature change of the working fluid. The term *specific heat* has been defined in Chapter 2 as the ratio of the heat transferred per unit mass by the working fluid in a process to the corresponding change in temperature of the fluid.

Mathematically,

$$c = \frac{q}{\Delta T} \qquad (5.13)$$

Several features of Eq. (5.13) have already been noted in Chapter 2 and are repeated here for emphasis. Heat is transferred energy and by convention is positive if added to a system and negative if extracted from a system. Also, the addition or removal of energy as work does not enter into the definition of specific heat. These concepts lead us to the conclusion that the specific heat of a process can be zero, positive, negative, or even infinite. Two processes proved themselves to be of particular interest, the constant-pressure process and the constant-volume process. For these processes the respective specific heats are

$$c_p = \left[\frac{q}{\Delta T}\right]_{p \text{ constant}} \qquad \text{(flow or nonflow)}$$

$$c_v = \left[\frac{q}{\Delta T}\right]_{v \text{ constant}} \qquad (5.14)$$

Throughout this chapter it will be necessary to invoke both the first and second laws to specify the path and state conditions as a gas undergoes a change of state. In Chapter 2 the first law was applied to the steady flow and nonflow constant-pressure processes, and the energy relation $q = \Delta h$ resulted. Although a complete discussion of the temperature and pressure dependence of the specific heat of a real gas is beyond the scope of this book, it may be noted that a gas whose equation of state is given by Eq. (5.9) has both its internal energy and enthalpy independent of pressure, and that these properties depend solely on temperature. Therefore, for the ideal gas for any process, flow or nonflow,

$$c_p = \frac{\Delta h}{\Delta T} \qquad (5.15a)$$

$$c_v = \frac{\Delta u}{\Delta T} \qquad (5.15b)$$

When internal energy or enthalpy data are available (such as in the Keenan and Kaye *Gas Tables*), an "average" value of c_p and c_v can readily be obtained.

$$\bar{c}_p = \frac{h_2 - h_1}{T_2 - T_1} \qquad (5.16)$$

$$\bar{c}_v = \frac{u_2 - u_1}{T_2 - T_1} \qquad (5.17)$$

For cases in which internal energy or enthalpy data are not available, equations have been developed either from empirical or spectroscopic data expressing the dependence of the specific heat on temperature. These equations are commonly of the following forms with A, B, and D as constants:

$$c = A + BT + DT^2 \qquad (5.18a)$$

$$c = A' + \frac{B'}{T} + \frac{D'}{T^2} \qquad (5.18b)$$

The mean or average specific heat of a substance can be defined as that value, when multiplied by the temperature interval, that will give the energy as heat interchanged during a process. Thus, if the specific heat varies as shown in Fig. 5.7, the mean value occurs when areas $abcd$ and $aefd$ are equal. For gases whose specific heats are of the form given by Eq. (5.18), the mean specific heats are, respectively,

$$\bar{c} = A + \frac{B}{2}(T_2 + T_1) + \frac{D}{3}(T_2^2 + T_2 T_1 + T_1^2) \qquad (5.19a)$$

$$\bar{c} = A' + \frac{B' \ln(T_2/T_1)}{T_2 - T_1} + \frac{D'}{T_2 T_1} \qquad (5.19b)$$

An alternate interpretation of the average specific heat can be illustrated graphically if reference is again made to Fig. 5.7. The c and T scales are plotted linearly, and $\bar{c}$ expresses the condition that the equal positive and negative areas cancel each other. In other words, area A equals area B. Note that the mean specific heat does not necessarily occur at the arithmetic mean temperature unless c is constant or a linear function of T.

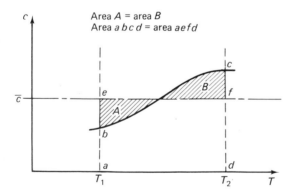

Figure 5.7 Mean specific heat

ILLUSTRATIVE PROBLEM 5.10

For nitrogen between 540°R and 9000°R, an equation for the instantaneous specific heat at constant pressure is

$$c_p = 0.338 - \frac{1.24 \times 10^2}{T} + \frac{4.15 \times 10^4}{T^2} \quad \text{Btu/lb °R}$$

Determine the mean specific heat at constant pressure between 80°F and 500°F.

Solution

This equation has the form of Eq. (5.18b) with $A'=0.338$, $B'=-1.24\times10^2$, and $D'=4.15\times10^4$. Therefore, from Eq. (5.19b), with temperatures in degrees Rankine,

$$\bar{c}_p = 0.338 - \frac{1.24\times10^2\ln(960/540)}{(960-540)} + \frac{4.15\times10^4}{(540)(960)}$$

$$= 0.248 \text{ Btu/lb }°R$$

ILLUSTRATIVE PROBLEM 5.11

Using the data for the properties of some gases at low pressure in the Appendix, solve Illustrative Problem 5.10.

Solution

The table in the Appendix does not give us the enthalpy data at 960°R and 540°R that we need. Interpolating,

T	$\bar{h}$	T	$\bar{h}$
$3\!\begin{pmatrix}537\\540\\600\end{pmatrix}\!63$	3729.5 3750.4 4167.9	$60\!\begin{pmatrix}900\\960\\1000\end{pmatrix}\!100$	6268.1 6694.0 6977.9

$$\bar{h}_{540} = 3729.5 + \frac{3}{63}(4167.9 - 3729.5)$$

$$\bar{h}_{960} = 6268.1 + \frac{60}{100}(6977.9 - 6268.1)$$

Note that $\bar{h}$ is given for a mass of 1 lb mole. To obtain the enthalpy per pound, it is necessary to divide the values of $\bar{h}$ by the molecular weight, 28.

$$\bar{c} = \frac{h_2 - h_1}{T_2 - T_1} = \frac{(6694.0 - 3750.4)}{28(960 - 540)} = 0.250 \text{ Btu/lb }°R$$

With the more extensive *Gas Tables*, these interpolations are avoided and the *Gas Tables* provide a relatively easy and accurate method of obtaining average specific heats.

For the ideal gas, certain unique and simple relations relating the specific heat at constant pressure to the specific heat at constant volume can be derived. Let us first recall the general definition of the term enthalpy,

$$h = u + \frac{pv}{J} \qquad (5.20)$$

The change in enthalpy between any two states is, therefore,

$$(h_2 - h_1) = (u_2 - u_1) + \frac{p_2 v_2}{J} - \frac{p_1 v_1}{J} \qquad (5.21)$$

But

$$(h_2 - h_1) = c_p(T_2 - T_1), \quad (u_2 - u_1) = c_v(T_2 - T_1) \quad \text{and} \quad pv = RT \qquad (5.22)$$

By substituting Eq. (5.22) into Eq. (5.21),

$$c_p(T_2 - T_1) = c_v(T_2 - T_1) + \frac{R}{J}(T_2 - T_1) \qquad (5.23)$$

Rearranging and simplifying Eq. (5.23) yields the desired result:

$$c_p - c_v = \frac{R}{J} \qquad (5.24)$$

In SI units the conversion factor J is not included. Therefore,

$$c_p - c_v = R \quad \text{(in SI)} \qquad (5.24a)$$

At this point it is often found convenient to express the results of Eq. (5.24) in terms of the ratio of the specific heats. By defining

$$k = \frac{c_p}{c_v} \qquad (5.25)$$

and dividing Eq. (5.25) by c_v

$$\frac{c_p}{c_v} - \frac{c_v}{c_v} = \frac{R}{Jc_v} \qquad (5.26)$$

Using the definition of k given by Eq. (5.25),

$$k - 1 = \frac{R}{Jc_v} \qquad (5.27)$$

and rearranging,

$$c_v = \frac{R}{J(k-1)} \qquad (5.28)$$

In SI,

$$c_v = \frac{R}{k-1} \qquad (5.28a)$$

Since $c_p = k c_v$

$$c_p = \frac{R}{J}\left(\frac{k}{k-1}\right) \qquad (5.29)$$

In SI units,

$$c_p = R\left(\frac{k}{k-1}\right) \qquad (5.29a)$$

ILLUSTRATIVE PROBLEM 5.12

Oxygen has a c_p of 0.24 Btu/lb °R at a given temperature. Determine c_v.

Solution

The molecular weight of oxygen is 32. R is, therefore, $1545/32 = 48.28$. Since $c_p - c_v = R/J$,

$$c_v = c_p - \frac{R}{J}$$

$$= 0.24 - \frac{48.28}{778} = 0.178 \text{ Btu/lb °R}$$

ILLUSTRATIVE PROBLEM 5.13

If k of oxygen is 1.4, determine c_p and c_v in SI units.

Solution

From Eq. (5.28a),

$$c_v = \frac{R}{k-1} = \frac{8.314/32}{1.4-1} = 0.6495 \ \frac{\text{kJ}}{\text{kg} \cdot \text{K}}$$

Since $c_p = kc_v$,

$$c_p = 1.4(0.6495) = 0.9093 \ \frac{kJ}{kg \cdot K}$$

ILLUSTRATIVE PROBLEM 5.14

A closed rigid container with a volume of 60 in.^{3} contains 0.0116 lb of a certain gas at 90 psia and 40°F. The gas is heated to 140°F and 108 psia, and the heat input is found to be 0.33 Btu. Assuming this to be a perfect gas, find the specific heat at constant pressure c_p.

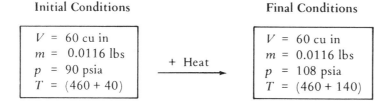

Figure **5.8** Illustrative Problem 5.14

Solution

When solving this type of problem, it is necessary to note carefully the information given and to write the correct energy equation for the process. Since the process is carried out at constant volume, the heat added equals the change in internal energy. Since the change in internal energy per pound for the ideal gas is $c_v(T_2 - T_1)$, the total change in internal energy for m pounds must equal the heat added. Thus

$$Q = m(u_2 - u_1) = mc_v(T_2 - T_1)$$

Using the data of the problem, $0.33 = 0.0116c_v(600 - 500)$, and

$$c_v = 0.284 \ \text{Btu/lb} \ °R$$

To obtain c_p, it is first necessary to obtain R. Enough information was given in the initial conditions of the problem to apply Eq. (5.8) for R, $pV = mRT$,

$$(90)(144)\left(\frac{60}{1728}\right) = 0.0116(R)(460 + 40)$$

and $$R = 77.8$$

Since

$$c_p - c_v = \frac{R}{J}$$

$$c_p = c_v + \frac{R}{J}$$

$$= 0.284 + \frac{77.8}{778} = 0.384$$

5.4 ENTROPY CHANGES OF THE IDEAL GAS

In the rest of this chapter, various nonflow processes of the ideal gas will be studied. It must be remembered that the energy quantities called work and heat depend on the path that the gas undergoes, whereas enthalpy, entropy, and internal energy are determined by the final and initial states of the fluid since they are properties.

Consider a gas that undergoes a change in state from A to B, as shown in Fig. 5.9a on pressure–volume coordinates. In this process (path A,B), the

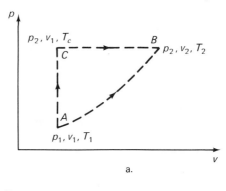

a.

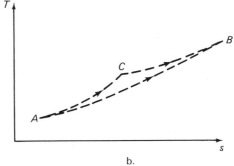

b.

Figure 5.9 General gas process

pressure, volume, and temperature change to the final values so that p_2, v_2, and T_2 are greater than p_1, v_1, and T_1.

To go from state A to state B, let us select the two separate reversible paths A,C and C,B. Path A,C is carried out at constant volume and path C,B is carried out at constant pressure. These paths are shown in Fig. 5.9a as dashed lines and are similarly shown on Ts coordinates in Fig. 5.9b. It is important to note that the properties at the initial and final states will determine the changes in enthalpy, entropy, and internal energy, but the path selected between these states will determine the energy interchange as both heat and work.

The change in entropy for a gas undergoing the reversible paths A,C and C,B can readily be determined. For the constant volume path, $q = \Delta u = c_v \Delta T$, and for the constant pressure path, $q = \Delta h = c_p \Delta T$. Therefore, from the definition of the property entropy,

$$\Delta s = \frac{q}{T} = \left(\frac{c_v \Delta T}{T}\right)_v + \left(\frac{c_p \Delta T}{T}\right)_p \qquad (5.30)$$

where the subscripts v and p refer to the constant-volume and constant pressure-processes, respectively.

To obtain the total change in entropy for a finite process between the temperature limits of T_2 and T_1, it is necessary to sum all the terms of Eq. (5.30) over the entire temperature range. Let us first assume that the specific heats are independent of temperature. It is necessary only to sum the $\Delta T/T$ values. This process has already been illustrated in Chapters 2 and 3, but it is worth repeating at this point. Figure 5.10 shows a plot of $1/T$ as a function of T. By selecting a value of ΔT, as shown, the shaded area is $\Delta T/T$. Thus the sum of the $\Delta T/T$ values is the area under the curve between the desired temperature limits. By the methods of the calculus it can be shown that this area is $\ln T_2/T_1$. As noted earlier, $\ln x = \log_e x = 2.3026 \log_{10} x$.

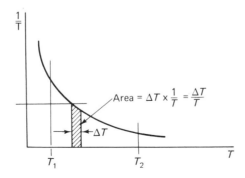

Figure 5.10 Evaluation of $\Delta T/T$

By performing the summation required by Eq. (5.30) and again noting that the specific heats are constant,

$$\Delta s = \left(c_v \ln \frac{T_c}{T_1} \right)_v + \left(c_p \ln \frac{T_2}{T_c} \right)_p \qquad (5.31)$$

Equation (5.31) can be put into a more useful form by noting that, for the constant volume process, Eq. (5.9) yields $T_c/T_1 = p_2/p_1$, and for the constant pressure process, $T_2/T_c = v_2/v_1$. Thus

$$\Delta s = c_v \ln \left(\frac{p_2}{p_1} \right) + c_p \ln \left(\frac{v_2}{v_1} \right) \qquad (5.32)$$

By dividing both sides of Eq. (5.32) by c_v and noting that $k = c_p/c_v$,

$$\frac{\Delta s}{c_v} = k \ln \left(\frac{v_2}{v_1} \right) + \ln \left(\frac{p_2}{p_1} \right) \qquad (5.33)$$

Another form of Eq. (5.32) can be derived by using Eq. (5.24):

$$\Delta s = c_p \ln \left(\frac{T_2}{T_1} \right) - \frac{R}{J} \ln \left(\frac{p_2}{p_1} \right) \qquad (5.34)$$

Equation (5.34) can also be derived in the following alternate way; from Chapter 3,

$$T\Delta s = \Delta h - (v\Delta p/J)$$

Dividing through by T and noting that $\Delta h = c_p \Delta T$ and $v/T = R/p$,

$$\Delta s = c_p \left(\frac{\Delta T}{T} \right) - \frac{R}{J} \left(\frac{\Delta p}{p} \right)$$

Summing each term on the right side of this equation gives us Eq. (5.34).

The utility of these considerations and equations will become apparent as the individual gas processes are studied. The student should note that Eqs. (5.31) through (5.34) are valid for *any process* of an *ideal gas* when the specific heats are *constant*. Note that in SI units, the J in the preceding equations is not necessary.

ILLUSTRATIVE PROBLEM 5.15

One pound of air (MW = 29) expands from 100 psia and 100°F to 15 psia and 0°F. Determine the change in entropy. Assume c_p of air is 0.24 Btu/lb °R and is constant.

Solution

On the basis of the data given, we can use Eq. (5.34) to solve this problem. Thus

$$\Delta s = 0.24 \ln \left(\frac{460}{460 + 100} \right) - \frac{R}{J} \ln \left(\frac{15}{100} \right)$$

We can make these logarithms positive quantities by noting that the $\log x = -\log 1/x$. Therefore,

$$-\Delta s = 0.24 \ln \left(\frac{460 + 100}{460} \right) - \frac{R}{J} \ln \left(\frac{100}{15} \right)$$

$$= 0.24 \ln \left(\frac{560}{460} \right) - \frac{1545/29}{778} \ln \left(\frac{100}{15} \right)$$

and $-\Delta s = 0.04714 - 0.1299 = -0.0828$ or $\Delta s = 0.0828$

ILLUSTRATIVE PROBLEM 5.16

Two kilograms of oxygen expand from 500 kPa and 100°C to 150 kPa and 0°C. Determine the change in entropy if $c_p = 0.9093$ kJ/kg·K and remains constant.

Solution

Using Eq. (5.34), and dropping J,

$$\Delta s = 0.9093 \ln \left(\frac{273}{273 + 100} \right) - \frac{8.314}{32} \ln \frac{150}{500}$$

$$= 0.02901 \text{ kJ/kg·K}$$

For 2 kg,

$$\Delta S = 2(0.02901) = 0.05802 \text{ kJ/K}$$

ILLUSTRATIVE PROBLEM 5.17

An ideal gas with constant specific heats undergoes a change during which its specific volume is halved and its entropy increases by an amount equal to one-quarter of its specific heat at constant volume. Assuming k is 1.4, what was the increase in pressure for this process?

Solution

From Eq. (5.33) and the data given,

$$\frac{\Delta s}{c_v} = k \ln\left(\frac{v_2}{v_1}\right) + \ln\left(\frac{p_2}{p_1}\right)$$

$$\frac{1/4 c_v}{c_v} = 1.4 \ln\left(\frac{1/2}{1}\right) + \ln\left(\frac{p_2}{p_1}\right)$$

or

$$\frac{1}{4} - 1.4 \ln\frac{1}{2} = \ln\left(\frac{p_2}{p_1}\right)$$

But $-1.4 \ln\frac{1}{2} = -1.4(\ln 1 - \ln 2) = -1.4(0 - 0.693) = 1.4(0.693)$. Thus

$$\frac{1}{4} + 1.4(0.693) = \ln\left(\frac{p_2}{p_1}\right)$$

$$\ln\left(\frac{p_2}{p_1}\right) = 1.22$$

and by taking antilogarithms

$$\frac{p_2}{p_1} = 3.4 \quad \text{or} \quad p_2 = 3.4 p_1$$

5.5 NONFLOW GAS PROCESSES

In the following portions of this section five nonflow gas processes are analyzed in detail. These processes are constant volume, constant pressure, isothermal, isentropic, and polytropic. The derivations in each case proceed from a consideration of the equation of state and the equation of the path. Paths shown as dashed lines indicate nonequilibrium paths.

5.5a Constant Volume Process (Isometric Process)

The constant volume process is best exemplified by a closed tank from which heat is either added or removed. In Fig. 5.11 the indicated path is one in which heat is being added.

From Eq. (5.9) the equation of the path can readily be written as

$$\frac{p_1}{T_1} = \frac{p_2}{T_2} \tag{5.35}$$

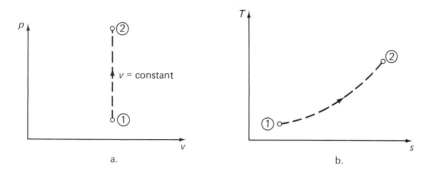

Figure 5.11 Constant volume process

The application of the first law yields the relationship between the heat added and the final state condition. Since there is no volume change, no work is done. Thus

$$q = u_2 - u_1 = c_v(T_2 - T_1) \tag{5.36}$$

Also $$W = 0 \tag{5.37}$$

since there is on change in volume.

The change in entropy for this process is given directly, by the defining equation for entropy or as the volume part of Eq. (5.31). In either case

$$\Delta s = c_v \ln\left(\frac{T_2}{T_1}\right) \tag{5.38}$$

Two further considerations complete all the necessary relations for the constant-volume process. The first of these states that the specific heat for this process is by definition c_v, and that we have assumed it to be constant. The second consideration (whose utility will appear later) determines the exponent in the equation $pv^n = $ constant that will make this equation fit the constant-volume process. By rearranging this equation,

$$\left(\frac{p_1}{p_2}\right)\left(\frac{v_1}{v_2}\right)^n = 1 \quad \text{or} \quad \frac{v_1}{v_2} = \left(\frac{p_2}{p_1}\right)^{1/n} \tag{5.39}$$

Since $v_1/v_2 = 1$, it becomes necessary for $1/n$ to be zero or

$$n = \infty \tag{5.40}$$

ILLUSTRATIVE PROBLEM 5.18

If $\frac{1}{2}$ lb of a gas is heated at constant volume from 70°F to 270°F, determine the change in entropy for this process. Assume that $c_v = 0.17$ Btu/lb °R.

Solution

For this process $T_1 = 530°R$, $T_2 = 730°R$. Therefore,

$$\Delta s = c_v \ln \left(\frac{T_2}{T_1} \right) = 0.17 \ln \left(\frac{730}{530} \right)$$

$$= 0.0544 \text{ Btu/lb } °R$$

$$\Delta S = \tfrac{1}{2}(0.0544) = 0.0272 \text{ Btu/}°R$$

ILLUSTRATIVE PROBLEM 5.19

If 0.2 kg of air is heated at constant volume from 20° to 100°C, determine the change in entropy for the process. Assume that c_v is constant and equal to 0.7186 kJ/kg·K.

Solution

$$\Delta s = c_v \ln \frac{T_2}{T_1} = 0.7186 \ln \left(\frac{100 + 273}{20 + 273} \right)$$

$$= 0.1735 \ \frac{\text{kJ}}{\text{kg} \cdot \text{K}}$$

For 0.2 kg,

$$\Delta S = 0.2(0.1735) = 0.03470 \ \frac{\text{kJ}}{\text{K}}$$

5.5b Constant Pressure Process (Isobaric Process)

The constant pressure process is a good approximation to many of the common physical processes with which we are familiar. The combustion of fuel in a boiler, the flow of fluids, the flow of air in ducts, and other processes can be used to illustrate constant pressure. Both the nonflow and flow processes yield to the following analysis: for an ideal gas, Eq. (5.9) once again gives us the equation of the path for this process.

$$\frac{v_1}{v_2} = \frac{T_1}{T_2} \tag{5.41}$$

From the first law, the constant-pressure process has as its energy equation (neglecting kinetic and potential energy terms)

$$q = h_2 - h_1 \tag{5.42}$$

and, consequently,

$$q = c_p(T_2 - T_1) \qquad (5.43)$$

where c_p is the specific heat of the process.

During the constant-pressure process shown in Fig. 5.12, work is removed as heat is added. The amount of work is the area under the pv curve, which is

$$p(v_2 - v_1) = p_2 v_2 - p_1 v_1 \qquad (5.44)$$

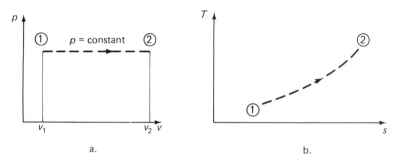

a.

b.

Figure 5.12 Constant pressure process

Application of Eq. (5.9) and reduction of the mechanical units of Eq. (5.44) to thermal units yields

$$p_2 v_2 - p_1 v_1 = \frac{R}{J}(T_2 - T_1) \qquad (5.45)$$

The exponent of pv^n which is applicable to this process is found as follows:

$$\left(\frac{p_2}{p_1}\right)\left(\frac{v_2}{v_1}\right)^n = 1 \quad \text{but} \quad \frac{p_2}{p_1} = 1$$

Therefore, $n = 0$ for a constant-pressure process.

Finally, the change in entropy for this process is

$$\Delta s = c_p \ln\left(\frac{T_2}{T_1}\right) \qquad (5.46)$$

ILLUSTRATIVE PROBLEM 5.20

In a gas turbine cycle, heat is added to the working fluid (air) at constant pressure. Determine the heat transferred, the increase in entropy, and the flow work change per pound of air if the initial pressure is 100 psia and the temperature goes from 70°F to 400°F. The specific heat c_p for this process is constant and equals 0.24 Btu/lb °F.

Solution

This process is shown graphically in Fig. 5.12. From the energy equation for the constant pressure process, the heat transferred is Δh. Therefore,

$$q = \Delta h = c_p(T_2 - T_1) = 0.24(860 - 530)$$
$$= 79.2 \text{ Btu/lb} \quad \text{(into the system)}$$

$$\Delta s = c_p \ln\left(\frac{T_2}{T_1}\right) = 0.24 \ln\left(\frac{860}{530}\right) = 0.116 \text{ Btu/lb } {}^\circ\text{R}$$

The flow work change is

$$\frac{p_2 v_2}{J} - \frac{p_1 v_1}{J} = \frac{R}{J}(T_2 - T_1)$$

$$= \frac{(1545/29)(860 - 530)}{778}$$

$$= 22.6 \text{ Btu/lb}$$

In addition to each of the assumptions made in all the processes being considered, it has further been tacitly assumed that these processes are carried out quasi-statically and without friction.

5.5c Constant Temperature Process (Isothermal Process)

The expansion process shown in Fig. 5.13 could conceivably be one in which a gas expands in a hot cylinder. Heat would be transferred from the hot cylinder walls to maintain the gas temperature constant. The path equation is

$$p_1 v_1 = p_2 v_2 = \text{constant} \tag{5.47}$$

and from the first law it can also be deduced that both the changes in enthalpy and internal energy for this process are zero since the temperature is constant. Therefore, the work of the isothermal process must exactly equal the heat transferred. Thus

$$q = \frac{W}{J} \tag{5.48}$$

or

$$q = W \quad \text{in SI} \tag{5.48a}$$

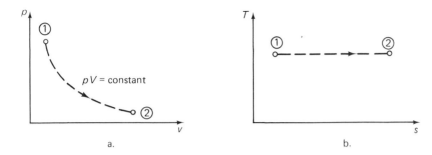

Figure 5.13 Isothermal process

Let us evaluate the change in entropy for the isothermal nonflow process from Eq. (5.32) as follows:

$$\Delta s = c_p \ln\left(\frac{v_2}{v_1}\right) + c_v \ln\left(\frac{p_2}{p_1}\right) \qquad (5.49)$$

Since

$$p_1 v_1 = p_2 v_2, \qquad (5.50)$$

$$\left(\frac{v_1}{v_2}\right) = \left(\frac{p_2}{p_1}\right) \qquad (5.51)$$

$$\Delta s = c_p \ln\left(\frac{v_2}{v_1}\right) + c_v \ln\left(\frac{v_1}{v_2}\right) \qquad (5.52)$$

However,

$$\ln\frac{v_1}{v_2} = -\ln\left(\frac{v_2}{v_1}\right) \qquad (5.53)$$

Therefore,

$$\Delta s = c_p \ln\left(\frac{v_2}{v_1}\right) - c_v \ln\left(\frac{v_2}{v_1}\right) \qquad (5.54)$$

Factoring,

$$\Delta s = \ln\left(\frac{v_2}{v_1}\right)(c_p - c_v) \qquad (5.55)$$

But $c_p - c_v = R/J$. Therefore,

$$\Delta s = \frac{R}{J} \ln\left(\frac{v_2}{v_1}\right) \qquad (5.56)$$

Equation (5.56) can also be written as

$$\Delta s = \frac{pv}{TJ} \ln\left(\frac{v_2}{v_1}\right) \qquad (5.57)$$

In SI units, Eq. (5.57) is

$$\Delta s = \frac{pv}{T} \ln\left(\frac{v_2}{v_1}\right) = R \ln\left(\frac{v_2}{v_1}\right) \qquad (5.57a)$$

We can now determine the energy interchange as heat and also the work by noting that

$$\Delta s = \frac{q}{T} \quad \text{or} \quad q = T(\Delta s) \qquad (5.58)$$

But from Eq. (5.48), $q = W/J$. This gives us

$$\frac{W}{J} = q = T\Delta s = \frac{RT}{J} \ln\left(\frac{v_2}{v_1}\right) = \frac{p_1 v_1}{J} \ln\left(\frac{v_2}{v_1}\right) = \frac{p_2 v_2}{J} \ln\left(\frac{v_2}{v_1}\right)$$

$$(5.59)$$

In SI units,

$$W = p_2 v_2 \ln\left(\frac{v_2}{v_1}\right) \qquad (5.59a)$$

Since there is no change in temperature for this process, and a finite quantity of energy as heat has crossed the system boundaries, the definition of specific heat requires that the specific heat of the isothermal process be infinite. Also, in order for both pv and pv^n to be the equation of the path, n must be unity.

ILLUSTRATIVE PROBLEM 5.21

If 0.1 lb of nitrogen is kept at a constant temperature of 200°F while its volume increases to twice its initial volume, determine the heat added and work out of the system.

Solution

From Eq. (5.59) we have

$$q = \frac{RT}{J} \ln\left(\frac{v_2}{v_1}\right)$$

$$= \frac{(1545/28)(460 + 200)}{778} \ln\left(\frac{2}{1}\right)$$

$$= 32.4 \text{ Btu/lb}$$

For 0.1 lb, $q = 0.1 \times 32.4 = 3.24$ Btu (added to system). The work out of the system is equal to the heat added; thus

$$\frac{W}{J} = 3.24 \text{ Btu} \quad \text{(out of system)}$$

ILLUSTRATIVE PROBLEM 5.22

If 1 kg of oxygen has its volume halved at a constant temperature of 50°C, determine the heat added and the work out of the system.

Solution

$$q = RT \ln \frac{v_2}{v_1} = \frac{8.314}{32}(273 + 50) \ln \frac{1}{2}$$

$$= -58.17 \frac{\text{kJ}}{\text{kg}} \quad \text{(heat out of system)}$$

Therefore, $\quad W = q = -58.17 \dfrac{\text{kJ}}{\text{kg}} \quad$ (into system)

5.5d Constant Entropy Process (Isentropic Process)

It will be recalled that the isentropic process is a reversible adiabatic process. An alternate definition is a process carried out with no change in entropy. Equation (5.33) serves to define this path:

$$\frac{\Delta s}{c_v} = k \ln\left(\frac{v_2}{v_1}\right) + \ln\left(\frac{p_2}{p_1}\right) = 0 \tag{5.33}$$

or

$$\ln\left(\frac{v_2}{v_1}\right)^k = \ln\left(\frac{p_1}{p_2}\right) \tag{5.60}$$

Taking antilogarithms and rearranging

$$p_1 v_1^k = p_2 v_2^k \tag{5.61}$$

Equation (5.61) is the path equation for this process, and by using the equation of state [Eq. (5.9)], it is possible to rewrite Eq. (5.61) in terms of pressures and temperatures as

$$\frac{v_2}{v_1} = \left(\frac{p_1}{p_2}\right)^{1/k} \tag{5.62}$$

and $p_1 v_1 / T_1 = p_2 v_2 / T_2$ from Eq. (5.9). Therefore,

$$\left(\frac{p_1}{p_2} \right) \left(\frac{T_2}{T_1} \right) = \left(\frac{p_1}{p_2} \right)^{1/k}$$

and rearranging

$$\frac{T_1}{T_2} = \left(\frac{p_1}{p_2} \right)^{(k-1)/k} \tag{5.63}$$

Similarly, we obtain the p,v relation from Eq. (5.61) as

$$\frac{p_1}{p_2} = \left(\frac{v_2}{v_1} \right)^k \quad \text{or} \quad p_1 v_1^k = p_2 v_2^k \tag{5.64}$$

From Eq. (5.9) we have $p_1/p_2 = (v_2/v_1)(T_1/T_2)$. Substitution into Eq. (5.64) yields

$$\frac{T_1}{T_2} = \left(\frac{v_2}{v_1} \right)^{k-1} \tag{5.65}$$

Equations (5.61), (5.63), and (5.65) define both the state and path of an ideal gas undergoing an isentropic change.

Since the energy interchange as heat is zero and there is a finite change in temperature, the specific heat for this process must be zero. Notice that the process specific heat is defined by the path and differs from the specific heat at constant pressure or the specific heat at constant volume. These other specific heats serve to define the enthalpy and internal energy of the gas at the state conditions at the end points of the path.

By the identification of pv^k with pv^n, the exponent n must equal k for the isentropic process.

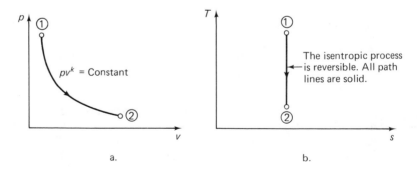

a.   b.

Figure 5.14 Isentropic process

The work of the nonflow process shown in Fig. 5.14 can be evaluated by noticing that the work done in a nonflow process in the absence of heat transfer equals the change in internal energy. Therefore,

$$\text{work} = u_1 - u_2$$

$$\text{work} = c_v(T_1 - T_2)$$

But

$$c_v = \frac{R}{J(k-1)}$$

Therefore,

$$\frac{W}{J} = \frac{R(T_1 - T_2)}{J(k-1)} \quad \text{or} \quad \frac{R(T_2 - T_1)}{J(1-k)} \; \text{Btu/lb} \qquad (5.66)$$

Again note that in SI units the conversion factor J is not included.

ILLUSTRATIVE PROBLEM 5.23

One pound of air expands isentropically from 5 atm absolute to 1 atm absolute. If the initial temperature is 1000°R, determine the final state and the work done by the air if k is 1.4 over this range of temperature.

Solution

From Eq. (5.63),

$$T_2 = T_1 \left(\frac{p_2}{p_1} \right)^{(k-1)/k}$$

$$= 1000 \left(\frac{1}{5} \right)^{(1.4-1)/1.4} = 632°\text{R}$$

From Eq. (5.66),

$$\text{work} = \frac{R}{J} \frac{(T_2 - T_1)}{(1-k)} = \frac{1545(632 - 1000)}{29(778)(1 - 1.4)} = 63 \; \text{Btu/lb} \quad \text{(out)}$$

ILLUSTRATIVE PROBLEM 5.24

If the initial temperature in Illustrative Problem 5.23 is 500°C, determine the final state and the work done.

Solution

$$T_2 = T_1\left(\frac{p_2}{p_1}\right)^{(k-1)/k}$$

$$= (500 + 273)\left(\frac{1}{5}\right)^{(1.4-1)/1.4} = 488.06 \text{ K} = 215.06°\text{C}$$

$$\text{work} = \frac{R(T_2 - T_1)}{(1-k)} = \frac{8.314}{29}\left(\frac{215.06 - 500}{1 - 1.4}\right) = 204.2 \frac{\text{kJ}}{\text{kg}} \quad (\text{out})$$

5.5e Polytropic Process

Each of the processes discussed in this section can have its path equation written in terms of

$$pv^n = \text{constant} \qquad (5.67)$$

which is known as the polytropic equation and is used, in general, to characterize any mechanically reversible nonadiabatic process. It is also used as an approximation for real processes. A diagram of the process is shown in Fig. 5.15. To recapitulate those processes already considered, see Table 5.3. If each of these processes is plotted on pv and Ts coordinates (basically the superposition of Figs. 5.11 to 5.14), it is possible to show the entire spectrum of n values (see Figs. 5.16 and 5.17).

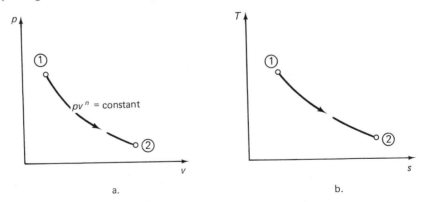

Figure 5.15 Polytropic process

TABLE 5.3

Process	n
Constant volume	∞
Constant pressure	0
Isothermal	1
Isentropic	k
Polytropic	$-\infty$ to $+\infty$

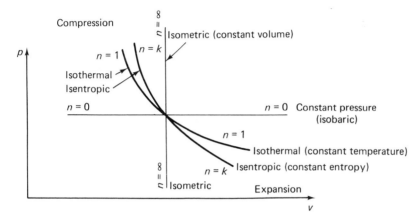

Figure 5.16 Polytropic processes

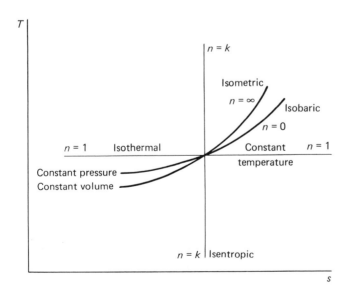

Figure 5.17 Polytropic processes

By comparison the pressure, temperature, and volume relations for the polytropic process corresponding to Eqs. (5.62), (5.63), and (5.65) can be written as follows:

$$\frac{v_2}{v_1} = \left(\frac{p_1}{p_2}\right)^{1/n} \tag{5.68}$$

$$\frac{p_1}{p_2} = \left(\frac{v_2}{v_1}\right)^{n} \quad \text{or} \quad p_1 v_1^n = p_2 v_2^n \tag{5.69}$$

$$\frac{T_1}{T_2} = \left(\frac{p_1}{p_2}\right)^{(n-1)/n} \tag{5.70}$$

$$\frac{T_1}{T_2} = \left(\frac{v_2}{v_1}\right)^{n-1} \tag{5.71}$$

The work of the polytropic process can be determined by the same method used to obtain the work of the isentropic process. The result is

$$\text{work} = \frac{p_2 v_2 - p_1 v_1}{1 - n} \tag{5.72}$$

and in terms of thermal units

$$\text{work} = \frac{R(T_2 - T_1)}{J(1 - n)} \tag{5.73}$$

To determine the specific heat of the polytropic process, we shall use the energy equation for the nonflow process:

$$q = (u_2 - u_1) + \frac{W}{J} \tag{5.74}$$

It is convenient to define the heat transferred by Eq. (5.75)

$$c_n(T_2 - T_1) = q \tag{5.75}$$

where c_n is the polytropic specific heat. Substitution of Eqs. (5.73) and (5.75) into Eq. (5.74) yields

$$c_n(T_2 - T_1) = c_v(T_2 - T_1) + \frac{R}{J} \frac{(T_2 - T_1)}{(1 - n)} \tag{5.76}$$

$$c_n = c_v + \frac{R}{J(1 - n)} \tag{5.77}$$

and

$$c_n = \frac{Jc_v - nJc_v + R}{J(1 - n)} \tag{5.78}$$

Using Eq. (5.29),

$$c_n = \frac{c_p - nc_v}{(1-n)} \qquad (5.79)$$

or

$$c_n = c_v\left(\frac{k-n}{1-n}\right) \qquad (5.80)$$

Notice that c_n can be positive or negative, depending upon the values of n and k.

Substitution of c_n into Eq. (5.75) gives the heat transferred in the polytropic process:

$$q = c_v\left(\frac{k-n}{1-n}\right)(T_2 - T_1) \qquad (5.81)$$

The change in entropy for the polytropic process can be arrived at by using Eq. (5.30) and assuming that c_n is independent of temperature:

$$\Delta s = \frac{q}{T} = \frac{c_n \Delta T}{T} \qquad (5.82)$$

Evaluating Eq. (5.82) as previously done by summing the $\Delta T/T$ yields

$$\Delta s = c_n \ln\left(\frac{T_2}{T_1}\right) \qquad (5.83)$$

ILLUSTRATIVE PROBLEM 5.25

For an internal combustion engine the expansion process can be characterized by $pv^{1.3} = $ constant. If the ratio of specific heats for this gas is 1.4, and the specific heat at constant pressure is 0.24 Btu/lb°F, determine the heat transferred as the gas expands from 1500°R to 600°R. Also evaluate the work done and the change in entropy for the process. R equals 53.3 for this gas.

Solution

From

$$\frac{c_p}{c_v} = k, \qquad c_v = \frac{0.24}{1.4} = 0.171$$

Therefore,

$$c_n = c_v\left(\frac{k-n}{1-n}\right) = 0.171\left(\frac{1.4-1.3}{1-1.3}\right) = -0.0570 \text{ Btu/lb °F}$$

The negative sign of c_n indicates that either the heat transfer for the process comes from the system or there is a negative temperature change while heat is transferred to the system.

The heat transferred is $c_n(T_2 - T_1)$. Therefore,

$$q = -0.0570(600 - 1500) = 51.3 \text{ Btu/lb} \quad \text{(to the system)}$$

The work done can be found using Eq. (5.73), giving us

$$\text{work} = \frac{R}{J} \frac{(T_2 - T_1)}{(1-n)} = \frac{53.3}{778} \left(\frac{600 - 1500}{1 - 1.3} \right)$$

$$= 205.5 \text{ Btu/lb} \quad \text{(from the system)}$$

The change in entropy Δs is given by

$$\Delta s = -0.0570 \ln \left(\frac{600}{1500} \right)$$

$$= -0.0570 \left(-\ln \frac{1500}{600} \right) = 0.0522 \text{ Btu/lb } °\text{R}$$

It must be kept in mind that in deriving the equations in this chapter the specific heats were assumed to be constants, independent of temperature. The same assumption was made for k. When the variation of these quantities does not permit us to assume an essentially constant average value, the methods of the calculus must be employed. For these techniques the student is referred to the references given at the end of this chapter.

Table 5.4 summarizes the results of the derivations made for nonflow processes. In this table the enthalpy and internal energies have also been tabulated, and it will be noted that these quantities depend only on the end states of the specified process and are independent of the path. This table has been included as a convenient reference. The student is cautioned against memorizing the table or using it without fully understanding the restrictions involved in each of the processes discussed.

The change in enthalpy and the change in internal energy for the ideal gas are useful quantities, and we can obtain these readily from the previous considerations in this chapter. Thus for enthalpy we can write

$$h_2 - h_1 = c_p(T_2 - T_1) \tag{5.84}$$

From Eq. (5.9) we have $T = pv/R$ and from Eq. (5.29) we have $c_p = R/J(k-1)$. Substitution of these quantities in Eq. (5.84) gives us

$$h_2 - h_1 = \frac{R}{J} \left(\frac{k}{k-1} \right) \left(\frac{p_2 v_2}{R} - \frac{p_1 v_1}{R} \right) \tag{5.85}$$

TABLE 5.4

IDEAL GAS RELATIONS (PER UNIT MASS OF GAS)

Process	Constant Volume V = constant (isometric)	Constant Pressure p = constant (isobaric or isopiestic)	Isothermal T = constant	Isentropic s = constant	Polytropic pv^n = constant
p, v, T	$\dfrac{T_1}{T_2} = \dfrac{p_1}{p_2}$	$\dfrac{T_1}{T_2} = \dfrac{v_1}{v_2}$	$p_1v_1 = p_2v_2$	$p_1v_1^k = p_2v_2^k$ $\dfrac{T_1}{T_2} = \left(\dfrac{v_2}{v_1}\right)^{k-1}$ $\dfrac{T_1}{T_2} = \left(\dfrac{p_1}{p_2}\right)^{(k-1)/k}$	$p_1v_1^n = p_2v_2^n$ $\dfrac{T_1}{T_2} = \left(\dfrac{v_2}{v_1}\right)^{n-1}$ $\dfrac{T_1}{T_2} = \left(\dfrac{p_1}{p_2}\right)^{(n-1)/n}$
W	0	$p(v_2 - v_1)$	$p_1v_1 \ln\dfrac{v_2}{v_1}$	$\dfrac{p_2v_2 - p_1v_1}{1-k}$	$\dfrac{p_2v_2 - p_1v_1}{1-n}$
$u_2 - u_1$	$c_v(T_2 - T_1)$	$c_v(T_2 - T_1)$	0	$c_v(T_2 - T_1)$	$c_v(T_2 - T_1)$
q	$c_v(T_2 - T_1)$	$c_p(T_2 - T_1)$	$p_1v_1 \ln\dfrac{v_2}{v_1}$	0	$c_n(T_2 - T_1)$
n	∞	0	1	k	$-\infty$ to $+\infty$
c	c_v	c_p	∞	0	$c_n = c_v\left(\dfrac{k-n}{1-n}\right)$
$h_2 - h_1$	$c_p(T_2 - T_1)$	$c_p(T_2 - T_1)$	0	$c_p(T_2 - T_1)$	$c_p(T_2 - T_1)$
$s_2 - s_1$	$c_v \ln\dfrac{T_2}{T_1}$	$c_p \ln\dfrac{T_2}{T_1}$	$R\left(\ln\dfrac{v_2}{v_1}\right)$	0	$c_n \ln\dfrac{T_2}{T_1}$

Note: The conversion factor J has been omitted from all equations. Care should be taken when using this table with English units.

231

Simplifying,

$$h_2 - h_1 = \frac{k}{J(k-1)}(p_2 v_2 - p_1 v_1) \tag{5.86}$$

or $\qquad h_2 - h_1 = \frac{k}{k-1}(p_2 v_2 - p_1 v_1)$ in SI units $\qquad$ (5.86a)

Similarly, for internal energy

$$u_2 - u_1 = c_v(T_2 - T_1)$$

and $\qquad u_2 - u_1 = \frac{1}{J(k-1)}(p_2 v_2 - p_1 v_1) \tag{5.87}$

or $\qquad u_2 - u_1 = \frac{1}{k-1}(p_2 v_2 - p_1 v_1)$ in SI units $\qquad$ (5.87a)

As a check on Eqs. (5.86) and (5.87), note that the ratio of $h_2 - h_1$ to $u_2 - u_1$ is the ratio of c_p to c_v, which it should be.

5.6 THE GAS TABLES

The *Gas Tables* provide a convenient and most useful set of tables for the computation of gas processes. By designating Eq. (5.9) as the equation of state, it has been possible to express the various thermodynamic properties of these gases in terms of their temperatures. For air at 32°F, the error in using this equation of state is of the order of 1 percent at 300 psia and only 0.1 percent at atmospheric pressure. In addition to using the equation of state of an ideal gas, the specific heats listed in these tables were based on spectroscopic data at zero pressure. The zero of entropy and enthalpy were chosen to be zero at zero degrees absolute. Use of the specific heats at zero pressure is equivalent to the assumption that the specific heat is a function of temperature only.

The outline of the *Gas Tables* can be easily developed by considering that the specific heats are temperature functions. The enthalpy values are listed as functions of the absolute temperature, and the change in enthalpy for a process is just the difference for the values tabulated at the final and initial temperatures. Since ideal gas relations are used,

$$u_2 - u_1 = (h_2 - h_1) - \frac{R}{J}(T_2 - T_1) \tag{5.88}$$

The general expression for the change in entropy of an ideal gas with a variable specific heat can be obtained, and the change in entropy per unit mass between states 1 and 2 is then

$$s_2 - s_1 = \phi_2 - \phi_1 - \frac{R}{J} \ln \frac{p_2}{p_1} \qquad (5.89)$$

where ϕ is a function of temperature given in the tables for each gas at each temperature. For an isentropic change,

$$\ln \frac{p_2}{p_1} = \frac{J}{R}(\phi_2 - \phi_1) \qquad (5.90)$$

The *Gas Tables*, at this point, define $p_2/p_1 = p_r$, where p_r is the relative pressure, and also define the relative volume as $v_r = \ln(v_2/v_1)$ for an isentropic process.

The *Gas Tables* also have adopted the definition that

$$v_r = \frac{RT}{p_r} \qquad (5.91)$$

with the units of R selected so that v_r is the specific volume in cubic feet per pound when the pressure is in psia for those tables based on a unit mass. When the mass is the pound mole, v_r is the molal specific volume in cubic feet per pound mole when the pressure is psia.

The following problems will serve to illustrate the use of the abridged air table, which will be found in Appendix 3.

ILLUSTRATIVE PROBLEM 5.26

Determine the change in enthalpy, internal energy, and entropy when air is heated at constant pressure from 500° to 1000°R.

Solution

From the table at 1000°R		From the table at 500°R	
$h =$	240.98 Btu/lb	$h =$	119.48 Btu/lb
$u =$	172.43 Btu/lb	$u =$	85.20 Btu/lb
$\phi =$	0.75042 Btu/lb °R	$\phi =$	0.58233 Btu/lb °R

The change in enthalpy is $h_2 - h_1 = 240.98 - 119.48 = 121.5$ Btu/lb. The change in internal energy is $u_2 - u_1 = 172.43 - 85.20 = 87.23$ Btu/lb. Since in the constant-pressure process $-R\ln(p_2/p_1)$ is zero,

$$\Delta s = \phi_2 - \phi_1 = 0.75042 - 0.58233 = 0.16809 \text{ Btu/lb °R}$$

ILLUSTRATIVE PROBLEM 5.27

Solve Illustrative Problem 5.23 using the *Gas Tables*.

Solution

In this problem the air expands from 5 atmospheres absolute to 1 atm absolute from an initial temperature of 1000 °R. At 1000 °R, $p_r = 12.298$ and $h = 240.98$ Btu/lb. The value of the final $p_r = 12.298/5 = 2.4596$. Interpolation in the air table yields the following:

T	p_r
620	2.249
	2.4596
640	2.514

$$620 + \frac{2.4596 - 2.249}{2.514 - 2.249} \times 20 = 635.9 \quad \text{or} \quad 636°\text{R}$$

The work done in an isentropic nonflow expansion is

$$\text{work} = u_1 - u_2 = 172.43 - 108.52 = 63.91 \text{ Btu/lb}$$

where the value of u_2 is obtained by interpolation at 636°R, and the value of u_1 is read from the air table at 1000°R.

The fact that the results found by using the *Gas Tables* agree well with those found from the ideal gas relations is not a coincidence. In all these problems the pressures were low and the temperatures were relatively high. Under these conditions it would be expected that these gases would behave much like ideal gases. The principal differences are caused by the fact that the specific heats vary with temperature. The *Gas Tables* take this variation into account and reduce the work of computations considerably.

5.7 GAS FLOW PROCESSES

In recent years, with the advent of missiles, high-speed aircraft, and the flow of gases in such devices as gas turbines and rocket exhaust nozzles, the area of fluid mechanics denoted as compressible flow has taken on increased importance. Many devices and flow regimes can be treated to a reasonable approximation by considering the flow to be one dimensional; that is, fluid properties are uniform over any cross section. Figure 5.18 shows a modern, high-speed, high-performance military airplane which can achieve speeds in excess of twice the local speed of sound. The speed of sound (acoustic velocity)

Figure 5.18 F-105 Fighter-Bomber, capable of speeds in excess of Mach 2 (Courtesy of Fairchild Republic Company)

in an ideal gas is given by

$$V_a = \sqrt{gkRT} \qquad (5.92)$$

where V_a is the speed of sound in feet per second, $g = 32.2$ ft/sec^2, k is the ratio of c_p/c_v, and T is the absolute temperature, in degrees Rankine. For air

$$V_a = 49.1\sqrt{T} \ \text{ft/sec} \qquad (5.93)$$

when T is in degrees Rankine. In SI units,

$$V_a = \sqrt{kRT} = 20.05\sqrt{T} \ \text{m/s} \qquad (5.93a)$$

when T is in degrees Kelvin.

ILLUSTRATIVE PROBLEM 5.28

Determine the velocity of sound in air at 1000°F. Using the data in Appendix III, determine the velocity of sound in hydrogen at this same temperature.

Solution

The velocity of sound in air at 1000°F is

$$V_a = 49.1\sqrt{(1000 + 460)} = 1876 \text{ ft/sec}$$

Hydrogen has a specific heat ratio of 1.41 and $R = 766.53$. Therefore,

$$\frac{V_{a_{\text{hydrogen}}}}{V_{a_{\text{air}}}} = \sqrt{\frac{(Rk)_{\text{hydrogen}}}{(Rk)_{\text{air}}}} = \sqrt{\frac{766.53 \times 1.41}{53.36 \times 1.40}} = 3.8$$

$$V_{a_{\text{hydrogen}}} = 3.8 V_{a_{\text{air}}} = 3.8 \times 1876 = 7130 \text{ ft/sec}$$

In the subsequent work in this chapter it will be found that the Mach number is an important parameter. It is defined as the ratio of the velocity at a point in a fluid to the velocity of sound at that point at a given instant of time. Denoting the local velocity by V and the velocity of sound as V_a.

$$M = \frac{V}{V_a} \qquad (5.94)$$

and

$$M^2 = \frac{V^2}{gkRT} \qquad (5.95)$$

where Eq. (5.95) is applicable only to an ideal gas. In SI, g is omitted.

ILLUSTRATIVE PROBLEM 5.29

Air is flowing in a duct at atmospheric pressure with a velocity of 1500 ft/sec. If the air temperature is 200°F, what is the Mach number?

Solution

The velocity of sound in air at 200°F is

$$V_a = 49.1\sqrt{T} = 49.1\sqrt{(200 + 460)} = 1262 \text{ ft/sec}$$

The Mach number is

$$M = \frac{V}{V_a} = \frac{1500}{1262} = 1.189$$

5.7a Adiabatic Flow

When studying the steady flow processes of gases, it is necessary to utilize the continuity equation, the equation of state, and the appropriate energy equation. Consider the special case of adiabatic flow without shaft work or elevation change. For this process the first law of thermodynamics yields

$$h + \frac{V^2}{2gJ} = h_1 + \frac{V_1^2}{2gJ} = h^0 \qquad (5.96)$$

Equation (5.96) defines the term stagnation enthalpy h^0. This terminology is best illustrated by referring to Fig. 5.19. At section "0" it is assumed that the

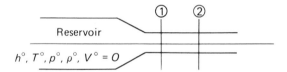

Figure 5.19 Stagnation conditions

area can be considered infinite or that the velocity is essentially zero. Thus from Eq. (5.96) the stagnation enthalpy is $h + V^2/2gJ$; $h_1^0 = h_1 + V_1^2/2gJ$ and $h^0 = h_1^0 = h_2^0 = $ constant. The stagnation enthalpy (or total enthalpy) is, therefore, a constant by definition for the process in question if it is adiabatic, if no work is done on or by the fluid, and if the fluid does not change in elevation.

The introduction of the terminology of the preceding paragraph requires a brief explanation. By referring to Fig. 5.20 it will be noted that an isentropic compression is shown on enthalpy–entropy coordinates by the line A, B. Since Eq. (5.96) is applicable, it follows that the change in enthalpy indicated in the diagram must equal $V^2/2gJ$ since the velocity at O conditions is zero. The final state (the O state) is commonly known as the *total*, state and the pressure, temperature, and density are known, respectively, as the total pressure, total temperature, and total density.

However, if the process is adiabatic but not isentropic, it may be shown as in Fig. 5.21. The final enthalpy will be the same as that for the isentropic case, but the entropy will be greater and consequently the final pressure at the end of the actual process will be less. The end state of the nonisentropic (actual)

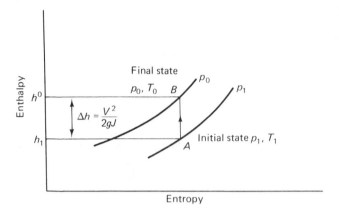

Figure 5.20 Isentropic stagnation

process is commonly called the *stagnation state*, and the properties at this state are called *stagnation properties*. By noting that the final enthalpies shown in Figs. 5.20 and 5.21 are equal, either the terminology of total or stagnation enthalpy for this state is correct. Again, for the ideal gas certain relevant and important conclusions may be drawn from this discussion. The final temperature of each process, that is, the total temperature and the stagnation temperatures, will be equal. The final pressures will not, in general, be equal. To recapitulate, the total state corresponds to an isentropic stagnation process and the stagnation state to an adiabatic process. Caution should be exercised in the use of this terminology. The literature contains many examples of differing definitions for these properties, and all terms used should be carefully defined.

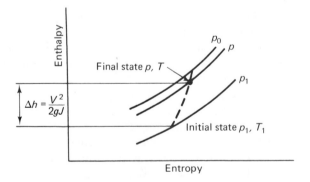

Figure 5.21 Adiabatic stagnation

ILLUSTRATIVE PROBLEM 5.30

Assume that a fluid is flowing in a device and that at some cross section the fluid velocity is 1000 ft/sec. If the fluid is saturated steam having an enthalpy of 1204.4 Btu/lb, determine its total enthalpy.

Solution

From the previous paragraph we can simply write

$$h^0 - h = \frac{V^2}{2gJ}$$

For this problem

$$h^0 - h = \frac{(1000)^2}{2 \times 32.2 \times 778} = 20 \text{ Btu/lb}$$

and

$$h^0 = 1204.4 + 20 = 1224.4 \text{ Btu/lb}$$

It will be noted for this problem that, if the initial velocity had been 100 ft/sec, Δh would have been 0.2 Btu/lb, and for most practical purposes the total properties and those of the flowing fluid would have been essentially the same. Thus for low-velocity fluids the difference in total and stream properties can be neglected.

5.7b Isentropic Flow of an Ideal Gas

For the isentropic flow of an ideal gas it is necessary only to recall that ideal refers to the equation of state of the gas and isentropic to the equation of the path. For an ideal gas with constant specific heat, it is possible to write the enthalpy (measured from a base of absolute zero) as

$$h^0 = c_p T^0 \tag{5.97}$$

Equation (5.96) can be written in the following form:

$$V^2 = 2gJ(h^0 - h_1) = 2gJc_p(T^0 - T_1) \tag{5.98}$$

By applying the equations of path and state to Eq. (5.98) and simplifying,

$$V_1 = \left[2gJc_p T^0 \left(1 - \left\{ \frac{p_1}{p_0} \right\}^{(k-1)/k} \right) \right]^{1/2} = \left[\frac{2gk}{k-1} \frac{p^0}{\rho^0} \left(1 - \left\{ \frac{p_1}{p_0} \right\}^{(k-1)/k} \right) \right]^{1/2}$$

$$\tag{5.99}$$

5.7c Converging Nozzle

We apply Eq. (5.99) to the throat of the section of minimum area *tt* (Fig. 5.22) and let p_t be the pressure at that section. The mass of gas passing through the

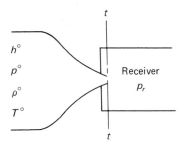

Figure 5.22 Converging nozzle

section tt per unit time is

$$\dot{m} = \rho_t A_t V_t = A_t \rho^0 \left(\frac{p_t}{p^0} \right)^{1/k} (V_t)$$

$$= A_t \left\{ \frac{2gk}{k-1} p^0 \rho^0 \left[\left(\frac{p_t}{p^0} \right)^{2/k} - \left(\frac{p_t}{p^0} \right)^{(k+1)/k} \right] \right\}^{1/2} \qquad (5.100)$$

The variation of $\dot{m}$ with p/p^0 is given by the curved line (partly dotted and partly solid) in Fig. 5.23, which shows that $\dot{m}$ reaches a maximum value for a

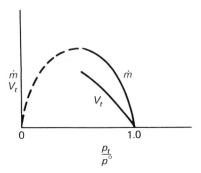

Figure 5.23 Mass flow variation in a nozzle

certain pressure ratio $p_t/p^0 = p_c/p^0$, where p_c is called the critical pressure and can be determined as follows: m is at its maximum when

$$\left[\left(\frac{p_t}{p^0} \right)^{2/k} - \left(\frac{p_t}{p^0} \right)^{(k+1)/k} \right]$$

is at a maximum.

By performing the required operations, using the methods of calculus, it is found that

$$\frac{p_t}{p^0} = \frac{p_c}{p^0} = \left(\frac{2}{k+1}\right)^{k/(k-1)} \qquad (5.101)$$

For air with $k = 1.4$, $p_c/p^0 = 0.53$. For superheated steam with $k = 1.3$, $p_t/p^0 = 0.546 = p_c/p^0$.

At the critical pressure ratio,

$$\frac{T_t}{T_0} = \frac{2}{k+1} \qquad (5.102)$$

$$\frac{V_{a_t}}{V_{a_0}} = \sqrt{\frac{2}{k+1}} \qquad (5.103)$$

$$V_t = \sqrt{\frac{2gk}{k+1}(p^0/\rho^0)} = \sqrt{\frac{2}{k+1}}\,(V_{a_0}) = V_{a_t} \qquad (5.104)$$

$$\dot{m}_{max} = A_t\left(\frac{2}{k+1}\right)^{1/(k-1)}\sqrt{\frac{2gk}{k+1}(p^0\rho^0)} \qquad (5.105)$$

In general, also,

$$\left(\frac{A}{A_t}\right)^2 = \frac{k-1}{2}\left\{\frac{\left(\dfrac{2}{k+1}\right)^{(k+1)/(k-1)}}{\left(\dfrac{p}{p^0}\right)^{2/k}\left[1 - \left(\dfrac{p}{p^0}\right)^{(k-1)/k}\right]}\right\} \qquad (5.106)$$

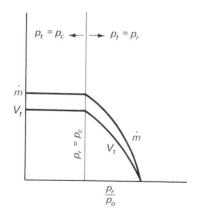

Figure 5.24 Choked flow

From the foregoing we can see that for a given nozzle throat area there is a maximum mass rate of flow of fluid that can pass through the nozzle. When the pressure ratio p_r/p^0 is above the critical value, $\dot{m}$ increases with decreasing p_t. After p_t reaches p_c, there is no further increase in $\dot{m}$, and the flow is said to be choked. Under such conditions the fluid leaving the nozzle decreases in pressure from p_c to p_r through irreversible flow processes. These flow conditions are shown in Fig. 5.24.

5.7d Converging and Diverging Nozzles (de Laval Nozzle)

In the preceding discussion it was shown for a converging nozzle that the maximum velocity the fluid will attain at the exit section is the local sonic velocity, and that the minimum pressure corresponding to sonic velocity at the exit is the critical pressure. To obtain a higher velocity and lower pressure at

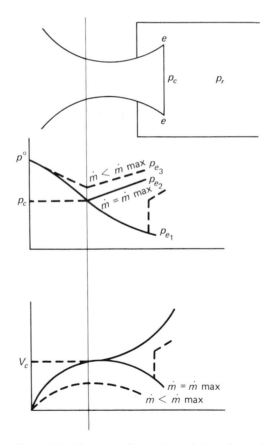

Figure 5.25 Flow conditions in a de Laval nozzle

the exit section of a nozzle, a divergent portion is added downstream of the throat section. The fluid continues to expand in the divergent portion, reaching V_{e_1} and p_{e_1} at the exit. The fluid could also be compressed in the divergent portion, reaching V_{e_2} and p_{e_2} at the exit. The process in the nozzle is determined by the pressure in the receiver. If $p_r = p_{e_1}$, the former occurs. If $p_r = p_{e_2}$, the latter occurs. If p_r lies between the two, the fluid would first follow the former and reach p_r at the nozzle exit, with a normal shock somewhere in the divergent portion of the nozzle or with compression waves in the receiver (see Fig. 5.25).

The foregoing discussion is for a mass flow rate in the nozzle equal to the maximum value. If the weight flow is below this value, the velocity at the throat is subsonic, and at the exit section of the nozzle $p = p_{e_3}$ and $V = V_{e_3}$.

To facilitate the use of many of the equations already developed, they have been placed into nondimensional form in terms of only two variables, namely the Mach number and the ratio of specific heats. Tables 30 and 53 of *Gas Tables* list the results of numerical computations of these one-dimensional compressible flow functions. In these tables the superscript * refers to conditions in which $M = 1$, and the subscript $_0$ refers to isentropic stagnation. With this notation in mind, the working nondimensional equations are

$$T_0 = \text{constant} = T_0^* \tag{5.107}$$

$$T^* = \text{constant} \tag{5.108}$$

$$p^0 = \text{constant} = p_0^* \tag{5.109}$$

$$p^* = \text{constant} \tag{5.110}$$

$$M^* = \frac{V}{V^*} = M \left\{ \frac{k-1}{2 \left[1 + \frac{1}{2}(k-1)M^2 \right]} \right\}^{1/2} \tag{5.111}$$

$$\frac{A}{A^*} = \frac{1}{M} \left\{ \frac{2 \left[1 + \frac{1}{2}(k-1)M^2 \right]^{(k+1)/2(k-1)}}{k+1} \right\} \tag{5.112}$$

$$\frac{T}{T^*} = \frac{k+1}{2 \left[1 + \frac{1}{2}(k-1)M^2 \right]} \tag{5.113}$$

$$\frac{\rho}{\rho^*} = \left\{ \frac{k+1}{2 \left[1 + \frac{1}{2}(k-1)M^2 \right]} \right\}^{1/(k-1)} \tag{5.114}$$

$$\frac{p}{p^*} = \left\{ \frac{k+1}{2 \left[1 + \frac{1}{2}(k-1)M^2 \right]} \right\}^{(k/k-1)} \tag{5.115}$$

Table 5.5 is abridged from Table 30 of the *Gas Tables*, and all the foregoing nondimensional equations are tabulated as functions of Mach number. The convenience of these equations as well as their use is illustrated by Illustrative Problems 5.31 and 5.32. The application of Table 5.5 is also demonstrated in these problems.

TABLE 5.5

ONE-DIMENSIONAL ISENTROPIC
COMPRESSIBLE FLOW FUNCTIONS FOR AN
IDEAL GAS WITH CONSTANT SPECIFIC HEAT
AND MOLECULAR WEIGHT AND $k=1.4$[†]

M	M^*	$\dfrac{A}{A^*}$	$\dfrac{p}{p_0}$	$\dfrac{\rho}{\rho_0}$	$\dfrac{T}{T_0}$
0	0	∞	1.00000	1.00000	1.00000
0.10	0.10943	5.8218	0.99303	0.99502	0.99800
0.20	0.21822	2.9635	0.97250	0.98027	0.99206
0.30	0.32572	2.0351	0.93947	0.95638	0.98232
0.40	0.43133	1.5901	0.89562	0.92428	0.96899
0.50	0.53452	1.3398	0.84302	0.88517	0.95238
0.60	0.63480	1.1882	0.78400	0.84045	0.93284
0.70	0.73179	1.09437	0.72092	0.79158	0.91075
0.80	0.82514	1.03823	0.65602	0.74000	0.88652
0.90	0.91460	1.00886	0.59126	0.68704	0.86058
1.00	1.00000	1.00000	0.52828	0.63394	0.83333
1.10	1.08124	1.00793	0.46835	0.58169	0.80515
1.20	1.1583	1.03044	0.41238	0.53114	0.77640
1.30	1.2311	1.06631	0.36092	0.48291	0.74738
1.40	1.2999	1.1149	0.31424	0.42742	0.71839
1.50	1.3646	1.1762	0.27240	0.39498	0.68965
1.60	1.4254	1.2502	0.23527	0.35573	0.66138
1.70	1.4825	1.3376	0.20259	0.31969	0.63372
1.80	1.5360	1.4390	0.17404	0.28682	0.60680
1.90	1.5861	1.5552	0.14924	0.25699	0.58072
2.00	1.6330	1.6875	0.12780	0.23005	0.55556
2.10	1.6769	1.8369	0.10935	0.20580	0.53135
2.20	1.7179	2.0050	0.09352	0.18405	0.50813
2.30	1.7563	2.1931	0.07997	0.16458	0.48591
2.40	1.7922	2.4031	0.06840	0.14720	0.46468
2.50	1.8258	2.6367	0.05853	0.13169	0.44444
2.60	1.8572	2.8960	0.05012	0.11787	0.42517
2.70	1.8865	3.1830	0.04295	0.10557	0.40684
2.80	1.9140	3.5001	0.03685	0.09462	0.38941
2.90	1.9398	3.8498	0.03165	0.08489	0.37286

TABLE 5.5 CONT'D

M	$M*$	$\dfrac{A}{A*}$	$\dfrac{p}{p_0}$	$\dfrac{\rho}{\rho_0}$	$\dfrac{T}{T_0}$
3.00	1.9640	4.2346	0.02722	0.07623	0.35714
3.50	2.0642	6.7896	0.01311	0.04523	0.28986
4.00	2.1381	10.719	0.00658	0.02766	0.23810
4.50	2.1936	16.562	0.00346	0.01745	0.19802
5.00	2.2361	25.000	$189(10)^{-5}$	0.01134	0.16667
6.00	2.2953	53.180	$633(10)^{-6}$	0.00519	0.12195
7.00	2.3333	104.143	$242(10)^{-6}$	0.00261	0.09259
8.00	2.3591	190.109	$102(10)^{-6}$	0.00141	0.07246
9.00	2.3772	327.189	$474(10)^{-7}$	0.000815	0.05814
10.00	2.3904	535.938	$236(10)^{-7}$	0.000495	0.04762
∞	2.4495	∞	0	0	0

†*Abridged from Table 30 in Gas Tables by Joseph H. Keenan and Joseph Kaye, John Wiley & Sons, Inc., New York, 1948.*

ILLUSTRATIVE PROBLEM 5.31

An isentropic convergent nozzle is used to evacuate air from a test cell that is maintained at stagnation pressure and temperature of 300 psia and 800°R, respectively. The nozzle has inlet and outlet areas of 2.035 and 1 ft², respectively. Constant-pressure specific heat is 0.24, the specific heat ratio is 1.4, and the gas constant R in consistent units is 53.35. Calculate the pressure, temperature, velocity, Mach number, and weight flow at the inlet and pressure and velocity if the Mach number at the outlet is unity.

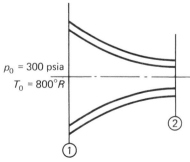

p_0 = 300 psia
T_0 = 800°R

M = 1, therefore state ② is the * state

Figure 5.26 Illustrative Problem 5.31

Solution

Refer to Fig. 5.26. For $k = 1.4$ and $M = 1$ (Table 5.5),

$$\frac{T^*}{T_0} = 0.8333$$

$$T^* = 800(0.8333) = 686.6°R$$

and
$$V_{a_t} = \sqrt{gkRT^*} = \sqrt{32.2 \times 1.4 \times 53.35 \times 686.6}$$
$$= 1270 \text{ ft/sec} = V_2$$

For

$$\frac{A}{A^*} = 2.035$$

the tables yield $M_1 = 0.3$ and

$$\frac{p^*}{p_0} = 0.52828, \qquad p^* = 300(0.52828) = 158.5 \text{ psia}$$

Also,

$$\frac{T_1}{T_0} = 0.98232 \quad \text{and} \quad \frac{p_1}{p_0} = 0.93947$$

Therefore,

$$T_1 = 800(0.98232) = 785.9°R$$

and
$$p_1 = 300(0.93947) = 281.8 \text{ psia}$$

From the inlet conditions derived,

$$V_{a_1} = \sqrt{gkRT_1} = \sqrt{32.2 \times 1.4 \times 53.35 \times 785.9} = 1375 \text{ ft/sec}$$

$$V_1 = M_1 V_{a_1} = 0.3(1375) = 412 \text{ ft/sec}$$

The specific volume at inlet is found from the equation of state for an ideal gas:

$$v = \frac{RT_1}{p_1} = \frac{53.35 \times 785.9}{281.8 \times 144} = 1.035 \text{ ft}^3/\text{lb}$$

and
$$\dot{m} = \rho A V = \frac{1}{1.035} \times 2.035 \times 412 = 810 \text{ lb/sec}$$

ILLUSTRATIVE PROBLEM 5.32

At a certain section of an air stream, the Mach number is 2.5, the stagnation temperature is 560°R, and the static pressure is 0.5 atm. Assuming that the flow is steady isentropic and follows one-dimensional theory, calculate the following at the point at which M is 2.5: (1) temperature, (2) stagnation pressure, (3) velocity, (4) specific volume, and (5) mass velocity.

Solution

This problem will be solved by two methods (A and B).

A. *By equations:* Assume that $k = 1.4$ and $R = 53.3$:

1. From Eqs. (5.112) and (5.113),

$$\frac{T}{T^*} = \frac{k+1}{2\left[1 + \frac{1}{2}(k-1)M^2\right]}$$

but from Eq. (5.102)

$$\frac{T^*}{T_0} = \left(\frac{2}{k+1}\right)$$

Therefore,

$$\frac{T^*}{T_0} \times \frac{T}{T^*} = \frac{T}{T_0} = \frac{1}{\left[1 + \frac{1}{2}(k-1)M^2\right]}$$

and

$$T = \frac{560}{1 + \frac{1}{2}(1.4-1)(2.5)^2} = \frac{560}{2.25} = 249°R$$

2.

$$\frac{p_0}{p} = \left(\frac{T_0}{T}\right)^{k/(k-1)}, \qquad p_0 = 0.5(14.7)\left(\frac{560}{249}\right)^{1.4/(1.4-1)} = 125.5 \text{ psia}$$

3.

$$V_a = \sqrt{gkRT} = \sqrt{32.2 \times 1.4 \times 53.3 \times 249} = 49.1\sqrt{249} = 775 \text{ ft/sec}$$
$$V = MV_a = 2.5 \times 775 = 1935 \text{ ft/sec}$$

4. From the equation of state,

$$v = \frac{RT}{p} = \frac{53.3 \times 249}{0.5(14.7)(144)} = 12.55 \text{ cu ft/lb}$$

5. Mass velocity is defined as the weight flow per unit area:

$$\frac{\dot{m}}{A} = \frac{AV}{A} = \frac{V}{v} = \frac{1935}{12.55} = 154.1 \ \text{lb}/\text{ft}^2/\text{sec}$$

B. *By the Gas Tables:* At $M = 2.5$, Table 5.5 gives
1.

$$\frac{T}{T_0} = 0.44444$$

2.

$$\frac{p}{p_0} = 0.05853$$

$$T = 560(0.44444) = 249°\text{R}$$

$$p = \frac{0.5 \times 14.7}{0.05853} = 125.5 \ \text{psia}$$

3. As before, 1935 ft/sec
4. As before, 12.55 cu ft/lb
5. As before, 154.1 lb/ft^2/sec

5.7e Actual Nozzle Performance

In the preceding sections certain idealizations were made regarding the character of the flow. Real fluids flowing in real devices deviate from these ideal conditions to some extent. There will always be frictional effects at the interface between the fluid and its containing walls; real fluids have viscosity and irreversible internal effects such as turbulence; temperature differences between the fluid and the walls give rise to nonadiabatic conditions; irreversible discontinuities (shocks) produce entropy increases, etc. Although it is beyond the scope of this book to investigate each of these irreversible processes, certain overall performance parameters have been established and are commonly used to express the performance of real fluids flowing in real nozzles.

The first of these performance changes is the nozzle efficiency. This parameter may be defined as

$$\eta = \frac{\text{actual change in enthalpy}}{\text{isentropic change in enthalpy}} \qquad (5.116)$$

or $\quad \eta = \dfrac{\text{actual kinetic energy at nozzle exit}}{\text{kinetic energy at exit for an isentropic expansion}}$

$$(5.117)$$

for an expansion to the same pressure at the exit of the nozzle. It is important to note that Eqs. (5.116) and (5.117) are strictly equivalent if the velocity entering the nozzle is zero or negligible. Figure 5.27 shows an isentropic

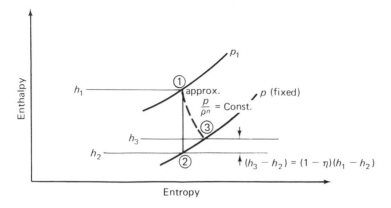

Figure 5.27 Nozzle coefficients

expansion from state ① to state ②. Also shown is a polytropic expansion characterized by a path equation $p/\rho^n =$ constant, where n is a function of the path. This approximation can be justified on the basis that the flow of a real fluid through a nozzle proceeds in such a rapid manner that it can be essentially adiabatic. Referring to Fig. 5.27, we note that the nozzle efficiency (for negligible entrance velocity) is

$$\eta = \frac{h_1 - h_3}{h_1 - h_2} \quad \text{or} \quad \frac{T_1 - T_3}{T_1 - T_2} \qquad (5.118)$$

for an ideal gas with constant specific heat. Equation (5.116) can also be written in terms of stagnation enthalpy by use of Eq. (5.96):

$$\eta = \frac{h_1^0 - h_3}{h_1^0 - h_2}$$

$$\eta = \frac{h_1 + (V_1^2/2gJ) - h_3}{h_1 + (V_1^2/2gJ) - h_2} \qquad (5.119)$$

When $V_1^2/2gJ$ is small, Eqs. (5.119) and (5.118) are essentially the same. Equation (5.119) should be used when this velocity term is not small and cannot be considered negligible compared to the other terms in these equations. Note that in SI units, the g and J are omitted.

For most nozzles, the efficiency varies from 90 percent upward, with larger nozzles having higher efficiencies. Fluids such as steam can show marked variations in efficiency, depending on the pressure and temperature range of operation. Saturated steam will immediately expand into the wet region, and a two-phase fluid composed of steam and water will result. Superheated steam will behave more nearly as an ideal gas until saturation is approached. At this time it will commence to behave as saturated steam and ultimately go into two-phase flow of steam and water. Because of this two-phase flow, it is possible for a real nozzle to have a mass flow rate exceeding that for isentropic flow between the same pressure ranges. This leads to the second performance index, the coefficient of discharge:

$$C_D = \frac{\text{actual mass rate of flow}}{\text{mass rate of flow for an isentropic expansion}} \qquad (5.120)$$

C_D can exceed unity, but it is usually of the order of 95 percent.

The foregoing parameters do not completely specify the performance of real fluids in real nozzles. This is readily shown from Eq. (5.120)

$$C_D = \frac{(\rho A V)_{\text{actual}}}{(\rho A V)_{\text{isentropic}}} = \frac{(\rho V)_{\text{actual}}}{(\rho V)_{\text{isentropic}}} \qquad (5.121)$$

Turbine designers are interested in the exit velocity of the nozzle as well as mass discharge. Taking the square root of both sides of Eq. (5.118) yields

$$\sqrt{\eta} = C_v = \frac{\sqrt{h_1 - h_3}}{\sqrt{h_1 - h_2}} = \frac{\text{actual exit velocity}}{\text{isentropic exit velocity}} \qquad (5.122)$$

for the same exit pressure. C_v is called the velocity coefficient. By defining the efficiency, coefficient of discharge, and coefficient of velocity we have thus completely specified the exit conditions in the real nozzle. The calculation of these coefficients is complex and beyond the scope of this study. For further discussions of these coefficients and tabulated values, the interested student is referred to the references at the end of this chapter.

5.8 REAL GASES

Many equations have been proposed to describe the pressure, volume, and temperature behavior of real gases where the simple equation of state for the ideal gas is inadequate. The earliest equation of state, based on elementary kinetic theory, was proposed by van der Waals. This equation is

$$\left(p + \frac{a}{v^2}\right)(v - b) = RT \qquad (5.123)$$

where v is the volume occupied by 1 lb mole of gas, R is the universal gas constant (1545), and a and b are constants for each gas. In the limit, as a and b go to zero, the van der Waals equation reduces to the ideal gas relation. This equation of state is most accurate when applied to gases that are removed from the saturated vapor state. It is possible to evaluate a and b in terms of the conditions at the critical state (the c state). When this is done, it will be found that the van der Waals equation of state can be rewritten in terms of the ratios p/p_c, T/T_c, and v/v_c. These ratios are known, respectively, as the reduced pressure, the reduced temperature, and the reduced specific volume, and are indicated by the symbols p_r, T_r, and v_r. Using this notation, we can show from the van der Waals equation that all gases have the same p, v, T relation when their reduced properties are the same. This is essentially the *law of corresponding states*. This law is not universally correct, and it has been modified in order to make it more generally applicable.

The utility of the law of corresponding states lies in the fact that a single curve (called a generalized compressibility chart) can be used to evaluate the p, v, T data for all gases. Most charts (made for various classes of gases) based on this principle use Z as the ordinate, where $Z = pv/RT$. A generalized compressibility chart is shown in Fig. 5.28.

ILLUSTRATIVE PROBLEM 5.33

Methane (CH_4, MW 16) has a critical temperature of 343°R and a critical pressure of 674 psia. Determine the specific volume of methane at 50°F and 500 psia, using both the ideal gas relation and Fig. 5.28.

Solution

$$p_r = \frac{p}{p_c} = \frac{500}{674} = 0.742$$

$$T_r = \frac{T}{T_c} = \frac{460 + 50}{343} = 1.485$$

Reading Fig. 5.28 at these values gives Z equal to 0.93. Therefore,

$$Z = 0.93 = \frac{pv}{RT}, \qquad v = 0.93 \frac{RT}{p}$$

and

$$v = \frac{0.93(1545/16)(510)}{500 \times 144} = 0.635 \text{ ft}^3/\text{lb}$$

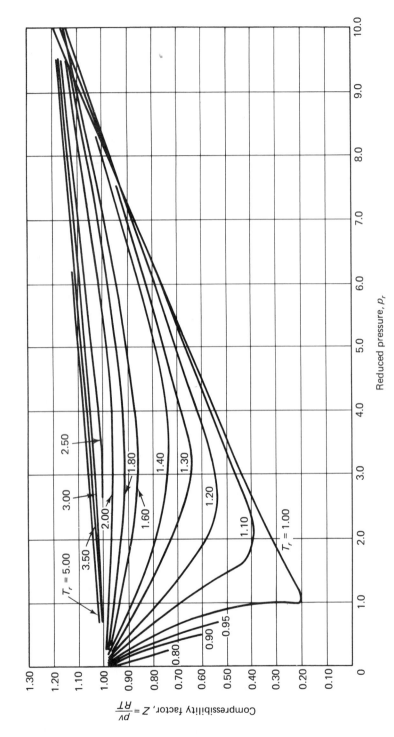

Figure 5.28 Compressibility factor versus reduced pressure for a series of reduced temperatures (low pressure range) (From B. F. Dodge, *Chemical Engineering Thermodynamics*, McGraw-Hill Book Co., New York, 1944)

252

For the ideal gas

$$v = \frac{RT}{p} = \frac{1545 \times 510}{16 \times 500 \times 144} = 0.683 \text{ ft}^3/\text{lb}$$

To obtain the other thermodynamic properties of the real gas, similar procedures based on the law of corresponding states have been developed. The interested reader is referred to the references at the end of this chapter for this information.

In general, the ideal gas relations yield more nearly correct results when the gas under consideration is at a pressure that is small compared to the critical pressure and when its temperature is much greater than the critical temperature. In other words, when $T_r \gg 1$ and $p_r \ll 1$, the ideal gas relations are usually applicable with negligible error.

5.9 CLOSURE

The material covered in this chapter will probably be used either directly or as a basis for further study as frequently as the material in any chapter in this book. At first glance this chapter may appear to be formidable to the student, since a large number of equations are developed for the situations studied. In actuality, for each of these situations we have always invoked three basic concepts: an equation of state, an equation of path, and an energy equation. Rather than attempting to memorize the derived formulas, each situation should be studied by the student to see how these three basic concepts apply. The subsequent mathematical manipulation and derived equations should be secondary to the fundamental application of the state, path, and energy equations. In addition, certain definitions are given throughout this chapter, and these should be thoroughly understood before proceeding further into the chapter.

The material on gas flow and real gases is intended as a brief introduction to topics about which volumes have been written. This material will, however, provide the background for any further studies in these fields.

REFERENCES

1 *Fluid Mechanics for Engineering Technology* by Irving Granet, Prentice-Hall, Inc., Englewood Cliffs, N.J., 1971.

2 *Elementary Thermodynamics*, 3rd Ed., by V. M. Faires, Macmillan, Inc., New York, 1957.

3 *Gas Tables* by J. H. Keenan and J. Kaye, John Wiley & Sons, Inc., New York, 1948.

4 *Thermodynamics*, 2nd Ed., by G. A. Hawkins, John Wiley & Sons, Inc., New York, 1951.

5 *Principles of Engineering Thermodynamics*, 2nd Ed., by P. J. Kiefer, G. F. Kinney, and M. C. Stuart, John Wiley & Sons, Inc., New York, 1954.

6 *Thermodynamics* by Enrico Fermi, Dover Publications, New York, 1956.

7 *Thermodynamics of Fluid Flow* by N. A. Hall, Prentice-Hall, Inc., Englewood Cliffs, N.J., 1951.

8 *The Dynamics and Thermodynamics of Fluid Flow*, Vol. 1, by A. H. Shapiro, Ronald Press Company, New York, 1953.

9 *Elements of Gasdynamics* by H. W. Liepmann and A. Roshko, John Wiley & Sons, Inc., New York, 1957.

10 *Thermodynamics* by G. J. Van Wylen, John Wiley & Sons, Inc., New York, 1960.

11 *Jet Propulsion and Gas Turbines* by M. J. Zuchrow, John Wiley & Sons, Inc., New York, 1948.

12 *Introduction to Gas Dynamics* by R. M. Rotty, John Wiley & Sons, Inc., New York, 1962.

13 *Introduction to Aerodynamics of a Compressible Fluid* by H. W. Liepmann and A. E. Puckett, John Wiley & Sons, Inc., New York, 1947.

14 *Chemical Engineering Thermodynamics* by B. F. Dodge, McGraw-Hill Book Co., New York, 1944.

15 *Basic Thermodynamics* by B. G. A. Skrotzki, McGraw-Hill Book Co., New York, 1963.

16 *Thermodynamics*, 2nd Ed., by F. P. Durham, Prentice Hall, Inc., Englewood Cliffs, N.J., 1959.

17 *Elementary Applied Thermodynamics* by Irving Granet, John Wiley & Sons, Inc., New York, 1965.

PROBLEMS

5.1 One pound of nitrogen initially at 14.7 psia and 32°F is compressed until its volume is halved and its pressure is increased by 50 percent. What is its final temperature?

5.2 One kilogram of nitrogen initially at 100 kPa and 0°C is expanded so that its volume is doubled while its pressure decreases to 0.3 times its initial value. What is the final temperature?

5.3 What is the density of air at 72°F and 160 psia (MW = 29)?

5.4 Determine the density of air at 20°C and 100 kPa (MW = 29).

5.5 A closed container having a volume of 5 cu ft is filled with methane (CH_4, MW = 16) at 68°F. If the tank contains 6 lb, determine the pressure in the tank.

5.6 An automobile tire is inflated to 26 psig on a cold morning when the temperature is 32°F. After prolonged high speed driving the tire temperature is 140°F. If the tire is considered to be rigid, what is its hot pressure?

5.7 A closed tank contains 8 cu ft of air at 17 psia and 125°F. If 60 Btu are added to the air, determine the final pressure. Assume $c_v = 0.17$ Btu/lb °R.

5.8 Three kilograms of CO_2 fills a tank having a volume of 0.2 m³ at 20°C. What is the pressure in the tank?

5.9 A tank of CO_2 is filled until the pressure is 5 MPa and the temperature is 100°C. If the volume of the tank is 1 m³, how much mass is there in the tank?

5.10 What is the final pressure in a closed tank after 60 kJ is added to 0.3 m³ of air that is at 150 kPa and 40°C? Assume that $c_p = 1.0061$ kJ/kg·K and $c_v = 0.7186$ kJ/kg·K.

5.11 An ideal gas has R of 80 and $k = 1.4$. Determine c_p and c_v of this gas.

5.12 An ideal gas has R equal to 29 and k equal to 1.3. Determine c_p and c_v of this gas in English units.

5.13 Do Problem 5.12 in SI units.

5.14 If the specific heat at constant pressure of a gas having a molecular weight of 18 is 0.45 Btu/lb °R, what is its specific heat at constant volume?

5.15 A gas has a specific heat at constant pressure of 0.34 Btu/lb °R, and a specific heat at constant volume of 0.272 Btu/lb °R. Determine the molecular weight of this gas.

5.16 If c_p of a gas is 5.2028 kJ/kg·K and its molecular weight is 4, determine c_v.

5.17 If c_p of a gas is 1.0426 kJ/kg·K and c_v is 0.7454 kJ/kg·K, determine the molecular weight and k of the gas.

5.18 If c_p of a gas is 0.3 Btu/lb·°R, what is c_v if the gas has a molecular weight of 28?

5.19 Nitrogen initially has a pressure of 55 psia and is at 80°F. If its final pressure after an isothermal expansion is 18 psia, what is its final specific volume?

5.20 A tank with a fixed volume contains O_2 at 30 psia and 60°F. Two pounds of O_2 is added to the contents so that the final pressure is 40 psia and the final temperature is 80°F. What is the volume of the tank?

5.21 Oxygen is initially at 30°C and 350 kPa. What is its final specific volume after it undergoes an isothermal expansion to 120 kPa?

5.22 How much work is required to isothermally compress 1 kg of air from 200 kPa to 2 MPa? Assume that c_p is 1.0061 kJ/kg·K, c_v is 0.7186 kJ/kg·K, and the air is at 20°C. (MW = 29)

5.23 If 0.1 lb of a gas is heated at constant volume from 90°F to 350°F, determine the increase in entropy for the process. Assume that $c_v = 0.22$ Btu/lb °R. Also determine the ratio of the final pressure to the initial pressure for this process.

5.24 If 0.05 kg of a gas is heated from 30° to 175°C, what is the entropy change if the process is carried out at constant volume and $c_v = 0.90$ kJ/kg·K?

5.25 One hundred Btu is added to 1 lb of air at constant volume whose initial conditions are 85°F and 35 psia. If $c_v = 0.19$ Btu/lb °R, determine the final pressure and final temperature and the change in entropy for the process. (MW = 29)

5.26 If 100 kJ is added to 0.5 kg of air at constant volume, and the initial conditions are 30°C and 200 kPa, and $c_v = 0.7$ kJ/kg·K, determine the final pressure, final temperature, and the change in entropy for the process. (MW = 29)

5.27 One pound of a gas at 80°F is heated until its entropy increase is 0.15 Btu/lb °R. If c_v is 0.21 Btu/lb °R and the process is carried out at constant volume, determine the final gas temperature.

5.28 Compute the new volume in a cylinder if air is cooled at constant pressure until its initial temperature of 500°F is reduced to 100°F. The initial volume of the cylinder is 10 cu ft.

5.29 An ideal gas has $R = 80$ and $k = 1.4$. If the gas undergoes a nonflow constant pressure process from 1000°F to 500°F, determine the work done, the change in internal energy, and the change in enthalpy for the process.

5.30 Determine the heat removed from the cylinder of Problem 5.28. Assume $c_p = 0.24$ Btu/lb °R and $c_v = 0.171$ Btu/lb °R.

5.31 An ideal gas (MW = 20) undergoes a nonflow constant-pressure process from 500° to 250°C. If k is 1.4, determine the work done, the change in internal energy, and the change in enthalpy for the process.

5.32 Determine the work done, the change in internal energy, and the heat that is supplied when air initially at 200 psia and 200°F expands in a cylinder at constant pressure from an initial volume of 20 cu ft to triple its initial volume. Assume $c_p = 0.24$ Btu/lb °R and $c_v = 0.171$ Btu/lb °R.

5.33 The initial pressure in the combustor of a gas turbine is 80 psia. If this process is carried out at constant pressure, determine the increase in entropy and the flow work change per pound of air if the air temperature goes from 85° to 550°F. Assume that $c_p = 0.24$ Btu/lb °R.

5.34 Carbon dioxide (MW = 44) is heated at constant pressure from 14.7 psia and 90°F to 500°F. If $k = 1.4$, determine the heat transferred and the change in entropy for the process. Assume that c_p is constant.

5.35 Carbon dioxide is heated from 100 kPa and 35°C to 250°C at constant pressure. If k equals 1.3, determine the heat transferred and the change in entropy for the process if c_p is constant. (MW = 44)

5.36 One pound of air is expanded isothermally until its final volume is 50 percent greater than its initial volume. If the temperature of the air is 150°F, how much heat was supplied and what is the change in entropy of this process?

5.37 One pound of argon (MW = 39.90) is isothermally compressed from 100°F and 20 psia to 600 psia. Calculate the final specific volume, the change in entropy, and the heat transferred.

5.38 Heat is added to air at constant temperature from initial conditions of 80 psia and 250°F to a final pressure of 25 psia. Determine the heat added and the change in entropy per pound of air for this process. (MW = 29)

5.39 How much work is required to isothermally compress 1 lb of air from 25 psia and 125°F to 250 psia?

5.40 An ideal gas expands isentropically from 120 psia and 200°F to 20 psia. Determine the final temperature for this nonflow process if $k = 1.4$.

5.41 Air is compressed isentropically from one atm absolute to 10 atm absolute. If the initial temperature is 70°F, determine the final temperature and the work required for this nonflow process if $k = 1.4$.

5.42 Solve Problem 5.40 using the *Gas Tables*.

5.43 Solve Problem 5.41 using the *Gas Tables*.

5.44 Air is expanded isentropically from a volume of 10 cu ft to a volume of 30 cu ft. If the initial temperature is 200°F, determine the final temperature.

5.45 An ideal gas expands isentropically from 600 kPa and 195°C to 110 kPa and 40°C. What is the k of this gas process?

5.46 A gas expands isentropically from 90 psia and 380°F to 15 psia and 100°F. Determine k for this gas.

5.47 Determine the final state and change in enthalpy and internal energy when air is expanded isentropically from 100 psia and 1000°R to 75 psia. Assume that $k = 1.4$. If all the work of this nonflow process could be recovered, how much work would be available?

5.48 A gas initially at 170 psia and 270°F is expanded to 40 psia and 90°F. Determine n for this process.

5.49 A process is carried out in which a gas is compressed from 14 to 28 psia, and its final volume is decreased to 60 percent of its initial volume. Determine n for this process.

5.50 One pound of nitrogen undergoes a process during which it changes from an initial state of 100 psia and 400°F to a final state of 300 psia and 650°F. Determine n for this process.

5.51 A gas that is initially at 1.16 MPa and 133°C is expanded to 275 kPa and 32°C. What is n for this process?

5.52 Air is compressed polytropically from 1 atm to 10 atm absolute. The initial temperature is 70°F and $n = 1.2$. Determine the work required for the compression if $c_v = 0.171$ Btu/lb °R.

5.53 Determine the entropy change and heat transferred for the polytropic process described in Problem 5.52.

5.54 If n of a nonflow process is 1.2, how much work is required to compress 1 kg of air from 120 kPa to 600 kPa if the air is initially at 30°C. Assume that k is 1.4 and MW is 29.

5.55 If n of a nonflow polytropic process is 1.18, determine the work required to compress 1 lb of air from 20 psia to 100 psia if the initial air temperature is 80°F.

5.56 An equation for the instantaneous specific heat of air is given as

$$c_p = 0.219 + \frac{0.342\,T}{10^4} - \frac{0.293\,T^2}{10^8} \qquad \text{where } T \text{ is in } °R$$

Determine the average specific heat of air between 340°F and 840°F.

5.57 Using the *Gas Tables*, solve Problem 5.56.

5.58 The instantaneous specific heat of carbon dioxide is given by

$$c_p = 0.368 - \frac{148.4}{T} + \frac{3.2 \times 10^4}{T^2} \qquad \text{where } T \text{ is in } °R$$

Determine the average specific heat of carbon dioxide between 500°R and 1000°R.

5.59 Carbon dioxide (MW = 44) has a critical pressure of 72.9 atm absolute and a critical temperature of 548°R. Determine the specific volume of this gas at atmospheric pressure (14.7 psia) and 1000°F, using Fig. 5.28. Compare it with the specific volume obtained from the ideal gas relation.

5.60 If the gas in Problem 5.59 is at 100 atm absolute, determine its specific volume and compare it to the value obtained from the ideal gas relation.

5.61 Air at 50°F and 500 psia is flowing in a duct at 100 ft/sec. What is its Mach number?

5.62 If air is slowed adiabatically from 500 to 300 ft/sec, determine its temperature rise if $c_p = 0.24$ Btu/lb °F.

5.63 Air is slowed adiabatically from a velocity of 500 ft/sec to another velocity. During the slowing-down process the air temperature rises 10°F. If c_p of air is 0.24 Btu/lb °F and constant, determine its final velocity.

5.64 Air is flowing at 500 ft/sec at a temperature of 300°F and a pressure of 25 psia. Determine its isentropic stagnation temperature and pressure.

5.65 Air flows in a nozzle. If the inlet velocity is negligible and the inlet pressure is 100 psia, determine the critical velocity in the nozzle if it is a converging–diverging nozzle. Assume that the inlet temperature is 100°F. What is the critical pressure?

5.66 Air is flowing in a duct at a Mach number of 2.5. Assuming that all processes are isentropic and that the stagnation temperature is 500°F, determine the air temperature for which the Mach number is 1.2.

chapter **6**

mixtures of ideal gases

6.1 INTRODUCTION

From the simple kinetic considerations of Chapter 1 it has been possible to deduce an equation of state to relate the pressure, temperature, and volume of a gas. This particular equation, $pv = RT$, formed the basis of most of the work in Chapter 5. As we have remarked several times, it is surprising that so simple an equation can represent real gases with any degree of accuracy. The success of this equation for a single gas leads us to hope that mixtures of gases can be represented equally well by an equally simple equation of state. To some extent this hope is realized for some real gaseous mixtures; but for others it has not been possible to write a simple p, v, T relation in terms of the properties of the individual components of the mixture. By use of semiempirical methods it has been found possible to correlate experimental p, v, T data for some gases, but no single method of correlation has yet been devised that will correlate all gaseous mixtures satisfactorily.

As a first approximation it will be assumed that the ideal gas relation can be extended and used for gas mixtures. The error in this procedure depends on the gases involved and the conditions of pressure and temperature of the mixture.

6.2 PRESSURE OF A MIXTURE

Consider that a mixture of several gases is contained in a volume V at a temperature T and that an absolute pressure gage placed on the volume would read a total mixture pressure p_m, as shown in Fig. 6.1a. In this gas mixture the various component gas molecules are in constant random motion, and the gas mixture is assumed to be homogeneous. For such a mixture Dalton's law (or Dalton's rule of additive pressures) is found to apply exactly if the ideal gas relation holds for the components and for the mixture. Dalton's law can be

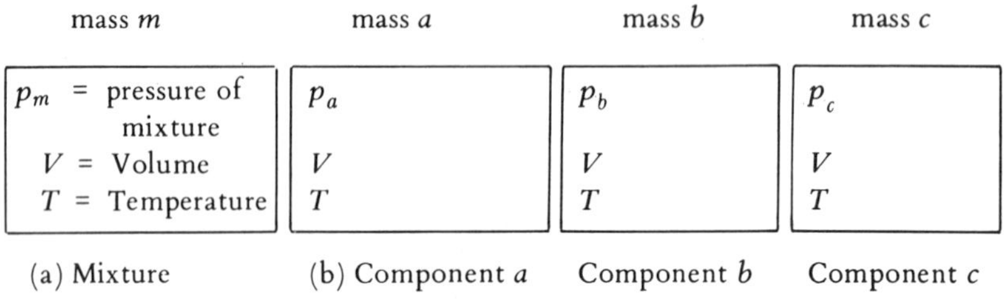

mass m	mass a	mass b	mass c
p_m = pressure of mixture V = Volume T = Temperature	p_a V T	p_b V T	p_c V T
(a) Mixture	(b) Component a	Component b	Component c

Figure 6.1 Dalton's law

stated as

1 Any gas is a vacuum to any other gas mixed with it.

2 The pressure of a mixture of gases is the sum of the pressures of its components when each alone occupies the volume of the mixture at the temperature of the mixture.*

Applying Dalton's law to the situation shown in Fig. 6.1, where the mixture m and each of the components are all shown to occupy equal volumes, yields

$$p_m = p_a + p_b + p_c \qquad (6.1)$$

where p_m is the total pressure of the mixture and p_a, p_b, and p_c represent the pressures that each of the constituent gases would exert if they alone occupied the total volume at the temperature of the mixture. These pressures are called the partial pressures of each gas. By assuming that the pressure–volume relationship for an ideal gas is applicable and denoting the molecular weight of the mixture as MW_m, we have

$$pV = mRT = m\left(\frac{1545\,T}{MW_m}\right) \qquad (5.8)$$

---

* *Thermodynamics* by J. H. Keenan, John Wiley & Sons, Inc., New York, 1941, p. 201.

and Eq. (6.1) can be written as

$$\frac{m_m}{\text{MW}_m} = \frac{m_a}{\text{MW}_a} + \frac{m_b}{\text{MW}_b} + \frac{m_c}{\text{MW}_c} \qquad (6.2a)$$

Before continuing, it will be convenient to recall certain items that were discussed briefly in Chapters 1 and 5. If the molecular weight of a substance is expressed in pounds, the resulting quantity is known as the pound molecular weight, a pound mole, or simply a mole. Thus 32 lb of oxygen constitutes 1 lb mole of oxygen, and 28.02 lb of nitrogen is 1 lb mole of nitrogen. It has also been found that 1 mole of a substance, whether it be solid, liquid, or gas, contains the same number of molecules as 1 mole of any other substance. The number of molecules in 1 mole is known as the Avogadro number, or Avogadro's constant. Thus, by application of the ideal gas equation of state, it is found that at a given pressure and temperature 1 mole of gas will occupy a fixed volume, regardless of the gas. This volume is known as the molar volume, and at 14.7 psia and 32°F it is 358 ft^3. Table 6.1 is a convenient listing of the molecular weights of various gases.

TABLE 6.1

MOLECULAR WEIGHTS OF GASES

GAS	CHEMICAL FORMULA	MOLECULAR WEIGHT
Acetylene	C_2H_2	26.02
Air		28.96
Ammonia	NH_3	17.024
Argon	A	39.90
Butane	C_4H_{10}	58.08
Carbon dioxide	CO_2	44.00
Carbon monoxide	CO	28.00
Dodecane	$C_{12}H_{26}$	170.3
Ethane	C_2H_6	30.05
Ethylene	C_2H_4	28.03
Helium	He	4.00
Hydrogen	H_2	2.016
Methane	CH_4	16.03
Nitrogen	N_2	28.02
Octane	C_8H_{18}	114.14
Oxygen	O_2	32.00
Propane	C_3H_8	44.06
Sulfur dioxide	SO_2	64.07
Water vapor	H_2O	18.01

With the foregoing in mind, it will be noted that the ratio of m/MW in Eq. (6.2a) is simply the number of moles of each component of the mixture. Denoting the moles of each constituent as n, with the appropriate subscripts,

$$n_m = n_a + n_b + n_c \qquad (6.2b)$$

In words, Eq. (6.2b) states that the number of moles of gas in a mixture, is equal to the sum of the moles of its constituent gases. It is also evident that the total mass of a gas mixture must equal the sum of the component masses. Referring to Fig. 6.1, we have

$$m_m = m_a + m_b + m_c \qquad (6.3)$$

The ratio n_a/n_m is the mole fraction x_a of gas a, and the ratio m_a/m_m is the weight fraction of gas a.

From Eqs. (6.1) and (5.8),

$$\frac{p_a}{p_m} = \frac{n_a}{n_m} = x_a, \qquad p_a = x_a p_m \qquad (6.4)$$

and from Eqs. (6.2) and (6.3),

$$n_m(\mathrm{MW}_m) = n_a(\mathrm{MW}_a) + n_b(\mathrm{MW}_b) + n_c(\mathrm{MW}_c)$$

or $$\mathrm{MW}_m = x_a \mathrm{MW}_a + x_b \mathrm{MW}_b + x_c \mathrm{MW}_c \qquad (6.5)$$

Since Eq. (6.5) is based on the fact that the mixture and its components are ideal gases and that the mixture can also be treated as a single ideal gas, the gas constant for the mixture can be written as

$$R_m = \frac{1545}{\mathrm{MW}_m} \qquad (6.6)$$

To sum up the foregoing,

1 The total pressure of a mixture of ideal gases is the sum of its partial pressures.

2 The mass of the mixture is the sum of the masses of the components of the mixture.

3 The total number of moles in the mixture equals the sum of the number of moles of the component gases of the mixture.

4 The partial pressure of a component equals the mole fraction of the component multiplied by the total pressure of the mixture.

5 The molecular weight of the mixture equals the sum of the products of mole fraction of each gas component multiplied by the molecular weight of each component gas.

6 The ideal gas equation of state is applicable to the components as well as to the entire mixture.

ILLUSTRATIVE PROBLEM 6.1

Dry air is a mixture of oxygen and nitrogen as the principle gases. Per pound of mixture there is 0.2315 lb of oxygen and 0.7685 lb of nitrogen. Determine (a) the number of moles of each gas, the total number of moles, and the mole fraction of each component; (b) the partial pressure of each component if the air is at 14.7 psia; (c) the molecular weight of the air; (d) the gas constant of the air.

Solution

As the basis of this calculation let us assume that we have 1 lb of mixture. Also let us take the molecular weight of oxygen to be 32.00 and nitrogen to be 28.02 (from Table 6.1).

(a) $n_{O_2} = \dfrac{0.2315}{32} = 0.00723$ mole of oxygen/lb of mixture

$n_{N_2} = \dfrac{0.7685}{28.02} = 0.02743$ mole of nitrogen/lb of mixture

$n_m = n_{O_2} + n_{N_2} = 0.00723 + 0.02743$

$n_m = 0.03466$ mole/lb of mixture

$x_{O_2} = \dfrac{n_{O_2}}{n_m} = \dfrac{0.00723}{0.03466} = 0.209$

$x_{N_2} = \dfrac{n_{N_2}}{n_m} = \dfrac{0.02743}{0.03466} = 0.791$

(Check: $x_{O_2} + x_{N_2} = 0.209 + 0.791 = 1.000$)

(b)

$p_{O_2} = x_{O_2}(14.7) = 0.209 \times 14.7 = 3.07$ psia

$p_{N_2} = x_{N_2}(14.7) = 0.791 \times 14.7 = 11.63$ psia

(c)

$\mathrm{MW}_m = x_{O_2}(32) + x_{N_2}(28.02) = 0.209 \times 32 + 0.791 \times 28.02 = 28.85$

(d)

$R_m = \dfrac{1545}{\mathrm{MW}_m} = \dfrac{1545}{28.85} = 53.55$ or   53.6

ILLUSTRATIVE PROBLEM 6.2

Gaseous Freon 12 (CCl_2F_2) is used to fill slowly a tank that initially contained air at atmospheric pressure and temperature to a final pressure of 1000 psia and room temperature. What is the mole fraction of air in the final mixture? Also find the molecular weight of the mixture and the partial pressure of the gases. Assume that the molecular weight of air is 29 and the molecular weight of Freon 12 is 120.9.

Solution

The partial pressure of the air is by definition 14.7 psia. Therefore, the partial pressure of the Freon 12 is $1000 - 14.7 = 985.3$ psia. The mole fraction of air is $14.7/1000 = 0.0147$, and the mole fraction of Freon 12 is $985.3/1000 = 0.9853$.
    The molecular weight of the mixture is

$$MW_m = 0.0147 \times 29 + 0.9853 \times 120.9 = 119.5$$

ILLUSTRATIVE PROBLEM 6.3

Ten pounds of air, 1 lb of carbon dioxide, and 5 lb of nitrogen are mixed at constant temperature until the mixture pressure is constant. The final mixture is at 100 psia. Determine the moles of each gas, the mole fraction of each gas, the partial pressure of each gas, the molecular weight of the mixture, and the gas constant of the mixture. Assume that the molecular weight of air is 29, of carbon dioxide, 44, and of nitrogen, 28.

Solution

Let us consider as a basis for the calculation that we have 16 lb of mixture. Therefore,

$$n_{air} = \frac{10}{29} = 0.345, \qquad n_{CO_2} = \frac{1}{44} = 0.023, \qquad n_{N_2} = \frac{5}{28} = 0.179$$

The total number of moles is $0.345 + 0.023 + 0.179 = 0.547$. The mole fractions are

$$x_{air} = \frac{0.345}{0.547} = 0.631, \quad x_{CO_2} = \frac{0.023}{0.547} = 0.041, \quad x_{N_2} = \frac{0.179}{0.547} = 0.327$$

$$p_{air} = 0.631 \times 100 = 63.1 \text{ psia}$$

$$p_{CO_2} = 0.041(100) = 4.1 \text{ psia}$$

$$p_{N_2} = 0.327(100) = 32.7 \text{ psia}$$

The molecular weight of the mixture is found from

$$\mathrm{MW}_m = 0.631(29) + 0.041(44) + (0.327)(28) = 29.3$$

and

$$R_m = \frac{1545}{29.3} = 52.7$$

6.3 VOLUME OF A MIXTURE

In arriving at Dalton's law in section 6.2, it was assumed that each gas in a mixture expands to fill the entire volume of the container at the temperature of the mixture. Let us assume that three gases, a, b, and c, are placed in separate containers, each having different volumes but each at the same pressure and temperature. This condition is shown in Fig. 6.2. If the three containers are brought together and the partitions are removed, the pressure and temperature of the mixture will remain constant, if these gases are ideal, and Dalton's law can be applied. The partial pressures will equal the initial pressure multiplied

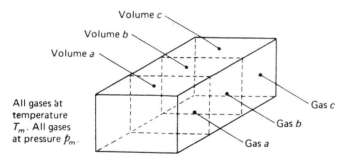

Figure 6.2 Law of additive volumes

by the ratio of the initial to final volume. Therefore,

$$p_m = p_{oa}\left(\frac{V_a}{V_m}\right) + p_{ob}\left(\frac{V_b}{V_m}\right) + p_{oc}\left(\frac{V_c}{V_m}\right) \qquad (6.7)$$

where p_{oa} is the initial pressure of a in its container, V_a is the *volume of a before mixing*, and V_m is the *volume of the mixture after mixing*. Since p_o of each gas is the same as the final pressure p_m,

$$1 = \frac{V_a}{V_m} + \frac{V_b}{V_m} + \frac{V_c}{V_m} \quad \text{or} \quad V_m = V_a + V_b + V_c \qquad (6.8)$$

Equation (6.8) is an expression of Amagat's law, which states that the volume of a mixture is the sum of the volumes that each constituent gas would occupy if each were at the pressure and temperature of the mixture.

By applying the equation of state of an ideal gas to Eq. (6.8),

$$\frac{V_a}{V_m} = \frac{n_a}{n_m} = x_a \tag{6.9}$$

That is, *the mole fraction also equals the volume fraction of the mixture.* The volume fraction is defined as the ratio of the partial volume of a constituent to the total volume of the mixture. Amagat's law and Dalton's law are equivalent to each other if the gases and the mixture are ideal gases. The following two examples will serve to illustrate the concept of mixture volume.

ILLUSTRATIVE PROBLEM 6.4

Five moles of oxygen at 14.7 psia and 70°F are adiabatically mixed with 10 moles of hydrogen at 14.7 psia and 70°F. Determine the mixture volume, the partial volume of the constituents, the mole fraction of each constituent, and the molecular weight of the resulting mixture. The molecular weight of oxygen is 32.0, and of hydrogen, 2.016 (see Table 6.1).

Solution

The total number of moles is $10 + 5 = 15$. Therefore, the mole fraction of each constituent is

$$x_{O_2} = \tfrac{5}{15} = \tfrac{1}{3}, \qquad x_{H_2} = \tfrac{10}{15} = \tfrac{2}{3}$$

The molecular weight of the final mixture is

$$\tfrac{1}{3}(32) + \tfrac{2}{3}(2.016) = 12.01$$

The partial volume of the oxygen can be found as follows: per pound of oxygen

$$(pv)_{O_2} = RT, \qquad 14.7 \times 144 \times (v_{O_2}) = \frac{1545(460 + 70)}{32}$$

and $\qquad v_{O_2} = 12.09$ cu ft/lb

Since there are 5 moles, each weighing 32 lb,

$$V_{O_2} = 12.09 \times 5 \times 32 = 1934 \text{ cu ft}$$

For the hydrogen, we can simplify the procedure by noting that the fraction of the total volume occupied by the oxygen is the same as its mole fraction. Therefore,

$$V_m = 3(1934) = 5802 \text{ cu ft}$$

and the hydrogen volume

$$V_{H_2} = 5802 - 1934 = 3868 \text{ cu ft}$$

We could obtain the partial volume of hydrogen by proceeding as we did for the oxygen. Thus

$$(pv)_{H_2} = RT, \qquad 14.7 \times 144 \times (v_{H_2}) = \frac{1545(460+70)}{2.016}$$

and $\qquad v_{H_2} = 191.88 \text{ cu ft/lb}$

For 10 moles of hydrogen, each weighing 2.016 lb, we have a total hydrogen volume of

$$V_{H_2} = 10 \times 2.016 \times 191.88 = 3868 \text{ cu ft}$$

which checks with the previous value. As an alternate to the foregoing we could also use the fact that at 14.7 psia and 32°F a mole of *any* gas occupies a volume of 358 cu ft. At 70°F and 14.7 psia, a mole occupies $358 \times [(460+70)/(460+32)] = 385.7$ cu ft. Therefore, 5 moles of oxygen occupy

$$V_{O_2} = 5 \times 385.7 = 1928 \text{ cu ft}$$

and 10 moles of hydrogen occupy

$$V_{H_2} = 10 \times 385.7 = 3857 \text{ cu ft}$$

Both values are in good agreement with the previous calculations.

ILLUSTRATIVE PROBLEM 6.5

A mixture contains 10 lb of carbon dioxide and 5 lb of nitrogen. If the mixture is at 70°F and 100 psia, determine the mixture volume, the partial volume of each constituent, the partial pressure of each constituent, the mole fraction of each constituent, and the molecular weight of the mixture (MW of $CO_2 = 44.0$; MW of $N_2 = 28.02$).

		CO_2		N_2	
Mixture		M = 10 lbs		M = 5 lbs	
Pressure = p_m		Volume = V_{CO_2}		Volume = V_{N_2}	
Temperature = T		Temperature = T		Temperature = T	
Volume = V_m		Pressure = p_m		Pressure = p_m	

Figure 6.3 Illustrative Problem 6.5

Solution

Referring to Fig. 6.3, we have for the CO_2

$$n_{CO_2} = \frac{10}{44} = 0.227 \text{ mole}$$

and for N_2

$$n_{N_2} = \frac{5}{28.02} = 0.178 \text{ mole}$$

The total moles in the mixture is therefore $0.227 + 0.178 = 0.405$ mole. Therefore,

$$x_{CO_2} = \frac{0.227}{0.405} = 0.560$$

and

$$x_{N_2} = \frac{0.178}{0.405} = 0.440$$

The molecular weight of the mixture is found from Eq. (6.5) as

$$MW_m = 0.560(44) + 0.440(28.02) = 37.0$$

Since the mixture is 15 lb (10 CO_2 + 5 N_2), the volume of the mixture is found from

$$p_m V_m = m_m R_m T_m, \qquad V_m = \frac{\dfrac{15 \times 1545}{37.0} \times (460 + 70)}{100 \times 144} = 23.05 \text{ cu ft}$$

The partial volume of carbon dioxide is the total volume multiplied by the mole fraction. Thus

$$V_{CO_2} = 23.05(0.560) = 12.91 \text{ cu ft}$$

and

$$V_{N_2} = 23.05(0.440) = 10.14 \text{ cu ft}$$

The partial pressure of each constituent is proportional to its mole fraction. For these conditions,

$$p_{CO_2} = 100(0.560) = 56.0 \text{ psia}$$

$$p_{N_2} = 100(0.440) = 44.0 \text{ psia}$$

6.4 MIXTURE COMPOSITION

When a gas mixture is analyzed, it is possible to state its composition correctly in several different ways. For instance, the moles of each constituent gas could be given; alternatively, the weight or partial volumes of each gas could be stated. The manner of expressing the analysis is completely arbitrary, and therefore it is necessary to be able to convert from one form of analysis to another.

If the moles (or mole fractions) are given, the volume fractions are immediately known. Conversely, if the volume fractions are known, the mole fractions are known. Since the mass of a gas is the product of the number of moles multiplied by the molecular weight, the conversion from a weight (gravimetric) analysis is readily achieved. The molecular weight of the mixture is also readily determined from Eq. (6.5).

ILLUSTRATIVE PROBLEM 6.6

A gas mixture consists of the following volume percentages: 40 percent CO_2, 10 percent N_2, 40 percent O_2, and 10 percent H_2. Determine the weight fraction of each gas in the mixture, the molecular weight of the mixture, and the gas constant of the mixture.

Solution

In solving this type of problem, we shall first assume a convenient volume for the gas mixture. Since we have percentages by volume for each constituent, we will assume that we have 100 volumes of gas mixture and set up Table 6.2. In the first column we tabulate the gas, and in the second column the given volume fractions are tabulated. Since the mole fraction equals the volume fraction, the values in column 3 are the same as those in column 2. The molecular weight is obtained from Table 6.1. Since the molecular weight of the mixture is the sum of the individual mole fractions multiplied by the respective molecular weights, the next column tabulates the product of mole fraction multiplied by molecular weight (column 3 multiplied by column 4). The sum of these entries is the molecular weight of the mixture, which, for this case, is 33.4. If we now consider that we have 33.4 lb of mixture and that the weight of each gas in the mixture is given by its product $(x)(MW)$, the weight fraction of each constituent is the entry in column 5 divided by 33.4. The value of R for the mixture is simply $1545/33.4 = 46.3$. The use of a tabular solution helps to simplify the calculations and is also a time saver when this type of repetitive calculation is involved.

TABLE 6.2

ILLUSTRATIVE PROBLEM 6.6

BASIS: 100 VOLUMES OF GAS MIXTURE

GAS	*2* *VOLUME* *FRACTION*	*3* *MOLE* *FRACTION* *(x)*	*4* *MOLECULAR* *WEIGHT* *(MW)*	*5* *3 × 4* *(x)(MW)*	*WEIGHT* *FRACTION*
CO_2	0.40	0.40	44.0	17.6	$17.6/33.4 = 0.527$
N_2	0.10	0.10	28.02	2.8	$2.8/33.4 = 0.084$
H_2	0.10	0.10	2.016	0.2	$0.2/33.4 = 0.006$
O_2	0.40	0.40	32.0	12.8	$12.8/33.4 = 0.383$
	1.00	1.00		$33.4 = MW_m$	$= 1.000$

The procedure when the weight (gravimetric) analysis is known and conversion to a volumetric basis is desired is similar to that given in the table. However, rather than assuming 100 volumes of gas, it is more convenient to use 100 lb of gas as the basis of the computations.

ILLUSTRATIVE PROBLEM 6.7

The result of Illustrative Problem 6.6 shows that the weight fractions of gases are $CO_2 = 0.527$, $N_2 = 0.084$, $H_2 = 0.006$, and $O_2 = 0.383$. Using these gases and weight fractions, determine the fraction by volume of each of the constituent gases of this mixture.

Solution

We will again use a tabular solution, as we did for Illustrative Problem 6.6, but for this calculation we will take as a basis 100 lb of mixture. The first three columns of Table 6.3 are similar to the items in Table 6.2 and are self-explanatory.

TABLE 6.3
ILLUSTRATIVE PROBLEM 6.7
BASIS: 100 POUNDS OF MIXTURE

	2	3	4	5	6
GAS	WEIGHT (lb)	MOLECULAR WEIGHT (MW)	WEIGHT / MOLECULAR WEIGHT = MOLES	MOLE FRACTION (MOLES/MOLE)	PERCENT VOLUME
CO_2	52.7	44	1.2	$1.2/3 = 0.4$	40
N_2	8.4	28.02	0.3	$0.3/3 = 0.1$	10
H_2	0.6	2.016	0.3	$0.3/3 = 0.1$	10
O_2	38.3	32	1.2	$1.2/3 = 0.4$	40
	100.0		Total moles = 3.0 $MW_m = 100/3 = 33.3$	1.0	100

273

Dividing column 2 by column 3 gives us weight/molecular weight or moles of each constituent. The total number of moles in the mixture is the sum of column 4, and the molecular weight of the mixture is the weight of the mixture (100 lb) divided by the number of moles, 3, or 33.3. Column 5, the mole fraction, is the moles listed in column 4 divided by the total moles in the mixture, which for this problem is 3.0. Since mole fraction is also volume fraction, the last column, percent volume, is just the fifth column multiplied by 100. It should also be noted that the volume percent is also the pressure percent of the various constituents of the mixture. Since this problem is the inverse of Illustrative Problem 6.6, the results obtained are found to be in good agreement for both problems.

ILLUSTRATIVE PROBLEM 6.8

Air consists of 23.18 percent O_2, 75.47 percent N_2, 1.30 percent A, and 0.05 percent CO_2 by weight. Determine the volumetric analysis.

Solution

This problem is a weight-to-volume conversion similar to Illustrative Problem 6.7. We set up Table 6.4 in the same manner as Table 6.3 and use the same procedure to solve the problem.

6.5 THERMODYNAMIC PROPERTIES OF A GAS MIXTURE

When several gases are mixed, it is assumed that the gas molecules will disperse until the mixture is completely homogeneous. It is also assumed that the components of the mixture will reach the same average temperature as the mixture. In Chapter 5 it was noted that the internal energy and enthalpy of the ideal gas are solely functions of the gas temperature. With this in mind, it would seem reasonable to state that these thermodynamic properties of a gas mixture (internal energy and enthalpy) are simply the sum of the properties of the gases of which the mixture is composed. This statement, combined with Dalton's law, can be considered as the Gibbs–Dalton law of mixtures. As before, this law is valid for the ideal gas, and deviations will be found when the components of a mixture differ considerably from the ideal gas law.

As a consequence of the Gibbs–Dalton law, we can write the following property relations for a mixture m composed of three gases, a, b, and c, on the basis that the properties of the mixture equal the sum of the properties of each component of the mixture when each of the components is assumed to occupy

TABLE 6.4

ILLUSTRATIVE PROBLEM 6.8

BASIS: 100 POUNDS OF MIXTURE

GAS	WEIGHT (lb)	MOLECULAR WEIGHT (MW)	$\dfrac{WEIGHT}{MOLECULAR\ WEIGHT}$ = MOLES	MOLE FRACTION	PERCENT VOLUME
O_2	23.18	32.00	0.724	0.210	21
N_2	75.47	28.02	2.693	0.780	78
A	1.30	39.90	0.033	0.010	1
CO_2	0.05	44.00	—	—	—
	100.00		3.45	1.00	100

$$MW_m = \frac{100}{3.45} = 28.99$$

the total volume at the temperature of the mixture, and the gases behave as ideal gases. Thus, for the internal energy and enthalpy of a mixture, we write

$$U_m = m_a u_a + m_b u_b + m_c u_c \qquad (6.10)$$

and
$$H_m = m_a h_a + m_b h_b + m_c h_c \qquad (6.11)$$

where U_m and H_m are the total internal energy and total enthalpy of the mixture, respectively. Since the total value of these properties is the product of the mass and the specific value of each property,

$$U_m = m_m u_m = m_a u_a + m_b u_b + m_c u_c \qquad (6.12)$$

and
$$H_m = m_m h_m = m_a h_a + m_b h_b + m_c h_c \qquad (6.13)$$

From Eqs. (6.12) and (6.13) the specific internal energy and the specific enthalpy of the mixture are

$$u_m = \left(\frac{m_a}{m_m}\right) u_a + \left(\frac{m_b}{m_m}\right) u_b + \left(\frac{m_c}{m_m}\right) u_c \qquad (6.14)$$

and
$$h_m = \left(\frac{m_a}{m_m}\right) h_a + \left(\frac{m_b}{m_m}\right) h_b + \left(\frac{m_c}{m_m}\right) h_c \qquad (6.15)$$

where $m_m = m_a + m_b + m_c$.

From Eqs. (6.14) and (6.15) we can also obtain the specific heat at constant volume and the specific heat at constant pressure for the mixture, since both internal energy and enthalpy for the ideal gas are only functions of the temperature of the mixture. Therefore,

$$c_{vm} = \left(\frac{m_a}{m_m}\right) c_{va} + \left(\frac{m_b}{m_m}\right) c_{vb} + \left(\frac{m_c}{m_m}\right) c_{vc} \qquad (6.16)$$

and
$$c_{pm} = \left(\frac{m_a}{m_m}\right) c_{pa} + \left(\frac{m_b}{m_m}\right) c_{pb} + \left(\frac{m_c}{m_m}\right) c_{pc} \qquad (6.17)$$

It should be noted that Eqs. (6.14) through (6.17) state that the mixture properties in question are each equal to the sum of the mass average of the individual properties of the components of the mixture.

ILLUSTRATIVE PROBLEM 6.9

In a steady-flow process, 160 lb/hr of oxygen and 196 lb/hr of nitrogen are mixed adiabatically. Both gases are at atmospheric pressure, but the oxygen is at 500°F and the nitrogen is at 200°F. Assume c_p of oxygen to be constant and equal to 0.23 Btu/lb °F, and c_p of nitrogen to also be constant and equal to 0.25 Btu/lb °F; determine the final temperature of the mixture. See Fig. 6.4.

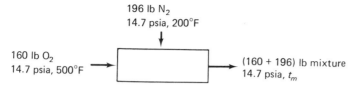

Figure 6.4 Illustrative Problem 6.9

Solution

The energy equation for the steady-flow adiabatic mixing process gives us the requirement that the enthalpy of the mixture must equal the enthalpies of the components, since $\Delta h = q = 0$. An alternate statement of this requirement is that the gain in enthalpy of the nitrogen must equal the decrease in enthalpy of the oxygen. Using this latter statement, that the change in enthalpy of the oxygen must equal the change in enthalpy of the nitrogen, yields

$$160(0.23)(500 - t_m) = 196(0.25)(t_m - 200)$$

where $mc_p(\Delta t)$ has been used for Δh. Solving,

$$t_m = 328.7°F$$

Using the requirement that the enthalpy of the mixture must equal the sum of the enthalpies of the components yields an alternate solution to this problem. Let us assume that at $0°F$ the enthalpy of each gas and of the mixture is zero. The enthalpy of the entering oxygen is $(160)(0.23)(500-0)$, and the enthalpy of the entering nitrogen is $196(0.25)(200-0)$. The enthalpy of the mixture is $(160+196)c_{pm}(t-0)$. Therefore,

$$(160)(0.23)(500-0)+(196)(0.25)(200-0)=(160+196)c_{pm}(t_m-0)$$

The required c_{pm} is obtained from Eq. (6.17):

$$c_{pm} = \frac{160}{(160+196)}(0.23) + \frac{196}{(160+196)}(0.25) = 0.241 \text{ Btu/lb °F}$$

Therefore,

$$t_m = \frac{(160)(0.23)(500-0)+(196)(0.25)(200-0)}{(160+196)(0.241)} = 328.7°F$$

The use of $0°F$ as a base was arbitrary but convenient. Any base would yield the same results. Also, either method used to solve this problem yields the same mixture temperature.

ILLUSTRATIVE PROBLEM 6.10

Assume that the process described in Illustrative Problem 6.9 is carried out as a nonflow mixing process. Also assume that c_v of the oxygen is 0.164 Btu/lb °F and the c_v of the nitrogen is 0.178 Btu/lb °F. Determine the final temperature of the mixture.

Solution

Since this is a nonflow process, the energy equation for this process requires the internal energy of the mixture to equal the sum of the internal energies of its components. Alternately, the decrease in internal energy of the oxygen must equal the increase in internal energy of the nitrogen. Using the latter statement,

$$(160)(0.164)(500 - t_m) = 196(0.178)(t_m - 200), \qquad t_m = 328.8°F$$

We obtained the same temperature for Illustrative Problems 6.9 and 6.10, since the ratio of c_p/c_v for both gases was deliberately taken to be the same. In effect, this constant was canceled from both sides of the equation.

In Chapter 5 we noted that the entropy of an ideal gas is in general a function of both pressure and temperature. For the mixture of ideal gases where each component of the mixture is taken to exist at its own partial pressure, we can write the following equation:

$$m_m(s_m) = m_a(s_a) + m_b(s_b) + m_c(s_c) \qquad (6.18)$$

where the individual entropies s_a, s_b, and s_c are evaluated per pound at the mixture temperature and the component partial pressure.

ILLUSTRATIVE PROBLEM 6.11

Two ideal gases having constant specific heats each at the same pressure and temperature are adiabatically mixed by removing the partition shown in Fig. 6.5. Assume gas a to have a molecular weight of MW_a and a mass of m_a lb.

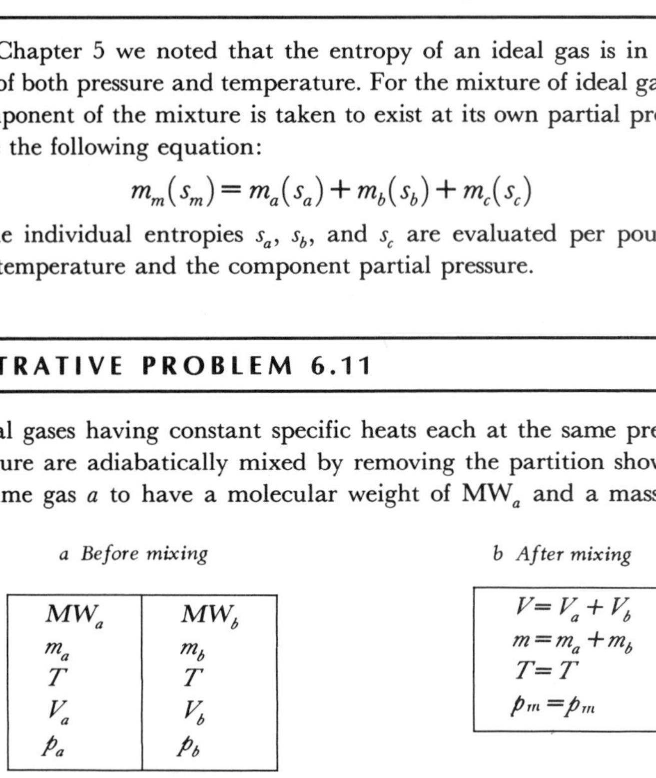

a Before mixing		b After mixing
MW_a MW_b		$V = V_a + V_b$
m_a m_b		$m = m_a + m_b$
T T		$T = T$
V_a V_b		$p_m = p_m$
p_a p_b		

Figure 6.5 Illustrative Problem 6.11

Assume gas b to have a molecular weight of MW_b and a mass of m_b lb. Determine the entropy change for this mixing process.

Solution

The general equation applicable to the change in entropy of an ideal gas due to both a pressure and temperature change is

$$\Delta s = c_p \ln\left(\frac{T_2}{T_1}\right) - \frac{R}{J}\ln\left(\frac{p_2}{p_1}\right) \quad (\text{Btu/lb} \,^\circ R) \qquad (5.34)$$

Since the process is carried out at constant temperature, the first term of Eq. (5.34) applied to this process is zero. Also, the final partial pressure of gas a is p_a, and the final partial pressure of gas b is p_b. Denoting the total pressure of the mixture as p_m,

$$\Delta S_a = - m_a \frac{R_a}{J} \ln\left(\frac{p_a}{p_m}\right)$$

and

$$\Delta S_b = - m_b \frac{R_b}{J} \ln\left(\frac{p_b}{p_m}\right)$$

The total change in entropy for the mixture for $m_a + m_b$ lb of mixture is

$$\Delta S = - \frac{m_a R_a}{J} \ln\left(\frac{p_a}{p_m}\right) - m_b \frac{R_b}{J} \ln\left(\frac{p_b}{p_m}\right)$$

However, $R = 1545/MW$. Therefore,

$$\Delta S = - \frac{m_a(1545)}{(MW_a)J} \ln\left(\frac{p_a}{p_m}\right) - \frac{m_b(1545)}{(MW_b)J} \ln\left(\frac{p_b}{p_m}\right)$$

We now note that $m_a/MW_a = n_a$, the number of moles of a; $m_b/(MW)_b = n_b$, the number of moles of b; $p_a/p_m = x_a$, the mole fraction of a; and $p_b/p_m = x_b$, the mole fraction of b:

$$\Delta S = - \frac{n_a(1545)}{J} \ln(x_a) - \frac{n_b(1545)}{J} \ln(x_b) \qquad (A)$$

Equation (A) is the desired result for the problem. However, it has an interesting conclusion in that the entropy increase due to the mixing process depends only on the moles of each gas present, but not upon the gas itself. Thus the mixing of 1 mole of oxygen with 1 mole of hydrogen will yield the same entropy increase as the mixing of 1 mole of argon with 1 mole of Freon. One point that should be noted at this time is that the adiabatic mixing of *identical* gases initially at the same pressure and temperature does not result in an increase in entropy and Eq. (A) is not applicable to this process. This has been called *Gibbs paradox*, and further discussion on it can be found in the references at the end of this chapter.

ILLUSTRATIVE PROBLEM 6.12

Determine the change in entropy for the process described in Illustrative Problem 6.9.

Solution

The change in entropy of the mixture is the sum of the changes in entropy of each component. For the oxygen, the temperature starts at 500°F (960°R) and decreases to 328.7°F. For the nitrogen, the temperature starts at 200°F (660°R) and increases to 328.7°F. Applying Eq. (5.34) and noting that the process is carried out at constant pressure, which makes the pressure term zero ($\ln 1 = 0$), *for the oxygen,*

$$\Delta s = c_p \ln\left(\frac{T_2}{T_1}\right) = 0.23 \ln\left(\frac{328.7 + 460}{500 + 460}\right)$$

$$= 0.23(\ln 788.7 - \ln 960) = -0.045 \text{ Btu/lb °F}$$

The total change in entropy of the oxygen is

$$\Delta S = 160(-0.045) = -7.20 \text{ Btu/°F}$$

For the nitrogen,

$$\Delta s = c_p \ln\left(\frac{T_2}{T_1}\right) = 0.25 \ln\left(\frac{328.7 + 460}{200 + 460}\right) = 0.045 \text{ Btu/lb °F}$$

The total change in entropy of the nitrogen is

$$\Delta S = 196(0.045) = 8.82 \text{ Btu/°F}$$

For the mixture, the total change in entropy is the sum of the changes of the constituent entropies. Therefore,

$$\Delta S = -7.20 + 8.82 = 1.62 \text{ Btu/°F}$$

Per pound of mixture,

$$\Delta s_m = \left(\frac{1.62}{196 + 160}\right) = 0.00455 \text{ Btu/lb °F} \quad \text{(increase per lb of mixture)}$$

As an alternate solution, assume an arbitrary datum of 0°F (460°R). The initial entropy of the oxygen above this base is

$$\Delta s = c_p \ln\left(\frac{T_2}{T_1}\right) = 0.23 \ln\left(\frac{500+460}{460}\right) = 0.169 \text{ Btu/lb °F}$$

The final entropy of the oxygen above this base is

$$\Delta s = c_p \ln\left(\frac{T_2}{T_1}\right) = 0.023 \ln\left(\frac{960}{460}\right) = 0.1240 \text{ Btu/lb °F}$$

The entropy change of the oxygen is, therefore,

$$\Delta s = 0.124 - 0.169 = -0.045 \text{ Btu/lb °F}$$

For the nitrogen,

$$\Delta s = c_p \ln\left(\frac{T_2}{T_1}\right) = 0.25 \ln\left(\frac{660}{460}\right)$$

$$= 0.090 \text{ Btu/lb °F} \quad \text{(above a base of 0°F) initially}$$

$$\Delta s = c_p \ln\left(\frac{T_2}{T_1}\right) = 0.25 \ln\left(\frac{460+328.7}{460}\right)$$

$$= 0.135 \text{ Btu/lb °F (above a base of 0°F) finally}$$

The entropy change of the nitrogen is, therefore,

$$\Delta s = 0.135 - 0.090 = 0.045 \text{ Btu/lb °F}$$

The remainder of the problem is as before. The advantage of this alternate method is that negative logarithms are avoided by choosing a reference temperature lower than any other temperature in the system.

6.6 AIR–WATER VAPOR MIXTURES*

A gas may be considered to be a vapor that is superheated. If the degree of superheat is high and the vapor is not close to critical conditions, it will usually behave as if it were an ideal gas. Although there are many exceptions to this

*The material in this section has been based largely on the *ASHRAE Guide and Data Book*, 1961, published by the American Society of Heating, Refrigerating, and Air-Conditioning Engineers, with permission.

generalization, it is found to be useful when treating air–water vapor mixtures. Air is a mixture of many gases, and dry air is defined as a mixture having the following composition by volume: oxygen, 20.95 percent; nitrogen, 78.09 percent; argon, 0.93 percent; carbon dioxide, 0.03 percent. In the treatment of air–water vapor mixtures it is common to treat air as a single gas with a molecular weight of 28.966.

Some of the concepts involved in dealing with air–water vapor mixtures can best be illustrated by referring to Fig. 6.6, a Ts diagram for an air–water vapor system. In general, atmospheric air contains superheated water vapor which may typically be at state B in Fig. 6.6. The dry-bulb temperature (T_1) is

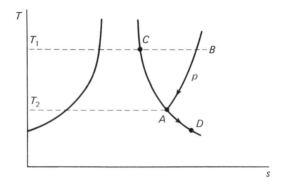

Figure 6.6 A Ts diagram for an air–water vapor system

the temperature of the mixture of air and water vapor at rest, and it is measured by an instrument (thermometer) that is not affected by the amount of moisture in the air or by thermal radiation. If the mixture of air and water vapor which is originally at B is cooled at constant pressure, it will follow the path from B to A along the constant-pressure line. In practice, the dew-point temperature is the temperature (T_2) at which condensation will just begin when the moist air mixture under consideration is cooled at constant pressure. If the mixture is cooled further, the water vapor will follow along the saturation line to D, and some moisture will condense. If water is added to the mixture at constant temperature, it will follow the path from B to C. Moist air is said to be saturated (C) when its condition is such that it can coexist in neutral equilibrium with an associated condensed moisture phase presenting a flat surface to it. The word neutral is used to exclude unstable states from the definition, and the flat surface is used to exclude surface-tension effects.

In addition to the quantities already defined, certain other terms describing air–water vapor mixtures require definition.

Relative Humidity (ϕ).

The relative humidity of any mixture of air and water vapor is defined as the ratio of the mole fraction of water vapor in the mixture to the mole fraction of water vapor in saturated air at the same dry-bulb temperature and barometric pressure.

Humidity Ratio (*W*). The humidity ratio of any mixture of air and water vapor is defined as the ratio of the mass of water vapor in the mixture to the mass of dry air in the mixture. The units of humidity ratio are pounds of water vapor per pound of dry air.

Specific Humidity. The term specific humidity has been and still is sometimes used for humidity ratio. They are synonymous.

Thermodynamic Wet Bulb Temperature. The thermodynamic wet bulb temperature is the temperature at which liquid or solidified water, by evaporating into air, can bring the air to saturation adiabatically at the same temperature. To illustrate the definition of the thermodynamic wet bulb temperature, consider the idealized system shown in Fig. 6.7. It is a steady-flow system in

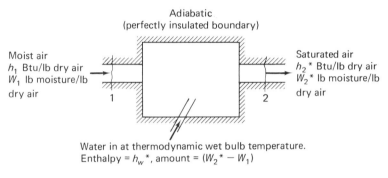

Figure 6.7 Adiabatic saturation process

which no work is done between sections 1 and 2, and no energy as heat enters or leaves. Water enters the system at the thermodynamic wet-bulb temperature, and air leaves the system saturated at the thermodynamic wet-bulb temperature. The energy equation for this process is, per pound of dry air,

$$h_1 + h_w^* (W_2^* - W_1) = h_2^* \qquad (6.19)$$

The * notation is used to denote properties at the thermodynamic wet bulb temperature, and the subscript w is used to denote water. The temperature corresponding to h_2^* for given values of h_1 and W_1 is the defined thermodynamic wet-bulb temperature. The process that we have just considered is also known as the *adiabatic saturation process*, and the thermodynamic wet bulb temperature is also known as the adiabatic saturation temperature. The usefulness of the foregoing discussion lies in the fact that the temperature of the saturated air–water vapor mixture leaving the duct is a function of the temperature, pressure, relative humidity of the entering mixture, and the exit pressure. Conversely, knowing the entering and exit pressures and temperatures, we can determine the relative humidity and humidity ratio of the entering air–water vapor mixture.

ILLUSTRATIVE PROBLEM 6.13

If the relative humidity of moist air is 50 percent when the mixture temperature is 80°F, determine the dew point of the air. Assume barometric pressure is 14.7 psia.

Solution

Referring to Fig. 6.6, it will be seen that the cooling of an air–water vapor mixture from *B* to *A* proceeds at constant pressure until the saturation curve is reached. The dew-point temperature of the air–water vapor mixture is equal to the saturation temperature, corresponding to the partial pressure of the water vapor. The relative humidity has been defined to be the ratio of the mole fraction of water vapor in the mixture to the mole fraction of water vapor in saturated air at the same dry bulb temperature and barometric pressure. It will be recalled from Section 6.2 that the partial pressure of a component equals the mole fraction of the component multiplied by the total pressure of the mixture. Since the relative humidity is a mole fraction ratio, it is also the ratio of the pressure of the vapor in the air to the saturation pressure corresponding to the temperature. At 80°F, the *Steam Tables* give us a saturation pressure of 0.5073 psia, and since the relative humidity is 50 percent, the vapor pressure of the water is $0.5 \times (0.5073) = 0.2537$ psia. Using the full *Steam Tables* or interpolating in the table in Appendix III yields a saturation temperature corresponding to 0.2537 psia as close to 60°F. This temperature is the desired dew point temperature.

ILLUSTRATIVE PROBLEM 6.14

Air at 90°F contains 0.005 lb of water vapor per pound of dry air. Determine the partial pressure of each component, the relative humidity, and the dew point temperature of the mixture if the mixture is at 14.7 psia.

Solution

To solve this problem, it is necessary to determine the properties of the saturated mixture at 90°F. If the air is saturated at 90°F, the partial pressure of the water vapor is found directly from the *Steam Tables* as 0.6988 psia, and the specific volume of the water vapor is 467.7 cu ft/lb of vapor. At this point let us assume that we have a container having a volume of 467.7 cu ft, and that it contains a saturated air–water vapor mixture at 90°F. Since the mixture is assumed to be saturated, there must be 1 lb of water vapor in the container, and the partial pressure of the dry air must be $14.7 - 0.6988 = 14.0$ psia. By applying the ideal gas equation to the air, we can determine the mass of air in the container. Thus

$$v_{\text{dry air}} = \frac{RT}{p_{\text{dry air}}} = \frac{1545}{28.966} \times \frac{(460+90)}{14.0 \times 144}$$

$$= 14.55 \text{ cu ft/lb dry air}$$

The mass of dry air in the 467.7 cu ft container is $467.7/14.55 = 32.1$ lb. The saturated mixture therefore contains 1 lb of water vapor per 32.1 lb of dry air or 0.0312 lb water vapor/lb dry air.

To obtain the relative humidity (ϕ), it is necessary to determine the mole fraction of water vapor for both the saturated mixture and the mixture in question. The saturated mixture contains 1 lb of water vapor or $1/18.016$ moles $= 0.055$ moles of water vapor and $32.1/28.966 = 1.109$ moles of dry air. Therefore, for the saturated mixture, the ratio of moles of water vapor to moles of mixture is $0.0555/(1.109+0.055) = 0.0477$. For the actual mixture, the moles of water vapor per pound of dry air is $0.005/18.016 = 0.000278$, and 1 lb of dry air is $1/28.966 = 0.0345$ moles. The moles of water vapor per mole of mixture at the conditions of the mixture is $0.000278/(0.0345 + 0.000278) = 0.00799$. From the definition of relative humidity, the relative humidity of this mixture is $0.00799/0.0477 = 0.168$ or 16.8 percent.

Since the mole ratio is also the ratio of the partial pressures for the ideal gas, ϕ can be expressed as the ratio of the partial pressure of the water vapor in the mixture to the partial pressure of the water vapor at saturation. Therefore, the partial pressure of the water vapor is $0.168 \times 0.6988 = 0.1173$ psia, and the partial pressure of the dry air in the mixture is $14.7 - 0.1173 = 14.58$ psia.

The dew point temperature is the saturation temperature corresponding to the partial pressure of the water vapor in the mixture. The saturation temperature corresponding to 0.1173 psia is found from the *Steam Tables* to be close to 39°F.

The adiabatic saturation of air is a process that is useful to analytically study the thermodynamics of air–water vapor mixtures. If this process had to be used each time one wished to obtain the relative humidity of an air–water vapor mixture, it would be impractical. Instead, a relatively simple method is used to establish the partial pressure of the water vapor based upon a temperature known as the wet-bulb temperature. The concept of the wet-bulb temperature can be developed by reference to Fig. 6.8. Two thermometers are placed in a moving air stream. The bulb of the wet-bulb thermometer is covered with a gauze that is immersed in clean water and acts to wick the water to the bulb. Air is continuously blown over the thermometer by a fan. At the wet-bulb thermometer, three actions occur. The first is that water will evaporate from the wick due to heat transfer to the air at the dry-bulb

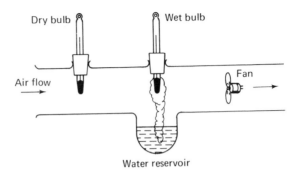

Figure 6.8 Steady flow apparatus for measuring wet- and dry-bulb temperature (From *Thermodynamics* by G. J. Van Wylen, John Wiley & Sons, Inc., New York, 1959, p. 223, with permission)

temperature; the second action is water evaporation from the wick due to radiant heat transfer from the surroundings; the last action is a diffusion of water vapor from the wick to the surrounding air–water vapor mixture. Due to these actions the temperature of the wet-bulb thermometer will be lower than the dry-bulb temperature. In practice, one method of obtaining the wet- and dry-bulb temperatures is by use of the sling psychrometer shown in Fig. 6.9. As shown, two thermometers are mounted on a sling, with the wet-bulb thermometer having a gauze wick around its bulb which is saturated with water. The sling is whirled around, which causes evaporation of water from the wick and lowers the temperature of the wet-bulb thermometer. When equilibrium is reached, both thermometers are read to obtain the wet- and dry-bulb temperatures. The sling psychrometer is an inexpensive portable device which is easy to use. An alternate device, known as an aspiration psychrometer, is shown in Fig. 6.10. In this device a small fan is used to draw air over the wet- and dry-bulb thermometers as shown. While less portable than the sling psychrometer, it gives continuous readings.

In principle, there is a difference between the wet-bulb temperature and the temperature of adiabatic saturation (the thermodynamic wet-bulb temperature). The wet-bulb temperature is a function of both heat and mass diffusion rates, while the adiabatic saturation temperature is a function of a thermodynamic equilibrium process. However, in practice, it has been found that for air–water vapor mixtures at atmospheric pressures and temperatures, the wet-bulb and adiabatic saturation temperatures are essentially the same. Thus the observed readings of the wet-bulb thermometer can be taken to be the same as the thermodynamic wet-bulb temperature defined by the adiabatic saturation process if the air velocity past the wick is approximately 1000 ft/min, and if the wick is exposed to radiation exchange with the surroundings at temperatures differing from the dry-bulb temperature by no more than 20°F. It must be noted as a caution that the wet-bulb temperature and adiabatic saturation temperatures deviate considerably from each other for other than air–water

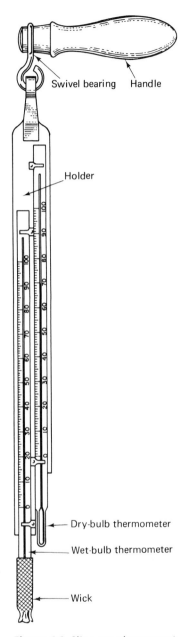

Swivel bearing   Handle

Holder

Dry-bulb thermometer

Wet-bulb thermometer

Wick

Figure 6.9 Sling psychrometer*

*Figures 6.9 and 6.10 are from *Thermal Engineering* by C. C. Dillio and E. P. Nye, International Textbook Co., Scranton, Pa., 1959, pp. 465, 466, with permission.

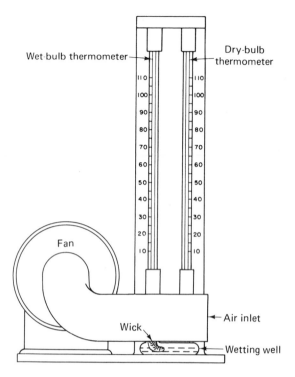

Figure 6.10 Aspiration psychrometer

vapor gas–vapor mixtures and for air–water vapor mixtures at conditions other than usual atmospheric conditions.

Problems concerning air–water vapor mixtures can be considerably simplified by using the ideal gas equations for each of the components. By denoting the subscripts a to be dry, v to be water vapor, vs to be saturated water vapor, s to be saturation, and m to mean mixture, the following relations can be derived:

Gas Constant of the Mixture.

$$R_m = \left(\frac{m_a}{m_a + m_v} \right) R_a + \left(\frac{m_v}{m_a + m_v} \right) R_v \qquad (6.20)$$

By dividing the numerator and denominator of each of the terms in parentheses by m_a,

$$R_m = \left[\frac{1}{1 + \dfrac{m_v}{m_a}} \right] R_a + \left(\frac{m_v/m_a}{1 + m_v/m_a} \right) R_v$$

But m_v/m_a is the humidity ratio W.

$$R_m = \left(\frac{1}{1+W}\right) R_a + \left(\frac{W}{1+W}\right) R_v \qquad (6.21)$$

Since W is a small number compared to unity, it is possible as a first approximation to use the gas constant of the mixture as the gas constant of dry air.

Relative Humidity. The relative humidity ϕ is

$$\phi = \frac{p_v}{p_{vs}} = \frac{v_{vs}}{v_v} = \left(\frac{\rho_v}{\rho_{vs}}\right) \qquad (6.22)$$

When the mixture is at the dew-point temperature, ϕ is 1.

Humidity Ratio.

$$W = \frac{m_v}{m_a} = \left(\frac{18.016}{28.966}\right)\left(\frac{p_v}{p_a}\right) = 0.622\left(\frac{p_v}{p_m - p_v}\right) \qquad (6.23)$$

In Eq. (6.23), 18.016 is the molecular weight of water vapor and 28.966 is the molecular weight of dry air.

Relative Humidity and Humidity Ratio. From Eqs. (6.22) and (6.23),

$$\phi p_{vs} = p_v \qquad (6.24)$$

Therefore,

$$W = 0.622\left(\frac{p_v}{p_a}\right) = 0.622\phi\left(\frac{p_{vs}}{p_a}\right) = \phi\left(\frac{p_{vs}}{p_a}\right)\left(\frac{R_a}{R_v}\right) = \phi\left(\frac{\rho_{vs}}{\rho_a}\right) = \phi\left(\frac{v_a}{v_{vs}}\right)$$

ILLUSTRATIVE PROBLEM 6.15

Solve Illustrative Problem 6.14 using Eqs. (6.20) through (6.24).

Solution

W is given as 0.005. Therefore,

$$W = 0.005 = 0.622\left(\frac{p_v}{p_m - p_v}\right)$$

with $p_m = 14.7$ psia. Thus $p_v = (0.005 \times 14.7)/(0.622 + 0.005) = 0.117$ psia, and $p_a = 14.7 - 0.117 = 14.58$ psia. Since $\phi = p_v/p_{vs}$, it is necessary to obtain p_{vs} from the *Steam Tables* at 90°F. This is 0.6988 psia. Therefore, $\phi = 0.117/0.6988 = 0.167 = 16.7$ percent. The dew-point temperature is the saturation temperature corresponding to 0.117 psia, which is found from the *Steam Tables* to be 39°F. The results of this problem and Illustrative Problem 6.14 are in good agreement.

ILLUSTRATIVE PROBLEM 6.16

Air at 90°F and 70 percent relative humidity is conditioned so that its final state is 80°F and 40 percent relative humidity. How much water was removed from the air? Assume that the barometer is at 14.7 psia.

Solution

The amount of water vapor removed (per pound of dry air) is the difference between the humidity ratio (specific humidity) at inlet and outlet of the conditioning unit. We shall therefore evaluate W for both specified conditions. Since $\phi = p_v/p_{vs}$,

$$\text{at } 90°\text{F}, \, p_{vs} = 0.6988 \text{ psia}$$
$$\text{at } 80°\text{F}, \, p_{vs} = 0.5073 \text{ psia}$$
$$\text{at } 90°\text{F}, \, p_v = 0.7 \times 0.6988 = 0.4892 \text{ psia}$$
$$\text{at } 80°\text{F}, \, p_v = 0.4 \times 0.5069 = 0.2028 \text{ psia}$$

But $p_a = p_m - p_v$. Thus

$$\text{at } 90°\text{F}, \, p_a = 14.7 - 0.4892 = 14.2108 \text{ psia}$$
$$\text{at } 80°\text{F}, \, p_a = 14.7 - 0.2028 = 14.4972 \text{ psia}$$

Since $\qquad W = 0.622 p_v/p_a$

$$\text{at } 90°\text{F}, \, W = 0.622 \left(\frac{0.4892}{14.2108} \right) = 0.0214 \text{ lb water/lb dry air}$$

$$\text{at } 80°\text{F}, \, W = 0.622 \left(\frac{0.2028}{14.4972} \right) = 0.0087 \text{ lb water/lb dry air}$$

The amount of water removed per pound of dry air is

$$0.0214 - 0.0087 = 0.0127 \text{ lb water removed/lb dry air}$$

A unit of weight commonly used in air conditioning work is the *grain*. By definition there are 7000 grains per pound. Using this definition, the water removal per pound of dry air in Illustrative Problem 6.16 is $7000 \times 0.0127 = 88.9$ grains/lb dry air.

6.7 THERMODYNAMIC PROPERTIES OF AIR–WATER VAPOR MIXTURES

The thermodynamic properties of air–water vapor mixtures can be determined from tabulated data available in the latest edition of the *ASHRAE Guide and Data Book*, published by the American Society of Heating, Refrigerating, and Air Conditioning Engineers. These data are tabulated from $-160°$ to $200°F$ for moist air at 29.921 in. Hg and are given for either perfectly dry or completely saturated air. By simple interpolation, the specific volume, enthalpy, or entropy of mixtures can be obtained. The interpolation formulas are given in the *Guide*.

For those designs or analyses that require accuracies which cannot be achieved by use of the ideal gas relations, these tables are invaluable. However, for those cases that can be dealt with by using ideal gas relations, it is possible to express the thermodynamic properties of air–water vapor mixtures in a relatively simple manner. It is convenient to express these properties per unit mass of dry air in the mixture, for example, Btu's per pound of dry air.

Specific Heat of the Mixture. The specific heat of the mixture in Btu's per pound per degree Fahrenheit (of dry air) is

$$c_{pm} = c_{pa} + W c_{pv} \qquad (6.25)$$

where $c_{pa} = 0.24$ Btu/lb °F and $c_{pv} = 0.44$ Btu/lb °F in the ordinary temperature range.

Enthalpy of the Mixture. The enthalpy of the mixture is given by

$$h_m = h_a + W h_v \qquad (6.26)$$

It is possible to express h_m accurately to within 0.1 percent between $32°$ and $100°F$ at 1 atm (29.921 in. Hg) by

$$h_m = (0.2402 + 0.44 W)t + 1061 W \qquad (6.27)$$

where t is the dry-bulb temperature in degrees Fahrenheit.

Entropy of the Mixture. The entropy of the mixture can be given as

$$s_m = s_a + W s_v \qquad (6.28)$$

where s_a and s_v are evaluated at the respective partial pressures in the mixture.

6.8 THE PSYCHROMETRIC CHART

Just as the Mollier chart was found to be useful in plotting the thermodynamic properties of a fluid, a psychrometric chart is found to be equally useful when dealing with air–water vapor mixtures (see Fig. 6.11). To understand the chart and its limitations fully, let us construct one in outline form. From the *Steam Tables* we have the following data:

TEMPERATURE (°F)	PRESSURE (psia)
32	0.08859
40	0.12166
50	0.17803
60	0.2563
70	0.3632
80	0.5073
90	0.6988
100	0.9503
110	1.2763
120	1.6945

If these data are plotted with the pressure of water vapor as the ordinate and the temperature (dry-bulb) as abscissa, the saturation curve is established as indicated in Fig. 6.12. From Eq. (6.22) the relative humidity is the ratio of p_v/p_{vs}. Thus by dividing the saturation pressures at each dry-bulb temperature into equal parts and connecting corresponding points, it is possible to construct lines of constant relative humidity. The outline of the 50 percent relative humidity line has been drawn on Fig. 6.12.

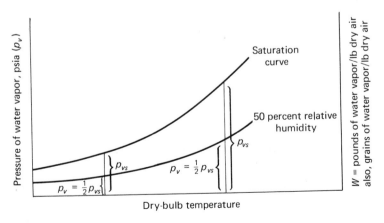

Figure 6.12 Skeleton psychrometric chart

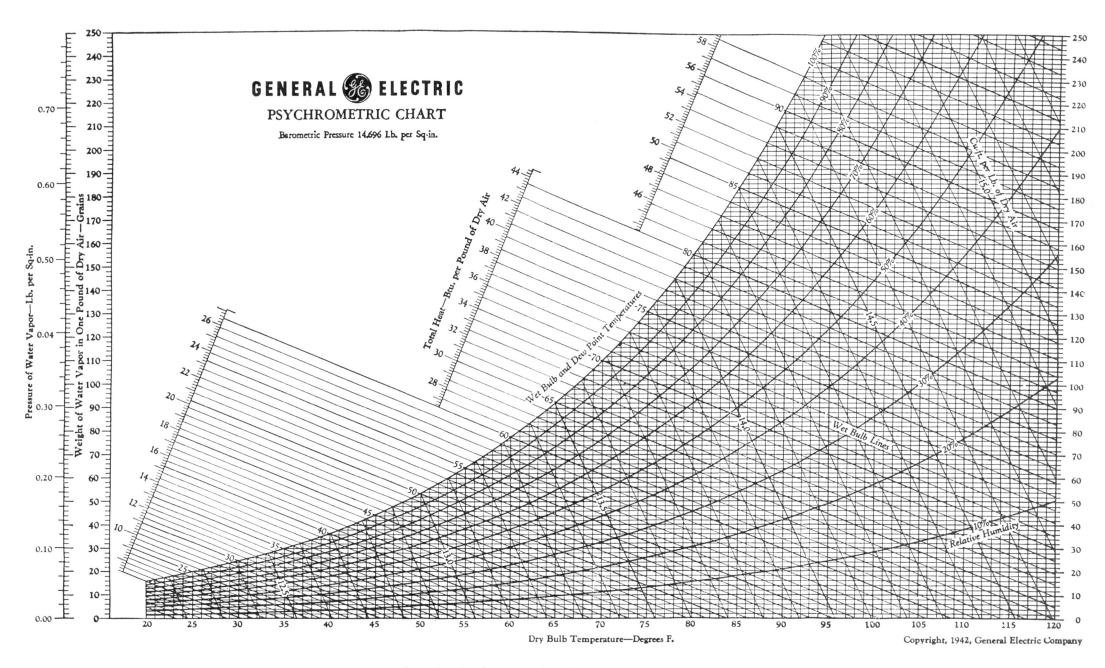

Figure 6.11 Psychrometric chart for air–water vapor mixtures

Let us further assume that the chart will apply for a given barometric pressure, say 29.921 in. Hg. From Eq. (6.23),

$$W = 0.622\left(\frac{p_v}{p_m - p_v}\right)$$

Since the mixture pressure has been assumed to be constant, W becomes a simple linear function of p_v. Thus the ordinate also becomes proportional to the weight of water vapor per pound of dry air. Since by definition there are 7000 grains/lb, we have plotted on the right ordinate of Fig. 6.12 an auxiliary scale of W in grains of water vapor per pound of dry air.

From Eq. (6.24) it is possible to evaluate the specific volume of the mixture per pound of dry air. Since ideal gas relations have been assumed, the specific volume of the air–water vapor mixture is a linear function of the humidity ratio W. Lines of constant specific volume are shown in Fig. 6.13.

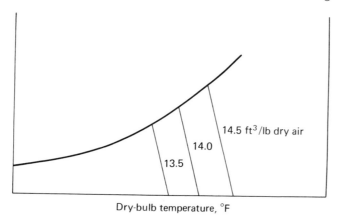

Figure 6.13 Skeleton psychrometric chart

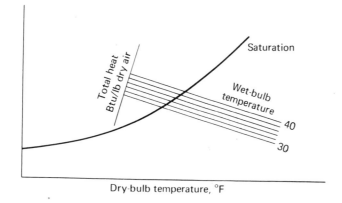

Figure 6.14 Skeleton psychrometric chart

By using the ideal gas relation and Eq. (6.27), the enthalpy of the mixture is also found to be linear with dry-bulb temperature and humidity ratio. Typical lines of constant enthalpy (total heat) are indicated in Fig. 6.14. Figure 6.14 also shows the lines of constant "total heat" and wet-bulb temperatures as the same. Actually, wet-bulb temperature lines are straight, but they are not parallel. However, the error is small enough to be negligible. For a further discussion of the conclusions regarding the relation of total heat to enthalpy, etc., the reader is referred to the ASHRAE publications.

ILLUSTRATIVE PROBLEM 6.17

Solve Illustrative Problem 6.13 using the psychrometric chart.

Solution

Entering Fig. 6.11 at a dry-bulb temperature of 80°F, we proceed vertically until we reach the 50 percent humidity curve. At this intersection, we proceed horizontally and read the dew-point temperature as approximately 60°F.

ILLUSTRATIVE PROBLEM 6.18

Solve Illustrative Problem 6.14 using the psychrometric chart.

Solution

In this problem we are given the moisture content of the air to be 0.005 lb/lb dry air. This corresponds to $0.005 \times 7000 = 35$ grains/lb dry air. Entering the chart at 90°F and proceeding vertically to 35 grains/lb of dry air, we find the dew point to be 39°F by proceeding horizontally to the intersection with the saturation curve. The relative humidity is approximately 17 percent. From the leftmost scale we read the pressure of water vapor to be 0.12 psia. The partial pressure of the air is $14.7 - 0.12 = 14.58$ psia. Comparing these results to Illustrative Problem 6.14 indicates good agreement between the results obtained by chart and by calculation.

ILLUSTRATIVE PROBLEM 6.19

Solve Illustrative Problem 6.16 using the psychrometric chart.

Solution

The initial conditions are 90°F and 70 percent relative humidity. Entering the chart at 90°F dry-bulb temperature and proceeding vertically to 70 percent relative humidity, we find the air to have 150 grains water vapor/lb of dry air. At the final condition of 80°F and 40 percent relative humidity, we read 61 grains of water/lb of dry air. The water removed is $150 - 61 = 89$ grains/lb of dry air or $89/7000 = 0.0127$ lb of water/lb of dry air removed.

Having constructed the chart, we can illustrate its usefulness best by showing typical processes on the chart.

Dew-Point Determination—Heating and Cooling Without Change in Moisture Content. From the definition of the dew point, it is apparent that a horizontal line on the chart (cooling at constant pressure of water vapor) extended to the saturation line will yield the dew-point temperature. This process of "sensible" heating or cooling (Fig. 6.15) is distinguished by a change in dry-bulb temperature, relative humidity, wet-bulb temperature, total heat, and specific volume, and by no change in moisture content, dew-point temperature, and vapor pressure of the moisture in the air.

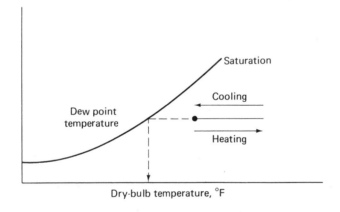

Figure 6.15 Sensible heating or cooling process

Figure 6.16 shows an example of chilled-water coils using extended surfaces (fins) to increase the heat transfer of the unit. This type of construction is usually used in larger installations where cooling (or heating) is accomplished by flowing the heat-transfer medium inside the tubes and passing the air over the external tube surface. When extended surfaces are used, they may be staggered or placed in line with the air flow. In those cases where frost may accumulate on the tube surface, plain tubes, rather than extended surface elements, are used. Coil performance is dependent on the way air flows over the outside of the tubes in relation to the way the heating or cooling fluid flows on the inside of the tubes. A discussion of the heat transfer in heat exchangers is given in Chapter 9.

Figure 6.16 Air cooling and heating coils

ILLUSTRATIVE PROBLEM 6.20

How much heat is required to sensibly heat air having a dry-bulb temperature of 50°F and a relative humidity of 50 percent to 80°F?

Solution

We first locate 50°F and 50 percent relative humidity on Fig. 6.11. At this state we read 26 grains of water/lb of dry air and a total heat of 16.1 Btu/lb of dry air. We now proceed horizontally to 80°F at a constant value of 26 grains of water/lb of dry air, and read a total heat of 23.4 Btu/lb of dry air. The heat required is therefore $23.4 - 16.1 = 7.3$ Btu/lb of dry air.

Humidifying of Air with No Change in Dry-Bulb Temperature. As shown in Fig. 6.17, this process is a vertical line on the psychrometric chart between the desired moisture limits. During this process there is an increase in relative humidity, wet-bulb temperature, total heat, specific volume, moisture

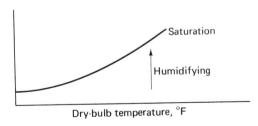

Figure 6.17 Humidification of air: Constant dry-bulb temperature

content, dew-point temperature, and vapor pressure of the moisture in the air. The addition of moisture to air is usually necessary for winter operation of air-conditioning systems. The process shown in Fig. 6.17 can be accomplished by using heated spray water whose temperature is kept above the dry-bulb temperature of the air. In the limit the air temperature approaches the final water temperature.

The control of the moisture content of air is one of the principal functions of air-conditioning systems. The addition of moisture is known as *humidification*, and the removal of moisture is known as *dehumidification*. The apparatus known as an air washer can be used to perform both processes, as well as to clean the air. Figure 6.18 shows the principle of the spray-type air washer. In essence, an air washer consists of a casing with one or more spray bands through which air flows, and at the outlet there is an eliminator to remove any entrained moisture. The operation of the spray washer can be summarized by noting that (1) if the final water temperature is held above the entering air dry-bulb temperature, the air is both heated and humidified; (2) if the final water temperature is kept below the entering air dry-bulb temperature, the air will be cooled and humidified; (3) if the final water temperature is held below the air's dew point, the air is both cooled and dehumidified.

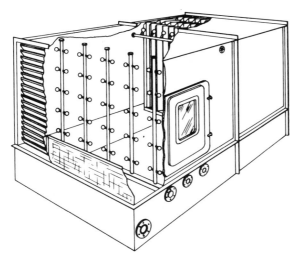

Figure 6.18 Spray type air washer (From *Refrigeration and Air Conditioning* by W. F. Stoecker, McGraw-Hill Book Company, New York, 1958, p. 291, with permission)

Evaporative Cooling of Air. If air is brought into contact with water that is at the wet-bulb temperature of the air, moisture will be added to the air at constant wet-bulb temperature. Since a line of constant wet-bulb temperature is also a line of constant total heat, the total heat for this process is constant. The heat "lost" by the incoming air serves to increase the moisture content of the final air, as given by Eq. (6.27). Although both the wet-bulb temperature and total heat of the air remain constant, the dry-bulb temperature and the specific volume decrease as the relative humidity, the moisture content, and vapor pressure of the moisture in the air increase. This process is shown in Fig 6.19. As the process proceeds along the line of constant wet-bulb temperature, the dry-bulb temperature and dew point of the leaving air approach the wet-bulb temperature of the air. The spray-type air washer shown in Fig. 6.18 can be used to accomplish this process. Since it is desired to obtain intimate contact between the air and water, another type of washer, shown in Fig. 6.20, is often used. In this unit the capillary action of glass filaments is used to thoroughly distribute water sprayed across the wetted surface. Air passing through the thoroughly soaked mass of glass fibers comes into intimate contact with a multiplicity of wetted surfaces. The excess water is collected in the bottom of the unit and recirculated. Evaporative cooling is one of the oldest methods of cooling known to man and is most successfully used in regions that are dry, such as in deserts. Portable evaporative coolers have been used in automobile and truck cabs in arid and desert regions for comfort control. For this method to be effective, there must be a large difference between the wet and dry-bulb temperatures of the air, making it ineffective in humid, tropic areas.

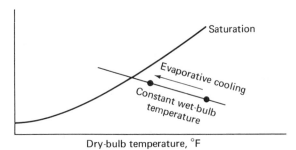

Dry-bulb temperature, °F

Figure 6.19 Evaporative cooling of air

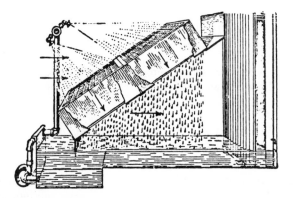

Figure 6.20 Capillary type of air washer

ILLUSTRATIVE PROBLEM 6.21

In an evaporative cooling process the exit air is found to be saturated at 50°F. If the entering air has a dry-bulb temperature of 80°F, determine the relative humidity of the entering air.

Solution

Since the exit air is saturated, we find the exit condition on the saturation curve corresponding to a wet-bulb temperature of 50°F. The process is carried out at constant total enthalpy, which is along a line of constant wet-bulb temperature. Proceeding along the 50°F wet-bulb temperature line of Fig. 6.11 diagonally to the right until it intersects with the vertical 80°F dry-bulb temperature line yields a relative humidity of approximately 4 percent.

Chemical Drying of Air. If air is passed over a drying agent which is not dissolved by the moisture extracted from the air and which does not retain an appreciable amount of the heat of vaporization liberated when the water is condensed, the process can be said to be carried out along a wet-bulb temperature line. If the adsorber retains an appreciable amount of this heat, the process takes place along a line below the wet-bulb temperature line. When the adsorber is soluble in water (such as calcium chloride), the process line is above or below the wet-bulb temperature line, depending on whether heat is liberated or absorbed when the adsorber goes into solution. This process is shown graphically in Fig. 6.21. Typical solid adsorbents are activated alumina, silica

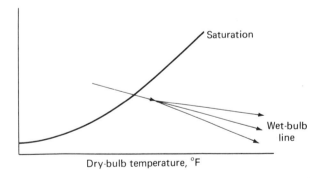

Figure 6.21 Chemical drying of air

gel, activated carbon, and bauxite. These remove water from an air stream only if the vapor pressure of the water in the adsorbent is less than the partial pressure of the water vapor in the surrounding air stream. In other words, the process is primarily one of condensation. The latent heat of vaporization and heat of adsorption have to be taken away by the surroundings. Thus the air stream, the adsorbent itself, and the adsorbent container all increase in temperature. Eventually, the sorbent temperature reaches a state of equilibrium, and the material has to be reactivated—heated to drive off the adsorbed moisture and cooled down for reuse.

Figure 6.22 shows a typical two-bed unit designed to operate continuously. Filtered air enters the unit and is ducted to one of the beds. While the first bed is working, the other is being reactivated by heating the sorbent (silica gel in this case) to approximately 300°F. Heating may be done by steam coils, electricity, gas, and so on.

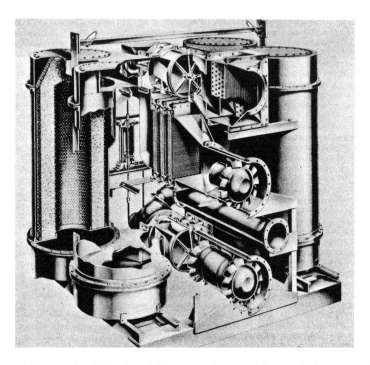

Figure 6.22 Two-bed solid dehumidifier (Reprinted with permission from *Power, The Engineer's Reference Library*, copyright by McGraw-Hill, Inc., New York)

Liquid sorbents such as the glycols, lithium chloride, calcium chloride, and lithium bromide functionally operate in a manner similar to the solid sorbents. These solutions must have concentrations such that their vapor pressure with respect to water is lower than that of the water vapor to be removed from the air. In the typical liquid-sorbent equipment, air passes through a tower into which the liquid sorbent is sprayed either in a fine mist or as a blanketing solution on the tower surfaces. Again, differences in partial pressure determine the absorption. Soon a state of equilibrium is reached. The sorbent solution, the air, and the equipment increase in temperature as latent and chemical absorption heats are taken up.

The warm, weak sorbent solution is first cooled. Then part is diverted for concentration. This is done by heating it to a vapor pressure well above that of the air blown over it; water in solution goes off with the air. After cooling, the concentrated solution rejoins the main stream to maintain proper density, the principal factor determining water absorption by liquid sorbents. Figure 6.23 shows a liquid sorbent unit in which the tower on the left fixes the moisture content of the conditioned air, while in the one on the right the sorbent releases its water and is reconcentrated.

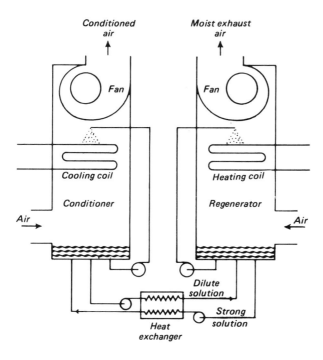

Figure 6.23 Dehumidifier (From *Refrigeration and Air Conditioning* by W. F. Stoecker, McGraw-Hill Book Company, New York, 1958, p. 293, with permission)

Cooling and Dehumidifying of Air.

If the cooling surface temperature is below the initial dew-point temperature, this process can be portrayed as a straight line extending from the initial condition to the surface temperature on the saturation curve. The final condition of the air will depend on the total heat extracted from the air. During this process the dry-bulb temperature, wet-bulb temperature, moisture content, specific volume, vapor pressure of the moisture, and total heat all decrease as indicated in Fig. 6.24. The coils shown in Fig. 6.16 can also be used for cooling and dehumidifying air by keeping the coil temperature below the dew point of the entering air.

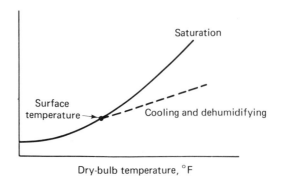

Figure 6.24 Cooling and dehumidifying process

Adiabatic Mixing of Air Streams. The mixing of two air streams at different initial conditions is quite commonly used in air-conditioning work. Let us assume that no condensation takes place during this process. Then, from Fig. 6.25, a mass balance on the dry air is

$$\dot{m}_{a_1} + \dot{m}_{a_2} = \dot{m}_a \qquad (6.29)$$

where $\dot{m}_{a_1}$ is the mass flow rate of dry air in stream 1, $\dot{m}_{a_2}$ is the mass flow rate of dry air in stream 2, and $\dot{m}_a$ is the mass flow rate of the combined streams. A mass balance on the water vapor yields

$$\dot{m}_{a_1} W_1 + \dot{m}_{a_2} W_2 = \dot{m}_a W \qquad (6.30)$$

For an adiabatic mixing process in which velocity and elevation terms are negligible and in which no work enters or leaves the system, an energy balance yields

$$\dot{m}_{a_1} h_{a_1} + \dot{m}_{a_2} h_{a_2} = \dot{m}_a h_a \qquad (6.31)$$

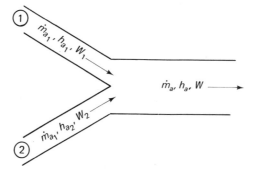

Figure 6.25 Adiabatic mixing of air streams

A combination of these equations yields

$$\frac{h_a - h_{a_2}}{h_a - h_{a_1}} = \frac{W_2 - W}{W - W_1} = \frac{\dot{m}_{a_1}}{\dot{m}_{a_2}} = \frac{l_1}{l_2} \qquad (6.32)$$

where l_1 and l_2 are the corresponding line segment lengths shown on Fig. 6.26. Equation (6.32) can be interpreted to mean that the mixing of air at one condition with air at another condition can be represented by a straight line connecting the initial and final conditions. The final mixture will lie along this line at a point determined by the relative quantities of air being mixed, as shown in Fig. 6.26.

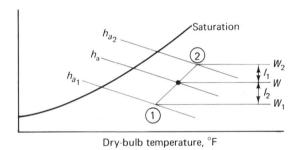

Dry-bulb temperature, °F

Figure 6.26 Adiabatic mixing of air streams

ILLUSTRATIVE PROBLEM 6.22

Indoor air at 75°F dry bulb and 50 percent relative humidity is to be mixed with outdoor air at 90°F dry bulb and 60 percent relative humidity. If 4 parts of indoor air is mixed with 1 part of outdoor air (by weight), what is the final mixture composition?

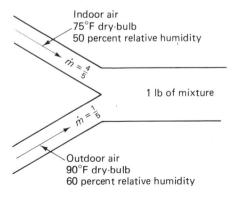

Figure 6.27 Illustrative Problem 6.22

Solution

As noted from Fig. 6.27, if we consider 1 lb of mixture, $\frac{4}{5}$ lb of indoor air and $\frac{1}{5}$ lb of outdoor air are mixed per pound of mixture. We now locate the two end states on the psychrometric chart and connect them with a straight line. The line connecting the end states is divided into 5 equal parts. Using the results of Eq. (6.32), we now proceed *from* the 75°F indoor air state 1 part *toward* the 90°F outdoor air state. This locates the state of the mixture, which is found to be a dry-bulb temperature of approximately 78°F, a wet-bulb temperature of approximately 66°F, and a relative humidity of approximately 54 percent.

The Cooling Tower. The cooling tower has been used in situations where the supply of water is limited or due to economic considerations. Recently, the effect on the environment due to the heat rejection to the cooling water of a power plant (thermal pollution) has become a factor in power-plant design. To minimize the environmental impact on rivers or other water sources, the cooling tower is used to cool the water discharged from the condensers, and this water is then recirculated. In effect, instead of using river or local water to carry off the heat rejected in the power plant, the atmosphere is used. The cooling tower is simply a device in which water is evaporatively cooled by air. In the natural-draft cooling tower, air is circulated through the tower in a horizontal direction while water is sprayed or trickled over wood filling. In the forced-draft cooling tower, a fan is used to positively circulate air countercurrent to the falling water. The fan can be located at the bottom of the tower, and this arrangement is known as forced-draft tower; if the fan is located at the top to prevent recirculation of the hot moist air, we have an induced-draft tower. Figure 6.28 shows a large bank of cooling towers used in a power

Figure 6.28 Large cooling tower installation

installation. We can analyze the action in the cooling tower by referring to the schematic diagram of Fig. 6.29. In this diagram, air flows from bottom to top of

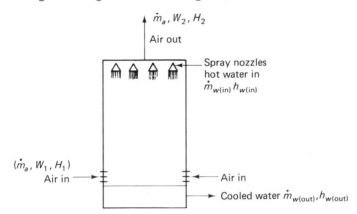

Figure 6.29 Schematic diagram of a cooling tower

the tower, and water droplets flow counter to the air stream and are in intimate contact with the counterflowing air stream. Heat is transferred to the air, raising its wet-bulb temperature, its dry-bulb temperature, and its moisture content. The evaporation of a small portion of the water accounts for the water cooling effect. The water that evaporates into the air stream must be replaced, and this replacement water is known as *makeup*. Referring to the symbols of Fig. 6.29, we can write a heat balance for the tower by considering the air and water streams separately.

For the air:

$$\text{heat pickup per lb of dry air} = H_2 - H_1, \text{ where } H = \text{total heat/lb dry air}$$

$$\text{total heat pickup} = \dot{m}_a(H_2 - H_1)$$

$$\text{moisture pickup per lb of dry air} = W_2 - W_1$$

$$\text{total moisture pickup} = \dot{m}_a(W_2 - W_1)$$

For the water:

$$\text{entering total enthalpy} = \dot{m}_{w(\text{in})}h_{w(\text{in})}$$

$$\text{leaving total enthalpy} = \dot{m}_{w(\text{out})}h_{w(\text{out})}$$

$$\text{total water enthalpy change} = \dot{m}_{w(\text{in})}h_{w(\text{in})} - \dot{m}_{w(\text{out})}h_{w(\text{out})}$$

$$\text{water evaporated} = \dot{m}_{w(\text{in})} - \dot{m}_{w(\text{out})}$$

Since the heat picked up by the air must equal the heat exchanged by the water, we have

$$\dot{m}_a(H_2 - H_1) = \dot{m}_{w(\text{in})}h_{w(\text{in})} - \dot{m}_{w(\text{out})}h_{w(\text{out})} \qquad (6.33)$$

The water picked up by the air must equal the water loss in the tower. Therefore,

$$\dot{m}_a(W_2 - W_1) = \dot{m}_{w(\text{in})} - \dot{m}_{w(\text{out})} \qquad (6.34)$$

Equations (6.33) and (6.34) provide the basic relations for the solution of cooling tower problems.

ILLUSTRATIVE PROBLEM 6.23

Hot water enters a cooling tower at the rate of 200,000 lb/hr at 100°F, and the water leaving is at 70°F. Air enters the tower at a dry-bulb temperature of 60°F with a 50 percent relative humidity and leaves at a dry-bulb temperature of 90°F with a relative humidity of 90 percent. Assuming atmospheric pressure is 14.7 psia and the psychrometric chart (Fig. 6.11) can be used, determine the amount of water lost per hour due to evaporation and the amount of air required per hour. The situation is summed up in Fig. 6.30.

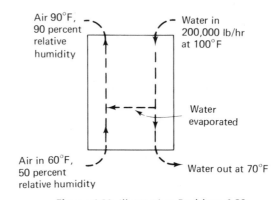

Figure 6.30 Illustrative Problem 6.23

Solution

Let us first obtain the necessary physical data required from the *Steam Tables* and the psychrometric chart.

For the water:

$$h_{100°\text{F}} = 68.05 \text{ Btu/lb}$$
$$h_{70°\text{F}} = 38.09 \text{ Btu/lb}$$

For the air:

at inlet $H = 20.4$ Btu/lb dry air
$W = 38.2$ grains/lb dry air
(at 60°F D.B. and 50% R.H.)

at outlet $H = 52.1$ Btu/lb dry air
$W = 194.0$ grains/lb dry air
(at 90°F D.B. and 90% R.H.)

Per pound of dry air, the heat interchange is $52.1 - 20.4 = 31.7$ Btu/lb dry air. Per pound of dry air, the moisture increase is $(194.0 - 38.2)/7000 = 0.0223$ lb/lb dry air. From Eq. (6.33),

$$\dot{m}_a(31.7) = 200{,}000(68.05) - \dot{m}_{w(\text{out})}(38.09)$$

From Eq. (6.34),

$$\dot{m}_a(0.0223) = 200{,}000 - \dot{m}_{w(\text{out})}$$

Solving the latter equation for $\dot{m}_{w(\text{out})}$,

$$\dot{m}_{w(\text{out})} = 200{,}000 - \dot{m}_a(0.0223)$$

Substituting this into the heat balance yields

$$\dot{m}_a(31.7) = 200{,}000(68.05) - 200{,}000(38.09) + \dot{m}_a(0.0223)(38.09)$$

Solving,

$$\dot{m}_a(31.7 - 0.85) = 200{,}000(68.05 - 38.09) = 5{,}992{,}000$$

$$\dot{m}_a = 194{,}230 \text{ lb/hr of dry air}$$

water evaporated (lost) $= 194{,}230 \times 0.0223 = 4331$ lb/hr

Note that the water evaporated is slightly over 2 percent of the incoming water, and this is the makeup that has to be furnished to the tower.

6.9 AIR CONDITIONING

In the previous sections of this chapter we have studied the properties of air–water vapor mixtures in some detail and the processes that these mixtures undergo, as well as the equipment in which the processes are carried out. The purpose of this section is to briefly study the factors that are involved in the design of air-conditioning systems that combine the elements that we have individually considered earlier in this chapter.

The term air conditioning as we will use it is meant to encompass the control of the properties of air in an enclosure such as a room or a building. If the object is to provide for the comfort of humans within an environment, it may be necessary to effectively control the dry-bulb temperature, the wet-bulb temperature, humidity, dust content, odors, bacteria, and toxic gases. The processes by which these objectives are attained are heating, cooling, ventilation, humidification, cleaning, and dehumidification. We have already considered the elements required for the control of dry-bulb temperature, wet-bulb temperature, and humidity. The removal of odors, gases, and dust is usually accomplished by passing the air through filter elements. In the *dry filter*, air is forced to flow through a screening material such as fiberglass, gauze, cellulose, or woven wool felt. Figure 6.31a shows a dry filter that is removable and cleanable. It uses wool felt arranged on a metal frame and can be vacuum cleaned, air blown, or dry cleaned. The dry filters serve best for relatively small air flows and light dust loadings. They are highly efficient and, when clean, offer relatively little resistance to air flow. Resistance builds up rapidly, however, and dust-holding capacity is relatively small. Change in resistance usually indicates when the filter should be replaced or cleaned.

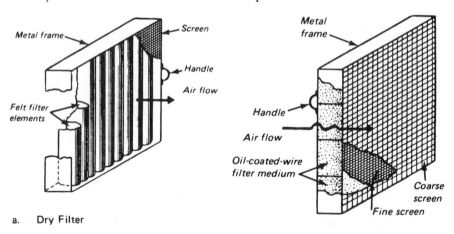

a. Dry Filter

b. Viscous Filter

Figure 6.31 Dry and viscous filters (Reprinted with permission from *Power, The Engineer's Reference Library*, copyright by McGraw-Hill, Inc., New York)

Other types of filters include viscous filters in which the filtering medium is coated with a sticky oil. Figure 6.31b shows this type of filter that can either be thrown away or can be cleaned and reused. The electrostatic precipitator shown in Fig. 6.32 utilizes the principle that a dust-particle exposed to an electric field becomes charged and migrates to one of the electrodes. The design uses a viscous material to hold the attracted particles, and it is cleaned by shutting down the unit for washing and recoating. The electrostatic precipitator removes microscopic particles, smoke, and pollen that mechanical filters cannot remove. Odors are usually removed by being adsorbed by activated charcoal units placed in ducts or in the air washers shown in Figs. 6.18 and 6.20.

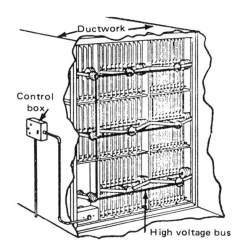

Figure 6.32 Electrostatic precipitator (Reprinted with permission from *Power, The Engineer's Reference Library*, copyright by McGraw-Hill, Inc., New York)

When we consider the human being and his effect on the environment when he is in a relatively confined space, we must consider the bodily processes that occur. Oxygen is inhaled, and a moist mixture less rich in oxygen and richer in carbon dioxide is exhaled into the enclosure. In addition, heat is transferred from the human, and moisture is evaporated to the environment. Body odors, smoke, and organic material are also added to the air. For a person at rest approximately 180 Btu/hr is given off as latent heat and 220 Btu/hr is given off as sensible heat. For a person working these values increase by approximately 25 percent. The term *latent heat* as used in air-conditioning work refers to the changes of liquid water to water vapor in humidification or the change of water vapor to liquid water in dehumidification. *Sensible heat* refers to the heating of dry air. One method of removing the heat, moisture, and odors that exist in a room is to ventilate the room. This process consists of supplying air to, or removing air from, the room. In ordinary residences, air infiltration usually provides sufficient ventilation. For an ordinary room in a dwelling, one air change per hour yields a ventilation rate of 10 cu ft/min when 600 cu ft are allotted per person. Table 6.5 shows some average ventilation rates used in practice.

TABLE 6.5*

AVERAGE VENTILATING PRACTICE (FRESH AIR)

Ordinary room of a dwelling	1 air change per hr and up
Toilets, rest rooms, etc.	2–5 air changes per hr
Public dining rooms	4–10 air changes per hr
Auditoriums	10–20 air changes per hr
Stores	2–5 air changes per hr

*From *Elements of Applied Energy* by F. T. Morse, copyright 1947 by Litton Educational Publishing, Inc. Reprinted by permission of Van Nostrand Reinhold Co., New York.

In hot weather the air-conditioning plant has to remove both sensible and latent heat (moisture). Some sources of the heat load are as follows:

1 Heat liberated by occupants—sensible and latent.

2 Infiltration of outside air—sensible and latent.

3 Process heat (industrial, cooking, etc.)—sensible and latent.

4 Heat infiltration from walls and partitions—sensible and latent.

5 Solar heat absorption through walls, roofs, windows, etc.—sensible.

6 Heat transfer between the exterior and interior of the building due to temperature differences—sensible.

7 Air brought in for ventilation—sensible and latent.

The detailed calculation of these heat loads is given in the latest edition of the *ASHRAE Guide* and will not be considered further. The references at the end of this chapter should be consulted as well as the *ASHRAE Guide* for these details. Also, Chapter 9 on heat transfer should be studied prior to performing such calculations.

Figure 6.33 shows a complete heating and cooling plant used in a recent commercial industrial installation. All the necessary processes of heating, cooling, cleaning, etc. are performed in this central plant. From this plant the treated air is ducted to the areas where it is used and some of the "used" air is returned for recirculation. Fans or blowers are required to circulate the air through the heating and cooling coils, filters, washers, ducts, outlets, grilles, and diffusers. Both axial and centrifugal fans are used for providing air circulation, and the choice depends upon the specific system requirements to which the fan is matched.

Securing proper distribution of air within a large room without creating drafts is difficult. Any air movement at a rate above 30 fpm in a room of seated people may seem uncomfortable to many. If the temperature and relative humidity are within comfort zone limits, somewhat higher velocities can be tolerated. Where people are moving about, velocities as high as 120 fpm can be

Figure 6.33 View of the district cooling and heating plant owned and operated by Houston Natural Gas Corp. at Nassau Bay, a commercial/residential project near Houston (Courtesy of Carrier Corp.).

used. Air can be withdrawn through grilles at up to 70 fpm without discomfort.

Over and above precautions taken to prevent undue drafts, it is desired to get even distribution of air despite the fact that incoming air may be different in temperature from the room air. Furthermore, some means of controlling air quantity at room inlets may be desirable. Thus a considerable variety of grilles and diffusers is available. Figure 6.34 shows some of the air distribution grilles and diffusers used in many air conditioning installations.

In the design of the air conditioning system the design outdoor dry-bulb and wet-bulb temperatures need to be known and also the dry- and wet-bulb temperature range in which humans can feel comfortable. For New York City, the design dry-bulb temperature is 95°F and the design wet-bulb temperature is 75°F. In Mobile, Alabama, the corresponding values are 95°F and 80°F. Extensive tabulations of the design dry-bulb and design wet-bulb temperatures for many cities in the United States will be found in the *ASHRAE Guide*. Also given in the *Guide* is the range of dry- and wet-bulb temperatures known as the human comfort zone as an area on the psychrometric chart. For this chart, the *Guide* should be consulted, but for most people the area enclosed by the 65° and 85°F dry-bulb temperatures and the 30 and 70 percent relative humidity lines defines the human comfort zone.

The design of any air-conditioning system is a complex interaction of many considerations, and the *ASHRAE Guide* is an invaluable source of data for any design study.

Grille has deflecting vanes so any desired air pattern can be set up

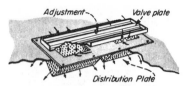

Valve plate and distribution space slow air down, smooth out the flow

An adjustable damper permits varying the volume of entering air

Latest diffusers mount flush with ceiling, blend with the decorations

Figure 6.34 Air distribution grilles and diffusers (Reprinted with permission from *Power, The Engineer's Reference Library*, copyright by McGraw-Hill, Inc., New York)

6.10 CLOSURE

As a logical extension of the ideal gas relation, we have considered a mixture of ideal gases to be an ideal gas having the equation of state of an ideal gas. With this as the basis, we have developed all the necessary thermodynamic properties of the mixture that are required for any process. The use of the ideal gas relation for mixtures represents an approximation to the behavior of real gas mixtures. For many engineering purposes, this procedure is satisfactory; for others it is not. When dealing with gases that individually deviate from the ideal gas relation, we may expect mixtures of such gases to deviate even more from the ideal gas.

A word of caution must be expressed at this point. The psychrometric chart of Fig. 6.11 is based on ideal gas relations and 29.921 in. Hg total pressure. For those applications that require greater accuracy than the chart can give or for total pressures varying ±1 in. Hg from 29.921 in., reference should be made to the *ASHRAE Guide* or other references at the end of this chapter.

REFERENCES

1 *Elementary Applied Thermodynamics* by Irving Granet, John Wiley & Sons, Inc., New York, 1965.

2 *Engineering Thermodynamics* by C. O. Mackey, W. M. Barnard, and F. O. Ellenwood, John Wiley & Sons, Inc., New York, 1957.

3 *Thermodynamics*, 2nd Ed., by G. A. Hawkins, John Wiley & Sons, Inc., New York, 1951.

4 *Thermodynamics* by J. P. Holman, McGraw-Hill Book Co., New York, 1969.

5 *Thermodynamics for Engineers* by M. A. Saad, Prentice-Hall, Inc., Englewood Cliffs, N.J., 1966.

6 *Thermodynamics* by G. J. Van Wylen, John Wiley & Sons, Inc., New York, 1959.

7 *Thermal Engineering* by C. C. Dillio and E. P. Nye, International Textbook Co., Inc., Scranton, Pa., 1959.

8 *Thermodynamics*, 2nd Ed., by F. P. Durham, Prentice-Hall, Inc., Englewood Cliffs, N.J., 1959.

9 *Thermodynamics* by J. H. Keenan, John Wiley & Sons, New York, 1941.

10 *Chemical Engineering Thermodynamics* by B. F. Dodge, McGraw-Hill Book Co., New York, 1944.

11 *Principles of Engineering Thermodynamics*, 2nd Ed., by P. J. Kiefer, G. F. Kinney, and M. C. Stuart, John Wiley & Sons, New York, 1954.

12 *Air Conditioning and Refrigeration* by W. H. Severns and J. F. Fellows, John Wiley & Sons, New York, 1958.

13 *Refrigeration and Air Conditioning*, 2nd Ed., by R. C. Jordon and G. B. Priester, Prentice-Hall, Englewood Cliffs, N.J., 1956.

14 *ASHRAE Guide and Data Book*, American Society of Heating, Refrigerating, and Air Conditioning Engineers, 1961.

15 *Concepts of Thermodynamics* by E. F. Obert, McGraw-Hill Book Co., New York, 1960.

16 *Elements of Applied Energy* by F. T. Morse, Van Nostrand Reinhold Co., New York, 1947.

17 *The Engineers Reference Library*, *Power Magazine*, McGraw-Hill Book Co., New York.

PROBLEMS

Use Table 6.1 for molecular weights of gases.

6.1 Show that at 14.7 psia and 32°F, a mole of any ideal gas occupies a volume of 358 cu ft.

6.2 A gas mixture consists of 1 lb of methane (CH_4) and 1 lb of oxygen (O_2). Determine the number of moles of each gas, the total number of moles, and the mole fraction of each component. Also determine the molecular weight of the mixture.

6.3 A mixture consists of 0.4 lb CO_2, 0.2 lb of CH_4, and 0.4 lb O_2. Determine the molecular weight and the gas constant of the mixture.

6.4 If the percentage by weight of a certain gas is CO (20 percent), N_2 (50 percent), O_2 (10 percent), and CH_4 (20 percent), compute the partial pressure of each constituent if the total mixture pressure is 100 psia.

6.5 A tank has a volume of 5 cu ft. If it contains 2 lb of O_2 and 3 lb of CO_2, compute the partial pressures of each constituent and the total pressure of the mixture. The temperature of the mixture is 70°F.

6.6 It is desired to produce a gas mixture containing 50 percent by volume of CO_2 and O_2. If this mixture contains 4 lb of CO_2, how many lb of O_2 is there in this mixture?

6.7 Determine the molecular weight and the gas constant of the mixture in Problem 6.6.

6.8 A mixture of 60 lb of O_2, 20 lb of N_2, and 10 lb of H_2 is at 140°F and 17 psia. Determine the volume of the mixture.

6.9 Three pounds of carbon dioxide (CO_2) are mixed with 7 lb of an unknown gas. If the resulting mixture occupies a volume of 50 cu ft when the mixture is at 50 psia and 200°F, determine the molecular weight of the unknown gas.

6.10 A mixture contains 10 lb of methane (CH_4) and 6 lb of oxygen (O_2). If the mixture is at 140°F and 75 psia, determine the mixture volume, the partial volume of each constituent, the partial pressure of each constituent, the mole fraction of each constituent, and the molecular weight of the mixture.

6.11 Two hundred cubic feet of hydrogen at 60 psia and room temperature is adiabatically mixed with 400 cu ft of nitrogen at 15 psia and room temperature. If the temperature of the room is 70°F, determine the molecular weight R and the final pressure of the mixture.

6.12 A mixture consists of 7 moles of oxygen (O_2), 3 moles of methane (CH_4), and 1 mole of nitrogen (N_2). Determine the volumetric analysis, the weight of the mixture, the molecular weight of the mixture, and the gas constant of the mixture.

6.13 A gas mixture consists of the following volume percentages: 40 percent CO, 20 percent CH_4, 30 percent N_2, and 10 percent O_2. Determine the weight fraction of each gas, the molecular weight of the mixture, and the gas constant of the mixture.

6.14 A gas mixture has a volumetric analysis of 25 percent N_2, 35 percent O_2, and 40 percent CH_4. Determine its gravimetric analysis, the molecular weight of the mixture, and the gas constant of the mixture.

6.15 The volumetric analysis of a gas mixture is 40 percent N_2, 40 percent O_2, and 20 percent CO_2. The mixture is at 100 psia and 100°F. Determine the partial pressure of each gas, the molecular weight of the mixture, the gravimetric (weight) analysis, and the gas constant of the mixture.

6.16 A gas mixture of oxygen, nitrogen, and methane occupies a container, and each constituent has a partial pressure of 50, 20, and 65 psia, respectively. Determine the gravimetric analysis, the volumetric analysis, the molecular weight of the mixture, and the gas constant of the mixture.

6.17 Determine the final temperature and pressure of a mixture of oxygen and nitrogen if 6 lb of oxygen at 70°F and 200 psia is mixed with 1 lb of nitrogen at 200°F and 100 psia. Use c_v of oxygen as 0.164 Btu/lb °F and c_v of nitrogen as 0.179 Btu/lb °F. The process is adiabatic.

6.18 Determine the final pressure and temperature of a mixture if it is made by mixing 10 cu ft of nitrogen at 120°F and 70 psia and 5 cu ft of oxygen at 60°F and 120 psia. Use c_v of oxygen as 0.164 Btu/lb °F and c_v of nitrogen as 0.179 Btu/lb °F. The process is adiabatic.

6.19 Determine c_v of the mixture in Problem 6.17.

6.20 Determine c_v of the mixture in Problem 6.18.

6.21 An air–water mixture at 100°F has a relative humidity of 40 percent. Calculate the partial pressure of the water vapor and its dew-point temperature.

6.22 Solve Problem 6.21 using the psychrometric chart.

6.23 An air–water vapor mixture at a dry-bulb temperature of 90°F and 14.7 psia is found to have a relative humidity of 50 percent. Calculate the dew point, the partial pressure of the water vapor, and the humidity ratio.

6.24 Solve Problem 6.23 using the psychrometric chart.

6.25 An air–water vapor mixture having a total pressure of 14.7 psia is found to have a humidity ratio of 0.010 lb of water vapor per pound of dry air. Calculate the relative humidity, the dew point, and the pressure of the water vapor if the dry-bulb temperature is 80°F.

6.26 Solve Problem 6.25 using the psychrometric chart.

6.27 The partial pressure of water vapor in an atmospheric pressure (14.7 psia) mixture is 0.4 psia. Calculate the relative humidity and the dew-point temperature if the dry-bulb temperature is 100°F.

6.28 Solve Problem 6.27 using the psychrometric chart.

6.29 Atmospheric air is sensibly cooled at constant pressure from an initial dry-bulb temperature of 80°F and 50 percent relative humidity to a final dry-bulb temperature of 60°F. Calculate the heat removed per pound of dry air. Assume that the mixture is at 14.7 psia. Use Eq. (6.27) for the enthalpy of the mixture.

6.30 Solve Problem 6.29 using the psychrometric chart.

6.31 Air is dehumidified at constant dry-bulb temperature. Calculate the heat removed per pound of dry air if the initial conditions are 90°F dry-bulb temperature, 40 percent relative humidity, and the final relative humidity is 20 percent. The mixture is at 14.7 psia.

6.32 Solve Problem 6.31 using the psychrometric chart.

6.33 Air is cooled adiabatically from 70°F dry bulb and 57 percent relative humidity until 90 percent relative humidity is reached. Calculate the final dry-bulb temperature and the initial and final dew-point temperatures.

6.34 Solve Problem 6.33 using the psychrometric chart.

6.35 Atmospheric air at 10 psia and 70°F dry bulb has a relative humidity of 50 percent. If the air is sensibly heated at constant pressure to 80°F dry bulb, what is the final relative humidity?

6.36 Even though the psychrometric chart (Fig. 6.11) is not applicable at this pressure, determine the final relative humidity in Problem 6.35 using the chart and compare results.

6.37 Determine the humidity ratio and dew-point temperature for air at a total pressure of 30.921 in. Hg if it is at 80°F dry-bulb temperature and 60 percent relative humidity.

6.38 Solve Problem 6.37 using the psychrometric chart. Comment.

6.39 To condition it, air is passed over a coil at 50°F. If the initial air is at 85°F dry bulb and 70 percent relative humidity, and a final 75°F dry-bulb air is specified, determine the final relative humidity, the amount of moisture removed per pound of dry air, and the amount of heat extracted per pound of dry air. (See Fig. 6.24 and use the psychrometric chart.)

6.40 Determine whether it is possible to obtain air at a dry bulb of 60°F and 70 percent relative humidity by evaporative cooling and then sensible heating if the initial air is at 70°F dry bulb and 10 percent relative humidity.

6.41 In Problem 6.40 what is the least value of the initial relative humidity that will permit the process to be completed?

6.42 What final conditions will be obtained when 200 lb/min of air at 85°F and 60 percent relative humidity is mixed with 300 lb/min of air at 50°F and 20 percent relative humidity? (Temperatures are dry-bulb values.) Use the psychrometric chart (Fig. 6.11).

6.43 If the flow quantities in Problem 6.42 were given in cubic feet per minute, that is, 200 cfm and 300 cfm, determine the final mixture conditions.

6.44 Water enters a cooling tower at 130°F and leaves at 100°F. Air at atmospheric pressure having an initial dry-bulb temperature of 60°F and a relative humidity of 60 percent leaves the tower saturated at 90°F. Calculate the weight of air required and the makeup water required (water lost by evaporation) if 150,000 lb/hr of water enters the tower.

6.45 Water is cooled in a cooling tower from 110°F to 80°F. Air enters the tower at 80°F and a relative humidity of 40 percent, and leaves at 95°F with a relative humidity of 90 percent. Determine the water entering that is cooled per pound of dry air and the makeup water required per pound of dry air.

chapter 7

power cycles

7.1 INTRODUCTION

A cycle has been defined as a series of thermodynamic processes during which the working fluid can be made to undergo changes involving energy transitions and subsequently is returned to its original state. The object of any practical cycle is to convert energy from one form to another more useful form. For instance, the energy bound in a fossil fuel is released by the chemical process of combustion and by undergoing appropriate thermodynamic processes is made to yield useful work at the shaft of an engine. Similarly, the energy of the nuclear-fission process is made to yield useful work that ultimately appears as electrical energy.

In the following sections several ideal cycles are discussed. They are "ideal" in the sense that they have been proposed as prototypes of practical cycles and, in the limit, their efficiencies approach a Carnot-cycle efficiency. These cycles usually bear the name of the person who either proposed them or developed them, and their composite study represents a large portion of applied thermodynamics. In practice, actual cycles deviate from the ideal because of unavoidable irreversibilities and for other practical reasons. The study of the ideal cycle, however, can and does yield invaluable results that are applicable to real cycles. Additionally, we will discuss the actual devices (hardware) used in the practical realization of these ideal cycles. Along with these descriptions we will see where the actual cycles deviate from the "ideal" cycles and the attempts made to make actual cycles approach ideal performance.

Power cycles are often classified by the character of the working fluid in the cycle. The two general classes of cycle are the vapor cycle and the gas cycle. The vapor cycle differs from the gas cycle in two respects. In the gas cycle, there is no change of phase of the working substance, and the compression work of the gas cycles can therefore represent a large percentage of the useful work output of the cycle. In the vapor cycle, the working substance is condensed to a liquid at the lower temperature of the cycle. This liquid is pumped to the desired delivery pressure. Since the liquid is essentially incompressible, it would be expected that the pump work of the vapor cycle would represent a small percentage of the useful work output of the cycle. Also, in the vapor cycle, the working substance may contain moisture when it is expanded in a turbine. Since this is undesirable, modifications are made in the vapor cycle to alleviate this condition.

7.2 CARNOT CYCLE

The conclusions reached in the study of the Carnot cycle were independent of the working medium, and it is pertinent to review this cycle briefly, as applied to both vapors and gases. It will be recalled that a Carnot cycle consists of two reversible isothermal stages and two isentropic stages. Figure 7.1a shows a Carnot cycle in which the working fluid is indicated as being in the wet vapor region. The line A, B represents the isentropic compression of the fluid from the lower temperature (and pressure) to the upper temperature of the cycle. At the upper temperature there is an isothermal and reversible reception of energy as heat from some reservoir. This transfer of the heat proceeds along path B, C with concurrent increase in the volume of the vapor. The fluid then expands isentropically along path C, D with energy extracted as work. As the fluid expands, the volume of the fluid increases. Finally, the wet fluid is condensed isothermally and reversibly at the lower temperature of the cycle. During the condensation process, the volume of the fluid decreases as heat is rejected to the sink of the system. The energy available is represented by area A, B, C, D, and the energy rejected is represented by area A', A, D, D' on the Ts diagram of Fig. 7.1a. The efficiency of a Carnot cycle is solely a function of the upper and lower temperatures and is given by

$$\eta_c = \frac{T_1 - T_2}{T_1} \times 100 \qquad (7.1)$$

Equation (7.1) is also the efficiency of any reversible heat engine operating between these constant temperature limits. All the heat is taken in or rejected at T_1 and T_2, respectively. Figure 7.1b shows the Carnot gas cycle plotted on pv coordinates. All the conclusions pertaining to the efficiency of the vapor cycle also pertain to the gas cycle, since we have already noted that the efficiency of a Carnot cycle is independent of the working fluid in the cycle.

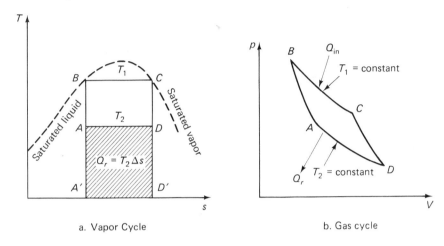

a. Vapor Cycle   b. Gas cycle

Figure 7.1 Carnot cycle

Unfortunately, there are certain practical limitations on the upper and lower temperatures. The upper temperature is limited by the strength of available materials, and the lower, by ambient conditions. Recent advances in the field of thermonuclear reactions have indicated that the upper temperature limitations may be removed by using magnetic fields to contain the working fluid. To date, the limits on the upper temperature of power cycles have depended on advances in the field of metallurgy.

ILLUSTRATIVE PROBLEM 7.1

An ideal Carnot heat cycle operates between 1000°F and 100°F. Compare the efficiency of this cycle with (a) two Carnot cycles operated in series between 1000°F to 500°F and 500°F to 100°F; (b) three Carnot cycles operated in series between 1000°F to 700°F, 700°F to 400°F, and 400°F to 100°F. The situation is shown in Fig. 7.2.

Solution

For the single unit

$$\eta_c = \left(\frac{T_1 - T_2}{T_1} \right) 100 = \left(\frac{1460 - 560}{1460} \right) 100 = 61.64\%$$

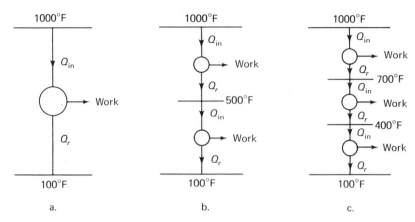

Figure 7.2 Illustrative Problem 7.1

(a) For the two units in series, the first one has an efficiency of η_1:

$$\eta_1 = \left(\frac{1460 - 960}{1460} \right) 100 = 34.25\%$$

Thus, for each Btu into it, 0.3425 Btu is converted to useful work and 0.6575 Btu is rejected to the second engine in series. The efficiency of the second engine, η_2, is

$$\eta_2 = \left(\frac{960 - 560}{960} \right) 100 = 41.67\%$$

Since 0.6575 Btu enters, the useful work out of the second engine is $0.6575 \times 0.4167 = 0.2740$ Btu. The total work output is $0.3425 + 0.2740 = 0.6165$ Btu. Since we assumed 1 Btu entered, this is an efficiency of 61.65 percent. Note that this is the same as the single engine operating between the same temperature extremes.

(b) For the three units in series, we proceed in the same manner:

$$\eta_1 = \left(\frac{1460 - 1160}{1460} \right) 100 = 20.55\%$$

$$\eta_2 = \left(\frac{1160 - 860}{1160} \right) 100 = 25.86\%$$

$$\eta_3 = \left(\frac{860 - 560}{860} \right) 100 = 34.88\%$$

The net work (based on 1 Btu entering) is $0.2055 + 0.2586(1 - 0.2055) + 0.3488$ $[1 - 0.2055 - (1 - 0.2055)(0.2586)] = 0.2055 + 0.2055 + 0.2054 = 0.6164$, which corresponds to an overall efficiency of 61.64 percent, the same as for the single engine and for two in series.

From Illustrative Problem 7.1 we note that the placement of intermediate Carnot engines in series between the given temperature limits does not change the overall efficiency of the system. In other words, the overall efficiency of any number of reversible engines in series operating between the same upper and lower temperature limits is the same as a single reversible engine operating between the same temperature limits regardless of the intermediate temperature (see Problem 7.3 and Chapter 3).

As noted, all the general conclusions reached for the Carnot vapor cycle hold true for any Carnot cycle utilizing any fluid as the working substance. Usually, it is desirable to strive for the maximum thermal efficiency for any thermodynamic cycle. However, it is important to note that in some special cases high thermal efficiency may require either extremely large pieces of equipment or excessive costs. As an example, let us consider a system designed to operate in space. Let us further assume that this system is operated as a Carnot vapor cycle with heat rejected to space by radiation only. For such a system operating in space, the size and weight of the equipment used to reject heat (the space radiator) becomes a limiting physical restriction. This space radiator requires protection against meteorites, and the shielding combined with the inherent weight of the heat-transfer elements usually makes the radiator the heaviest component of the space-propulsion system. It is readily apparent that it would be desirable to keep the size and weight of the radiator to a minimum from both launch and operating considerations.

Consider the Carnot cycle shown in Fig. 7.1. The upper temperature of the cycle is assumed fixed by the metallurgical limits imposed by the heat source, and the lower temperature is assumed to be a variable. Also, the heat rejection is proportional to the fourth power of the lower (radiating) absolute temperature (see Chapter 9). Under these assumptions, we can determine that the efficiency of a Carnot cycle that will yield the minimum weight of the radiator is 25 percent. Thus it follows that any Carnot cycle operated in space will have a maximum work output with a *minimum radiator surface area* (weight) if its efficiency is 25 percent. Obviously, this requires $T_2 = \frac{3}{4} T_1$. The analysis we have made can be extended to real cycles. If this is done, it will be found that the equivalent Carnot efficiency for such a cycle in which the maximum work for the minimum-sized radiator is desired will be approximately 24 percent.

The foregoing discussion has been used to illustrate the fact that thermodynamic efficiency alone may not be the governing consideration in the design of a cycle or in the setting of component operating conditions. It is necessary in each case to be able to analyze the system and to determine the parameters of importance. Only then will it be possible to optimize the system with respect to these parameters. For example, conflicts may occur when a system is optimized with respect to more than one parameter, and it will then become necessary to compromise. Many items other than technical items (cost for one) will dictate the final decision.

7.3 THE RANKINE CYCLE

The Carnot cycle described in Section 7.2 cannot be used in a practical device for many reasons. Historically, the prototype of actual vapor cycles was the simple Rankine cycle. The elements of this cycle are shown in Fig. 7.3; the *Ts* and *hs* diagrams for the ideal Rankine cycle are illustrated in Fig. 7.4.

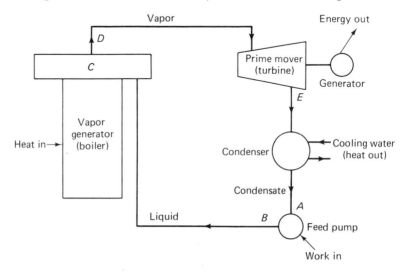

Figure 7.3 Elements of the simple Rankine cycle

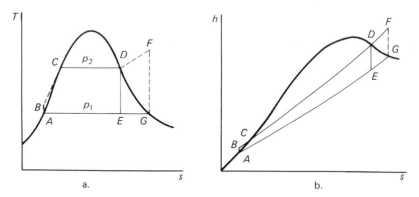

Figure 7.4 Rankine cycle

As indicated in the schematic of Fig. 7.3, this cycle consists of four distinct processes. Starting with the feed pump, the liquid supplied to the boiler is first brought to the boiler pressure. In the ideal cycle, the liquid supplied to the pump is assumed to be saturated at the lowest pressure of the cycle. In an actual cycle, the liquid is usually slightly subcooled to prevent vapor bubbles from forming in the pump (which causes a process known as *cavitation*, which will subsequently damage the pump). For the ideal cycle, the compression process is taken to be isentropic, and the final state of the liquid supplied to the boiler is subcooled at the boiler pressure. This subcooled liquid is heated to saturation in the boiler, and it is subsequently vaporized to yield the steam for the prime mover in the cycle. The energy for the heating and vaporizing of the liquid is provided by the combustion of fuel in the boiler. If superheating of the vapor is desired, it is also accomplished in the boiler (also called a steam generator). The vapor leaves the steam generator and is expanded isentropically in a prime mover (such as a turbine or steam engine) to provide the work output of the cycle. After the expansion process is completed, the working substance is piped to the condenser, where it rejects heat to the cooling water.

Figure 7.5 gives an idea of the size and complexity of a modern electric generating station. The station shown is the Ravenswood station of New York City's Con Edison system. The three generators at the plant have a total electrical capability in excess of 1,700,000 kilowatts. The plant is located on the east bank of the East River, whose water is used as cooling water in the condensers. In the foreground can be seen the complex electrical substation equipment that ties this plant into the Con Edison system. The size of the plant can be visualized by comparing it to the automobiles parked near the buildings and to the six-story houses in the lower right of the photograph. Unit 3 of this station is a 1000-MW unit with a boiler capable of generating 6.5×10^6 lb/hr of steam at 2750 psia and 1000°F with a single reheat. This boiler is designed for a pressure of 2990 psia, and it will operate about 5 percent above its nominal pressure of 2400 psi. Feedwater enters the economizer at a tempera-

Figure 7.5 Con Edison's Ravenswood station (Courtesy of Con Edison, New York)

ture of 480°F, and steam enters the reheater at 650°F. The boiler is a twin-furnace unit and, outside of size, marks one important step forward: one furnace and one-half of the boiler are able to keep operating if the other half fails. Load reduction would be only 500 MW. Each half of the boiler has its own drum and circulating system and its own air and gas ductwork. Hot air for combustion is supplied by four regenerative airheaters. Fuel is heavy oil, and steam air heaters preheat it to about 150°F with the used air going to the main air heaters. Steam temperature and feedwater regulation, as well as combustion, are electronically controlled with solid-state parts; valves and dampers are pneumatically actuated.

7.3a The Steam Generator

The term *boiler* is often used to broadly describe the device known more properly as a steam-generating unit. The boiler section of a steam generator refers to the elements in which the change of state from water to steam takes place. The steam generator consists of the boiler section, the superheater, reheater economizer, air heater, fuel system, air system, and ash-removal system. Thus a complete steam generator is a combination of many elements, all integrated to yield an economical, efficient, reliable unit.

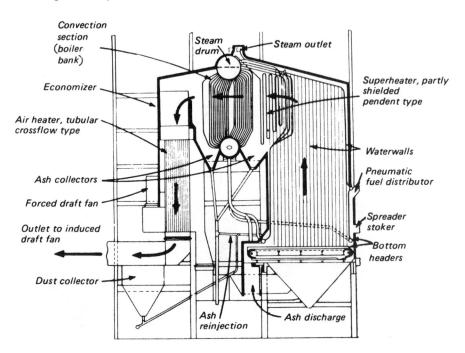

Figure 7.6 Modern water-tube steam generator (Reprinted with permission from Power, special report "Steam Generation," copyright by McGraw-Hill, Inc., 1964)

Let us examine the unit shown in Fig. 7.6 and trace out all the elements that constitute this type of steam generator. The unit shown is known as a water-tube unit in which steam is generated within the tubes and the combustion gases are outside the tubes. The path of the water can be traced out by noting that after leaving the feed pumps it is usually pumped into the steam drum. The water is subcooled at the pump exit, and in the steam drum it mixes with a steam–water mixture. This causes some of the steam to condense in the steam drum in order to heat the feed to saturation temperature. Depending on the particular design, it is possible for as much as 30 percent of the steam actually generated to be condensed to heat the feedwater in the steam drum. The steam drum acts as a collecting device and releasing point for the steam generated. In the water-tube boiler, water and steam flow in a relatively large number of externally heated paths. Circulation of the steam–water mixture in the tubes can be brought about in two ways. The first is illustrated in Fig. 7.7

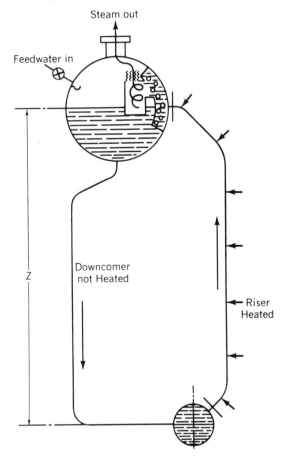

Figure 7.7 Schematic of natural circulation (Courtesy of Babcock and Wilcox Company)

and is called natural circulation. In the circuit shown, steam is formed on the heated side. The steam–water mixture weighs less than the cooler mixture on the unheated downcomer side and is displaced by water circulating convectively in the circuit. The difference in force between the water leg in the downcomer and the steam–water mixture in the riser causes flow to occur. An equilibrium velocity is reached in the circuit when the force difference between the downcomer and riser equals the flow losses in the circuits. If the available pressure difference is greater than the flow resistance in the circuits, the flow will increase until a balance point is reached between available force and resistance. The steam–water mixture then goes to the steam drum, where the steam is released and the water is returned to the downcomer circuit. Unless adequate circulation is maintained, it is possible to have a stationary local steam pocket, which in turn leads to local overheating of the tube and ultimately to tube failure (burnout).

It will be recalled that at the critical point there is no distinction between the vapor and liquid. Also, as the critical point is approached the difference in density between the liquid and vapor decreases. Figure 7.8 shows this effect. To assure adequate circulation at all loads, some steam generators use a pump to overcome circuit resistance. If this is done, it is usually done in high-pressure units where natural circulation forces are relatively small or in low-pressure units to give freedom of tube layout. Figure 7.9a shows a schematic of a forced-circulation unit with a drum for steam separation. Figure 7.9b shows a schematic of a once-through forced circulation steam generator where all the

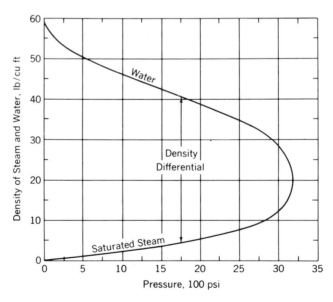

Figure 7.8 Specific weight of steam and water (Courtesy of Babcock and Wilcox Company)

water entering the tubes is vaporized and leaves the tubes as steam. As indicated, for pressures below the critical pressure, a separator may be used to remove any moisture in the steam.

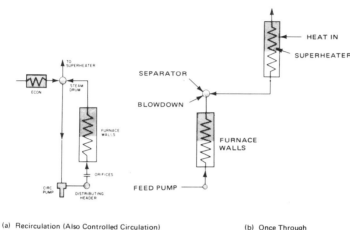

(a) Recirculation (Also Controlled Circulation)   (b) Once Through

Figure 7.9 Forced circulation steam generators (Courtesy of Combustion Engineering, Inc.)

The steam drum plays an important role in most boiler designs. The steam drum is the place where the cleaning and drying of the saturated steam is performed, where the feedwater is distributed, and it provides protection for the unit. Large-diameter steam drums provide conservative steam release rates per square foot of separation surface, assuring high steam purity and stable water levels even with fluctuating loads. Figure 7.10 shows the interior of a steam drum in which steam enters the drum through a primary separator, which removes carryover of water from the discharge of the generating tube and returns it to the drum water. The steam then passes through the closely spaced Z-shaped steel fins of the water-cooled condenser tube elements, being, in effect, washed and scrubbed in its own condensate. In this design, sectionalized dryer cartons remove the remaining moisture from the steam before it enters the superheater. Steam drum diameters are of the order of 60 in. in many installations.

Clean steam is important because modern turbines operate at rated capacity and high rates of speed for long periods, and it is essential from the standpoint of safety to these prime movers, as well as to maintenance of their efficiency and capacity, that the blades remain clean. Deposits, however, are selective. Also, superheater tubing may overheat if solids are deposited in them.

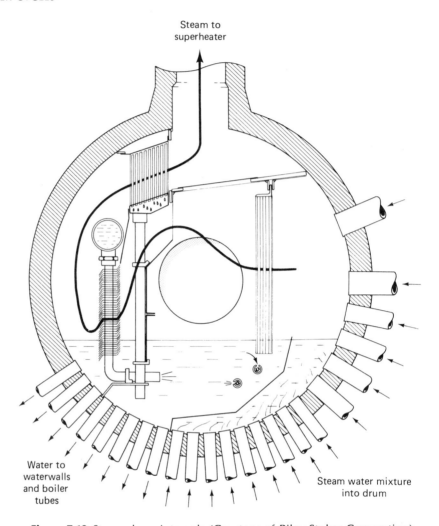

Steam to
superheater

Water to
waterwalls
and boiler
tubes

Steam water mixture
into drum

Figure 7.10 Steam drum internals (Courtesy of Riley Stoker Corporation)

Since solids in steam are carried by the moisture associated with it, steam purification (as to solids, not gases) is primarily a matter of moisture removal. Modern power boilers deliver steam containing less than one part impurities per million. This is truly remarkable, since boiler-water impurity concentrations may run from a few to thousands of parts per million. It is interesting to note that steam is probably the purest substance produced commercially—purer than 99.9999 percent. Commercially distilled water would be intolerably dirty as steam. While drum size has an important bearing on steam purity, internal baffling is even more effective. All such baffles are designed to use gravity, centrifugal force, and inertia to accomplish separation. Preliminary separation of water from steam is obtained by the manner in which the mixture is delivered from the tubes to the drum and by baffles which change the direction of flow. Since foam promotes carryover, baffles which direct the water toward a foam blanket to beat down minute bubbles have been used. A secondary separator may remove most of the moisture still remaining in the steam, after which the steam passes through a drier. Driers usually consist of several layers of screen or closely spaced undulated plates. They permit passage of steam without much resistance, while offering a large area on which droplets may deposit.

In the design of the drum internals shown in Fig. 7.11, the separation of water from steam is done in cyclones installed along the length of the drum with steam scrubbers above the cyclones. This procedure is often supplemented by a third step, steam washing. Here pure water is sprayed into the scrubbers to wash out silica vapor from the steam and return it to the water.

Figure 7.11 Steam drum internals (Courtesy of Babcock and Wilcox Company)

For the controlled circulation boiler (see the schematic of Fig. 7.9a), the steam drum internals used for the separation of steam and water are not limited by the pressure drop since a pump provides the circulation. In the unit shown in Fig. 7.12, the same basic elements are used to dry the steam, but

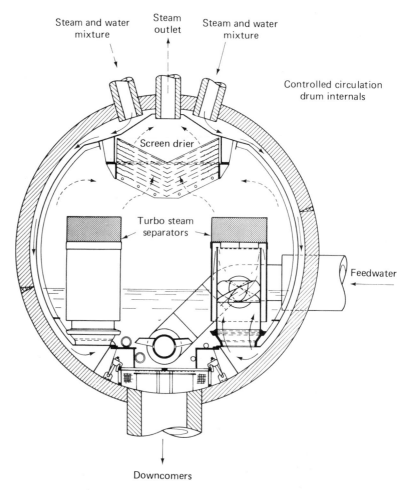

Figure 7.12 Drum internal design for controlled circulation boiler (Courtesy of Combustion Engineering Inc.)

cylindrical baffles within the drum circulate steam and water in contact with the entire circumference of the drum. By doing this, the drum metal temperature is caused to closely follow the water temperature at all times. Variation in metal temperature at different parts of the drum therefore does not become a limiting factor in the rate at which a unit can be heated or cooled, and this greatly expedites load pickup as well as emergency repairs. Boilers which are fed through a single nozzle, as contrasted to a series of tubes from an economizer, require an internal pipe or trough to distribute the feedwater uniformly lengthwise in the drum. Feedwater is somewhat (and may be considerably) cooler than boiler water. It is usually discharged above the water level to avoid temperature shock to the structure. Distribution is important to obtain the uniform mixing which is desirable to avoid turbulence and promote residual internal feed treatment. Figure 7.13 shows the boiler bank of a shop-erected boiler. Even for a relatively small unit, the large number of tubes that constitute this bank is quite evident.

Figure 7.13 Boiler bank of a shop-erected unit (Courtesy of Combustion Engineering Inc.)

If we now return to the steam generator of Fig. 7.6, we can determine the relative amounts of heat that are absorbed by the various sections of this unit by referring to Fig. 7.14, which shows the relative percent of heat-transfer

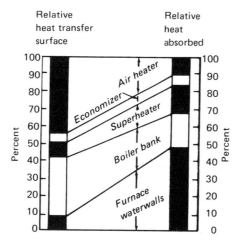

Figure 7.14 Heat absorption in a modern steam generator (Reprinted with permission from *Power*, special report "Steam Generation," copyright by McGraw-Hill, Inc., June 1964)

surface for the furnace waterwalls, the boiler bank, superheater, economizer, and air heater, and the relative percentage of the total heat absorbed by each of these sections. The generation of steam in these units is also accomplished in the furnace waterwalls. The combustion of the fuel (coal, oil, or gas) should be completed within the furnace. If the flame should continue into the tube bank of the boiler or superheater, damaging local high temperatures can occur. If, for some reason, the gas temperature in the furnace should fall below the ignition point, incomplete combustion and smoke will occur. When a furnace is designed, both the volume, which is related to the time required for combustion, and the radiant heat absorbing area, which is related to the gas temperature leaving the furnace, must be considered. Satisfactory heat release rates vary with furnace size, proportion of heat-transfer surfaces, construction, and type of fuel. For fuel oil, an acceptable maximum for medium-sized water cooled furnaces is about 35,000 Btu/cu ft/hr, coal allows about 20,000 to 25,000 Btu/cu ft/hr, and natural gas allows a slightly higher rate than oil.

Heat release rates per square foot of effective radiant heat absorbing surface vary widely—from perhaps 60,000 to 200,000 Btu/hr. Average heat absorption rates are somewhat less than half these figures. As might be expected, the rates of heat release and heat absorption differ considerably in different parts of the furnace. Large gas and oil furnaces are generally limited to average heat release rates of about 150,000 Btu/sq ft/hr and coal furnaces to about 100,000 Btu/sq ft/hr.

The original purpose of waterwalls was to protect or supplant the refractories used in furnace construction and to lower the ashpit temperature to prevent slagging. Brickwork failures and firmly adhering slag accretions limited firing rate, shortened operating periods, and caused expensive maintenance. In modern boilers, furnace cooling is used to the fullest extent consistent with economy of design and firing characteristics. In all cases, the furnace water cooling surface is made part of the "boiler" circulation; it may often be difficult to distinguish between "furnace" and "boiler" in this respect. Any furnace cooling will improve refractory maintenance, at least by reducing the severity of the temperature conditions to which it is subjected. Large furnaces, however, are usually completely enclosed in a heat-absorbing envelope.

Figure 7.15 shows typical design variations for water-cooled walls. In the construction shown in Fig. 7.15a, the tubes are spaced apart and the wall surface is composed of part firebrick. The brick is usually backed with several layers of insulation and a strong steel casing. Reinforced metal lath is often used in wall construction. This type of construction is used where moderate cooling is desired.

The most common form of waterwall is shown in Fig. 7.15b where the adjacent tubes are tangent or, as shown, staggered. This arrangement offers high heat-absorbing capability in the area of maximum heat release. The tube surface is backed by solid block or plastic insulation and a strong steel casing.

By removing every other tube and welding fins on the tubes, we obtain the construction shown in Fig. 7.15c. The adjacent fins (shown on the right side

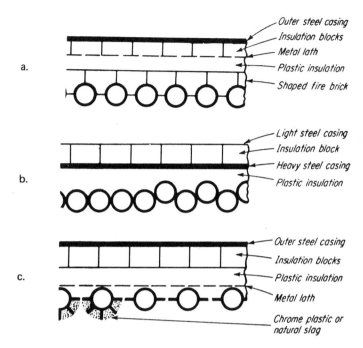

a.
- Outer steel casing
- Insulation blocks
- Metal lath
- Plastic insulation
- Shaped fire brick

b.
- Light steel casing
- Insulation block
- Heavy steel casing
- Plastic insulation

c.
- Outer steel casing
- Insulation blocks
- Plastic insulation
- Metal lath
- Chrome plastic or natural slag

Figure 7.15 Typical design variations of water-cooled walls (Reprinted with permission from *Power*, special report, "Steam Generation," copyright by McGraw-Hill, Inc., June 1964)

of the figure) are often welded to assure furnace tightness. In some designs, steel lugs are welded to the tubes as shown on the left side of Fig. 7.15c, and the protruding lugs are covered with a chrome-base refractory or slag. The backing construction is similar to that shown for the construction used in Figure 7.15b.

Figure 7.16 shows the type of welded-wall furnace construction used by one manufacturer. In this construction $3\frac{1}{4}$-in. outside-diameter tubes are employed with narrow $\frac{3}{4}$-in. fins. The entire furnace is constructed in this manner to assure tightness against gas leakage and to produce uniform heat absorption rates.

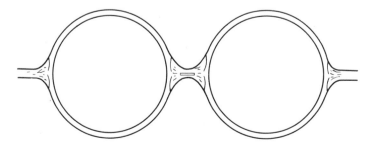

Figure 7.16 Welded waterwall (Courtesy of Riley Stoker Corporation)

Before leaving the furnace, let us briefly consider the fuel system. There are three common fuels used for steam generation: coal, oil, and gas. Each fuel requires different preparation and handling equipment, as well as different furnace design considerations.

The stoker is one of the oldest methods of burning coal, and it is still widely used today, mostly in smaller units, industrial installations, and with certain fuels, including refuse. The advantage of the stoker is the minimal cost of fuel preparation, ease of ash disposal, and the ability to operate satisfactorily over wide load ranges. The disadvantage of stoker operation lies in the difficulty of building and maintaining stokers of sufficient size to reliably fire large boilers. Also, a failure of a stoker shuts down an entire unit, while the failure of a single burner or coal pulverizer will, at worst, force a reduction in the load that the unit can carry.

Stokers may be classified in two general types, depending on whether the coal is fed from below or above the fuel bed, as underfeed and overfeed stokers.

Underfeed stokers, either single- or (rarely) multiple-retort, consist essentially of a trough or troughs into which coal is pushed by rams or screws. Part of the combustion air is introduced into the fuel bed through tuyeres or grate bars. Movement of the fuel discourages the formation of large coke masses. Volatile matter is distilled off the coal in these troughs or retorts and burns above the incandescent fuel bed. The partly coked and somewhat caked coal then falls onto the air-admitting tuyeres or grate bars, where the fixed carbon is burned out. Progressively, the fuel is pushed sidewise or forward until the refuse is discharged to the ashpit.

The most common type of stoker is the overfeed stoker. The traveling grate overfeed stoker is illustrated in Fig. 7.17. The basic operation of the

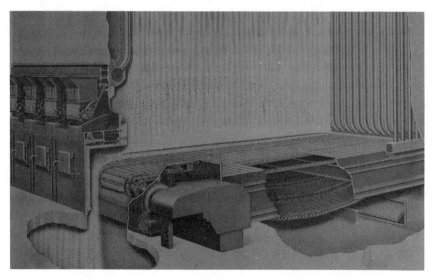

Figure 7.17 Traveling grate spreader stoker (Courtesy of Detroit Stoker Co.)

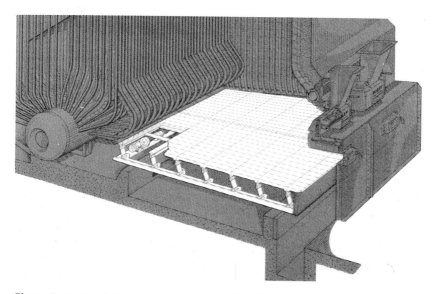

Figure 7.18 Oscillating grate spreader stoker (Courtesy of Riley Stoker Corp.)

traveling grate stoker is to provide a surface on which the fuel is supported throughout the combustion process; as the surface moves, fuel is fed on one end and the ash is deposited on the other end in the ashpit. Figure 7.18 shows an oscillating-grate stoker in which the fuel supporting surface oscillates in the plane in which the fuel moves. The oscillation causes the coal to move in the desired direction. Both of the units shown in Figs. 7.17 and 7.18 are also known as spreader stokers, since the coal is thrown (propelled) by a distributor onto the grate. With mechanical distributors, the smaller particles fall toward the front of the grate and the larger pieces to the rear. To permit these large pieces a longer time to burn, the grates of continuous discharge stokers are made to travel forward toward the ashpit located under the front of the stoker.

Stokers are proportioned on the basis of grate heat release rates, which may range from 200,000 Btu/hr for small single-retort stokers to 1,000,000 Btu/hr or more for large spreader stokers (where part of the fuel is burned in suspension), all rates being per square foot of projected grate surface. This area determines the furnace cross section. Furnace volumes are proportioned on the basis of furnace heat-release rates, which may range from 25,000 to 50,000 Btu/cu ft hr, depending on installation, size, type of stoker, probable load factor, and the amount of furnace heat absorbing area.

Traveling grate stokers are used in sizes from about 50 sq ft (10,000 lb of steam/hr) to 670 sq ft (275,000 lb of steam/hr). Dump-type spreader stokers might cover the same range, but since grate lengths over 16 ft are awkward to operate, a practical limitation corresponds to about 125,000 lb of steam/hr. Not subject to the length limitation, the continuous-discharge stoker may range up to 200,000 lb of steam/hr or more. Figure 7.6 shows a traveling-grate stoker installed in a steam-generating unit.

Pulverized coal units have largely replaced stoker installations in large sizes. In the direct firing system shown in Fig. 7.19, the raw coal is first fed to

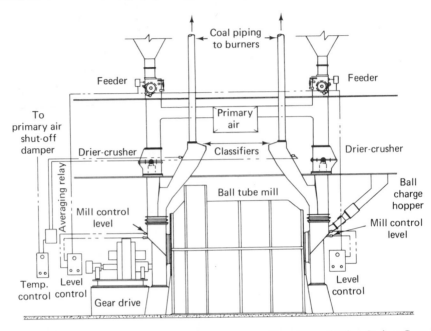

Figure 7.19 Typical ball mill pulverizing system (Courtesy of Riley Stoker Corp.)

feeders which maintain an uninterrupted positive coal feed regardless of coal moisture. A typical drum-type feeder is shown in Fig. 7.20a. As raw coal enters

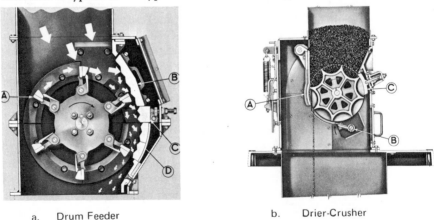

a.   Drum Feeder   b.   Drier-Crusher

Figure 7.20 Pulverized coal system components (Courtesy of Riley Stoker Corp.)

the feeder it is dropped into the semicircular pockets of the rotating feeder drum. A spring-loaded release apron Ⓐ located on the discharge side of the feeder drum levels off coal in each pocket before it is discharged into the coal chute. An adjustable wiper blade Ⓑ, geared to the feeder drum, cleans each pocket at each drum revolution. Coal, usually precrushed, is uniformly fed to the mill. An adjustable apron plate Ⓒ at the rear of the drum acts as a seal to prevent fine coal from sifting down behind the drum.

From the feeder, the coal then goes to the drier-crusher, which is illustrated in Fig. 7.20b. Raw coal enters the drier-crusher with preheated primary air (plus furnace gas when necessary). Violent intermixing of coal and preheated air is created by rotating swing hammers which operate at constant speed. At this stage, the coal's surface moisture is removed, and the coal is crushed by impact against the swing hammers Ⓐ, the breaker plate Ⓑ, the adjustable crusher block Ⓒ, and the solid grid section Ⓓ, all of which are made of alloy material. The resulting dry granulated coal is fed to the mill for final pulverization together with primary air.

As is to be expected, there has been a wide variation in the devices designed to pulverize various coals, and each may be particularly suitable for some application. The characteristics to be desired are dependable performance, uniform or adjustable product, low operating cost (principally low power cost), low maintenance cost, quick response, quiet operation, and ability to handle wet coal.

One type of coal pulverizer is shown in Fig. 7.21. This unit is known as a ball mill. This unit consists of a cylinder containing steel balls which crush the coal as the cylinder rotates. As the balls must roll or drop on the coal charge, the speed (hence, capacity) is limited to that at which centrifugal force would overcome gravity and the balls cease to roll. At the exit of the unit there is a classifier which permits coal particles of desired fineness to go to the burner and returns the coarser particles to the mill for further grinding.

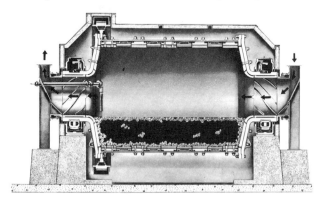

Figure 7.21 Ball mill pulverizer (Courtesy of Riley Stoker Co.)

The grinding elements are simple, but the ball mill is noisy in operation, control of fineness is poor, and power consumption per ton of product is high, particularly at light loads. Performance has been improved by baffling the mill and sweeping it with air to remove the pulverized product. The rather large amount of coal storage in the mill makes it responsive to a sudden load increase, but this characteristic becomes a liability in the event of a sudden loss of load, that is, trip-out. This type of mill is particularly suitable for grinding anthracites and similar fuels.

Another type of mill is shown in Fig. 7.22. This type of mill is an impact mill. Coal and primary air enter the crusher-drier section Ⓐ of the pulverizer where the coal is granulated by impact against tough swing hammers Ⓑ. Here, much of the remaining moisture in the coal is removed by the flash-drying turbulent action induced by rapid swing hammer rotation. Foreign materials in the coal are efficiently conveyed to a tramp metal pocket for removal. Dried coal, in the granulated state, passes through a grid section Ⓒ, with oversize coal particles being retained above the grids for recrushing. Dry, fine granulated coal then enters the first-effect stage of the pulverizer for fine pulverization. Tungsten carbide clad impeller clips Ⓓ and wear-resisting plates having extension blades convey the coal and air to the second effect. It is then finely pulverized by impact and attrition between tungsten carbide clad stationary pegs Ⓔ and moving pegs Ⓕ. Specially designed peripheral liner plates help to further pulverize the coal granules. A rejector assembly equipped with tungsten clad rejector arms Ⓖ returns the coarse coal particles for further pulverization. Coal of the desired fineness is permitted to enter the fan section. An integral, primary air-fan delivers pulverized coal and primary air through coal piping to the burners.

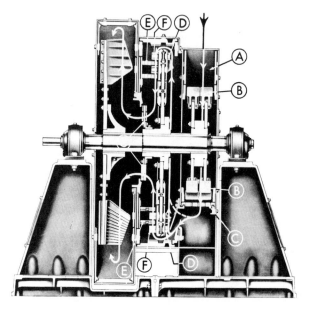

Figure 7.22 Combined crusher-drier pulverizer (Courtesy of Riley Stoker Corp.)

The roller mill is another type of pulverizer. In this device the material to be pulverized is thrown against a vertical ring and ground by rollers suspended from a rotating spider that swing out against the ring by centrifugal force. Figure 7.23 shows a C-E (Combustion Engineering) Raymond bowl mill and exhauster. This unit is designed for center feed of coal. This mill pulverizer dries and classifies the coal, and the exhauster delivers the pulverized coal through a distribution system to the burners. A two-stage classifier permits particles of a given fineness to enter the distribution system and returns coarser particles to the mill for further grinding. A feeder is used with this system in the same manner (in principle) as the one described previously for the ball mill.

Figure 7.23 C-E Raymond bowl mill with central feed (Courtesy of Combustion Engineering, Inc.)

Once the coal particles are ground to the proper fineness, the coal air mixture goes to the burners. Complete combustion requires that, at a temperature sufficiently high for ignition, every particle of fuel must come in contact with oxygen long enough for the combustion reaction to occur. Turbulence is necessary to scavenge combustion products from the surface of fuel particles and to supply oxygen. Fuel streams enter a furnace at a velocity considerably above the rate of flame propagation. Ignition stability depends on a flow pattern from the burner which causes eddy currents at the stream edges. Proper control of the flame shape also assures uniform heat absorption in all water-walls and avoids direct flame impingement on the furnace tubes.

One method of firing, known as corner firing, is illustrated in Fig. 7.24. In this method the burners are located in the corners of the furnace with separate

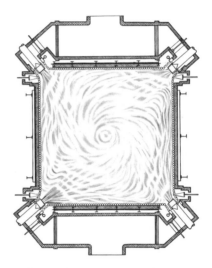

Figure 7.24 Corner firing (Courtesy of Combustion Engineering, Inc.)

air nozzles above and below each fuel nozzle. The fuel and air are injected in several relatively small streams from the four corners of the furnace. This arrangement imparts cyclonic or rotary motion to the fuel–air streams within the furnace. The impinging and scrubbing action of the streams upon one another produces the turbulence and mixing of fuel and air necessary for rapid and complete combustion. Nearly all the heat from combustion is thus distributed throughout the furnace and is available for radiant absorption by the maximum amount of waterwall surface. In addition to using fixed burners, tilting tangent burners are also used. These have adjustable tips pivoted to the end of the fuel nozzle and air ports. Individual operating rods are linked together at the burner front and are operated simultaneously, tilting the assembly upward or downward. The drive unit (either electric motor or pneumatic actuator) may be operated manually by remote control or automatically by steam temperature control. The use of the tilting burner for varying load conditions for steam generation and superheat control can be best illustrated by referring to Figs. 7.24, 7.25.

When the fuel–air streams are directed downward, combustion is completed lower in the furnace, resulting in greater heat absorption by the waterwall surface and lower temperature of the gas leaving the furnace. The opposite effect results from directing the fuel–air streams upward, thus reducing the heat absorption in the lower part of the furnace, resulting in less total heat absorption and higher gas temperature leaving the furnace. For steam tempera-

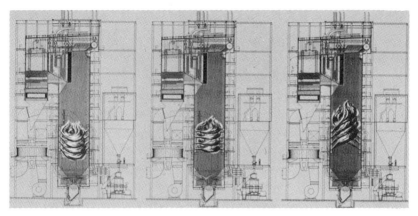

Figure 7.25 Operation of tilting burners (Courtesy of Combustion Engineering, Inc.)

ture control from partial load to full load, the furnace is designed for the desired exit gas temperature with maximum upward burner tilt at the minimum load control point. Cooling of exit gas temperature with increasing load is provided by a corresponding downward tilt of burners to utilize more surface for heat absorption. Tangential firing can also be used for oil and gas firing. Figure 7.26 shows a fixed tangential burner with nozzles for pulverized coal, oil, natural gas, and blast furnace gas. The two large nozzles at the bottom are for blast furnace gas.

For conventional horizontal firing from fixed burners, a unit such as the one shown in Fig. 7.27 is used. This unit has a central coal nozzle with internal ribs in the form of rifling. The coal nozzle is surrounded by a housing that is provided with adjustable vanes for controlling the air rotation and resulting flame shape. A central tube provides for the insertion of an oil or gas ignition torch. Adjustable deflectors in the burner inlet uniformly distribute the fuel around the periphery of the nozzle inlet. This compensates for any segregation caused by turns in the fuel pipe leading to the burners. After the proper setting is determined for the desired uniform distribution, the deflectors remain in position.

After passing the deflectors, the mixture of coal and primary air enters the nozzle tangentially. The spiral ribs in the nozzle maintain uniform distribution in the main body of the nozzle and assure a uniform mixture around the outlet periphery.

The secondary air from the outer housing also enters tangentially through a series of adjustable vanes and combines with the primary air and fuel mixture, resulting in turbulence and thorough mixing. The length of the flame may be varied by changing the angle of the adjustable vanes. The burners are usually placed in the front or rear wall of the furnace so that the flame can expand and utilize the furnace volume effectively without impingement on the walls. These burners may be designed to burn coal, oil, or gas, either one fuel alone or any combination of fuels.

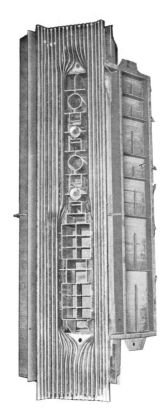

Figure 7.26 Combination burner (Courtesy of Combustion Engineering Inc.)

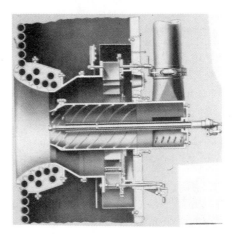

Figure 7.27 C-E type R horizontal burner (Courtesy of Combustion Engineering, Inc.)

Oil burner guns for power boilers are usually described by the method used in atomizing the oil at the tip. These methods are mechanical atomizing, steam or air atomizing, inside or outside mix type, and rotary cup. These types are illustrated in Fig. 7.28.

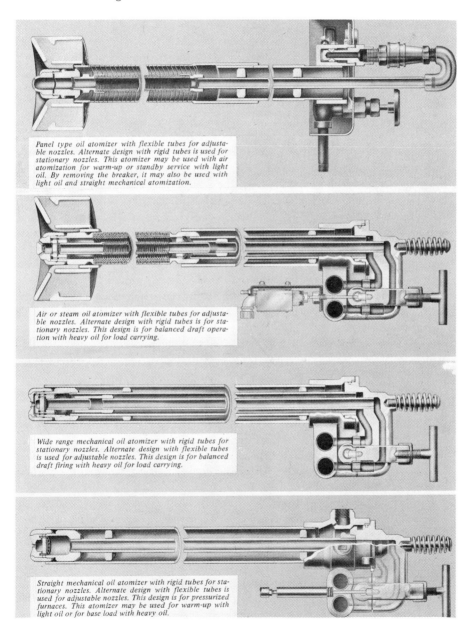

Panel type oil atomizer with flexible tubes for adjustable nozzles. Alternate design with rigid tubes is used for stationary nozzles. This atomizer may be used with air atomization for warm-up or standby service with light oil. By removing the breaker, it may also be used with light oil and straight mechanical atomization.

Air or steam oil atomizer with flexible tubes for adjustable nozzles. Alternate design with rigid tubes is for stationary nozzles. This design is for balanced draft operation with heavy oil for load carrying.

Wide range mechanical oil atomizer with rigid tubes for stationary nozzles. Alternate design with flexible tubes is used for adjustable nozzles. This design is for balanced draft firing with heavy oil for load carrying.

Straight mechanical oil atomizer with rigid tubes for stationary nozzles. Alternate design with flexible tubes is used for adjustable nozzles. This design is for pressurized furnaces. This atomizer may be used for warm-up with light oil or for base load with heavy oil.

Figure 7.28 Types of oil burners (Courtesy of Combustion Engineering, Inc.)

Rotary cup burners depend for atomization on centrifugal force. Energy is imparted to the oil on a rapidly spinning cup, droplets flying off the rim as a mist. In steam atomizing burners, streams of oil and steam impinge in a mixing chamber where the energy in the steam heats and atomizes the oil, and the mixture then enters the furnace. Oil viscosity need be only low enough to permit pumping.

Mechanical atomizing oil burners depend on the energy in the oil by virtue of its pressure for atomization, that is, the conversion of this energy to velocity. The oil flows through tangential passages in the burner tip and emerges through a central hole with sufficient rotative velocity to cause atomization, mixture droplets flying off from the tip circumferentially. The required oil viscosity necessitates heating the heavier oils.

The firing rate of all burners is controlled by varying oil pressure: for a given system resistance, the pressure variation is as the square of the rating. The atomizing effect of steam and rotary cup burners is not dependent on oil pressure drop through a nozzle; hence these burners function satisfactorily over a wide load range. This is not true of straight mechanical atomizing burners since energy for atomization depends on pressure, about 100 psig minimum. Unless the system is designed for very high pressure at maximum load, atomization is poor, and the burners drool or throw large droplets of oil at low load. While this can be accommodated by changing tips, it necessitates taking burners out of service successively, which temporarily upsets air distribution. The limitation can be minimized by the use of wide-range mechanical burners. In this type of design, oil is pumped to the burner tip at a constant rate, passing through tangential slots at high velocity. Part of the rapidly spinning oil passes into the furnace, the balance being returned through another passage to a tank or booster pump inlet. The firing rate is controlled by varying the return line pressure.

While the steam atomizing burner has some advantages, particularly for starting and low-load operation, there is often an objection to the use of steam. The amount of atomizing steam is less than 1 percent of that generated at full load, but its use entails the loss of treated water. There is a slight increase in flue gas moisture, with its implications as to air heater or economizer corrosion. In terms of energy, there is very little difference between steam and mechanical burners in atomization cost.

Gas burner nozzles may be designed with a series of small holes for distribution of gas in the air stream or a single nozzle opening of suitable size. The choice depends on the application, method of air admission, and cleanliness of the gas. Some gas burners premix part of the combustion air. Blast-furnace gas burners must be large enough to pass large volumes of low calorific gas containing considerable dust. Small jets firing such a gas would soon be plugged with dirt. Many of the burners already described for coal and oil can also be used for gas when properly designed. Quite often combination burners that are capable of firing any of these fuels are used. The use of these combination burners gives the operator flexibility in the fuel that he can fire, depending upon the supply and the economics at any given time.

One word of caution should be expressed at this time, prior to leaving the topic of fuel burning. Resumption of fuel flow to a hot furnace after accidental flame failure may cause a very serious explosion. Oil and gas burners are therefore often monitored by flame-failure devices utilizing radiation-sensitive eyes which will shut off fuel and/or sound an alarm in the event of such failure. A further refinement may include controls which will prevent relighting until the furnace has been purged.

We have already seen from the Carnot cycle that one way to increase the efficiency of the theoretical cycle is to increase the upper temperature of the cycle. For the practical cycle we must also consider the effect of moisture in the steam on the steam turbine. Moisture in the steam can cause severe turbine blade erosion and even failure of a unit. Thus superheating eliminates any water from entering the turbine, and more importantly it also minimizes the moisture in the steam in the last stages of the turbine. When we discuss the turbine and the reheat cycle, we will consider the effect of moisture and reheating of the partially expanded steam in the turbine further. For the present, we will note that from both cycle and practical considerations, super-heating is used in all power generating stations.

The arrangement of the superheater surface in a steam generator is of considerable importance since different locations will give rise to different superheater outlet temperature characteristics. The conventional way of classi-fying superheaters is either as convection or radiant types. Some idea of the location of the superheater sections of a modern steam generator can be obtained by referring to Fig. 2.27 (repeated). This figure shows a pulverized-coal-fired unit with both radiant and convection heat-transfer surfaces. Since the amount of tubing (total length) needed depends upon the rate of heat absorption, the most economical superheater would be one where the tubing was closely spaced and placed in the highest heat-release portion of the steam generator. However, the heat transfer to superheated steam is very low when compared to the heat-transfer rate for boiling water, and such a design could lead to unsafe metal temperatures in the superheater. As a practical matter, the startup rate in units with radiant superheaters is often dictated by the metal temperature in the superheater before a positive steam flow is established. The purpose for both convection and radiant superheaters in the unit shown can be shown from the following reasoning. For best turbine operation it is desirable to have the temperature of the steam entering the turbine stay constant (or as nearly constant) as possible as the load varies. As the load increases, the effective radiant heat transfer in the furnace does not increase as quickly as the steam flow increases. Thus, as load increases, the steam temperature out of the radiant superheater decreases. For the convection type of superheater we have a different situation. As the load increases, the mass flow of gases and their average temperature increase faster than the flow of steam. Therefore, as the

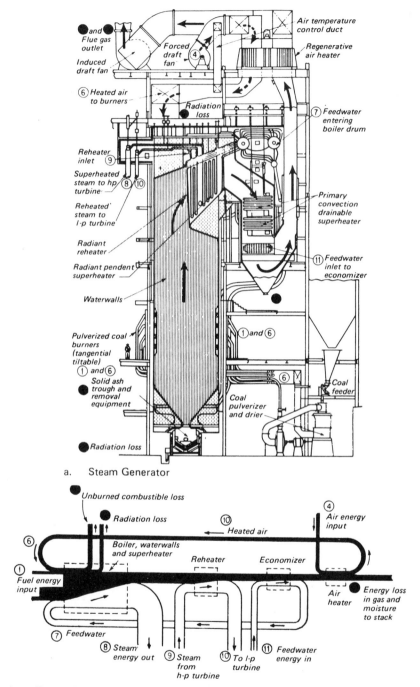

Air temperature control duct

and Flue gas outlet

Regenerative air heater

Induced draft fan

Forced draft fan (4)

(6) Heated air to burners

Radiation loss

(7) Feedwater entering boiler drum

Reheater inlet (9)

Superheated steam to hp (8)(10) turbine

Reheated steam to l-p turbine

Primary convection drainable superheater

Radiant reheater

Radiant pendent superheater

Waterwalls

(11) Feedwater inlet to economizer

(1) and (6)

Pulverized coal burners (tangential tiltable)
(1) and (6)

Solid ash trough and removal equipment

(6)

Coal feeder

Coal pulverizer and drier

Radiation loss

a.   Steam Generator

Unburned combustible loss

Radiation loss

(10)   Heated air

(4) Air energy input

(6)

Boiler, waterwalls and superheater

Reheater

Economizer

(1) Fuel energy input

Air heater

Energy loss in gas and moisture to stack

(7) Feedwater

(8) Steam energy out

(9) Steam from h-p turbine

(10) To l-p turbine

(11) Feedwater energy in

b.   Energy Diagram

Figure 2.27 Modern steam generator (repeated) (Reprinted with permission from Power, special report "Steam Generation," copyright by McGraw-Hill, Inc., June 1964)

load increases, the characteristic of a convection superheater is a rising outlet temperature. Figure 7.29 shows this effect and also the combined characteristic

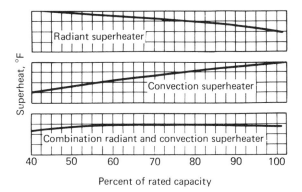

Figure 7.29 Typical superheater characteristics

when both types of superheater are used. It will be seen that the combined characteristic is reasonably flat over a large portion of the load range. In many applications it is essential that the final steam temperature be kept constant over a wide range of load. Where the inherent characteristic of the superheater is not flat over the desired load range, several methods of regulating the final steam temperature are sometimes incorporated individually or in combination in the steam generator. These include the use of gas bypass dampers, burner tilt, gas recirculation from the economizer outlet to the furnace, desuperheating by introducing water between superheater sections, desuperheating using a heat exchanger in the steam drum, use of separately fired superheaters, and others.

After leaving the superheater and boiler bank sections of the steam generator, the exhaust gases are still at a relatively high temperature, and it is very often economical (especially in large central station units) to make provisions to use this heat to heat the incoming feedwater in an economizer or to heat the incoming air in an air heater, or both. The reduction of exit gas temperature to a low value is attractive from an efficiency standpoint. However, temperature is limited practically by the metal temperature at which condensation of vapors from the combustion products occurs. These condensed vapors contain sulfurous and sulfuric acid and are highly corrosive; they also act as a binder for ash particles, promoting deposit formation, although in some instances larger fly-ash particles tend to scrub the surface. The end products of the combustion of a given coal cannot be predicted accurately, so the exact dew-point temperature cannot be forecast. The important consideration is not an average cold end metal temperature, but the minimum metal temperature under disadvantageous operating conditions and the duration of these conditions.

The economizer is usually a steel tube heat exchanger having longitudinal fins or gilled rings with the feedwater flowing inside the tubes and the combustion gases flowing over the tubes. Cast iron is used, especially where the flue-gas temperature is low and acid condensation may be expected. The use of extended surface (fins) is to increase the heat transfer per linear foot of tubing, since economizers operate at relatively low temperature differentials and require large surface areas. When located within the boiler setting, the economizer is most commonly placed before the air heater. Figure 7.30 shows an extended-surface economizer.

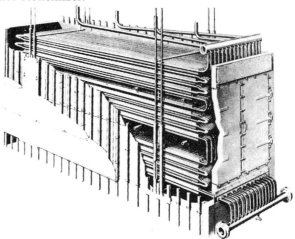

Figure 7.30 Extended surface economizer (Courtesy of Combustion Engineering, Inc.)

Air heaters are of two general types, recuperative and regenerative. Tubular heaters are of the former type and Ljungstrom heaters of the latter type. Almost all are designed for counterflow to achieve greater mean temperature differences. Selection of type for a given installation depends on factors such as space, arrangement, and performance. In power boiler installations, where it is desired to reduce the combustion gas exit temperature as low as possible (compatible to the dew-point temperature of the gas), air heaters become very large.

The regenerative (Ljungstrom) air heater shown in Fig. 7.31 consists of a rotating heat-storage element turning at about 2 to 3 rpm. Hot gases pass through one-half of the unit, with air passing in counterflow through the other half. As the rotor rotates, the combustion gases transfer heat to the heat-storage elements, which are subsequently exposed to the cold incoming air.

The tubular type of air heater is essentially a nest of tubes enclosed in a steel casing. One unit of this type is shown in Fig. 7.32. In this design the tubes are vertical, with air flowing outside of the tubes and combustion gases flowing inside the tubes. Other arrangements of surface are possible: air inside the tubes and gas outside, horizontal tubes, integral with the boiler, external to the boiler, and so on.

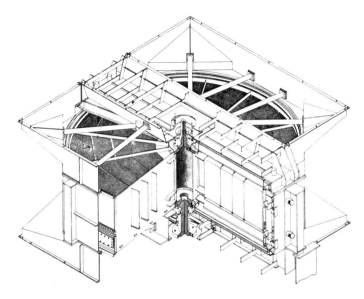

Figure 7.31 Ljungstrom regenerative air heater (Courtesy of Combustion Engineering, Inc.)

The trend in large central station steam generators has been toward high pressures and temperatures dictated by the economics of higher efficiency (with attendant decreased operating costs) against the initial increased cost necessitated by the high pressure and temperature. When a steam generator is designed to operate above the critical pressure of 3203.6 psia, certain physical phenomena must be considered. As heat is applied to the fluid at constant pressure, there is a continuous increase in the temperature of the fluid, and at no point does the fluid temperature remain constant. There is no clearly defined boundary between the liquid and vapor phase, but there is a continuous increase in the specific volume and temperature. During this time the working fluid is homogeneous, with no boiling. Thus in boilers designed for supercritical pressures there can be no circulation in the sense that steam disengages from the steam–water mixture, and water is recirculated via downcomers to the heat absorption surfaces. Therefore, supercritical boilers are of the once-through or monotube type in which water enters at one end and emerges at the other as superheated steam, with the boiler feed pump supplying the positive circulation. In actual units, many such once-through paths are provided in parallel.

Figure 7.33 shows a supercritical steam generator designed to produce 6.4×10^6 lb/hr at 3500 psig and 1000°F. At startup or low loads it operates as a controlled circulation unit. This is a twin furnace fired with pulverized coal. Water flow goes from the economizer to the center wall. From the center wall the flow goes to the outer walls and then to the rear gas pass walls. After going

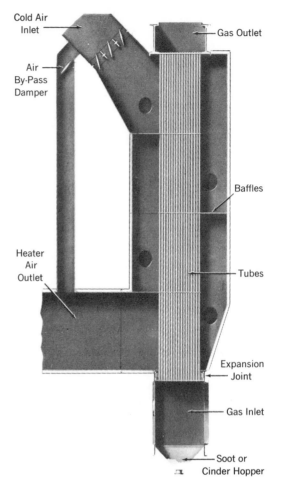

Figure 7.32 Tubular air heater (Courtesy of Babcock and Wilcox Company)

through four superheater sections, the steam is discharged to the high-pressure turbine. After expansion through the high-pressure turbine, the steam is returned to the two-section reheater prior to entering the low-pressure turbine.

A principal advantage of the once-through boiler is that it does not require circulating pumps or drums. Energy required for circulation is provided by the feed pump. The design is well suited to quick starts and rapid load changes since it utilizes small diameter tubes, has no drum, and provides positive circulation under all operating conditions. It is also adapted to the use of radiant superheaters, because this surface is always protected by flow during startup.

The principal disadvantage is the requirement of extremely pure boiler water, since all solids present must be deposited in the tubes or carried along with the steam as dust.

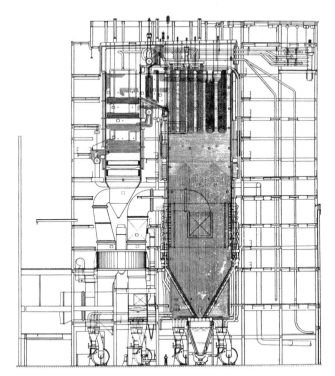

Figure 7.33 Supercritical steam generator (Courtesy of Combustion Engineering, Inc.)

In addition to the steam generators that we have discussed, other units are commonly used in smaller sizes. Many of these are built and completely equipped with combustion controls prior to shipment. These are the "packaged" or shop-assembled boilers. Quite often it is possible to classify these units according to their basic tube arrangements, that is, A type, D type, and O type, as shown in Fig. 7.34. The A type has two small lower drums with an

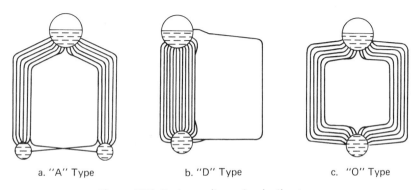

a. "A" Type   b. "D" Type   c. "O" Type

Figure 7.34 Basic medium-size boiler types

upper drum for steam–water separation. Most steam generation occurs in the furnace walls. In the D type unit, most of the steam is generated in the tube bank. In the O type, steam generation is mostly in the furnace walls. The O type is usually longer than the A and D types for equal steam capacity.

In the smallest-sized generator, a type of unit called the firetube boiler is often used. In this boiler, steam generation occurs with the hot combustion gases flowing in the tubes and with water outside of the tubes. Due to their limited use for power generation we will not discuss this class of boiler.

7.3b Steam Turbine

The steam leaves the steam generator and goes to the turbine where it expands to give useful work. There are many different types, sizes, and shapes of turbines depending upon the specific application. Some idea of the size range can be obtained from Fig. 7.35, which shows a small single-stage turbine and a large central station multistage turbine. Due to the large number of combinations possible, let us start our discussion with the blading and the basic principles used to convert the energy in the steam to useful work. The two classifications of blading used are *impulse* blading and *reaction* blading. The basic action that occurs in impulse blading is that the expansion of steam takes place in the nozzles of the turbine and not in the blading. In the simple single impulse stage shown in Fig. 7.36a, the nozzles direct the steam into the moving blades (buckets) mounted on the rotor (see also Fig. 7.35). In the single impulse stage, all the pressure drop is shown to occur in the nozzles. As the steam flows

Figure 7.35 Comparison of turbine sizes: (a) 20-inch wheel diameter, single stage turbine (Courtesy of Worthington Corp.); (b) large turbine during shop fabrication (Courtesy of Westinghouse Electric Corp.)

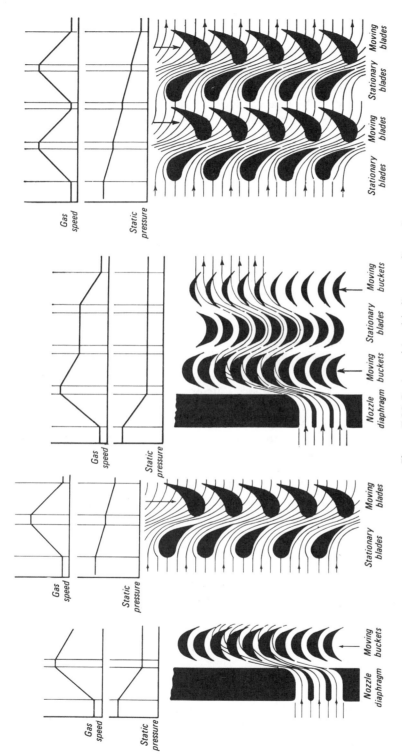

Figure 7.36 Basic turbine blading configurations

355

through the passages of the moving vanes, it is turned by the symmetrical moving blades in an axial direction, and at the same time the steam does work on the blades. Thus the final velocity of the steam is lower than at entry, and also the enthalpy of the steam is lower. When two or more such stages are placed in series, this is known as *pressure-compounding* (also known as Rateau staging). In a pressure-compounded impulse turbine, the pressure drop is taken in equal steps in the alternate fixed nozzles. In Fig. 7.36c we have a velocity-compound impulse blading situation (also known as Curtis staging). In this arrangement the complete expansion of the steam takes place in the fixed nozzles before the first stage. The steam gives up part of its kinetic energy in the first row of moving blades and is reversed in direction in the fixed blades. The fixed blading directs the steam into the second row of blades, where the remainder of the kinetic energy is absorbed.

In the reaction blading shown in Fig. 7.36b (also known as Parson's blading), a partial pressure drop occurs in the fixed blades, and the velocity of the steam is increased. The steam then flows between moving blades that are shaped to act as nozzles. A further pressure drop occurs in the moving blades, increasing the velocity of the steam relative to the blades. This expansion in the moving blades causes a reaction against the blades that does work in driving the rotor. Sufficient stages are employed to expand the steam down to the desired exhaust pressure. The right side of Fig. 7.36c shows reaction stages being fed from velocity-compounded impulse staging. This is frequently done in multistage turbines where reaction staging is used in the latter stages due to their increased efficiency under these conditions.

There are two basic turbine types that depend upon the exhaust-steam conditions. In the condensing type, the exhaust steam leaves at below atmospheric pressure, while in the noncondensing type the steam is exhausted at pressures above atmospheric. In addition, extraction methods can be further categorized as straightflow, reheat, automatic, or nonautomatic. Figure 7.37 shows the common basic turbine types.

Figure 7.38 shows a straight noncondensing steam turbine that is used for industrial applications. This turbine is used in applications requiring large quantities of single pressure steam for process or other use, and where the unit can be operated in parallel with other units that can absorb load variations. This type of turbine is usually controlled by an exhaust pressure governor which maintains the desired pressure of the process steam exhausted from the turbine. Noncondensing turbines are also used in topping arrangements, with steam exhausting to existing generating equipment to increase overall plant efficiency and output.

Figure 7.39 is also an industrial-type turbine, but the unit is a double automatic extraction condensing steam turbine. As shown, this turbine consists of high, intermediate, and low pressure sections. Units of this type are used in applications demanding continuous steam at two pressure levels. During times of high process flow, the steam flowing to the condenser generates the electric

Non-condensing

A straight non-condensing turbine is the economic choice when all exhaust steam can be used for process or heating.

If high-pressure steam is available for the turbine and the lower pressure exhaust can be used to supply other prime movers or a process, a non-condensing turbine can be applied to increase power output for the same fuel consumption.

Condensing

A straight condensing turbine is used when electrical power generation is the only concern and it must be produced on a minimum amount of steam. To improve the plant's efficiency these units can be provided with multiple uncontrolled extraction openings for feedwater heating.

Condensing controlled extraction

A condensing controlled extraction turbine bleeds off part of the main steam flow at one (single extraction) or two (double extraction) points. It is applied where process steam is required at pressures below the inlet pressure.

Condensing mixed-pressure

A condensing mixed-pressure turbine automatically uses as much low-pressure steam as available, supplementing it with as much high-pressure steam as required to carry the load. This type is used when more power must be generated than is possible with the available low-pressure steam.

Mixed-pressure extraction

This unit operates either as a mixed-pressure or an extraction turbine, depending on steam balance. As the turbine generates power, it holds constant pressure on the low-pressure steam line, extracting or admitting steam as required.

Non-condensing controlled extraction

A non-condensing controlled extraction turbine bleeds part of the main steam flow at one (single extraction) or two (double extraction) points. It is applied where process steam is required at several different pressures with variable or intermittent flows.

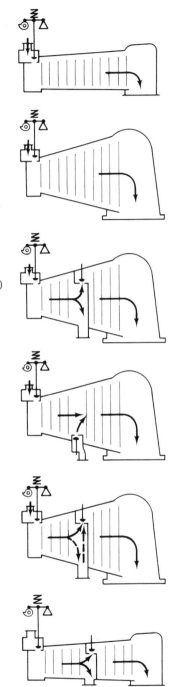

Figure 7.37 Basic turbine types (Courtesy of Worthington Corp.)

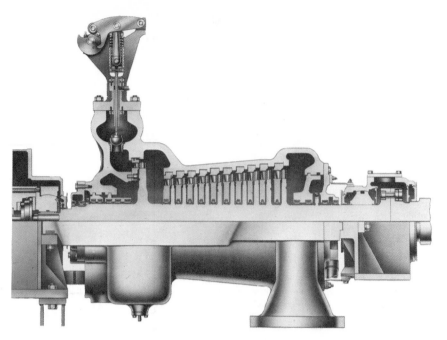

Figure 7.38 Straight noncondensing steam turbine (Courtesy of General Electric Co.)

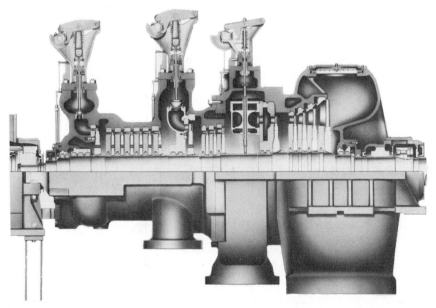

Figure 7.39 Double automatic extraction condensing steam turbine (Courtesy of General Electric Co.)

power. An automatic electro-hydraulic control maintains the extraction pressures even when the load on the unit fluctuates and extraction steam flows vary. Once the desired extraction pressure for the process is set, the turbine automatically holds that pressure. The steam flow is regulated by cam-operated upper inlet control popper valves. These valves are designed to assure efficient handling and accurate governing of large volumes of steam.

The design of a large turbine for power generation may differ in detail from the units we have discussed thus far. Figure 7.40 shows a 3600 rpm,

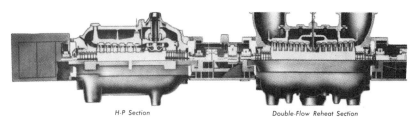

H-P Section   Double-Flow Reheat Section

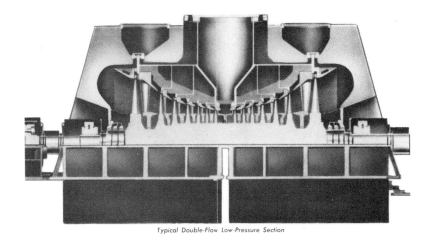

Typical Double-Flow Low-Pressure Section

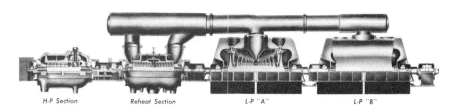

H-P Section   Reheat Section   L-P "A"   L-P "B"

Figure 7.40 Tandem-compound reheat steam turbine (Courtesy of General Electric Co.)

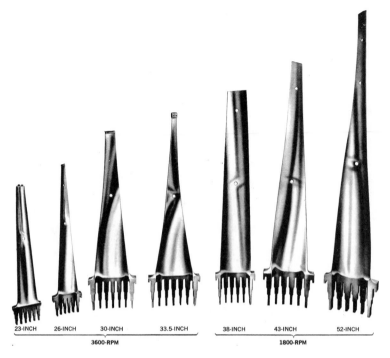

Figure 7.41 Typical turbine blading (Courtesy of General Electric Co.)

tandem-compound, four-flow, reheat steam turbine. This turbine is rated from 550,000 to 850,000 kW, with steam conditions to 3500 psig and steam at 1000°F. The 850,000 kW size has 33.5-in.-high last-stage buckets. The exhaust from the high pressure portion to the reheater in the furnace, where the temperature is again raised to 1000°F. From the reheater the steam returns to the double-flow intermediate section. The steam enters at the center of the reheat section and splits into two flow streams in opposite directions along the shaft of this section. After leaving the reheat section the steam flows to the two low pressure sections. Each low pressure section is a double-flow section receiving steam at a central inlet. The steam divides and flows through low pressure stages in opposite directions. These last stages are frequently followed by diffusers which recover some of the kinetic energy from the steam before the steam flows to the condenser below. The latter stage blades are warped, since the diameter is large and the blade velocity variation from tip to hub is also very large. Some typical turbine blades are shown in Fig. 7.41.

7.3 RANKINE CYCLE (continued)

Let us return to the simple Rankine cycle shown in Figs. 7.3 and 7.4 and consider some of the processes that occur.

Process A–B

For steady flow isentropic pumping of the feedwater it is assumed that the inlet condition to the pump corresponds to saturation at the lowest pressure of the cycle. The compression is assumed to be isentropic, and differences in potential and kinetic energies at inlet and outlet to the pump are negligible. For this ideal process the work in is

$$W = J(h_B - h_A)_s \text{ ft lb/lb} \qquad (7.2)$$

or
$$W = (h_B - h_A)_s \text{ kJ/kg} \qquad (7.2a)$$

where the subscript s denotes an isentropic compression. Since the water is essentially incompressible, it is possible to approximate Eq. (7.2) as

$$W \cong (p_2 - p_1)v_f \text{ ft lb/lb} \qquad (7.3)$$

or
$$W \cong (p_2 - p_1)v_f \text{ kJ/kg} \qquad (7.3a)$$

where p_2 is the high pressure of the cycle, p_1 is the low pressure of the cycle, and v_f is the specific volume of saturated liquid at the inlet temperature to the pump.

Process B–C

This process is the heating of the subcooled water to saturation by steam in the drum. We will consider that this occurs as part of the boiler process $(B–D)$ and not evaluate it separately. However, it is considered as part of the boiler design by the designer.

Process B–D

The liquid leaves the pump at the delivery pressure to the boiler. In the ideal cycle, pressure losses in the pipelines are negligible. Thus the process of heating in the boiler and subsequent vaporization (and superheat) can be considered to be a steady flow process carried out at constant pressure. For this process, neglecting differences in potential and kinetic energies at inlet and outlet of the boiler,

$$q = (h_D - h_B) \text{ Btu/lb or kJ/kg} \qquad (7.4a)$$

or
$$q = (h_F - h_B) \text{ Btu/lb or kJ/kg} \qquad (7.4b)$$
$$\text{(if superheat is used)}$$

It should be noted that q is the energy required by the working fluid, not the energy released in the steam generator. Also, devices such as attemperators or desuperheaters, which are used to control the final steam temperature leaving the superheater, have to be accounted for in an energy balance of a steam generator.

Process D–E

After leaving the boiler the steam is piped to the turbine. Once again friction losses will be neglected, as will differences in potential and kinetic energies at the inlet and outlet of the turbine. For the turbine, assuming an isentropic expansion,

$$W = (h_D - h_E)_s \quad \text{Btu/lb or kJ/kg} \tag{7.5a}$$

or
$$W = (h_F - h_G)_s \quad \text{Btu/lb or kJ/kg} \tag{7.5b}$$
$$\text{(if superheat is used)}$$

The presence of moisture in the turbine can lead to mechanical difficulties such as excessive erosion of the turbine blades. This is highly undesirable, and to alleviate this condition superheating of the steam is often used. This increases the efficiency of the unit (as deduced from the Carnot cycle) and decreases the amount of moisture in the turbine exhaust (see Fig. 7.4).

Figure 7.42 illustrates an expansion of steam from 500 psia to a final pressure of $1\frac{1}{2}$ in Hg. On the *hs* coordinates this ideal expansion is a vertical line. If the expansion is not isentropic, there is an increase in entropy, and the final state point must lie on the $1\frac{1}{2}$ in. Hg line at an increased value of *s*. As shown in Fig. 7.42, the final enthalpy is required to be higher for the nonisentropic expansion than for the isentropic case. In other words, the change in enthalpy for the isentropic expansion is greater than the change in

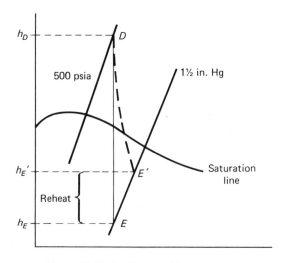

Figure 7.42 Rankine turbine expansion

enthalpy for the nonisentropic expansion between the same pressure limits. The nonisentropic expansion has been shown as a dashed line. Actually, this line is not the path of the expansion, since the expansion is irreversible and non-equilibrium states cannot be drawn on an *hs* diagram. The difference in enthalpy $(h'_E - h_E)$ is called reheat, since all the mechanical irreversibilities increase the final enthalpy, or "reheat" the fluid. To account for the nonideal effects in the turbine, the internal turbine efficiency is introduced as the ratio of the work is actually done to the work that could be done ideally. The student should note that this procedure corresponds to the method used to define nozzle efficiencies in Chapter 5. Therefore, the internal turbine efficiency η_t is

$$\eta_t = \frac{h_D - h_{E'}}{h_D - h_E} \qquad (5.116a)$$

Process E–A

After leaving the turbine the fluid (which is usually wet steam) is piped to the condenser. Since the specific volume is high and we wish to keep the pressure losses in pipelines and equipment small, the piping and condenser are usually quite large at this part of the cycle. If pressure losses, kinetic terms, and potential terms are negligible and it is assumed that the equipment is well insulated, the heat rejected to the cooling water is

$$q_r = (h_E - h_A) \text{ Btu/lb or kJ/kg} \qquad (7.6a)$$

or

$$q_r = (h_G - h_A) \text{ Btu/lb or kJ/kg} \qquad (7.6b)$$
$$\text{(if superheat is used)}$$

This energy is rejected to the cooling water and raises the temperature of the cooling water. In the ideal cycle the condensed steam is assumed to be saturated and is returned to the inlet of the circulating pump with no pressure drop or heat loss in the piping. Actually, as we have noted, the condensate is usually slightly subcooled before leaving the condenser. A large surface condenser is shown in Fig. 7.43. Note the size of the man in relation to the size of the equipment.

By definition, the thermal efficiency of any cycle is the useful (net) work out of the cycle divided by the thermal energy supplied (input) to the cycle. Therefore, the efficiency of the ideal Rankine cycle (without superheat) is

$$\eta_R = \frac{\text{turbine work out} - \text{pump work}}{\text{heat supplied in boiler}} = \frac{(h_D - h_E)_s - (h_B - h_A)_s}{h_D - h_B}$$
$$(7.7)$$

Figure 7.43 Large surface condenser (Courtesy of Foster Wheeler Corp.)

If the pump work is small, as it usually is, it can be neglected, and the efficiency of the ideal Rankine cycle becomes

$$\eta'_R = \frac{(h_D - h_E)_s}{(h_D - h_B)} \qquad (7.8)$$

$$\text{with superheat, } \eta'_R = \frac{(h_F - h_G)_s}{(h_F - h_B)} \qquad (7.8a)$$

The engine which operates on the expansion of steam between the boiler and the condenser in the Rankine cycle is called the Rankine engine. If the expansion is isentropic, the maximum amount of work obtainable from the expansion is $(h_D - h_E)_s$, or $(h_F - h_G)_s$ if superheating is used. If pump work is neglected, the efficiency of the Rankine cycle is the same as that of the Rankine engine.

ILLUSTRATIVE PROBLEM 7.2

The maximum and minimum pressures in a Rankine cycle are 400 and 14.696 psia. The steam is exhausted from the engine as saturated vapor. (a) Sketch the cycle on temperature–entropy and on enthalpy–entropy diagrams. (b) Find the thermal efficiency of the cycle.

Solution

(a) Figure 7.4 with the cycle extending into the superheat region and expanding along $F \rightarrow G$ is the appropriate diagram for this process. (b) This problem can be solved either by use of the Mollier chart or the *Steam Tables*. If the chart is used, 14.696 psia is first located on the saturated vapor line. Since the expansion, $F \rightarrow G$, is isentropic, a vertical line on the chart is the path of the process. The point corresponding to F in Fig. 7.4 is found where this vertical line intersects 400 psia. At this point the enthalpy is 1515 Btu/lb and the corresponding temperature is approximately 980°F. Saturated vapor at 14.696 psia has an enthalpy of 1150.5 Btu/lb (from the Mollier chart). The *Steam Tables* show that saturated liquid at 14.696 psia has an enthalpy of 180.15 Btu/lb. In terms of Fig. 7.4,

$$h_B = 180.15, \qquad h_F = 1515, \qquad h_G = 1150.5$$

Neglecting pump work

$$\eta_R' = \frac{1515 - 1150.5}{1515 - 180.15} \times 100 = 27.3\%$$

The pump work is

$$\frac{(p_2 - p_1)v_f}{J} = \frac{(400 - 14.696)}{778} \times 144 \times 0.0167 = 1.19 \text{ Btu/lb}$$

The efficiency of the cycle including pump work is

$$\eta_R = \frac{(1515 - 1150.5) - (1.19)}{1515 - 180.15} \times 100 = 27.2\%$$

Neglecting pump work is obviously justified in this case. An alternate solution is obtained by using the *Steam Tables*: at 14.696 psia and saturation, $s_g = 1.7567$; therefore, at 400 psia $s = 1.7567$. From Table 3 (at 400 psia)

s	h	t
1.7632	1523.6	1000
1.7567	1514.2	982.4
1.7558	1512.9	980

The remainder of the problem proceeds along similar lines with essentially the same results. The use of the Mollier chart greatly facilitates the solution of this problem.

7.4 RATING OF POWER-PLANT CYCLES

To evaluate the merit of the power-plant cycles, several yardsticks are employed. One of these, the type efficiency, is quite useful. The type efficiency is defined as the ratio of the ideal thermal efficiency of a given cycle divided by the efficiency of a Carnot cycle operating between the same maximum and minimum temperature limits. In essence, it measures the approach of a prototype ideal cycle to the Carnot cycle between the same maximum and minimum temperature limits.

ILLUSTRATIVE PROBLEM 7.3

What is the type efficiency of the ideal Rankine cycle of Illustrative Problem 7.2?

Solution

The Carnot cycle would operate between 982.4° and 212°F. Its efficiency is

$$\eta_c = \left(\frac{T_1 - T_2}{T_1} \right) 100$$

$$= \frac{(982.4 + 460) - (212 + 460)}{(982.4 + 460)} \times 100 = 53.4\%$$

The type efficiency would be

$$\frac{\eta_R'}{\eta_C'} 100 = \left(\frac{27.3}{53.4} \right) 100 = 51.1\%$$

In other words, at best, this cycle is only 51.1 percent as efficient as the Carnot cycle operating between the same temperature limits.

For actual cycles, the thermal efficiency is defined as the net work output of the system divided by the energy as heat supplied to the system. In evaluating the thermal efficiency, it is necessary to take care that the proper accounting of energies is carried out. This can best be illustrated by reference to Illustrative Problem 7.4.

ILLUSTRATIVE PROBLEM 7.4

In the Rankine cycle of Illustrative Problem 7.2, 50 Btu/lb of steam is lost by heat transfer from the turbine to the surroundings. What is the thermal efficiency of this cycle?

Solution

From Illustrative Problem 7.2 it was found that the useful (ideal) work is $1515 - 1150.5 = 364.5$ Btu/lb of steam if pump work is neglected. Because of the heat losses, 50 Btu/lb of the 364.5 Btu/lb becomes unavailable. Thus $364.5 - 50 = 314.5$ Btu/lb is available. The thermal efficiency of the cycle (neglecting pump work) is

$$\eta = \left(\frac{314.5}{1515 - 180.15} \right) 100 = 23.6\%$$

The heat rate and steam rate of a cycle are also figures of merit, which have been used to describe cycle performance. The heat rate (actual or ideal) is defined as the amount of energy supplied per horsepower-hour or kilowatt-hour of net output of the cycle. Therefore, heat rate equals energy supplied per horsepower-hour (or kilowatt-hour) divided by η_R (or η_R'). Thus

$$\text{heat rate} = \frac{2545}{\eta_R(\text{or } \eta_R')} \quad \text{(Btu per horsepower-hour)} \quad (7.9a)$$

$$= \frac{3413}{\eta_R(\text{or } \eta_R')} \quad \text{(Btu per kilowatt-hour)} \quad (7.9b)$$

The denominator in Eq. (7.9) can be the thermal efficiency of any cycle. It is not restricted to the Rankine cycle. It is left as an exercise for the student to verify the constants 2545 and 3413 used in Eq. (7.9).

The steam rate of a cycle is defined as the ratio of the steam supplied per net horsepower-hour or kilowatt-hour. Therefore,

$$\text{Steam rate} = \frac{\text{pounds of steam supplied per hour}}{\text{net output in horsepower- or kilowatt-hour}}$$

$$(7.10)$$

ILLUSTRATIVE PROBLEM 7.5

Determine the heat rate and the steam rate per kilowatt-hour of plant output in Illustrative Problem 7.2.

Solution

Neglecting pump work

$$\text{heat rate} = \frac{3413}{0.273} = 12,500 \text{ Btu/kw-hr}$$

Per pound of steam, $1515 - 1150.5 = 364.5$ Btu is delivered. Since 1 kw-hr $= 3413$ Btu, the steam rate becomes $3413/364.5 = 9.36$ lb of steam/kw-hr.

7.5 THE REHEAT CYCLE

The simple Rankine cycle suffers from the fact that heat is added while the temperature varies, and excess moisture during the expansion process is detrimental to the performance and life of the turbine. Superheating tends to help the turbine, but thermodynamically it would not appear to yield much of an increase in the thermal efficiency of the cycle. To achieve a higher thermal efficiency and to help solve the turbine problem, the reheat cycle was proposed. The basis of this cycle is an attempt to approach Carnot-cycle efficiency by adding heat in increments at the highest possible temperature level. The steam is permitted to expand part of the way in the turbine and is then returned to the boiler, where it is heated again (reheated) and subsequently reexpanded through the turbine. Although there is no theoretical limit to the number of stages of reheat that can be employed in a cycle, two, or at most three, are used in practice. A schematic and a *Ts* diagram of this cycle are shown in Fig. 7.44.

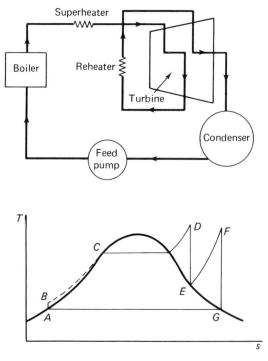

Figure 7.44 Simple reheat cycle

It will be noted that this cycle is similar to the Rankine cycle, with the addition of the constant pressure heating from E to F and the second isentropic expansion from F to G. In an actual cycle, pressure and heat losses will occur in each part of the cycle, but for the present it will be assumed that all processes are carried out to prevent these losses from occurring. Neglecting pump work, the energy supplied to the cycle per pound of fluid circulated is the sum of the heat supplied during the original heating plus that supplied during reheating. Thus the heat in is $(h_D - h_B) + (h_F - h_E)$, which can also be written as $(h_D - h_A)$ $+ (h_F - h_E)$ when pump work is neglected. The work out of the cycle is due to the two expansions. Thus the work out is $(h_D - h_E)_s + (h_F - h_G)_s$.

The efficiency of the cycle is

$$\eta_{\text{reheat}} = \frac{(h_D - h_E)_s + (h_F - h_G)_s}{(h_D - h_A) + (h_F - h_E)} = \frac{(h_D - h_G) + (h_F - h_E)}{(h_D - h_A) + (h_F - h_E)} \quad (7.11)$$

A reheat cycle is sometimes called an "ideal" reheat cycle if, in the first expansion, it is expanded isentropically to saturated vapor and during the subsequent reheat it is brought back to the same enthalpy that it had before expansion; that is, $h_D = h_F$.

ILLUSTRATIVE PROBLEM 7.6

Assume that the simple Rankine cycle described in Illustrative Problem 7.2 is made into a reheat cycle by first expanding the steam to 200 psia and then reheating it to the enthalpy that it had prior to the first expansion. If the final expansion is carried out to 14.696 psia, determine the efficiency of the reheat cycle and compare it to the simple cycle.

Solution

The Mollier chart provides a convenient way of solving this problem. Expanding from 980°F, 400 psia, $s = 1.7567$ to 200 psia yields a final enthalpy of 1413 Btu/lb. Expanding from 200 psia and an enthalpy of 1515 Btu/lb to 14.696 psia yields a final enthalpy of 1205 Btu/lb.

$$\eta_{\text{reheat}} = \left[\frac{(1515 - 1205) + (1515 - 1413)}{(1515 - 180.15) + (1515 - 1413)} \right] 100 = 28.7\%$$

It is apparent that for the conditions of this problem the increase in efficiency is not very large. The final condition of the fluid after the second expansion is superheated steam at 14.696 psia. By condensing at this relatively high pressure condition, a large amount of heat is rejected to the condenser cooling water.

7.6 THE REGENERATIVE CYCLE

As indicated in the preceding discussion, reheating is limited in its ability to improve the thermodynamic cycle efficiency and finds greatest usefulness in the reduction of moisture in the turbine. However, since the largest single loss of energy in a power plant occurs at the condenser in which heat is rejected to the coolant, it is pertinent to consider methods of reducing this rejected heat and improving cycle efficiency.

In both the ideal Rankine and reheat cycles the condensate is returned to the boiler at the lowest temperature of the cycle. The fluid is heated to saturation by direct mixing in the steam drum of the boiler, by furnace radiation in the boiler tubes, or by gas convection heating by the flue gases in the economizer section of the unit. These methods depend on large temperature differences and are inherently irreversible. Rather than resorting to such procedures, which involve the internal arrangement of the boiler and its heat-transfer circuit, let us consider a method of feedwater heating which, although idealized, leads to certain interesting and practical conclusions.

The most desirable method of heating the condensate would be by a continuous reversible method. Presuming that this is possible and imagining that the heating can be made to occur reversibly by an interchange within the turbine and in equilibrium with the expanding fluid, the Ts diagram will be given as shown in Fig. 7.45. This diagram assumes saturated vapor at the initiation of expansion. Curve AB' is parallel to CD since it was postulated that the heating is reversible. It will be noted that the increase in entropy during heating equals the decrease during the expansion and cooling of the vapor, and area $A'ABB'$ equals area $CD'D$. Thus the cycle is equivalent to a Carnot cycle operating between the maximum and minimum temperatures T_1 and T_2. The efficiency is therefore given by Eq. (7.1).

It is interesting to note that by allowing the working fluid to deliver work and to transfer heat simultaneously in the manner indicated, the ideal-cycle efficiency approaches the Carnot efficiency as a limit.

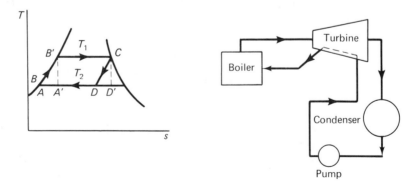

Figure 7.45 Ideal regenerative cycle

In practice, this ideal cycle is approached by allowing the condensate from the feed pump to be heated in a separate heater (or heaters) by steam extracted from the turbine after it has partly expanded and done work. The extracted steam may mix directly with the condensate (as in an openheater) or may exchange heat indirectly and condense (as in a closed heater). A schematic of a practical cycle is shown in Fig. 7.46.

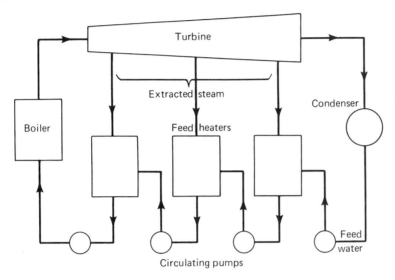

Figure 7.46 Regenerative cycle

In large central station installations, from one up to a dozen feedwater heaters are often used. These can attain lengths of over 60 ft, diameters up to 7 ft, and have over 30,000 sq ft of surface. Figure 7.47 shows a straight condensing type of feedwater heater with steam entering at the center and flowing logitudinally, in a baffled path, on the outside of the tubes. Vents are

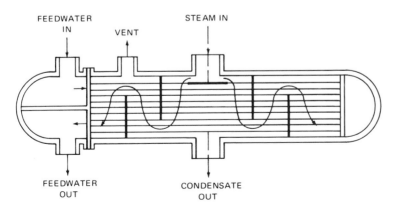

Figure 7.47 Straight condensing feedwater heater

provided to prevent the buildup of noncondensable gases in the heater, and are especially important where pressures are less than atmospheric pressure. Also, deaerators are often used in conjunction with feedwater heaters or as separate units to reduce the quantity of oxygen and other noncondensable gases in the feedwater to acceptable levels.

By combining the regenerative cycle with the reheat cycle, the modern regenerative–reheat cycle is obtained. An analysis of such a cycle involves writing a heat balance around each of the heaters to determine the quantities extracted. A subsequent heat balance around the cycle then establishes the cycle output and efficiency.

7.7 OTHER POWER-PLANT CYCLES

In the discussion so far, water has been the working fluid of the cycle because of its abundance, ease of handling, and nontoxicity. Actually, water has many disadvantages as a working fluid for a power-plant cycle. The vapor pressure of water is high; this necessitates thick piping and thick pressure vessels and gives rise to other design problems. From the standpoint of thermal efficiency, the high pressure is not necessary, since it is temperature that controls the efficiency of a cycle. Superheated steam is also a poor heat transfer fluid, and from the equipment standpoint requires larger heat-transfer surfaces and limits the heat inputs to the surface. Thermodynamically, it means that large temperature differences must exist in parts of the equipment in order to transfer the heat. This obviously is not desirable.

Other qualities that make water undesirable are that it changes phase in the turbine, its lowest temperature in the cycle takes it below atmospheric pressure, requiring leaktight construction and pumps on the condenser, and it is corrosive and needs conditioning in order to be used in boilers. It also has a high specific heat of the vapor and a high specific heat of the liquid, which means that the temperature varies as heat is added (from the *Ts* diagram it will be seen that a nearly vertical line for the water-heating part of the cycle makes it approach the Carnot cycle; a very low specific heat of the liquid is therefore desired).

In the binary vapor cycle some of the advantages of water are utilized in conjunction with another fluid which has merit in other parts of the cycle. In the arrangement used in conventional power plants (as opposed to nuclear), mercury has been the high-temperature working fluid, and the heat rejected by the mercury part of the cycle has been the heat source for the steam part of the cycle. A schematic of such a cycle is shown in Fig. 7.48. For a further discussion of this cycle the student is referred to specialized texts on power plants.

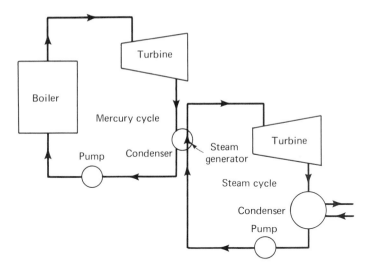

Figure 7.48 Binary fluid cycle

7.8 NUCLEAR REACTOR POWER CYCLES

The advent of nuclear power for central stations, marine, and naval power plants has necessitated the study of the power production cycle from viewpoints that are novel when compared to the technology that has been discussed earlier in this chapter. The extent of the use of nuclear plants for power production can be realized when the present and future installed capacities are studied. At present 13% of the electrical energy produced in the U.S. is derived from central station nuclear power plants. In addition, 94 plants are in some stage of planning or construction, stretching to the end of the century. The events that occurred in March 1979 at the Three Mile Island plant in Pa and the subsequent reappraisal of the problem involving safety by the Nuclear Regulatory Commission, has caused the power industry to re-evaluate its position or the use of nuclear power. At present the outcome is unclear but as noted by the General Accounting Office, the limiting of or the stoppage of nuclear power generation will probably cause the U.S. to severely limit the use of electricity.

All commercial power reactors in the United States generate electricity by first generating steam which is then used to drive a turbine. Thus we may consider the nuclear reactor and its fissionable material to be a fuel in a special container. To orient our discussion of the power-generating aspects of nuclear reactors, reference is made to Fig. 7.50, which shows a simplified comparison of nuclear and conventional power systems. The fundamental process used for the production of power in a nuclear reactor is called the *fission process*. In this process the nuclei of certain heavy atoms are bombarded by neutrons, causing the nuclei to split, releasing heat, two or three additional neutrons, and fission

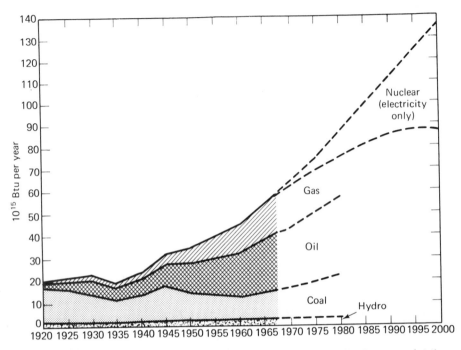

Figure 7.49 United States energy consumption. *Source*: U.S. Bureau of Mines Resources in *America's Future*, Special LMFBR Study, AEC (Courtesy of Consolidated Edison Co.)

fragments (as many as 80 different elements have been identified as fission fragments). The uranium isotopes U^{233} and U^{235} are fissionable as is plutonium 239 (Pu^{239}). In addition, thorium 232 (Th^{232}) and uranium 238 (U^{238}) are fertile materials which may be transmuted to fissionable U^{233} and Pu^{239}. Due to the fission process, a large energy release occurs, which in engineering units would yield approximately 3.6×10^6 Btu(1×10^7 kW-hr) for each pound of material fissioned. From the standpoint of heat production, this is over $2\frac{1}{2}$ million times greater than an equal weight of coal. For the fission process to be self-sustaining, each fission must produce enough neutrons to replace those lost due to leakage from the system, those captured in nonfissioning processes, and those captured by fissioning nuclei in a process known as resonance capture, and provide a neutron for the next fission process to occur. In general, approximately 2.5 neutrons must be produced per fission to have a self-sustaining chain reaction occur. When the reaction is self-sustaining, the reactor is said to be *critical*. A given reactor having given fuel composition and geometry has a given size for which the reaction will be self-sustaining, and the size is known as the *critical size*. It is important to note that once criticality is reached, the power output of a nuclear reactor is not related to the size of the reactor. The most important consideration is the ability to remove the heat produced

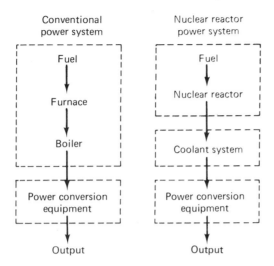

Conventional power system

Nuclear reactor power system

Figure 7.50 Comparison of conventional and nuclear power systems

from the system. This is quite different from conventional thermal systems where the heat output is directly related to the rate at which fuel is fired.

Associated with any nuclear reactor are problems of shielding personnel from the radioactive processes occurring within the reactor, designing of the system to cope with any leakage or accident, coolant stability, adequate heat removal, shielding of any circulating radioactive liquids, handling of radioactive fuel, chemical and metallurgical problems, and so on. Many of these problems have dictated solutions that often override any considerations of thermal efficiency in such a cycle. Without going into all these considerations for each of the reactor systems currently in use, we will briefly consider their basic power production cycles in the following paragraphs.

7.8a Pressurized Water Reactor (PWR)

The ideal reactor coolant is one that would have good heat-transfer properties while being a good moderator (slower down of neutrons) and also not be affected by the nuclear processes and reactions occurring in the reactor. Ordinary (light) water is suitable as a coolant and is used in many reactor systems as coolant-moderator. Because of questions concerning the stability of parallel coolant circuits when boiling occurs, many reactors have been proposed and built using nonboiling ordinary water as the coolant. These systems are known as pressurized water reactors (PWR). As shown schematically in Fig. 7.51, primary water is circulated within the reactor to remove the heat and act as moderator. The water from the reactor is circulated through a heat exchanger (steam generator), where it produces steam. The primary water returns to the reactor and the secondary steam expands through the turbine to

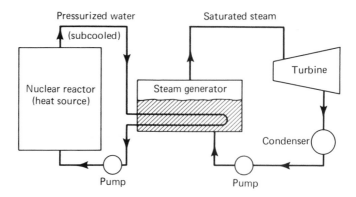

Figure 7.51 Pressurized water reactor system

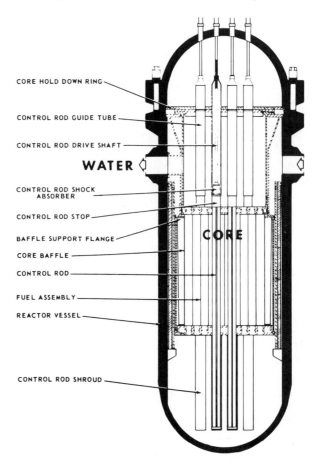

Figure 7.52 Typical PWR reactor vessel

produce power. Due to the requirement that no steam be produced in the primary coolant circuit and the properties of water, even low primary water temperatures (under the critical temperature) require primary pressures of 1500 to 2000 psia. Some idea of the complexity of the reactor vessel for a PWR system can be obtained from Fig. 7.52, which is a cross section of a typical reactor vessel.

Since the steam produced in the heat exchanger is saturated, its temperature is lower than the average temperature of the primary water. If the steam goes directly to the turbine, problems occur that are associated with steam expanding into the wet region. Also, the thermal performance (efficiency) of such a low-temperature cycle is very poor. One way to alleviate the turbine problem and increase the overall plant thermal performance is to superheat the

Figure 7.53 Indian Point Station (Courtesy of Consolidated Edison Co.)

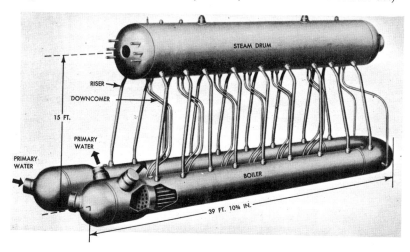

Figure 7.54 Indian Point steam generator

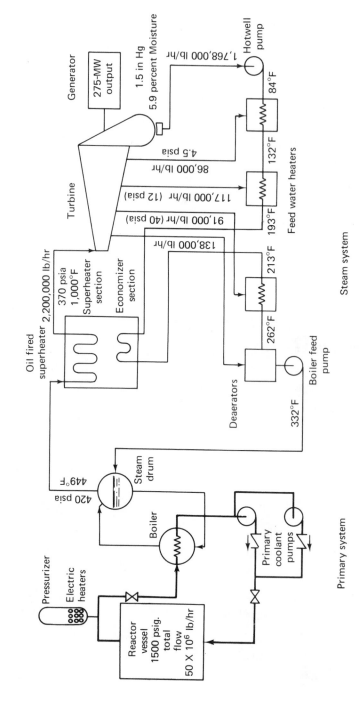

Figure 7.55 Heat balance of an Indian Point loop

Steam system

Primary system

Generator

275-MW output

1.5 in Hg
5.9 percent Moisture

1,768,000 lb/hr

Hotwell pump

84°F

132°F

4.5 psia

86,000 lb/hr

Turbine

117,000 lb/hr (12 psia)

91,000 lb/hr (40 psia)

193°F

Feed water heaters

138,000 lb/hr

213°F

Oil fired superheater 2,200,000 lb/hr

370 psia
1,000°F
Superheater section

Economizer section

262°F

Deaerators

332°F

Boiler feed pump

Steam drum

449°F

420 psia

Boiler

Primary coolant pumps

Pressurizer

Electric heaters

Reactor vessel 1500 psig. total flow 50 × 10⁶ lb/hr

steam from the heat exchanger in a separate fossil-fueled superheater. One plant that utilizes this arrangement is the Indian Point Station of New York's Consolidated Edison System, which is shown in Fig. 7.53. This plant has a design capacity of 2000 MW. The core of the reactor contains a small amount of highly enriched uranium and thorium. Some of the thorium is transmuted to U^{233}, which supplements the original fuel loading. The reactor vessel for the plant is 41 ft, $5\frac{1}{2}$ in. high, has an inside diameter of 9 ft 9 in., a wall thickness of $6\frac{15}{16}$ in. with the inside of the vessel clad with 0.109 in. type 304 stainless steel.

Since the primary water is radioactive to some extent, it is desired in this system to keep the primary water and steam circuits separate. This is accomplished for each of the reactor loops in a steam generator of the type shown in Fig. 7.54. As shown, primary water circulates within the tubes, and steam and water circulate outside of the tubes. The steam drum, risers, and downcomers provide the usual functions of these elements. The heat balance of a loop of this system is shown in Fig. 7.55.

One further point should be noted; the entire reactor system and its associated heat transfer loops are in a 160 ft diameter steel containment sphere having a wall thickness of 1 in. and are enclosed in a concrete shielding structure.

7.8b Boiling-Water Reactor (BWR)

After a great deal of research, it was found possible to satisfactorily operate nuclear reactors with steam generation (boiling) occurring within the reactor. This type of reactor uses ordinary water as the coolant and moderator, and this allows operating pressures of about half those found in PWR systems. Also the steam generator and its circulating system are eliminated.

The Oyster Creek unit shown in Fig. 7.56 is such a single cycle, 515-MW unit. Feedwater enters the reactor vessel at the top of the core. Here it is mixed with the recirculated coolant and flows down between core and vessel walls. Recirculating flow, affording primary output control, is fed to external circulating pumps, which return it to the bottom of the vessel and up through the core. Steam generated within the core passes through steam separators and driers. Moisture content entering the turbine is about 0.1 percent. Considerable reduction in reactor vessel thickness is possible compared to the PWR. Bottom entry control rods are an important feature of BWR vessels. Space above the core is then free for steam separators and driers. Since scramming by gravity is no longer possible, very reliable mechanical or piston-type control rod drive is essential. Radiation exposure in the vicinity of BWR is negligible. Pressure suppression containment, trapping radioactive steam and fission products, eliminates the familiar containment sphere. But the removal through the stack of radioactive carryover from the condenser can pose a problem.

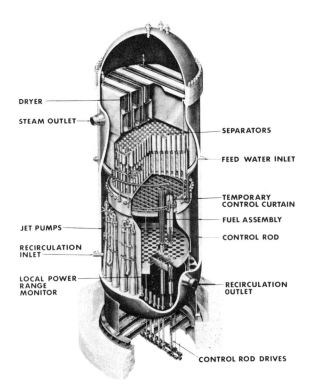

DRYER

STEAM OUTLET

SEPARATORS

FEED WATER INLET

TEMPORARY
CONTROL CURTAIN

FUEL ASSEMBLY

JET PUMPS

CONTROL ROD

RECIRCULATION
INLET

LOCAL POWER
RANGE
MONITOR

RECIRCULATION
OUTLET

CONTROL ROD DRIVES

Figure 7.56 Oyster Creek boiling water reactor

Operational control of the BWR presents a problem in that the reactor is not self-controlling. A sudden increase in steam demand by the turbine reduces reactor pressure, which causes water to flash to steam in the reactor core. This reduces the reactivity of the reactor and steam output at the time that it should be increased. One way that this is overcome is to bypass excess steam past the turbine at part-load conditions. Any sudden load increase then closes the bypass valve, increasing steam flow to the turbine without affecting reactor pressure. Another method is to increase coolant flow by controlling the circulating pumps. This maintains reactor pressure by counteracting the tendency of core coolant to flash into steam.

Boiling water reactors using nuclear superheat have also been built. The use of nuclear superheat has led to turbine steam conditions approaching those found in modern fossil fueled plants. Without further discussion, it is noted that problems associated with nuclear superheat are problems with the fuel elements at the high reactor temperature, inadvertent flooding of the superheater, and steam carryover causing erosion and scaling of the fuel elements.

7.8c Liquid-Metal Fast Breeder Reactor (LMFBR)

The basic fuel for light-water reactors is uranium 235, which is one of the few fissionable materials found in nature. As it is mined, natural uranium contains only about 0.7 percent fissionable U^{235}. The balance is nonfissionable U^{238}. To produce heat in a light-water reactor, the natural uranium is enriched by partially removing the U^{238} from it until the concentration of U^{235} reaches about 3 percent. The result is a small quantity of enriched uranium and a relatively large quantity of depleted uranium. The enriched uranium is made into fuel assemblies, and the depleted uranium is stockpiled, since it still contains a small percentage of U^{235} and may have other uses. Recent Atomic Energy Commission figures place the U.S. reserves of uranium recoverable at current prices at 243,000 tons, enough to meet projected requirements for the next 11 years.

Domestic uranium will be able to carry the light-water reactor program well through the 1990s and past such time that the breeder reactor becomes a significant source for nuclear fuel. Yet, unless the fast breeder development program moves ahead the date of commercial introduction will slip further ahead in the future, bringing with such slippage the possibility or probability of a uranium fuel shortage. Light-water reactors use ordinary water as both "moderator" and coolant, and this feature is the very reason that they cannot efficiently "breed," or produce more fuel than they consume. The moderator slows down the neutrons producing the chain reaction so that they are very efficient in splitting or fissioning the U^{235} fuel. The slow neutrons, however, are not efficient at converting U^{238} into Pu^{239}.

In the fast breeder reactor, which uses no moderator, the fission process is carried forward by "fast" neutrons, which are very efficient in splitting the Pu^{239} nucleus. The splitting of the Pu^{239} nucleus in a fast reactor's fuel core emits more neutrons, which then can strike the U^{238} atoms surrounding the core. This creates more Pu^{239} atoms than the fission process is using up, thus creating the condition called *breeding*. In the typical fast breeder now under development, 1.3 new Pu^{239} atoms are created for every one burned up or fissioned. The *breeding ratio* is therefore said to be 1.3.

The fast breeder reactor has a very compact fuel core, and the nuclear reactions produce great quantities of heat. To move the heat out of the reactor for use in power production, a very efficient coolant must be used. The coolant must also have desirable nuclear properties that will not slow down, or "moderate," fast neutrons. The coolant used is sodium. Being a metal, sodium has a good heat transfer property, it melts and flows as a liquid at fairly low temperatures, and it will not interfere significantly with fast neutron reaction. Its vapor pressure is also low.

In the sodium-cooled fast breeder reactor shown schematically in Fig. 7.57 (which is often called the liquid-metal fast breeder reactor, LMFBR) the sodium coolant in the *primary loop* flows through pipes into the bottom of the

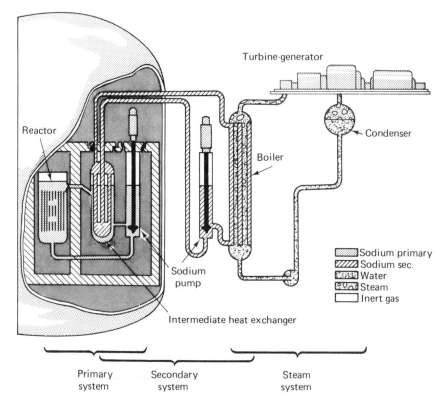

Figure 7.57 Flow diagram of liquid-metal fast breeder reactor

reactor and picks up heat as it moves up past the fuel assemblies. The primary sodium (which is radioactive) then is circulated through a heat exchanger, where it flows through tubes and gives up its heat to other sodium flowing outside the tubes, in what is called the secondary loop. The heated sodium in the secondary loop then flows through a steam generator, where it gives up its heat to water flowing outside the tubes. The heat converts the water into steam, and the steam then drives a turbine generator to produce electricity. The secondary loop is used for two reasons. The first is for safety; sodium and water react violently, and if a single loop were used this high-pressure water could enter and react with primary sodium to cause a catastrophic reaction in the reactor coolant loop. The second reason for the use of a secondary system is the fact that the primary sodium is radioactive and could activate the water. Figure 7.58 shows (in the upper part) a model of the LMFBR demonstration plant and (in the lower part) an artist's rendering of this plant. Figure 7.59 shows the arrangement of the Enrico Fermi Atomic Power Plant, which is also a fast breeder reactor using a sodium primary loop, a sodium secondary loop, and a separate steam generator.

Figure 7.58 Liquid-metal fast breeder reactor demonstration plant (Courtesy of Westinghouse Electric Corp.)

Other power producing nuclear reactor cycles are used. Among these are the gas-cooled reactor (GCR) that is popular in England and is the basis of the Philadelphia Electric 40-MW, high temperature gas cooled reactor (HTGR) and the heavy water reactor used in Canada (CANDU). We will not discuss these and other cycles since they present no new principles from a power production standpoint.

While the nuclear reactor power generation system is being developed rapidly, there are several questions that have been raised concerning it. Due to low thermal performance, these plants reject more heat per kilowatt generated than do conventional power plants, which leads to problems concerning effects on the ecology, for example, thermal pollution. In addition, the placing of a nuclear reactor in or near centers of population usually causes great public concern and in some cases has led to the abandoning of projects. Since concern

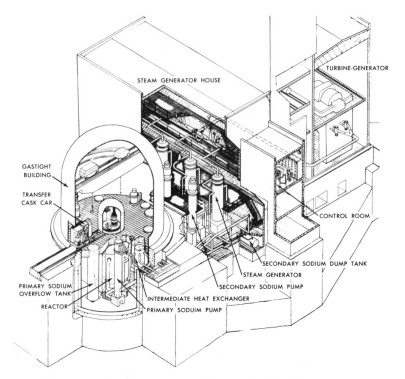

Figure 7.59 Enrico Fermi liquid-metal fast breeder reactor

regarding safety, possible radioactive leakage, and the like is justified, it must enter the plans of utility companies when additional generating capacity is being considered for a given system. As a result, the Westinghouse Electric Company and Tenneco, Inc., have proposed floating nuclear power plants to overcome many of these problems. Recently, Public Service Electric and Gas Co. of New Jersey contracted with Westinghouse-Tenneco's offshore power systems subsidiary for the construction of a floating power plant consisting of two units each having a capacity of 1150 MW at a site 12 miles northeast of Atlantic City and just within the 3-mile limit.* It is claimed that the temperature increase outside the breakwater will be less than 2 degrees in an area of approximately 5 acres, and that the rise plus the presence of the breakwater shown in Fig. 7.60 will result in an improvement in the aquatic population in the area, whereas in rivers this heat can be a problem to aquatic life. Also, land use in densely populated areas (both in terms of cost and obtaining licenses) for nuclear plants is becoming a problem while the offshore plant poses no such problem. Lastly, such a floating power plant can be located near utility load

*Mechanical Engineering, December 1972, p. 35.

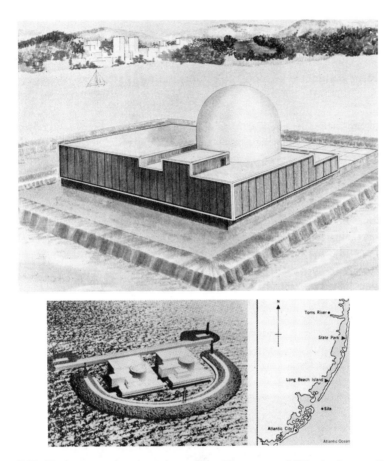

Figure 7.60 Platform-mounted nuclear plant (Courtesy of Westinghouse Electric Corp. and *Mechanical Engineering*, December 1972, p. 35)

centers in the heavily populated coastal areas. The events at Three Mile Island have placed doubts that this plant will ever be completed or ever go beyond the conceptual stage.

7.9 GAS CYCLES

7.9a Internal Combustion Engine

The power plants that we use for propelling cars, boats, etc., are commonly known as internal-combustion engines since the release of energy is by combustion within the engine. Mobile power plants have been developed to a high state of reliability and are commonplace in everyday life. Reliability is essentially a term that describes the level of development of the mechanical system. Thus we expect, as the usual occurrence, that a car will start easily and that a trip will be completed without mechanical failure. However, the size, weight, and cost of fuel of a given engine are all functions of the thermal efficiency of the unit.

In the earlier sections of this chapter our attention was focused on systems in which the release of energy by combustion occurred external to the device or engine that converted this energy to useful work. Several limitations occur when this is done. In the combustion device, temperatures are maintained as high as possible. This leads to problems associated with the strength of the heat-transfer surfaces (tubing) and requires large amounts of expensive, bulky insulation. The working fluid of the cycle is contained within tubular elements, and to keep thermal stresses and pressure stresses within the strength capabilities of the tube material the heat-transfer rates must be limited. This leads to the need for large heat-transfer surfaces requiring large-sized units. Many of these objections can be overcome by releasing the energy in the fuel within the engine. In any device it is usually true that the average temperature rather than the peak temperature of the working fluid will govern the strength limits of the material. In a periodic device (such as the automotive engine) the average temperature is kept reasonable by maintaining the duration of the peak temperature for a small fraction of the total cycle time.

Figure 7.61 Modern 400-cubic inch displacement V-8 engine (Courtesy of Ford Motor Co.)

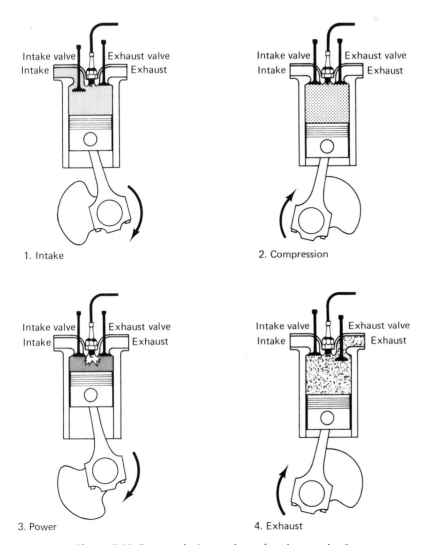

Figure 7.62 Four-cycle internal-combustion engine*

Before considering the prototype ideal cycles of the internal-combustion engine, let us first describe the engine and then make those idealizations required for the analysis of the cycle. Figure 7.61 shows a 400-cu in. displacement V-8 automotive engine. This is a complex device having over 1000 parts, of which almost 400 move. To understand this engine we will consider the four-cycle reciprocating engine, which is the most commonly used. The four events that take place in the cycle are illustrated in Fig. 7.62 and are as follows:

---

*Figures 7.62, 7.63, 7.65, and 7.67 are from "How an Internal Engine Works," Renwal Products Co., Fairless Hills, Pa., 1960.

1 *Intake*: Consider the piston to be at the uppermost part of its stroke known as top dead center (t.d.c.). As the piston starts downward, it creates a partial vacuum in the cylinder. At this time the intake valve is open and a mixture of air and vaporized gasoline is drawn into the cylinder from the intake manifold past the open intake valve.

2 *Compression*: When the piston reaches the end of its downward stroke, the piston is said to be at bottom dead center (b.d.c.). At this point the intake valve closes and stays closed as the piston moves upward. Since the fuel–air mixture is totally confined within the cylinder, it is compressed as the piston moves upward. Both intake and exhaust valves remain closed.

3 *Power*: Ideally, when the piston again reaches top dead center and the fuel–air mixture is at its maximum compression, an electrical spark ignites the fuel–air mixture, causing combustion to occur. The large pressure force created by the combustion causes the piston to be driven downward. This driven downward motion of the piston is the power stroke of the cycle. In actual engines ignition can occur before, at or even after top dead center, based upon details that we will not consider. Also, both the intake and exhaust valves remain closed during the power stroke.

4 *Exhaust*: At the end of the power stroke the gases have fully expanded and the exhaust valve now opens. The upward motion of the piston causes the spent combustion gases to flow out of the cylinder past the open exhaust valve and into the exhaust manifold. At top dead center the exhaust valve closes and the cycle starts over again.

The four stroke cycle just described produces one power stroke for each piston for two revolutions of the main shaft (crankshaft). The arrangement of the basic components of a V-8 engine is shown in Fig. 2.11 (repeated) and is also shown schematically in Fig. 7.63. The cylinder block is usually a cast, accurately machined housing for the cylinders, pistons, and connecting rods. All the other elements are supported by the cylinder block (or blocks) or bolted to it. At the top of the block (Fig. 2.11 repeated) are the cylinder heads which are also shown schematically in Fig. 7.63. To prevent melting of the metal parts, cooling must be provided. This can either be done by air cooling or water cooling. Water cooling is the commonest method used, and this water must circulate within the block and the heads. Thus a series of matching openings is provided in the blocks and heads for water circulation.

The valves in the internal combustion engine are subjected to the severest conditions of all the elements of the engine. Operating as often as 2000 times per minute, they are required to be leakproof even though they are subjected to the direct pressure and temperature of the combustion occurring within the cylinders. Also, they must operate at the precisely correct moment in the cycle

FUEL AND AIR IN

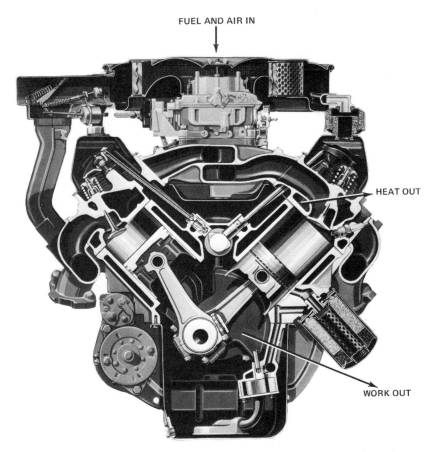

HEAT OUT

WORK OUT

Figure 2.11 A 429-cubic inch displacement V-8 engine (Courtesy of Ford Motor Corp.) (repeated)

without valve bounce or chatter. The actuation of the valves is performed by one cam for each valve on the camshaft that is driven by the crankshaft. Since the four-cycle engine produces one power stroke per piston for two revolutions of the crankshaft, the camshaft is geared to rotate one revolution for each two revolutions of the crankshaft. The cam shape must be accurately designed to open the intake and exhaust valves precisely, hold them open for the necessary length of time, and close them all as dictated by the cycle.

Figure 7.64 shows a carburetor used on an automotive engine. The carburetor is the device in which the gasoline is vaporized and mixed with the air in proper proportions to produce a detonatable mixture to be used in the cylinders of the engine. As shown schematically in Fig. 7.65, air enters at the top of the carburetor and moves through a venturi tube where a suction is created at the throat of the venturi. At this section there is a fuel jet, and the suction draws fuel into the air stream from the jet. Fresh fuel is fed to

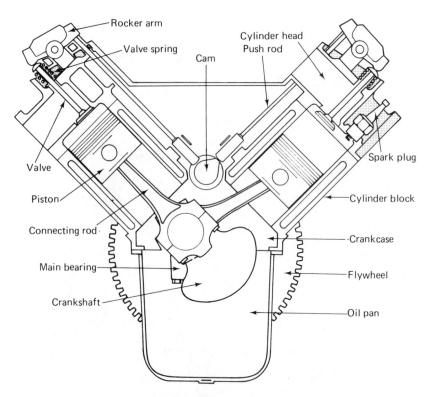

Figure 7.63 Mechanical elements of a V-type engine

the carburetor by the engine's fuel pump into the float chamber. The level in the float chamber is kept constant by a float that regulates fuel flow. The operating conditions of an internal combustion engine vary widely, requiring differing proportions of fuel in the fuel–air mixture. When an engine is cold it requires more fuel in the mixture (a rich mixture), and when the engine warms up, the mixture must be leaned. The foregoing is accomplished by the choke; when it is closed, very little air is drawn into the carburetor, but the suction created by the downward stroke of the pistons draws fuel into the engine. The resultant fuel–air mixture is rich in fuel. As the engine warms up the choke gradually opens, until at full opening, a steady fuel–air ratio of approximately 16:1 is reached. As shown in Fig. 7.64, the entire choke action is automatically regulated by a thermostatic spring. On top of the carburetor (Fig. 2.11, repeated) is a large air cleaner designed to remove dust and dirt particles from the incoming air and also to act as an air silencer and flame arrester. In modern cars equipped with pollutant-reduction devices, some of the exhaust gases are recirculated (EGR) through the carburetor to the engine to reduce nitrogen and hydrocarbon emissions from the engine. Also, part of the crank-case vapors are recirculated through the carburetor. As shown in Fig. 2.11

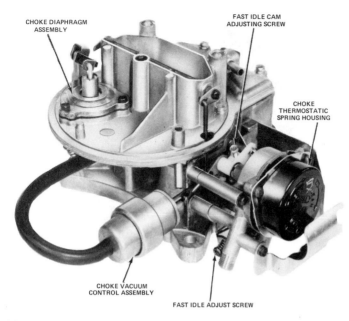

CHOKE DIAPHRAGM
ASSEMBLY

FAST IDLE CAM
ADJUSTING SCREW

CHOKE
THERMOSTATIC
SPRING HOUSING

CHOKE VACUUM
CONTROL ASSEMBLY

FAST IDLE ADJUST SCREW

Figure 7.64 Automotive carburetor (Courtesy of Ford Motor Co.)

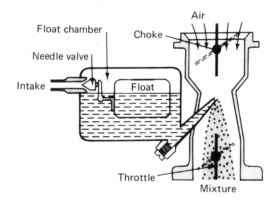

Float chamber

Needle valve

Intake

Float

Air

Choke

Throttle

Mixture

Figure 7.65 Schematic of a carburetor

(repeated), the air filter also filters the recirculated gases before they enter the carburetor.

Many different arrangements of the cylinders and the manner in which they are grouped are possible. We have already seen and described the V-8 engine in Figs. 2.11 (repeated) and 7.63. Figure 7.66 shows an in-line six-cylinder engine with a 200 cu in. piston displacement. In addition to the V-8 and in-line arrangements, there are others, as shown in Fig. 7.67, that are used in specific applications. Although it is not shown here, we shall spend some time discussing the rotating combustion (Wankel) engine next.

Figure 7.66 In-line six-cylinder engine (Courtesy of Ford Motor Co.)

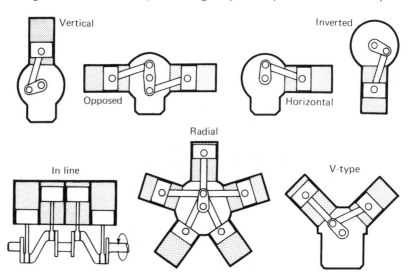

Figure 7.67 Internal-combustion cylinder arrangement

7.9b Rotating Combustion Engine: Wankel Engine

The rotating combustion engine was first conceived by a German inventor, Felix Wankel, in 1954. Since the early 1960s intense development work on this engine has taken place throughout the world. At present the Wankel has been produced in sizes ranging from $\frac{1}{2}$ hp to 400 hp and powers approximately 500,000 automobiles worldwide. To obtain an idea of the relative size and simplicity of the rotating combustion engine when compared to a conventional reciprocating automotive engine one only has to note the following: a V-8 engine of 195 hp has 1029 parts and 388 of these parts move. The engine weighs more than 600 lb and takes up 15 cu ft in the engine compartment. In contrast, a 185-hp Wankel engine has only 633 parts, 154 of which move, weighs 237 lb and occupies 5 cu ft. In addition, there are no valves in the Wankel engine. Figure 7.68 shows this engine and a total parts layout for it.

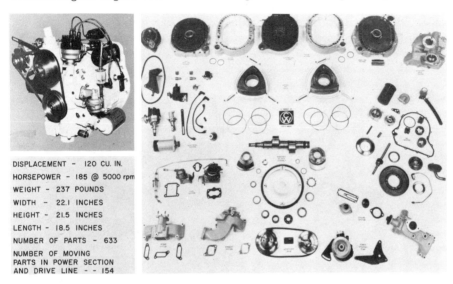

DISPLACEMENT - 120 CU. IN.
HORSEPOWER - 185 @ 5000 rpm
WEIGHT - 237 POUNDS
WIDTH - 22.1 INCHES
HEIGHT - 21.5 INCHES
LENGTH - 18.5 INCHES
NUMBER OF PARTS - 633
NUMBER OF MOVING PARTS IN POWER SECTION AND DRIVE LINE - - 154

Figure 7.68 Vehicular Wankel (rotating combustion) engine (Courtesy of Curtiss-Wright Corporation)

The engine shown in Figure 7.68 was built by the Curtiss-Wright Corporation of Woodridge, New Jersey, and is designated as the RC2-60, where RC stands for rotating combustion, 2 means 2 rotors and chambers, and 60 designates that each rotor-chamber combination has a displacement of 60 cu in. The basic engine components of the RC-2 are shown in Fig. 7.69.

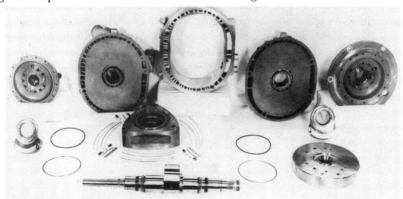

Figure 7.69 Basic engine components of the RC-2 engine (Courtesy of Curtiss-Wright Corporation)

The Wankel engine operates on the four-stroke Otto cycle, as indicated in Fig. 7.70. As shown in both Figs. 7.68 and 7.69, there are two major moving assemblies in the Wankel engine, a three-sided rotor and a main shaft. The rotor operates inside a chamber which is essentially an ellipse with sides pointed in. The mathematical name of the shape of the chamber is an epitrochoid. This shape is needed due to the motion of the rotor, which rotates on an eccentric axis off the main shaft in a wobbling motion. The cycle shown in Fig. 7.70 starts when one of the apex points passes the intake port, causing

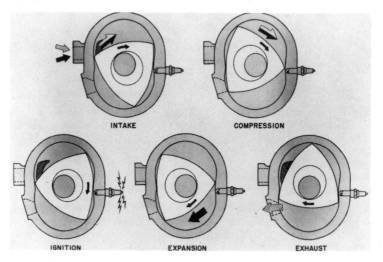

INTAKE COMPRESSION

IGNITION EXPANSION EXHAUST

Figure 7.70 Wankel engine combustion cycle (Courtesy of Curtiss-Wright Corporation)

the fuel–air mixture to flow into the housing in the volume between the rotor and housing. As the rotor turns, the volume between the rotor and chamber decreases, which effectively compresses the fuel–air mixture. Seals at each apex of the rotor prevent mixing or dilution of the gases contained in each portion of the chamber. As the rotor keeps on turning, the fuel–air mixture is ignited at the time when its volume is at its minimum. The combustion of the fuel–air mixture causes a thrust on the rotor to keep it turning and at the same time causes the combustion gases to expand. At the end of expansion, the exhaust port is uncovered and the combustion gases leave through this port.

Thus far we have considered only one face of the three-lobed rotor during the course of one revolution. It must be remembered that during this same revolution the other two faces of the rotor are undergoing the same cycle. Thus the torque output of the Wankel engine is positive for about two-thirds of one shaft revolution, as compared to one-quarter of the two shaft revolutions required to complete a single cycle of a four-cycle reciprocating engine. This is due to the fact that there is a 1 : 3 rotor-to-crankshaft speed ratio in the Wankel engine, requiring three shaft revolutions for one complete rotor revolution to fire all three rotor flanks. A single-cylinder reciprocating engine fires once in two shaft revolutions, giving a three-cylinder reciprocating engine three power pulses in two shaft revolutions. On the basis of torque output, the Wankel single-rotor engine approaches the three-cylinder reciprocating engine. If we consider power, the single rotor Wankel engine power output is twice the power output of the same displacement reciprocating four-cycle engine. This is due to the fact that for every mainshaft revolution there is one firing, similar to the two-cycle engine. Also, it must be noted that in the piston engine the piston comes to a complete halt every time it reverses direction, and that due to its linear motion a connecting rod and crank are needed to convert its up-and-down motion into torque. As a result of these factors, the Wankel engine gives smooth torque output at all speeds without dynamic unbalance even when one rotor is used.

The advantages of the Wankel engine can be summarized as follows:

1 Fewer moving parts: no valves, connecting rods, and so on.

2 High power to weight ratio and small volume.

3 The rotor center of gravity and rotational axis remain at a fixed eccentricity from the shaft centerline so that even a single rotor engine can attain complete dynamic balance with simple shaft counterweights.

4 Smooth torque and power output at all speeds.

One of the Wankel engine's most serious engineering problems was the design of the apex seals that are used to seal off the three compartments from each other. Some of the initial engines built for automotive use seldom ran for more than 15,000 to 20,000 miles before the seals wore out. At the present time it is claimed that seal lifetimes in automotive applications are in the 60,000- to 100,000-mile range, which is nearing the life of piston rings in conventional engines. The RX-7 automotive engine has an engine warranty of 75,000 miles. Another problem that occurred during the initial development of the Wankel engine was its poor fuel economy, which was about half the miles per gallon of a comparative conventional automotive engine. The principal factors contributing to this poor mileage were the positioning of the spark plugs, insufficient distance between the inlet and exhaust ports, and the already mentioned seal problem. Using a modified side entry port, repositioned spark plug, and the latest seals, current versions of the Wankel engine indicate that they are reaching the same fuel consumption levels as comparable powered conventional reciprocating engines.

The poor fuel economy noted in the original Wankel engines led to its reputation as a "dirty" engine, that is, a high emitter of atmospheric pollutants. Without any controls, an improved version of the Wankel engine still gave off twice as many hydrocarbon emissions, a little more carbon monoxide, and one-fifth to one-half of the oxides of nitrogen as a comparable reciprocating engine without controls. By using a lean mixture, exhaust gas recirculation (EGR), and a device known as a thermal converter, reducton of 75 to 90 percent of the hydrocarbon emissions was achieved. The catalytic or thermal converter is basically a device in which the partly burned gases from the engine are reignited and burned. A thermal converter is a cylindrical device made of stainless steel with internal baffles. When exposed to engine exhaust gases, the baffles become hot enough to complete the combustion of hydrocarbons with the addition of air.

One of the characteristics that makes the Wankel desirable is the fact that its high power to weight ratio yields a powerful engine and thus frees space to be used for emission-control devices. Moreover, as noted, the use of the catalytic reactor or thermal converter has already been shown to significantly reduce hydrocarbon emissions in this engine. The close coupling of the engine to the converter, higher exhaust temperatures, rapid warm-up, and lack of dependence on lead or lead additives in the fuel makes the Wankel engine particularly compatible with converters. The most convincing final argument for the Wankel engine lies in the tighter limits imposed on the oxides of nitrogen, a noxious pollution component formed in the flame front within the combustion chamber. While present data show a conventional reciprocating engine may lose as much as 30 percent of its fuel economy to reduce the level of oxides of nitrogen by a factor of 4 from current levels, the Wankel engine has oxide of nitrogen levels which already range from one-fifth to one-half of those of current reciprocating engines. The Wankel achieves these levels because of a lower burning rate, yielding lower peak internal temperatures and higher gas exhaust temperatures that are more compatible with the converters for hydrocarbon emission control, as already mentioned.

The Wankel engine has at this time successfully demonstrated a high level of durability, reliability, and performance in such diverse applications as automobiles, boats, trucks, lawnmowers, tanks, and power-generating sets. Industrial long-life units, snowmobiles, and small air-cooled industrial units are already in the development stage. It must be remembered that the rotary combustion engine is still in its initial stages of technological development while the conventional reciprocating engine has reached an asymptotically flat portion of its technological growth curves. The adoption of the Wankel engine will depend upon the ability to achieve a clean engine with good fuel economy.

7.9c Air-Standard Analysis of the Otto Cycle

The introduction of fuel into an internal combustion engine gives rise to a variable mass in the cycle. Also, at the end of the cycle the entire charge is discarded, and a fresh charge is introduced to undergo a new cycle identical to the first. During the actual processes, both heat and work are interchanged at each portion of the cycle. The mass, specific heats, and state of the working fluid are all variable. Under these circumstances, the analysis of a cycle becomes quite difficult. To simplify the analysis, certain idealized cycles have been proposed as prototypes of the actual engine cycles. These models are considered for the rest of this chapter. In the analysis of each of the cycles, the following assumptions are made:

1 Each process is carried out reversibly. Friction, pressure differences, turbulence, and the like, are neglected.

2 The working fluid is an ideal gas, and all relations already derived for the ideal gas are applicable.

3 The necessary energy is added or removed to achieve the desired state changes.

4 The working fluid is a gas with constant specific heats.

It is apparent from these assumptions (and their implications) that the analysis of an engine cycle based on them is quite artificial. However, certain generalizations can be arrived at from this analysis, called the *air-standard* analysis, and as such it can be quite useful.

The Otto cycle is the prototype for most internal-combustion engines commonly in use. Regardless of the number of strokes required to complete the cycle, it is conceived of as consisting of four separate and distinct processes. As shown in the *Ts* and *pv* diagrams in Fig. 7.71, the Otto cycle consists of (after

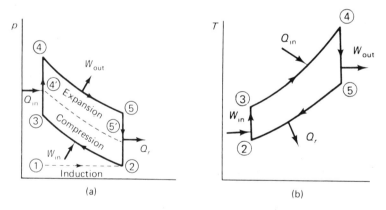

Figure 7.71 Otto cycle

induction of the gas) an isentropic compression followed by the reversible constant-volume addition of heat, then an isentropic expansion from which work is extracted, and finally a reversible constant-volume rejection of heat. Subsequently, the cycle is repeated. It will be noted that each step is an idealization of the events that we have previously described for the internal-combustion engine. Also note that each portion of the cycle is a nonflow process.

Referring to Fig. 7.71, we have the nonflow energy equation for the nonflow reception of heat (step ③ to ④) as

$$q_{in} = c_v(T_4 - T_3) \text{ Btu/lb} \qquad (7.12)$$

Similarly, the heat rejected during the constant-volume reversible expansion (step ⑤ to ②) is

$$q_r = c_v(T_5 - T_2) \text{ Btu/lb} \qquad (7.13)$$

The net work in thermal units available from the cycle is the difference between q_{in} and q_r:

$$W = (q_{in} - q_r) \text{ Btu/lb} \qquad (7.14)$$

The efficiency of the cycle is

$$\eta_{Otto} = \frac{W}{q_{in}} = \frac{q_{in} - q_r}{q_{in}} = 1 - \frac{q_r}{q_{in}} \qquad (7.15a)$$

and

$$\eta_{Otto} = 1 - \frac{c_v(T_5 - T_2)}{c_v(T_4 - T_3)} = 1 - \frac{(T_5 - T_2)}{(T_4 - T_3)} \qquad (7.15b)$$

From Fig. 7.71 it will be noted that the volumetric limits of the expansion and compression portions of the cycle are equal. From equations developed in Chapter 5,

$$\frac{T_4}{T_5} = \frac{T_3}{T_2} \quad \text{or} \quad \frac{T_2}{T_5} = \frac{T_3}{T_4} \qquad (7.16)$$

By adding unity to both sides of Eq. (7.16),

$$1 - \frac{T_2}{T_5} = 1 - \frac{T_3}{T_4} \quad \text{or} \quad \frac{T_5 - T_2}{T_5} = \frac{T_4 - T_3}{T_4} \qquad (7.17)$$

By substituting Eq. (7.17) into Eq. (7.15b),

$$\eta_{Otto} = 1 - \frac{T_5}{T_4} = 1 - \frac{T_2}{T_3} = 1 - \left(\frac{v_3}{v_2}\right)^{(k-1)} \qquad (7.18)$$

where we have used the equation of path for the isentropic compression to relate temperature and volumes from Table 5.4.

At this time we will introduce a term called the *compression ratio*, r_c, which is defined as

$$r_c = \frac{v_2}{v_3} \qquad (7.19)$$

Note that the compresson ratio defined in this manner is the ratio of two volumes, not two pressures as is commonly thought. Using this definition of compression ratio, we have the efficiency of the Otto cycle as

$$\eta_{\text{Otto}} = 1 - \left(\frac{1}{r_c}\right)^{(k-1)} \qquad (7.20)$$

It is emphasized that the term compression ratio is not the ratio of the peak to inlet pressure; it is the ratio of the volume before compression to the volume after compression.

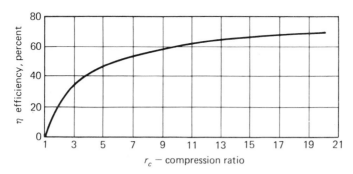

Figure 7.72 Efficiency of Otto cycle

Figure 7.72 is a plot of Eq. (7.20) for $k = 1.4$. It is apparent that an increase in compression ratio yields an increased cycle efficiency. However, it will be noted that the efficiency increases at a decreasing rate, and an increase in compression ratio from 10 to 15 yields an increase in efficiency of only 6 percent. Until the mid 1960s, the compression ratio of the automotive engine was generally being increased in an effort to get more power out of a given engine. It was not uncommon to have engines with compression ratios in excess of 10, requiring highly leaded fuels to prevent preignition and detonation of the fuel–air mixture in the compression and ignition portions of the cycle. Environmental considerations, with the attendant desire to limit the pollutants from these engines, have led to engines having lower compression ratios. The highest compression ratio in the 1972 Ford Motor Co. engines (Ford, Mercury, Lincoln) was 8.8, with a police interceptor engine having a compression ratio of 8.6 and the more modestly powered engines having compression ratios as low as 8.0. Thus considerations other than thermal efficiency govern the design of the internal-combustion engine for specific applications.

Returning to the air-standard Otto cycle, another point must be emphasized. The Otto air-standard cycle efficiency is determined only by the ratio of v_2 to v_3. Thus the cycle operating between the limits of ②, ③, ④, and ⑤ in Fig. 7.71 will have the same efficiency as the cycle operated between ②', ③', ④', and ⑤'. The heat in, work out, and heat rejected will be different for each cycle, but the efficiency will be the same. However, a Carnot cycle having as its maximum temperature the upper temperature of the Otto cycle and as its lower temperature the lowest temperature of the Otto cycle will always have a thermal efficiency that is greater than the Otto cycle. This can be determined from Fig. 7.71 as follows: as heat is added to the Otto cycle, its maximum temperature T_4 is increased, but its efficiency is constant if v_2/v_3 is constant. The Carnot cycle efficiency increases as its peak cycle temperature is increased. In the limit the least value of the efficiency of a Carnot cycle will be $1 - T_2/T_3$, which is the maximum efficiency of the Otto cycle.

ILLUSTRATIVE PROBLEM 7.7

Compute the efficiency of an air-standard Otto cycle if the compression ratio is 7 and $k = 1.4$. Compare this with a Carnot cycle operating between the same temperature limits if the lowest temperature of the cycle is 70°F and the peak temperature is 700°, 1000°, and 3000°F. Plot η versus temperature.

Solution

The efficiency of the Otto cycle is only a function of the compression ratio. Therefore, for the entire range of this problem η is constant and equal to

$$\eta_{\text{Otto}} = \left(1 - \frac{1}{7^{0.4}}\right)100 = 54.1\%$$

For the Carnot cycle

$$\eta_C = 1 - \frac{T_2}{T_4}$$

At 700°F

$$\eta_C = \left(1 - \frac{530}{1160}\right)100 = 54.3\%$$

At 1000°F

$$\eta_C = \left(1 - \frac{530}{1460}\right)100 = 63.7\%$$

At 3000°F

$$\eta_C = \left(1 - \frac{530}{3460}\right)100 = 84.7\%$$

These data are plotted in Fig. 7.73.

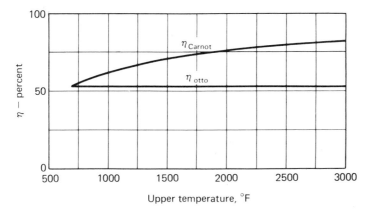

Figure 7.73 Solution of Illustrative Problem 7.7

ILLUSTRATIVE PROBLEM 7.8

Assuming c_v to be 0.172, determine the heat added and the heat rejected per pound of fluid during the constant-volume portions of Illustrative Problem 7.7 for the case in which the peak temperature of the cycle is 1000°F. Also compute the work output per pound of fluid. Determine the efficiency of the Otto cycle based on these values and compare it with the results of Illustrative Problem 7.7.

Solution

By referring to Fig. 7.71 and using the relations developed in Chapter 5,

$$\frac{T_3}{T_2} = \left(\frac{v_2}{v_3}\right)^{k-1} = (7)^{0.4} = 2.18$$

$$T_3 = (2.18)(530) = 1155.4°R$$

$$q_{in} = c_v(T_4 - T_3) = 0.172(1460 - 1155.4) = 52.39 \text{ Btu/lb}$$

To determine T_5, further use is made of Table 5.4:

$$q_r = c_v(T_5 - T_2), \qquad \frac{T_5}{T_4} = \left(\frac{v_3}{v_2}\right)^{k-1} = \frac{1}{2.18}$$

Therefore,

$$T_5 = \frac{1460}{2.18} = 669.72$$

$$= c_v(T_5 - T_2) = 0.172(669.72 - 530) = 24.03 \text{ Btu/lb}$$

The net work out is

$$q_{in} - q_r = 52.39 - 24.03 = 28.36 \text{ Btu}$$

Therefore,

$$\eta_{Otto} = \left(\frac{28.36}{52.39}\right)100 = 54.1\%$$

This value of efficiency agrees well with the results of Illustrative Problem 7.7.

ILLUSTRATIVE PROBLEM 7.9

An Otto cycle operates with a compression ratio of 8. If 50 kJ are added to the cycle which has as its lower pressure 150 kPa and as its lowest temperature 20°C. Determine the peak temperature of the cycle if $c_v = 0.7186$ kJ/kg·K and $k = 1.4$. Assume 1 kg of working fluid.

Solution

Refer to Fig. 7.71 and

$$\frac{T_3}{T_2} = \left(\frac{v_2}{v_3}\right)^{k-1} = 8^{0.4} = 2.297$$

Therefore,

$$T_3 = 2.297(20 + 273) = 673.14 \text{ K}$$

But

$$q_{in} = c_v(T_4 - T_3)$$

Therefore,

$$50 = 0.7186(T_4 - T_3)$$
$$69.58 = T_4 - T_3$$

and

$$T_4 = 742.72 \text{ K} = 469.72°\text{C}$$

The mean effective pressure of a cycle (mep) is defined as the work out of a cycle divided by the volume swept out by the piston. In Fig. 7.74 it is the shaded area (work) divided by $(v_2 - v_3)$. It becomes that number (the horizontal dotted line) which when multiplied by the base yields the same shaded area. As such, it is the mathematical mean ordinate of Fig. 7.74. The area of the rectangle [(mep)×$(v_2 - v_3)$] equals the area enclosed by the cycle ②, ③, ④, ⑤. The value of the mean effective pressure can be obtained by integrating the

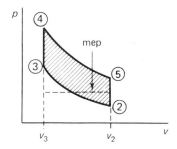

Figure 7.74 *pv* diagram of Otto cycle

area shown in Fig. 7.74 and dividing by $(v_2 - v_3)$. However, it can also be obtained as follows:

The work out of the cycle equals $q_{in} - q_r$ in thermal units of Btu's per pound:

$$q_{in} - q_r = c_v(T_4 - T_3) - c_v(T_5 - T_2)$$

In terms of pressure and volumes we can show that

$$q_{in} - q_r = \frac{1}{k-1} \left[v_3(p_4 - p_3) - v_2(p_5 - p_2) \right]$$

in mechanical units of ft lb/lb. Dividing by $(v_2 - v_3)$,

$$\text{mep} = \frac{1}{k-1} \left[\frac{v_3(p_4 - p_3) - v_2(p_5 - p_2)}{v_2 - v_3} \right] \qquad (7.21)$$

or

$$\text{mep} = \frac{1}{k-1} \left[\frac{(p_4 - r_c^k p_2)\left[1 - \left(\frac{1}{r_c}\right)^{k-1}\right]}{r_c - 1} \right] \qquad (7.22)$$

The mean effective pressure is useful in evaluating the ability to produce power. Since the product of piston travel and piston area is piston volume (displacement), the relative power-producing capability of two pistons can be established by comparing the product of mep times displacement in each case.

ILLUSTRATIVE PROBLEM 7.10

Determine the power output of a cylinder having a cross-sectional area of A square inches, a length of stroke of L inches, a mean effective pressure of p_m psi, and making N power strokes per minute.

Solution

The force on the piston is $(p_m A)$ pounds. Since the mean effective pressure is equivalent to a constant force on the piston over the length of the piston stroke, the work done per power stroke is $(p_m A)L$. For N power strokes per minute $hp = p_m LAN/33,000$. Note that if p_m is in psi, A should be in square inches while L is in feet. Also, N is *not* the rpm of the engine; it is the number of power strokes per minute, which for a four-cycle engine is rpm/2.

ILLUSTRATIVE PROBLEM 7.11

It is common practice to denote the total volumetric displacement in litres. Using this notation to mean (LA), determine the power output of an engine having a mean effective pressure of p_m kPa, and making N power strokes per minute.

Solution

The basic solution is the same as for Illustrative Problem 7.10 with due respect to units. The displacement (LA) in $cm^3/1000$ needs to be converted to m^3.

$$cm^3 \times \frac{1}{(cm/m)^3} = cm^3 \times \frac{1}{(100)^3} = cm^3 \times 10^{-6} \quad \text{or} \quad litres \times 10^{-3}$$

One horsepower is equal to $746\ W = 746\ N \cdot m/s$. Per minute,

$$1\ hp = 746 \times 60 = 44760\ \frac{N \cdot m}{min}$$

Therefore,

$$hp = \frac{p_m \times 10^3 \times (LA)10^{-3} \times N}{44760} = \frac{p_m LAN}{44760}$$

where LA is expressed in litres, p_m in kPa, and N in power strokes per minute.

ILLUSTRATIVE PROBLEM 7.12

Using the results of Illustrative Problem 7.11, determine the horsepower of a 2.0-liter engine that has a mep of 1 MPa operating at 4000 rpm. The engine is a four-cycle engine.

Solution

$$hp = \frac{p_m LAN}{44760} = \frac{1000 \times 2 \times (4000/2)}{44760} = 89.4\ hp$$

ILLUSTRATIVE PROBLEM 7.13

Refer to Figure 7.71a (modified and repeated) and note that the difference in volume, $V_2 - V_3$, is commonly called the *displacement volume* and V_3 is the *clearance volume*. Derive an expression for the compression ratio in terms of the displacement volume and clearance volume.

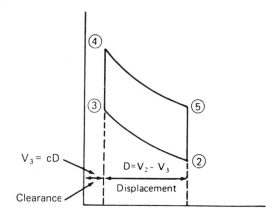

Figure 7.71a (modified and repeated)

Solution

To simplify the analysis, let us call the clearance volume a fraction (c) of the displacement volume D. Thus $V_3 = cD$ and $V_2 - V_3 = D$. By our definition of compression ratio,

$$r_c = \frac{v_2}{v_3} = \frac{V_2}{V_3} = \frac{D + cD}{cD} = \frac{1 + c}{c}$$

ILLUSTRATIVE PROBLEM 7.14

An Otto engine has a clearance equal to 20 percent of its displacement. What is its compression ratio?

Solution

From Illustrative Problem 7.13,

$$r_c = \frac{1 + c}{c} = \frac{1 + 0.2}{0.2} = \frac{6}{1}$$

ILLUSTRATIVE PROBLEM 7.15

Determine the mean effective pressure of a four-cycle, six-cylinder engine which has a 100-hp output at 4000 rpm. The cylinder bore is 3 in. and the stroke is 4 in.

Solution

Based upon the results of Illustrative Problem 7.9, we have

$$\text{hp} = \frac{p_m LAN}{33,000}$$

with $L = 4/12$ ft, $A = \pi/4(3)^2 \times 6$, and $N = 4000/2$ (since there are six cylinders and a four-cycle engine). Therefore,

$$p_m = \frac{100 \times 33,000}{\dfrac{4}{12} \times \dfrac{\pi(3)^2 \times 6}{4} \times \dfrac{4000}{2}} = 116.7 \text{ psia}$$

7.9d Diesel Engine (Compression Ignition Engine)

In the Otto (or spark ignition) cycle the fuel is mixed with the air prior to the compression stroke of the cycle. Ignition occurs due to an externally timed electrical spark. Due to the fact that the fuel–air mixture is compressed, it is necessary to use volatile, readily vaporized fuels that can be distributed uniformly into the incoming air. Also, the compression of the fuel–air mixture can cause it to become prematurely ignited during the compression stroke of the cycle leading to the familiar phenomenon of "knock" in the engine. Recent emphasis on ecological considerations has placed severe limitations on the use of leaded fuels to prevent preignition and nonuniform burning of the fuel, with the already noted decrease in the compression ratio being used in modern spark ignition engines.

In the diesel engine the air is first compressed to a pressure and temperature sufficient to ignite the fuel, which is injected at the end of the compression stroke. Since there is no fuel present during the compression stroke, much higher compression ratios are used in the compression ignition engine than in the spark ignition engine. Figure 7.75 shows a cross section of a V-type diesel engine from which it will be seen that many of the mechanical features are the same as for the spark ignition engine. This particular unit is made with piston bores of $13\frac{1}{2}$ in., strokes of $16\frac{1}{2}$ in., in 12, 16, or 20 cylinders; it operates at 400 to 515 rpm and is built in sizes ranging from 3000 to 6150 hp. Also, this is a dual fuel engine that can use diesel oil or gas (natural or manufactured) as the

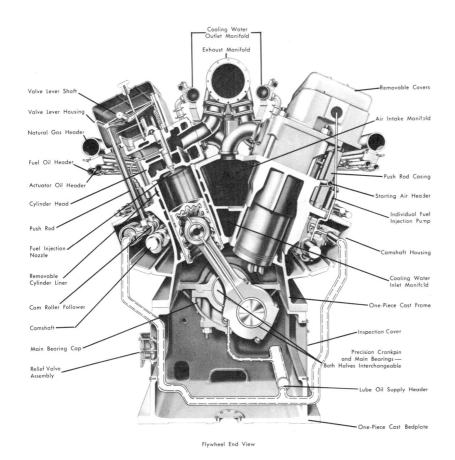

Cooling Water Outlet Manifold
Exhaust Manifold
Removable Covers
Air Intake Manifold
Valve Lever Shaft
Valve Lever Housing
Natural Gas Header
Fuel Oil Header
Push Rod Casing
Actuator Oil Header
Starting Air Header
Cylinder Head
Individual Fuel Injection Pump
Push Rod
Fuel Injection Nozzle
Camshaft Housing
Removable Cylinder Liner
Cooling Water Inlet Manifold
Cam Roller Follower
One-Piece Cast Frame
Camshaft
Inspection Cover
Main Bearing Cap
Precision Crankpin and Main Bearings — Both Halves Interchangeable
Relief Valve Assembly
Lube Oil Supply Header
One-Piece Cast Bedplate

Flywheel End View

Figure 7.75 V-type dual fuel diesel engine (Courtesy of Nordberg Div. of Rex Chainbelt, Inc.)

fuel. When using gas, a small amount of pilot oil is also injected to initiate combustion. Should the gas supply be interrupted, this engine automatically switches to fuel oil operation. Notice that in this figure there is no electrical ignition system and that the engine is started using compressed air.

Before proceeding further, let us compare the features of the spark ignition and compression ignition engines.

Features in Common.

1 Both utilize the same mechanical patterns, that is, in line, V, and so on.

2 Both are similarly cooled and lubricated.

3 The valving and valve actions are similar.

4 Both use external starting systems.

5 Both are made in two- and four-cycle types.

Differing Features.

1 Ignition in the spark ignition engine is initiated by an electrical spark at or near the completion of the compression stroke of the fuel–air mixture. In the compression ignition engine, air alone is compressed, and fuel ignition occurs when the fuel is injected into the cylinder at or near top dead center.

2 The prototype of the spark ignition engine is constant-volume combustion. In the compression ignition engine, constant-pressure combustion is the prototype.

3 Control of the spark ignition engine is accomplished by varying the quantity of fuel–air mixture while keeping a constant mixture composition. In the compression ignition engine, control is achieved by varying the fuel input to a constant mass of charging air.

4 Spark ignition engines use an electrical ignition system and a carburetor. Compression ignition engines have no electrical ignition system and no carburetor, but they do have some form of high pressure fuel injection system.

5 Spark ignition engines are restricted either to gases or readily vaporized fuels. Compression ignition engines do not have this limitation. The usual fuel is a refined crude petroleum oil. Surprisingly, both compression ignition and spark ignition engines are prone to detonation. The fuel qualities that suppress detonation in the spark ignition engine aggravate this condition in the compression ignition engine.

Figure 7.76 shows an opposed piston type of diesel engine. This engine is indicative of the variation in mechanical arrangements possible with the diesel engine. The operating cycle of this engine is as follows:

1 Air under blower pressure charges the cylinder via intake ports encircling the top of the cylinder liner.

2 Converging pistons close exhaust and intake ports, entrapping clean air.

3 Pistons converge, compressing air trapped in the cylinder.

4 Fuel injects into the combustion chamber between the pistons.

5 Heat of compression ignites air fuel mixture.

6 Pressures resulting from combustion force the pistons apart, delivering power to both crankshafts.

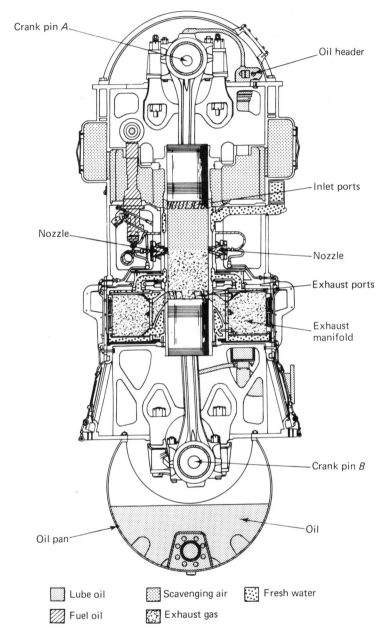

Figure 7.76 Opposed piston diesel engine (Courtesy of Colt Industries, Fairbanks Morse Power Systems Div.)

7 Exhaust ports encircling bottom of cylinder liner open. Unimpeded by valves, burned gases escape. (No power is lost in operating push rods or rocker assemblies.)

8 Intake ports open, admitting clean air under blower pressure and sweeping all burned gases from compression chamber in one direction (uniflow scavenging via exhaust ports) as the cycle repeats.

To increase the performance of diesels, a turbine-type supercharger of the type shown in Fig. 7.77 is frequently used. This is a self-contained unit composed of a gas turbine and a centrifugal blower mounted on a common shaft. The exhaust gases from the cylinders flow to the gas turbine where they drive the blower, which provides air for combustion and scavenging of exhaust gases from the cylinders. The use of a supercharger can increase the output of an engine as much as 50 percent. The injection of fuel into the cylinders of the compression ignition engine is one of the most exacting and difficult requirements for this type of engine. As an example, a 100-hp diesel operating at 750 rpm requires the droplets of oil to be injected with the injection and burning

Figure 7.77 Turbine-type supercharger (Courtesy of Colt Industries, Fairbanks Morse Power Systems Div.)

completed in 0.01 second. The fuel system must have the following characteristics:

1 It must accurately measure the fuel.

2 Since the air is compressed to at least 500 psi, the fuel must be delivered under high pressure. The fuel system in some engines compresses the fuel to pressures up to 30,000 psi.

3 The timing of the fuel injection into the cylinder is critical.

4 The rate of fuel injection must be accurately controlled.

5 The fuel must be atomized to assure uniform combustion.

6 The fuel must be dispersed properly in the chamber.

Figures 7.75 and 7.76 show fuel injection nozzles installed on diesel engines. In general three types of fuel systems are used for diesel engines:

1 *Unit system*: In this system a single injection pump is used per cylinder. This pump provides the fuel pressurization, metering, and timing function. Each unit is usually mechanically operated off a cam shaft.

2 *Common rail system*: In this system the fuel is kept under pressure at all times in a plenum chamber. Timed valves permit flow during the injection portion of the cycle, and the mechanically operated injection valve provides the timing and metering functions.

3 *Distributor system*: The metering of the fuel for all cylinders is carried out at low pressure by a single injection pump. Fuel is distributed through a distribution valve which directs the metered fuel to the individual injection valves. The injection valves have mechanically operated plungers to raise the oil pressure to the required injection pressure. In this system the injection valve pressurizes the fuel and also times the fuel injection. However, it does not meter the fuel.

Although diesel engines have been built in small sizes, such as for automotive use, most diesels are large, relatively slow machines. An idea of the size of a diesel-generator set (rated at 3250 kW output at the generator) that is used for a nuclear power plant for emergency power can be obtained from Fig. 7.78. This unit is shipped as a single unit with the generator directly coupled to the diesel engine.

Figure 7.78 A 3250 kW diesel generator set (Courtesy of Colt Industries, Fairbanks Morse Power Systems Div.)

7.9e Air-Standard Analysis of the Diesel Cycle

All the assumptions made for the air-standard analysis of the Otto cycle regarding the working fluid and its properties apply to the present analysis of the idealized diesel cycle.

The idealized air-standard diesel cycle consists of four processes. The first is an isentropic compression of the air after it has been inducted into the cylinder. At the end of the compression process, fuel is injected and combustion is assumed to occur at constant pressure. Subsequent to the heat release by combustion, the gas is expanded isentropically to produce work, and finally heat is rejected at constant volume. The gas is assumed to be recycled rather than rejected. Figure 7.79 shows the ideal diesel cycle on both pv and Ts coordinates.

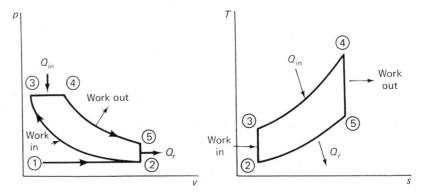

Figure 7.79 Diesel cycle

Heat is received (reversibly) during the nonflow constant-pressure process, ③ to ④. The energy equation for a constant-pressure process (flow or nonflow) yields

$$q_{in} = c_p(T_4 - T_3) \text{ Btu/lb} \tag{7.23}$$

The energy rejected during the constant-volume process is

$$q_r = c_v(T_5 - T_2) \text{ Btu/lb} \tag{7.24}$$

The net work available from the cycle is

$$W = q_{in} - q_r = c_p(T_4 - T_3) - c_v(T_5 - T_2) \text{ Btu/lb} \tag{7.25}$$

The efficiency thus becomes

$$\eta_{diesel} = \frac{c_p(T_4 - T_3) - c_v(T_5 - T_2)}{c_p(T_4 - T_3)} = 1 - \frac{1}{k}\left(\frac{T_5 - T_2}{T_4 - T_3}\right) \tag{7.26}$$

At this point it becomes conventional to introduce two terms and to define them as follows:

$$\text{compression ratio } r_c = \frac{v_2}{v_3} \qquad (7.27)$$

$$\text{expansion ratio } r_e = \frac{v_5}{v_4} \qquad (7.28)$$

Based upon the nonflow processes discussed in Chapter 5, we can write

$$\frac{T_3}{T_2} = (r_c)^{k-1} \quad \text{and} \quad \frac{T_5}{T_4} = \frac{1}{(r_e)^{k-1}} \qquad (7.29)$$

Since heat is received at constant pressure

$$\frac{T_4}{T_3} = \frac{v_4}{v_3} \qquad (7.30)$$

The ratio of

$$\frac{r_c}{r_e} = \frac{v_2/v_3}{v_5/v_4} = \frac{v_4 v_2}{v_3 v_5} \quad \left(\text{and since } v_2 = v_5\right) = \frac{v_4}{v_3} \qquad (7.31)$$

This ratio v_4/v_3 is called the cutoff ratio. Therefore,

$$\frac{T_4}{T_3} = \frac{r_c}{r_e} \qquad (7.32)$$

By substituting Eqs. (7.27) through (7.32) into Eq. (7.26) and rearranging,

$$\eta_{\text{diesel}} = 1 - \frac{1}{k}\left[\frac{(r_c/r_e)^k - 1}{(r_c/r_e - 1)(r_c^{k-1})}\right] = 1 - \left(\frac{1}{r_c}\right)^{k-1}\left[\frac{(v_4/v_3)^k - 1}{k(v_4/v_3 - 1)}\right] \qquad (7.33)$$

Equation (7.33) shows that the efficiency of the diesel cycle is only a function of the two ratios r_c and r_e. The term $[(r_c/r_e)^k - 1]/k[(r_c/r_e - 1)]$ requires examination to determine whether the diesel cycle is more or less efficient than the Otto cycle. Since v_4/v_3 is always greater than unity, it follows that this term is greater than unity. Therefore, by comparing Eq. (7.33) with Eq. (7.20) it can be concluded that the efficiency of the Otto cycle is greater than the efficiency of the diesel cycle for the same compression ratio. We can also arrive at this conclusion by referring to Fig. 7.80, which is a plot on pv and Ts coordinates of

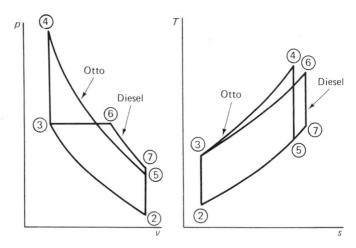

Figure 7.80 Otto and diesel cycles having same compression ratio and heat addition (From *Thermodynamics*, 2nd Ed. by F. P. Durham, Prentice-Hall, Inc. Englewoods Cliffs, N.J., 1959, p. 163, with permission)

a diesel and Otto cycle having the same compression ratio. The heat rejected in the diesel cycle (area under curve ⑥ to ① in the *Ts* plane) is greater than the heat rejected in the Otto cycle (area under curve ④ to ①). Since both cycles were assumed to receive the same amount of heat, the efficiency of the Otto cycle must be greater than that of a diesel cycle having the same heat addition and the same compression ratio.

However, as noted earlier in this section, the diesel cycle can be operated at much higher compression ratios than the Otto cycle and can, therefore, have a higher efficiency than the Otto cycle. It should be further noted that as v_4/v_3 is increased there is also a decrease in the efficiency of the diesel cycle. Values between 2 and $2\frac{1}{2}$ are generally used as the upper limits of v_4/v_3. The mean effective pressure of the diesel cycle is obtained in a similar manner to that used to obtain the mean effective pressure of the Otto cycle. The work of the diesel cycle is given by Eq. (7.25). Dividing it by the volume swept out by the piston yields

$$\text{mep}_{\text{diesel}} = \left[\frac{c_p(T_4 - T_3) - c_v(T_5 - T_2)}{v_2 - v_3} \right] J \qquad (7.34)$$

By suitably rearranging Eq. (7.34), the mean effective pressure of the diesel cycle can be expressed in terms of pressures and volumes. Also, in SI units, J is not needed.

ILLUSTRATIVE PROBLEM 7.16

An air-standard diesel engine has a compression ratio of 16 and a cutoff ratio of 2. Find the efficiency and temperature of the exhaust, using $k = 1.4$ with the cycle starting at 14 psia and 100°F.

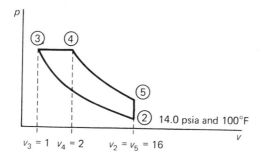

Figure 7.81 Illustrative Problem 7.16

Solution

From Fig. 7.81, values of the volumes can be assigned as shown. The cutoff ratio v_4/v_3 is given as 2. Therefore, $v_4 = 2v_3 = 2$. From Eq. (7.33),

$$\eta_{\text{diesel}} = 1 - \left(\frac{1}{r_c}\right)^{k-1}\left[\frac{(v_4/v_3)^k - 1}{k(v_4/v_3 - 1)}\right]$$

For $k = 1.4$,

$$\eta_{\text{diesel}} = 1 - \left(\frac{1}{16}\right)^{0.4}\left[\frac{(2)^{1.4} - 1}{1.4(2-1)}\right] = 0.614 = 61.4\%$$

From Eq. (7.29),

$$\frac{T_3}{T_2} = r_c^{k-1} \quad \text{and} \quad \frac{T_5}{T_4} = \frac{1}{r_e^{k-1}}$$

But

$$\frac{T_4}{T_3} = \frac{v_4}{v_3} = \frac{r_c}{r_e}$$

Substituting for T_3 and T_4 in terms of T_2, v_4, and v_3,

$$T_5 = T_2\left(\frac{v_4}{v_3}\right)^k$$

Therefore

$$T_5 = (100 + 460)(2)^{1.4} = 1478°\text{R} = 1018°\text{F}$$

ILLUSTRATIVE PROBLEM 7.17

In Illustrative Problem 7.16, determine the net work per pound of gas and the mean effective pressure. Assume $c_v = 0.172$ Btu/lb °F and $c_p = 0.24$ Btu/lb °F.

Solution

From Illustrative Problem 7.16,

$$q_r = c_v(T_5 - T_2) = 0.172(1018 - 100) = 157.9 \text{ Btu/lb}$$

Note that

$$\eta_{\text{diesel}} = 1 - \frac{q_r}{q_{\text{in}}}$$

Therefore,

$$\frac{q_r}{1 - \eta} = q_{\text{in}}$$

$$q_{\text{in}} = \frac{157.9}{(1 - 0.614)} = 409.1 \text{ Btu/lb}$$

$$\text{net work out} = J(q_{\text{in}} - q_r)$$
$$= 778(409.1 - 157.9)$$
$$= 195{,}430 \text{ ft lb/lb}$$

The mean effective pressure is net work divided by $(v_2 - v_3)$:

$$\text{mep} = \frac{195{,}430}{15 \times 144} = 90.5 \text{ psi}$$

7.9f Brayton Cycle

The discussion of gas cycles has so far been limited to intermittent cycles. However, the gas turbine has recently become quite important, both from an aircraft propulsion standpoint and for the production of power in stationary power plants. The emerging prominence of this device is due primarily to the mechanical development of its components and the metallurgical development of alloys that can be used at elevated temperatures. The prototype cycle for this device is the Brayton (or Joule) cycle. Its elements are shown in the *pv* and *Ts* diagrams in Fig. 7.82.

The gas is isentropically compressed along path ① to ②, and heat is added at constant pressure along path ② to ③. The gas then undergoes an isentropic expansion to its initial pressure, and heat is rejected at constant pressure. All the processes are reversible in the ideal cycle.

Before we analyze the Brayton cycle, let us look at the hardware used in conjunction with this cycle. There are three basic elements: the compressor, the

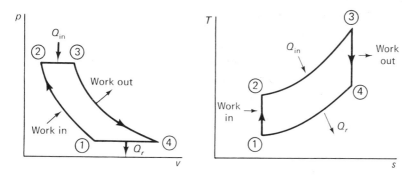

Figure 7.82 Ideal Brayton cycle

combustor, and the turbine in the simple cycle. Of these, the compressor and turbine play the key role in the power-generation cycle.

The compression of the air in a gas-turbine cycle is usually accomplished in two types of compressors, the centrifugal compressor and the axial flow compressor. In the axial flow compressor the blades have airfoil shapes and are arranged in concentric rings (stages) along the axis of the compressor shaft. In the usual design, each moving blade is followed by a stationary or fixed blade. Figure 7.83 shows the inlet to an axial flow unit and the compressor blading

Figure 7.83 Axial flow gas-turbine compressor (Courtesy of Pratt & Whitney Aircraft Div. of United Aircraft Corporation)

behind the inlet shroud. The moving blades impart a helical velocity to the air, increasing its velocity in each moving stage, while the stationary blades are shaped to act as diffusers, slowing up the air but at the same time increasing its pressure. Since the specific volume of the air decreases as the pressure increases, blade heights decrease as the air progresses along the axis of the compressor. Also, blade angles are varied due to the differing air speeds and flow patterns as the air proceeds along the compressor axis. Figure 7.84a shows the air path through the fixed and moving blades and also the rise in pressure along the axis of the compressor. It will be noted that each stage imparts approximately the same pressure rate as the preceding stage. Thus, if each stage produces a

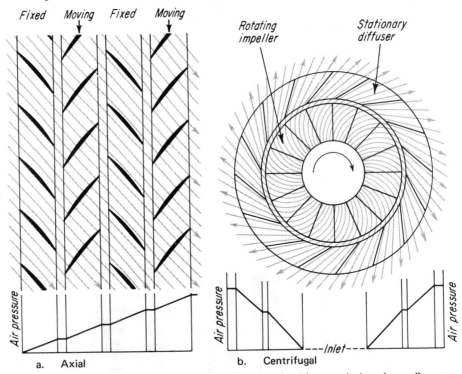

Figure 7.84 Basic flow in compressors (Reprinted with permission from *Power, The Engineer's Reference Library,* copyright by McGraw-Hill, Inc., New York)

pressure ratio of 1.1 : 1 (that is, a 10 percent increase), 8 stages will produce a total pressure rise of $(1.1)^8 = 2.14$, and 16 stages will produce an overall pressure rise of $(1.1)^{16} = 4.6$. The action of the centrifugal compressor is shown schematically in Fig. 7.84b. Air is taken in at the center (or eye) of the impeller. The rotation of the impeller causes the air to flow in a radial direction at high speed into the stationary diffuser. The air is slowed in the diffuser with an attendant increase in pressure. By varying the shape of the rotor blades and diffuser passages, it is possible to achieve almost any pressure characteristic as a function of rotor speed. Figure 7.85 shows a medium-sized, high-speed compressor having a first stage of axial compression and a second stage of centrifugal compression.

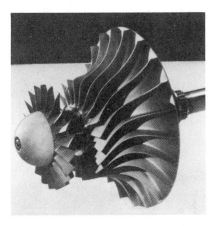

Figure 7.85 Combination aixal flow–centrifugal compressor (Reprinted with permission from *Power, The Engineer's Reference Library,* copyright by McGraw-Hill, Inc., New York)

The gas turbine is similar to the steam turbine and utilizes both the impose and reaction effects. Gas turbines have lower overall pressure drops than steam turbines, and consequently they have fewer stages and less change in blade height from inlet to exhaust.

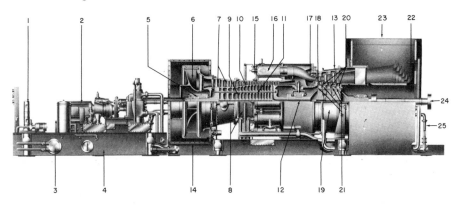

Figure 7.86 Single-shaft gas turbine (Courtesy of General Electric Co.)

Figure 7.86 shows a simple-cycle, single-shaft industrial gas turbine. Referring to the numbers in this figure, the following features are noted:

  2 Starting device: motor, steam turbine, or expansion (air) turbine.

  6 Radial inlet casing: provides uniform circumferential inlet flow to compressor.

  8 Compressor: axial flow.

15 Fuel nozzles.

16 Combustion chambers.

19 Three-stage impulse turbine.

Figure 7.87 is a schematic of a single-cycle, two-shaft arrangement in which atmospheric air is compressed in the compressor and then directed to the combustion chamber where it is mixed with fuel and then burned. The hot

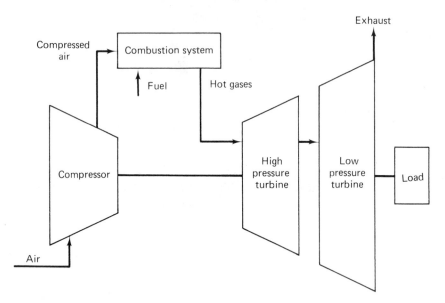

Figure 7.87 Schematic of a single-cycle, two-shaft design

gases expand through the high-pressure (first stage) and low-pressure (second stage) turbines, driving the compressor and load, respectively. Hot gases then expand to the atmosphere. This arrangement, which mechanically decouples the compressor from the turbine, gives increased flow flexibility in speed and load application. Figure 7.88 shows a complete gas-turbine power system. It consists of a two-stage, reaction-type free turbine connected to a gas generator through a diffuser duct. The compressor of this unit is split into two sections mechanically independent of each other. The first eight compressor stages (low-pressure compressor) are driven by the second and third turbine stages. Seven additional compressor stages (high-pressure compressor) are driven by the first turbine stage through a shaft which is independent of and concentric with the low-pressure drive shaft. The combustion section houses eight separate burner cans arranged circumferentially and interconnected by crossover tubes. The coupling between the gas generator and free turbine permits rapid response to varying power requirements. The air turbine requires a pressure of 45 psig for normal starting cycles.

Figure 7.88 Gas turbine power unit (Courtesy of Pratt & Whitney Div. of United Aircraft Corporation)

7.9g Air-Standard Brayton Cycle Analysis

Let us now return to the ideal Brayton cycle shown in Fig. 7.82 (repeated). The heat input in the constant-pressure nonflow process per pound is

$$q_{in} = c_p(T_3 - T_2) \qquad (7.35)$$

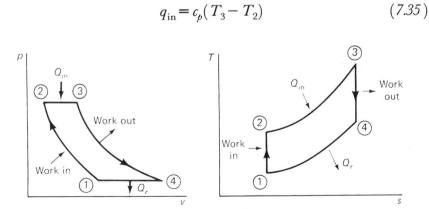

Figure 7.82 Ideal Brayton cycle (repeated)

and for the constant-pressure nonflow heat rejection part of the cycle ④ to ①,

$$q_r = c_p(T_4 - T_1) \qquad (7.36)$$

The net work is

$$q_{in} - q_r = c_p(T_3 - T_2) - c_p(T_4 - T_1) \quad \text{in thermal units} \quad (7.37)$$

Thus

$$\eta_{Brayton} = \frac{c_p(T_3 - T_2) - c_p(T_4 - T_1)}{c_p(T_3 - T_2)} = 1 - \frac{T_4 - T_1}{T_3 - T_2} \qquad (7.38)$$

However,

$$\frac{T_4}{T_1} = \frac{T_3}{T_2} \quad \text{and} \quad \frac{T_4 - T_1}{T_1} = \frac{T_3 - T_2}{T_2} \qquad (7.39)$$

Therefore,

$$\eta_{Brayton} = 1 - \frac{T_1}{T_2} = 1 - \left(\frac{v_2}{v_1}\right)^{k-1} \qquad (7.40)$$

Denoting v_1/v_2 as r_c,

$$\eta_{Brayton} = \left[1 - \left(\frac{1}{r_c}\right)^{k-1}\right] 100 \qquad (7.41)$$

In terms of pressures (in which p_2/p_1 is called the pressure ratio),

$$\eta_{Brayton} = \left[1 - \left(\frac{1}{p_2/p_1}\right)^{(k-1)/k}\right] 100 \qquad (7.42)$$

Comparison of Eq. (7.41) with Eq. (7.20) yields the conclusion that the efficiency of the Brayton cycle is equal to the efficiency of the Otto cycle for the same compression ratio. Therefore, we can also conclude that the efficiency of the ideal Brayton cycle is solely a function of the compression ratio and is not a function of the peak temperature of the cycle.

ILLUSTRATIVE PROBLEM 7.18

A Brayton cycle is operated with a compression ratio of 7. Assuming that $k = 1.4$ and $c_p = 0.24$, determine the heat in, the work out, the heat rejected, and the efficiency of the cycle if the peak temperature of the cycle is 1500°F and the initial conditions are 14.7 psia and 70°F. R for air is 53.3.

Solution

We can calculate the efficiency as

$$\eta_{\text{Brayton}} = 1 - \left(\frac{1}{r_c}\right)^{k-1} = 1 - \left(\frac{1}{7}\right)^{1.4-1} = 0.537 \quad \text{or} \quad 53.7\%$$

If we base our calculation on 1 lb of gas and use subscripts that correspond to points ①, ②, ③, and ④ of Fig. 7.82, we have

$$v_1 = \frac{RT_1}{p_1} = \frac{53.3(460 + 70)}{14.7 \times 144} = 13.35 \text{ cu ft/lb}$$

Since $\qquad r_c = 7, \qquad v_2 = v_1/7$

Therefore, $\qquad v_2 = \dfrac{13.35}{7} = 1.91 \text{ cu ft/lb}$

After the isentropic compression,

$$T_2(v_2)^{k-1} = T_1(v_1)^{k-1}$$

Thus

$$T_2 = T_1\left(\frac{v_1}{v_2}\right)^{k-1} = 530(7)^{(1.4-1)} = 1145°\text{R} = 685°\text{F}$$

T_3 is given at 1500°F. Therefore, the heat in is

$$q_{\text{in}} = c_p(T_3 - T_2) = 0.24(1500 - 685) = 195.6 \text{ Btu/lb}$$

Since efficiency can be stated to be work out divided by heat in,

$$0.537 = \frac{W/J}{q_{\text{in}}}, \qquad \frac{W}{J} = 0.537(195.6) = 105.0 \text{ Btu/lb}$$

The heat rejected is

$$q_{\text{in}} - \frac{W}{J} = 195.6 - 105.0 = 90.6 \text{ Btu/lb}$$

This problem can also be solved using the *Gas Tables*. In addition, a check is provided by solving for all the temperatures of the cycle and then solving for the efficiency.

The foregoing discussion has been of a working fluid that is returned to pass through the cycle after each sequence of events is completed. Such a cycle is known as a *closed* cycle. One application of a closed-cycle gas turbine plant is in conjunction with a nuclear reactor. The elements of this cycle are shown in Fig. 7.89 with the nuclear reactor being the heat source.

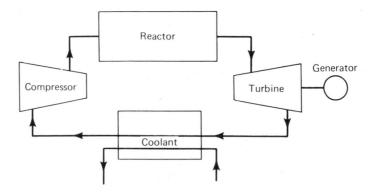

Figure 7.89 Elements of a closed-cycle gas turbine plant

The *open*-cycle gas turbine system is a steady flow system in which the working fluid is continuously discharged, and fresh fuel and air are continuously being added to maintain a steady flow of gases. The elements of this cycle are indicated in Fig. 7.90. The cold air is compressed and flows to the

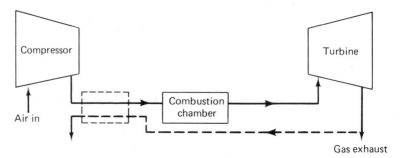

Figure 7.90 Open-cycle gas turbine plant

combustion chamber where fuel is continuously supplied and burned to heat the fluid. The combustion gases are then expanded in the turbine to provide work. The successful operation of the gas turbine requires that the net output of the turbine be greater than the work required by the compressor. It also requires that the mechanical efficiencies of these components be high; otherwise, the losses in these pieces of equipment may decrease useful output of the system to a point at which it might become uneconomical. Figure 7.91 shows an aircraft turbine being installed. This unit operates on the open Brayton cycle. Another application of the open gas-turbine cycle is shown in Fig. 7.92. This figure depicts the steam and gas turbine combined cycle plant which

Figure 7.91 Aircraft gas turbine (Courtesy of Pratt & Whitney Div. of United Aircraft Corp.)

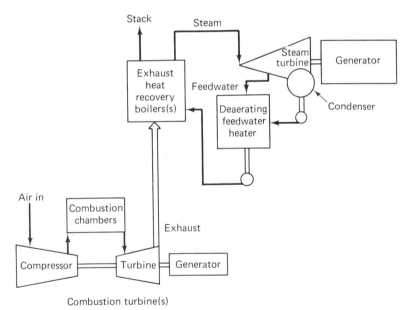

Figure 7.92 General Electric STAG combined cycle

General Electric calls the STAG cycle (STAG is an acronym for *steam and gas turbine*). The high-temperature exhaust gases from the open-cycle gas turbine generate steam in a forced circulation heat recovery steam generator.

The use of regeneration in vapor cycles has been shown to increase the efficiency of these cycles. Similarly, regeneration can be used to increase the efficiency of the Brayton cycle. Such an arrangement is indicated in Fig. 7.90 by the dotted lines. The exhaust gas leaving the turbine is used to preheat the air after it leaves the compressor and before entering the combustion chamber. If the same quantity of fuel is used, a higher gas temperature is obtained at the inlet to the turbine. If a constant temperature to the turbine is desired, regeneration decreases the amount of fuel required to achieve this temperature.

7.9h Stirling Cycle

The Stirling cycle has for some time been only of historical interest, since it has not been used as the prototype for practical power-producing systems. Recently, in this country and abroad, interest has been revived and engines based on the Stirling cycle have been built and successfully operated. This development has been due to the possibility of using these engines for power production in space.

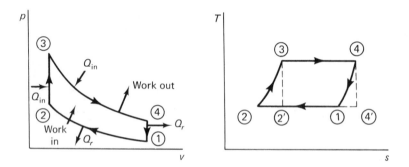

Figure 7.93 Stirling cycle

The elements of this cycle are shown in Fig. 7.93. It consists of two isothermal and two constant-volume processes. During the isothermal compression, heat is rejected by cooling the air in the compressor. Heat is added during the constant-volume portion of the cycle (② to ③). The gas is then isothermally expanded, and more heat is added. The gas finally rejects heat during the constant-volume position of the cycle (④ to ①). If all these paths were carried out reversibly, the efficiency of the Stirling cycle would equal that of the Carnot cycle between the same maximum and minimum temperature limits. This can be seen from the Ts diagram in Fig. 7.93. Paths ② to ③ and ④ to ① are parallel, and the cycle can be "squared off" to yield the Carnot cycle shown as 2'344'. The inability of actual devices to achieve this limiting efficiency arises principally from the heat transfer processes and pressure losses in the engine and its associated piping.

7.10 DIRECT ENERGY CONVERSION

In all the devices and cycles that we have discussed thus far, the generation of electrical power from an energy source required the transfer of the energy from the source to a working fluid, which, by undergoing circulation and other manipulation in a complex "prime mover" (turbine, engine, and so on), ultimately yielded the desired electrical output. Recent progress has been made in the development of direct energy conversion systems in which the energy of the fuel is converted directly to electrical energy without the use of a circulating fluid or any moving parts. At present we will just qualitatively describe four of these systems and their limitations. These are

1 The thermoelectric converter

2 The fuel cell

3 The thermionic converter

4 The magnetohydrodynamic generator

7.10a Thermoelectric Converter

The first of these direct energy conversion devices, the thermoelectric converter, is based upon the fact that a voltage is generated when two unlike conductors are connected at their ends with the ends kept at different temperatures. If the circuit is closed through a load resistance, current will flow through the load.

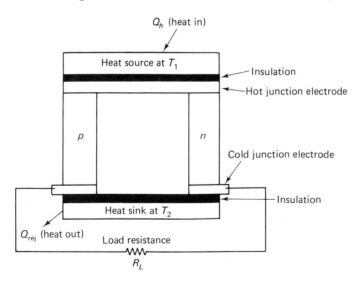

Figure 7.94 Thermoelectric converter

This phenomenon has already been noted and is used to measure temperature in the thermocouple which we described in Chapter 1. An associated phenomenon, known as the Peltier effect, is discussed in Chapter 8 in conjunction with the thermoelectric refrigerator. Figure 7.94 shows a simple thermoelectric energy converter. The desirable characteristics of the materials used in such a device are as follows:

1 Low internal electrical resistance to reduce internal heat generation resulting from current flow in the materials.

2 Low thermal conductivity (high thermal resistance) to reduce heat conduction from the heat source to the sink.

3 High values of open-circuit voltage. Most metals produce open-circuit voltages of the order of microvolts per degree of temperature difference.

The most suitable materials are the semiconductors, such as lead telluride, germanium–silicon alloys, and germanium telluride. The thermoelectric converter is basically a form of heat engine receiving heat from a source, rejecting heat to a sink, and converting heat to electrical work. Thus it has as its theoretical upper limit the Carnot-cycle efficiency. Due to losses, the Carnot-cycle limit is not even approached and although, in theory, the thermoelectric converter is capable of operating at efficiencies greater than 10 percent, most of the devices built to date have shown efficiencies much lower than this figure. With development and using semiconductors, a thermal efficiency approaching 20 percent is a reasonable objective. Due to their reliability and lack of moving parts, they have been used in such diverse applications as converting waste heat from kerosene lamps to power radio receivers in rural areas and in conjunction with radioisotope heat sources to power long-life unattended ocean buoys.

7.10b Fuel Cell

The fuel cell is an electrochemical device that resembles a car battery. As can be seen from Fig. 7.95, it is unlike the battery in that it does not feed on itself. The fuel and the oxidant are consumed, and the electrodes stay intact. The components and structure of a fuel cell vary with the physical state of the reactants. Since gases, liquids, and solids have been used as fuel and oxidants, the structures and components of fuel cells have wide variations. Highly reactive hydrazine and almost inert carbon have drastically different requirements, just as fluorine and air must be handled differently. But even the same reactant pair (hydrogen and oxygen) is being utilized in a number of systems quite unlike each other. Regardless of the system, reactants must be admitted and heat and products removed approximately in proportion to the electric power demands. The ideal voltage output of a fuel cell at no load is approxi-

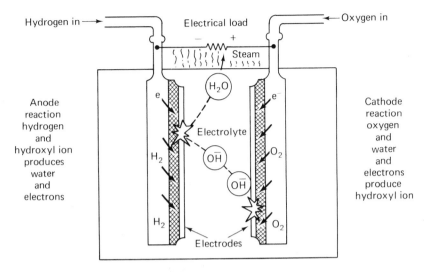

Figure 7.95 Basic fuel cell

mately $1\frac{1}{4}$ V for a hydrogen–oxygen cell and depends to some extent on the reactants used.

Figure 7.96 shows a complete fuel cell system. The system must provide for storage of at least one reactant (the fuel) or both reactants if air is not used

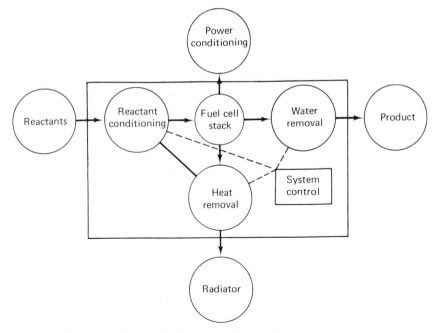

Figure 7.96 Complete fuel cell system

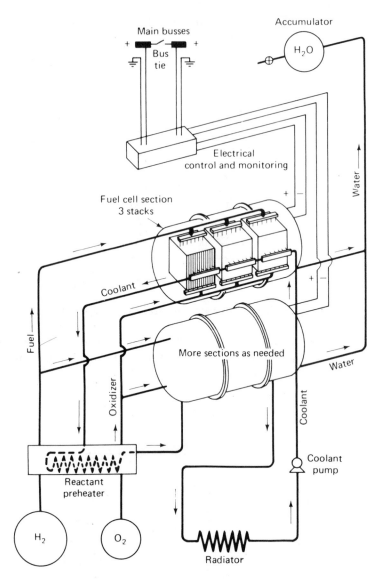

Figure 7.97 Gemini fuel-cell system

as the oxidant. The system as shown must be capable of adjusting the flow of reactants according to demand while removing the products of the reaction and the heat generated. In some cases, such as water on a space vehicle, the product must also be stored. Where many cells are stacked to obtain the required voltage and power output, supply and removal must be uniform to all cells in the stack, the cells must perform uniformly, and they must all have good external electrical connections. Figure 7.97 schematically shows a fuel-cell system that was used in the project Gemini space vehicles. More than 30 cells were connected in series, in each of the three stacks, which are connected in parallel.

The fuel cell is not a heat engine, and it is therefore not limited by the Carnot efficiency. If we consider the function of the cell to be the conversion of chemical to electrical energy, then the maximum theoretical efficiency of a fuel cell is 100 percent.

7.10c Thermionic Converter

The thermionic converter is basically a high temperature device that converts thermal energy to electricity by literally boiling off electrons from the hot cathode, which then travel to the cold anode. Figure 7.98 shows a schematic of this device in which the electrical circuit is completed by the external load, R_L. In principle, this device is a heat engine that uses electrons as the working fluid. Therefore, the upper limit of its efficiency is that of a Carnot engine operating between the temperature limits of the cathode and anode. Efficiencies of 10 percent have been achieved with cathode temperatures of 3200°F when the Carnot efficiency was 50 percent. Since electron emission is an exponential function of temperature, high cathode temperatures yield high power densities. Efficiencies of the order of 18 percent have been achieved in a thermionic converter with a cathode temperature of 4500°F.

There are several problems associated with the operation of the thermionic converter. The first of these arises from the distribution of the electrons in the gap between electrodes. When the gap is maintained as nearly as possible as a "perfect" vacuum, it is necessary to keep the spacing of the electrodes as small as 0.001 in.; otherwise, the retarding potential (space–charge effects) becomes too large for satisfactory operation of the converter. These spacings are extremely difficult to maintain, especially with the large temperature differences between the anode and cathode. To reduce the space–charge effect and at the same time maintain reasonable spacings (of

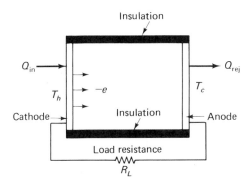

Figure 7.98 Schematic of a thermionic converter

the order of 0.040 in.), most present-day thermionic converters use cesium gas in the interelectrode space. Cesium is relatively easily ionized with positively charged ions which tend to neutralize and negate the space–charge effect.

In addition to the space–charge problem, the thermionic converter performance is also degraded by heat radiated from the cathode to the anode, which is ultimately lost from the anode, and heat conducted from the cathode to the anode. Thus, to achieve high efficiencies in a thermionic converter, it is necessary to reduce the effects of space–charge, to minimize radiation and conduction losses, and to keep the internal resistance of the converter to a minimum. It will be noted from the foregoing that mechanical design plays a vital role in the ultimate performance of a thermionic converter.

7.10d Magnetohydrodynamic Generator

When a conductor is moved through a magnetic field, an electromotive force results, and if the circuit is closed, a current will flow. This phenomenon is the basis of operation of all rotating electrical generators in which the rotor turns conductors in a magnetic field to produce electricity. The basic concept of the magnetohydrodynamic (MHD) converter is exactly this principle, with the conductor being a high-speed ionized gas. Figure 7.99 shows the replacement of the conducting wires of a conventional electric generator by a highly ionized gas called a *plasma*. The electrical properties of a plasma are determined by the density of free electrons in the gas. The ionization of the gas (and consequently its electrical conductivity) can be achieved in several ways (high gas temperatures, seeding of a gas with readily ionized atoms such as cesium, nuclear radiation of the gas, and others). When this ionized gas (plasma) flows at right angles to the magnetic field (Fig. 7.99), a force is generated at right angles to both the velocity of flow and the magnetic field. This force drives the electrons and ions to the pickup electrodes, giving rise to a current when the electrodes are connected to an external load.

In the MHD cycle, the gas is first compressed, heat is added at constant pressure, and the gas is then accelerated in a nozzle before passing through the magnetic field. If we consider the overall cycle, such as the Rankine cycle shown in Fig. 7.3 or the Brayton cycle shown in Fig. 7.82, it will be seen that the MHD converter has basically replaced the turbine and generator. The Ts diagram of the ideal cycle is the same as that we had for the ideal Brayton cycle with the isentropic expansion yielding electrical work output, heat addition being at constant pressure, and heat rejection occurring at constant pressure. This device is obviously a heat engine device, and it is subject to the efficiency limitations of the Carnot cycle. Some of the factors that cause losses in the MHD converter are heat transfer losses through the electrodes, internal electrical resistance losses in the plasma, energy required and losses in the magnets, and fluid friction losses associated with high speed gas flow.

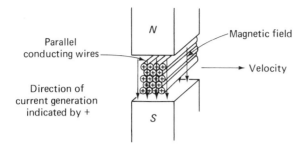

a. Conventional generator

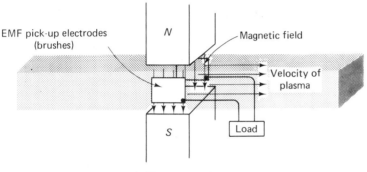

b. Plasma generator

Figure 7.99 Magnetohydrodynamic generator principle

Due to the losses noted, it is found that the MHD converter is best suited for large sized central stations in which the reject heat from the MHD converter is used as the input to a conventional power cycle. Using this binary type of cycle, it is estimated that practical efficiencies approaching 50 percent can be achieved.

7.11 CLOSURE

The length of this chapter is due primarily to the amount of descriptive material that has been included. Experience has shown that theoretical considerations of cycles and their characteristics does not give a sufficient grasp of this topic. It is most important to be able to relate the physical methods of realizing an ideal cycle to the cycle itself. Only in this manner can the student appreciate why certain assumptions are made and the problem confronting the engineer in building devices to make idealizations become working devices.

To those who are familiar with portions of this material (for example, the internal combustion engine), some of the material may appear to be unnecessary and as a consequence they may tend to skip over other descriptive portions of the chapter. It is strongly urged that all the descriptive portions be studied prior to, and reviewed after studying the ideal cycles.

REFERENCES

1 *Thermodynamics*, 6th Ed., by V. M. Faires and M. S. Simmang, Macmillan Inc., New York, 1978.

2 *Power* Special Reports:
"Steam Turbines" by B. G. A. Skrotzki, June 1962.
"Gas Turbines" by B. G. A. Skrotzki, December 1963.
"Steam Generation" by R. J. Bender, June 1964.
"Nuclear Power Reactors" by R. K. Evans, March 1965.
"Heat Exchangers" by R. G. Schweiger, June 1970.

3 "Energetics," series of seven articles appearing in *Mechanical Engineering*, June through December, 1966.

4 *How an Internal Combustion Engine Works* by Renwal Products Co., Fairless Hills, Pa., 1960.

5 *Modern Steam Generating Equipment* by E. A. Ferris, Combustion Engineering, Inc., New York, 1960.

6 *Engineering Thermodynamics* by W. C. Reynolds and H. C. Perkins, McGraw-Hill Book Co., New York, 1970.

7 *Thermodynamics* by J. P. Holman, McGraw-Hill Book Co., New York, 1969.

8 *Elementary Applied Thermodynamics* by Irving Granet, John Wiley & Sons, Inc., New York, 1965.

9 "The Little Engine That Could Be an Answer to Pollution" by G. Alexander, *New York Times Magazine*, Oct. 3, 1971.

10 "A Survey of Curtiss-Wright's 1958–1971 Rotary Combustion Engine Technological Developments" by C. Jones, Society of Automotive Engineers, National Automobile Engineering Meeting, Detroit, Mich., May 1972, Paper 720468.

11 "Westinghouse Liquid Metal Fast Breeder Reactor" by V. J. Rinaldi, Westinghouse Technical Paper 282-165A, prepared by Westinghouse Advanced Reactors Division, Madison, Pa., May 1962.

12 *Elements of Applied Energy* by F. T. Moore, Litton Educational Publishing, Inc., New York, 1947.

13 *Thermal Engineering* by H. L. Solberg, O. C. Cromer, and A. R. Spalding, John Wiley & Sons, Inc., New York, 1960.

14 *Thermodynamics*, 2nd Ed., by F. P. Durham, Prentice-Hall, Inc., Englewood Cliffs, N.J., 1959.

15 *Basic Thermodynamics* by B. G. A. Skrotzki, McGraw-Hill Book Co., New York, 1963.

16 *Power Reactors*, U.S.A.E.C. Technical Information Service, May, 1958.

17 "The Effect of Fast Breeder Reactors on Uranium Requirements" by Karl Cohen, General Electric Co. Delivered at Governor's Conference on Uranium, Casper, Wyo, November 1, 1968.

18 *Principles of Nuclear Reactor Engineering* by S. Glasstone, Van Nostrand Reinhold Co., New York, 1955.

19 "Nuclear Power Plant of TVA at Browns Ferry" by J. R. Parrish, G. M. Roy, and F. G. Baily, presented at American Power Conference, April 25–27, 1967, Chicago, Ill.

20 *Engineering Thermodynamics with Applications* by M. D. Burghardt, Harper & Row, Publishers, New York, 1978.

PROBLEMS

Use $c_p = 0.24$ Btu/lb°F, $c_v = 0.171$ Btu/lb°F, $c_p = 1.0061$ kJ/kg·K, and $c_v = 0.7186$ kJ/kg·K for air unless otherwise noted. Assume that these specific heats are constant and that the molecular weight of air is 29.

7.1 A Carnot cycle is operated with its maximum temperature equal to 1000°R. If the cycle efficiency is such that 100 Btu/hr is rejected, what is the sink temperature if 500 Btu/hr enters at the upper temperature?

7.2 A Carnot vapor cycle uses water as the working fluid. If the cycle operates within the wet region (Fig. 7.1) and upper pressure is 500 psia while lower pressure is 20 psia, determine the cycle efficiency.

7.3 Two ideal reversible heat engines are operated in series, the first receiving heat at a temperature T_1, and the second rejecting heat at a temperature T_2. Prove that this arrangement is as efficient as a single reversible engine operating between the same minimum and maximum temperatures.

7.4 A Carnot cycle is operated between 1000 K and 200 K. If 1 MJ/hr enters as heat, how much heat is rejected, what is the thermal efficiency of the cycle, and how much work is obtained from the cycle?

7.5 A turbine manufacturer specifies that the maximum steam temperature in the turbine is to be 1000°F and that the last stage of the turbine is to have a moisture content not exceeding 10 percent by weight. If the expansion is carried out reversibly and adiabatically from 800 psia, what is the state of the steam as it leaves the turbine? Use the Mollier chart.

7.6 In Problem 7.5 the steam is expanded irreversibly. If the actual $\Delta h = 90$ percent of the Δh that would be present if the process were carried out isentropically, what is the final moisture that would leave the turbine if the final pressure was that of Problem 7.5?

7.7 What is the internal efficiency of the turbine in Problem 7.6?

7.8 If the condenser pressure in a Rankine cycle is 1 psia and the maximum pressure in the cycle is 600 psia, calculate the efficiency of the ideal cycle for saturated vapor. Use the Mollier chart and neglect pump work.

7.9 If the vapor in Problem 7.8 has 200°F superheat, calculate the efficiency of the ideal Rankine cycle.

7.10 What is the pump work in Problem 7.8?

7.11 What is the thermal efficiency of the Rankine cycle in Problem 7.8 if pump work is included?

7.12 Repeat Problem 7.8 for an initial pressure of 400 psia.

7.13 Repeat Problem 7.9 for an initial pressure of 400 psia.

7.14 A Rankine cycle is operated with a turbine inlet pressure of 600 psia and 600°F. Determine the efficiency if the expansion is to 1 psia. Use the Mollier diagram and neglect pump work.

7.15 Determine the efficiency of the cycle in Problem 7.14 if the expansion is carried out to 10 psia. Compare results with those obtained in Problem 7.14.

7.16 A Rankine cycle is operated with a turbine inlet pressure of 500 psia and a temperature of 620°F. If the engine expansion is to 2 psia, what is the efficiency of the cycle? Neglect pump work.

7.17 Steam is expanded to 10 percent moisture at 2 psia in a Rankine cycle. If the initial pressure is 500 psia, what is the efficiency of the cycle? Neglect pump work.

7.18 Steam is expanded to 12 percent moisture at 1 psia in a Rankine cycle. If the initial pressure is 400 psia, what is the efficiency of the cycle? Neglect pump work.

7.19 Determine the type efficiency of the cycle of Problem 7.8.

7.20 Determine the type efficiency of the cycle of Problem 7.12.

7.21 Determine the type efficiency of the cycle of Problem 7.14.

7.22 Determine the heat rate in Btu/kilowatt-hr for Problem 7.14.

7.23 Determine the heat rate in Btu/kilowatt-hr for Problem 7.15.

7.24 Determine the ideal steam rate for Problem 7.14.

7.25 Determine the ideal steam rate for Problem 7.15.

7.26 If the specific heat of the condenser cooling water is assumed to be unity, and it is desired to limit the condenser cooling water temperature change to 50°F in the condenser, determine the pounds of cooling water required per pound of steam for the ideal Rankine cycle operated from 600 psia and 600°F to 2 psia. The condensate is assumed to be saturated liquid.

7.27 A reheat cycle is operated to decrease the amount of moisture in the final steam from a turbine. If the steam, initially at 1000 psia and 800°F, is permitted to expand only to saturation and is reheated to its initial enthalpy, what will the moisture content of the final steam be if it is expanded reversibly to 2 in. Hg?

7.28 If the steam in Problem 7.27 is reheated by the addition of one-half of the initial decrease in enthalpy, what will the moisture content of the final steam be after a reversible expansion to 2 in. Hg?

7.29 A reheat cycle is operated from 500 psia and 500°F to a final pressure of 1 in. Hg. If the amount of reheat added is $\frac{1}{2}\Delta h$ from the initial conditions to saturated vapor, determine the efficiency of the cycle. (h_f at 1 in. Hg is 47.09 Btu/lb; temperature is close to 79°F.)

7.30 What is the type efficiency of the cycle in Problem 7.29?

7.31 In a reheat cycle the steam is expanded from 700 psia and 600°F to 100 psia. It is subsequently reheated until the steam has the same degrees of superheat as it had initially. If the final pressure of the cycle is 1 psia, determine its efficiency.

7.32 Starting with 500°F and 500 psia and assuming that the steam in a reheat cycle is reheated to an enthalpy equal to its initial enthalpy, determine the efficiency of this cycle if the final pressure is 1 psia and the initial expansion is carried out to 100 psia.

7.33 Assume that the final pressure in a reheat cycle is 1 psia and the first expansion is to saturated vapor. If the steam is reheated to its initial enthalpy, determine the efficiency of the cycle for an initial pressure of 500 psia and initial temperature of 600°F.

7.34 An air-standard Otto cycle is operated with a compression ratio of 6. If k has values of 1.1, 1.2, 1.3, 1.4, determine the efficiency of the cycle. Plot the efficiency as a function of k.

7.35 An air-standard Otto cycle has 2000 kJ/kg added as heat. The initial conditions are 20°C and 150 kPa. If the compression ratio is 7, determine the thermal efficiency of the cycle, the temperature and pressure at each point in the cycle, and its mean effective pressure.

7.36 An air-standard Otto cycle with a compression ratio of 7 has air at 70°F and 15 psia at the start of the compression portion of the cycle. If 800 Btu/lb is added as heat, determine the pressure and temperature in each portion of the cycle, the thermal efficiency of the cycle, and its mean effective pressure.

7.37 An air-standard Otto cycle has 1400 kJ/kg added as heat. The initial conditions are 20°C and 100 kPa. If the compression ratio is 7, determine the thermal efficiency of the cycle, the temperature and pressure at each point in the cycle, and its mean effective pressure.

7.38 An air-standard Otto cycle has 500 Btu/lb added as heat. If the initial conditions are 70°F and 20 psia and the compression ratio is 7, determine the thermal efficiency of the cycle, the temperature and pressure at each point in the cycle, and its mean effective pressure.

7.39 An air-standard Otto cycle has 300 Btu/lb added as heat. If the initial conditions are 50°F and 15 psia and the compression ratio is 8, determine the thermal efficiency of the cycle, the temperature and pressure at each point in the cycle, and its mean effective pressure.

7.40 The mean effective pressure of an Otto cycle is 100 psia. If the displacement of an engine is 144 in.^{3}, what horsepower can the engine deliver? This is a four-cycle engine operating at 3600 rpm.

7.41 The mean effective pressure of an Otto engine is 1 Mpa. The displacement of the engine is 3.8 litres. If the engine is operated as a four-cycle engine at 4000 rpm, what is its horsepower?

7.42 An air-standard diesel cycle is operated with a compression ratio of 25. The inlet conditions to the cycle are 14.7 psia and 70°F. The gas is to be used after the expansion cycle to heat some process liquid in a heat exchanger. For this purpose the temperature at the end of the expansion is to be 500°F. Determine the efficiency of the cycle.

7.43 Assuming the engine in Problem 7.41 is a diesel engine, determine its horsepower.

7.44 An air-standard diesel cycle is operated with a compression ratio of 20. The ratio of $(v_4 - v_3)/(v_2 - v_3)$ is variable. Determine the efficiency of the cycle for values of the volume ratio of 0.01, 0.04, 0.08, and 0.1. Plot the results. Use $k = 1.4$.

7.45 An air-standard diesel engine has 1000 kJ/kg added as heat. At the beginning of the compression the temperature is 20°C and the pressure is 150 kPa. If the compression ratio is 20, determine the maximum pressure and temperature in the cycle.

7.46 Derive the following expression for the mean effective pressure in an air-standard diesel.

$$\text{mep}_{\text{diesel}} = p_1 \left[\frac{kr_C^k(v_3/v_2 - 1) - r_C\left[(v_3/v_2)^k - 1\right]}{(k-1)(r_C - 1)} \right]$$

7.47 The net heat input to a diesel cycle is 100 Btu/lb. If the initial conditions to the cycle are 14.7 psia and 60°F and the compression ratio is 20, determine the efficiency of the cycle, the net work out of the cycle, and its mean effective pressure. Assume that 1 lb of air is used per cycle.

7.48 An air-standard diesel engine has 500 Btu/lb added as heat. At the beginning of the compression the temperature is 70°F and the pressure is 20 psia. If the compression ratio is 20, determine the maximum pressure and temperature in the cycle.

7.49 A cycle operates on air for which the constant-volume and constant-pressure specific heats are 0.17 and 0.24 Btu/lb °R, respectively. All processes contained within the cycle are reversible and consist of (a) a constant-volume heat addition of 300 Btu/lb of air, which was initially at 15 psia and 70°F; (b) an adiabatic expansion to a temperature of 800°F; and (c) a constant-pressure heat rejection of a magnitude that will return the air to 15 psia and 70°F. Determine the net work of this cycle in Btu's per pound of air.

7.50 A gas-turbine cycle is operated with a pressure ratio of 5:1; that is, the pressure after compression is five times the pressure before compression. What is the efficiency of this cycle?

7.51 A Brayton cycle is operated to yield maximum work out of the cycle. If the compression ratio of the cycle is 4, the initial temperature to the cycle is 70°F, and the temperature at the start of the heat-rejection portion of the cycle is 500°F, what is the peak temperature in the cycle?

7.52 A Brayton cycle is operated to yield maximum work out of the cycle. If the compression ratio of the cycle is 4, the initial temperature of the cycle is 20°C, and the temperature at the start of the heat rejection portion of the cycle is 240°C, what is the peak temperature in the cycle?

7.53 A Brayton cycle has a compression ratio of 5. If the initial temperature is 70°F and the initial pressure is 15 psia and 1000 Btu/lb is added as heat, what is the thermal efficiency of the cycle?

7.54 A Brayton cycle has a compression ratio of 5. If the initial temperature is 20°C, the initial pressure is 100 kPa, and 1000 kJ/kg is added as heat, what is the temperature at each point in the cycle and what is the thermal efficiency of the cycle?

7.55 A Brayton cycle is operated with a compression ratio of 8. The inlet conditions are 14.7 psia and 90°F. Determine the thermal efficiency of this cycle. If the compressor in this cycle is 90 percent efficient mechanically and the turbine is also 90 percent efficient mechanically, determine the overall efficiency of the cycle.

7.56 A turbine receives air at 1 MPa, 600 K, and discharges to a pressure of 150 kPa. The actual temperature at discharge is 400 K. What is the internal engine efficiency of the turbine?

7.57 A turbine receives air at 150 psia, 1000°R, and discharges to a pressure of 15 psia. The actual temperature at discharge is 600°R. What is the internal engine efficiency of the turbine?

chapter **8**

refrigeration

8.1 INTRODUCTION

In previous chapters, consideration was given to those cycles that (by the proper placing of elements) could yield useful work from a heat source. By the simple expedient of rearranging the sequence of events in these cycles, it is possible (in principle) to remove heat from a region of lower temperature and to deliver it to a region of higher temperature by the input of mechanical work. This removal of heat by the use of mechanical energy has been called the *refrigerating effect*. In more general terms, refrigeration can be defined as the art of maintaining a body at temperatures below its surroundings or, alternatively, as the removal of heat from a place in which it is undesirable to a place in which it is not.

The history of refrigeration can be traced back thousands of years with natural ice providing the cooling effect desired. The field of refrigeration on a large scale was first developed in the 19th century, and in the middle 1800s the harvesting, storing, and shipping of natural ice became one of the leading industries of the New England states. By the end of the 19th century, mechanical refrigeration had become a practical reality, and the refrigeration industry as we know it today was in existence. Along with the use of industrial refrigeration for food preservation, chemical production, metallurgical applications, medicine, and so on, another facet of the refrigeration process appeared, the control of the temperature and humidity of the environment, which is commonly called air conditioning. It is interesting to note that in 1904 a 450-ton air conditioning system had been installed to air condition the New York Stock Exchange.

The Carnot cycle has served to establish the performance criteria of power cycles; in this chapter the study of the reversed Carnot cycle will yield many of the thermodynamic limitations and performance criteria for refrigeration cycles.

8.2 THE REVERSED CARNOT CYCLE

It will be remembered that the Carnot cycle consists of four reversible processes: two isothermals and two isentropics. In the direct cycle, in which the production of useful work is the primary objective, the elements are arranged so that the energy-flow diagram is as shown in Fig. 8.1. Energy flows into the system from a reservoir at constant temperature T_1, work leaves the system through the agency of the prime mover, and heat is rejected to the receiver at constant temperature T_2. The Ts diagram of the cycle is repeated in Fig. 8.2. Since this ideal cycle can be treated independently of the working fluid, property lines are not shown on the diagram.

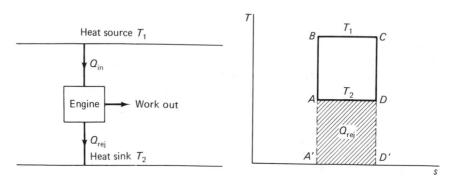

Figure 8.1 Direct Carnot cycle   **Figure 8.2** Direct Carnot cycle

For the reversed cycle the energy flow diagram is as shown in Fig. 8.3. Note that in this case the work of the engine serves to take heat from the reservoir (sink at T_2) and rejects it to the source at T_1. The Ts diagram for the reversed cycle is shown in Fig. 8.4, and the areas are interpreted as various energy items corresponding to Fig. 8.3. By considering these figures, certain general and important conclusions can be obtained for the reversed cycle. First, however, notice that the area $ABCD$ of Fig. 8.4 measures the net work supplied to the cycle, and the area $A'ADD'$ on this same figure represents the heat removed from the colder region (at T_2).

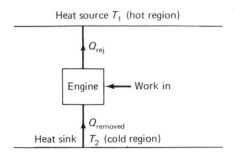

Figure 8.3 Reversed Carnot cycle

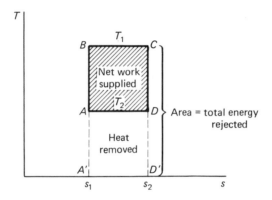

Figure 8.4 Reversed Carnot cycle

If the interest is in removing the greatest amount of heat from the sink, it is desirable to do so with the least possible energy input to the system. This mode of operation is equivalent to operating at the maximum efficiency.

To evaluate the maximum efficiency system, the same reasoning used for the direct cycle will serve to answer the question of the optimum efficiency conditions for operation of the reversed cycle. Consider a reversible engine operating as shown schematically in Fig. 8.3. The amount of energy rejected at T_1 will equal the work in plus the heat removed from the lower temperature region at T_2. It has already been demonstrated that a reversible engine operating between two temperatures is the most efficient engine possible. Therefore, the energy rejected by the reversed cycle can be used in a reversible engine operating in a direct manner (see Fig. 8.1). The work out of the direct cycle will equal that required by the reversed cycle, and the energy rejected by the direct engine cycle will be equal to that removed by the reversed cycle. Let it now be assumed that the reversed cycle (Fig. 8.3) is more efficient than a reversible engine operating in the same mode between the same temperature limits. For a given work input this cycle will be capable of removing more energy from the sink at T_2 than the reversible engine could. However, the more efficient engine (reversed one) operating in a direct manner will, for a given work output between the same temperature limits, remove less energy from T_1 and reject more energy to T_2 than the equivalent energy amounts for the "more efficient than reversible engine." The inescapable conclusion of such a condition of combined operation is that, without the use of energy or an external agency, heat is removed continuously from a lower temperature region and made to flow to a higher temperature region. This is an obvious violation of the second law, and it must be concluded that the most efficient reversed engine cycle operating between two temperatures is a reversible engine, and, therefore, a reversed Carnot cycle represents the most efficient possible refrigerating cycle.

Based on the foregoing, let us now establish a figure of merit for the refrigeration cycle. For the direct power cycle, we were interested in the amount of work that was obtained from a given heat supply, and this ratio was termed the efficiency of the power cycle. For the reversed cycle we are interested in the amount of work required to remove a given amount of heat from the low-temperature reservoir. This ratio of refrigeration effect to work input is known as the *coefficient of performance* (COP). Thus

$$\text{COP} = \frac{\text{refrigeration effect}}{\text{work input}} \qquad (8.1)$$

For the reversed Carnot cycle shown in Figs. 8.3 and 8.4, the heat removed from the reservoir at T_2 is $T_2(s_2 - s_1)$, and the work supplied is $(T_1 - T_2)(s_2 - s_1)$.

$$\text{COP}_{\text{Carnot refrigeration}} = \frac{T_2(s_2 - s_1)}{(T_1 - T_2)(s_2 - s_1)} = \frac{T_2}{T_1 - T_2} \qquad (8.2)$$

Notice that the COP for an ideal refrigeration cycle is greater than unity. To summarize the foregoing,

1 The COP of a Carnot cycle is a function only of the upper and lower temperatures of the cycle and increases as the difference between the upper and lower temperatures is decreased. These conclusions are independent of the working fluid of the cycle.

2 Equation (8.2) indicates that, for maximum COP, T_2 should be kept to a minimum. In most cases either the atmosphere or some nearby body of water is the practical heat sink.

3 Any deviations of the actual cycle from the ideal processes predicated for the Carnot cycle lead to values of COP less than the ideal.

ILLUSTRATIVE PROBLEM 8.1

A Carnot refrigeration cycle is used to keep a freezer at 32°F. If the room to which the heat is rejected is at 70°F, calculate, for a heat removal of 1000 Btu/min, (a) the COP of the cycle, (b) the work required, and (c) the heat rejected to the room. The data are shown in Fig. 8.5.

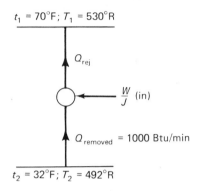

$t_1 = 70°F; T_1 = 530°R$

Q_{rej}

$\dfrac{W}{J}$ (in)

$Q_{removed} = 1000$ Btu/min

$t_2 = 32°F; T_2 = 492°R$

Figure 8.5 Illustrative Problem 8.1

Solution

a. The COP is given by Eq. (8.2) for the reversed Carnot cycle. Thus

$$\text{COP} = \frac{T_2}{T_1 - T_2} = \frac{492}{530 - 492} = 12.95$$

b. Since the COP is defined as the ratio of the refrigeration effect to the work input, the work input is the refrigeration effect divided by the COP. Therefore,

$$\frac{W}{J} = \frac{1000}{12.95} = 77.2 \text{ Btu/min}$$

c. Q_{rej} is the sum of the refrigeration effect plus the work into the cycle. Thus

$$Q_{rej} = 1000 + 77.2 = 1077.2 \text{ Btu/min}$$

8.3 DEFINED RATINGS

It is unfortunate that a certain terminology grows up with every segment of technology. This terminology invariably remains, even though it may be both inconsistent and misleading. For refrigeration, the basic unit is derived from the rate of energy removal from the cold region equivalent to that necessary to fuse (solidify) water at 32°F at the rate of 1 ton every 24 hr. Unfortunately, the rate of energy removal is also commonly used to define a quantity of energy. By arbitrary definition, the standard ton (commercial) of refrigeration is defined by

$$1 \text{ standard commercial ton} = 288{,}000 \text{ Btu/day}$$

or $12{,}000 \text{ Btu/hr}$ or 200 Btu/min

Also,

$$1 \text{ standard ton} = 288{,}000 \text{ Btu}$$

From the definition of COP, it is evident that the product of COP and power input yields the rate at which heat is being removed, or

$$\text{rate of heat removal} = (\text{COP}) \times (\text{power input}) \text{ (hp or kW)}$$
$$(8.3)$$

Equation (8.3) leads to the following ratings:

$$\frac{\text{horsepower}}{\text{ton of refrigeration}} = \frac{200}{42.4 \times \text{COP}} = \frac{4.717}{\text{COP}} \qquad (8.4)$$

$$\frac{\text{kilowatts}}{\text{ton of refrigeration}} = \frac{200}{56.93 \times \text{COP}} = \frac{3.514}{\text{COP}} \qquad (8.5)$$

It is left as an exercise for the student to derive Eqs. (8.4) and (8.5). The following example will serve to illustrate the foregoing concepts.

ILLUSTRATIVE PROBLEM 8.2

A refrigeration cycle operates between 20° and 70°F. (a) Determine the maximum COP for the cycle. (b) It is found that the actual COP is 2. How much more horsepower per ton of refrigeration effect is required by the actual cycle over the minimum possible requirement?

Solution

Refer to Fig. 8.3.

$$\text{COP}_{ideal} = \frac{460 + 20}{(460 + 70) - (460 + 20)} = 9.6$$

The minimum horsepower per ton of refrigeration [Eq. (8.4)] is therefore $4.717/9.6 = 0.49$ hp/ton. The actual COP is stated to be 2; therefore, the actual horsepower per ton of refrigeration is $4.717/2 = 2.36$ hp/ton. The horsepower required by the actual cycle over the minimum is

$$
\begin{array}{r}
2.36 \\
-0.49 \\
\hline
1.87 \text{ hp/ton}
\end{array}
$$

8.4 REFRIGERATION CYCLES

To discuss the various refrigeration cycles that are in common use, we will first look at the "ideal" or prototype of each cycle to understand the basic thermodynamics involved and then consider how the practical realization of these cycles is accomplished.

At present, there are several common refrigeration cycles in use:

1 Vapor-compression cycle

2 Gas cycle refrigeration

3 Absorption refrigeration cycle

4 Vacuum refrigeration cycle

8.4a Vapor Compression Cycle

Just as it was found possible to reverse the Carnot cycle, it is equally possible in principle to reverse the Rankine cycle. An elementary vapor-compression cycle is shown in Fig. 8.6, and a corresponding *Ts* diagram is shown in Fig. 8.7.

The cycle consists of an expansion of the fluid from the saturation point to the wet region (path ① to ②). During this process (throttling), the enthalpy stays essentially constant (see Chapter 2). However, the pressure and temperature of the working fluid decrease, and the fluid becomes a vapor–liquid mixture at state ②. The cooled working fluid (refrigerant) then passes to the evaporator, and there (path ② to ③) heat enters from the region or fluid to be cooled. This part of the process is carried out at constant temperature and constant pressure (ideally), since the working fluid is in the wet region. The next part of the cycle (path ③ to ④) is a compression phase. If the compression proceeds from point ③ to point ④ on Fig. 8.7, the refrigerant will start from the saturated vapor point and then proceed into the superheated vapor range. This path is called *dry compression*. An alternate path (③a to ④a) is shown where the refrigerant is initially "wet" and is just brought to saturation conditions by the compression process. This path has been called *wet*

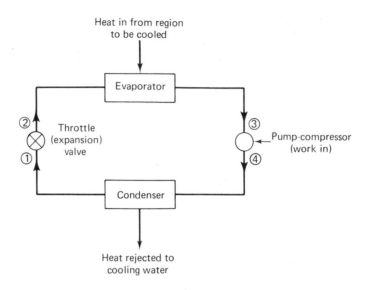

Figure 8.6 Simple vapor compression cycle

compression for obvious reasons. From considerations of the cycle and the Ts diagram (Fig. 8.7), it can be demonstrated that it is more efficient to operate the cycle with wet compression. However, most vapor-compression cycles operate with dry compression, since the loss in efficiency is small, while the practical problems of the compressor design and operation are considerably eased. The last path of the cycle (path ④ to ①) rejects heat at essentially constant pressure until the saturated liquid line is reached. Once again the Ts diagram shows an alternate path (①a to ②a). In practice, it would be difficult to just achieve point ① for all loads on the system, and some further cooling to point ①a would be expected.

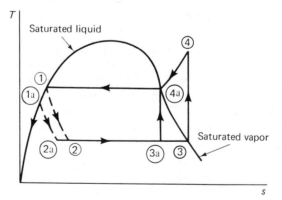

Figure 8.7 Simple vapor compression cycle

Assuming that all processes are carried out without pressure or heat losses (other than specified), and neglecting kinetic energy and potential energy differences, it is possible to analyze the system as follows:

1 Path ① to ②, throttling:

$$h_1 = h_2 \qquad (8.6)$$

2 Path ② to ③, evaporator (cooling effect):

$$q_{in} = h_3 - h_2 = h_3 - h_1 \qquad (8.7)$$

3 Path ③ to ④, compressor:

$$\text{work} = h_4 - h_3 \qquad (8.8)$$

(For the refrigeration cycle, work in to the cycle is taken to be positive.)

4 Path ④ to ①, condenser (heat removal):

$$q_{rej} = h_4 - h_1 \qquad (8.9)$$

From these quantities it will be noted that the energy removed in the condenser must numerically equal the heat gain in the evaporator, plus the work of the compressor. The refrigerating capability, however, is only the evaporator effect.

The weight of refrigerant circulated per ton of refrigeration can readily be found from the definition of the ton and the heat absorbed by the evaporator:

$$\frac{\text{weight of refrigerant}}{\text{minute}} = \frac{200 \times \text{tons}}{h_3 - h_2} = \frac{200 \times \text{tons}}{h_3 - h_1} \qquad (8.10)$$

The definition of the COP (in terms of this cycle) is the ratio of the heat absorbed in the evaporator to the net work into the cycle. In consistent heat units this can be written as

$$\text{COP} = \frac{h_3 - h_1}{h_4 - h_3} \qquad (8.11)$$

For the ideal cycle the work per ton of refrigeration will be given by

$$\text{horsepower/ton} = 4.717 \left(\frac{h_4 - h_3}{h_3 - h_1} \right) \qquad (8.12)$$

Note that this is the definition given in Eq. (8.4).

ILLUSTRATIVE PROBLEM 8.3

An ammonia refrigerator plant is to operate between a saturated liquid at 120 psia at the condenser outlet and a saturated vapor at 15 psia at the evaporator outlet. If a capacity of 30 tons is desired, compute the following on the basis of an ideal cycle only:

1 Coefficient of performance.
2 Work of compression, Btu's per pound.
3 Refrigerating effect, Btu's per pound.
4 Pounds per minute of ammonia required.
5 Ideal horsepower per ton of refrigeration.

Solution

At 120 psia the corresponding saturation temperature is 66°F. Referring to Fig. 8.7, the enthalpies are

$h_1 = 116.0$ Btu/lb   (values from appendix of ammonia properties)
$h_2 = 116.0$ Btu/lb   (throttling gives us $h_1 = h_2$)
$h_3 = 602.4$ Btu/lb

From the consideration that $s_3 = s_4$, h_4 is found: at 15 psia $s_3 = 1.3938$; therefore, by interpolation in the superheat tables at 120 psia, $t_4 = 237.4°F$ and $h_4 = 733.4$ Btu/lb.

1 $\text{COP} = \dfrac{602.4 - 116.0}{733.4 - 602.4} = 3.71$

2 The work of compression is

$$h_4 - h_3 = 733.4 - 602.4 = 131.0 \text{ Btu/lb}$$

3 The refrigerating effect is

$$h_3 - h_1 = 602.4 - 116.0 = 486.4 \text{ Btu/lb}$$

4 The pounds per minute of ammonia required for circulation equals

$$\frac{200 \times 30}{602.4 - 116.0} = 12.33 \text{ lb/min}$$

5 The ideal horsepower per ton of refrigeration equals

$$4.717 \left(\frac{733.4 - 602.4}{602.4 - 116.0} \right) = 1.27 \text{ hp/ton}$$

Before proceeding further with our discussion of refrigeration cycles, let us first look at some of the components used and their arrangement in practice. In a typical home refrigerator the compressor is usually physically in the rear near the bottom of the unit. The motor and compressor are usually located in a single housing with the electrical leads for the motor passing through the housing. While this is done to prevent leakage of refrigerant, it imposes the requirement that the refrigerant should be inert with respect to the insulation. One common refrigerant, Freon, cannot be used with natural rubber since this class of refrigerant acts as a solvent with certain types of insulating materials and varnishes. Also, the electrical resistance of the refrigerant is of the utmost importance in hermetically sealed units such as used in home refrigerators where the motor windings are exposed to the refrigerant. Figure 8.8 shows a diagrammatic layout of a refrigerating system for a domestic-type refrigerator.

The condenser is physically arranged so that room air flows past the condenser by natural convection. The expansion valve is a long capillary tube, and the evaporator is shown around the outside of the freezing compartment inside the refrigerator. The pressures shown in Fig. 8.8 are typical for the use of sulfur dioxide as the refrigerant. Although the compressor shown schematically is a reciprocating unit, small, efficient, and economical rotary units are available for home refrigeration use.

Starting at point 3 of Fig. 8.8, the vaporous refrigerant enters the compressor at low pressure and temperature. An isentropic compression (ideally) raises the pressure and temperature to p_2 and t_2. The saturation temperature corresponding to p_2 must be some value above atmospheric temperature, or above the temperature of the cooling water that may be used in the condenser. Leaving the compressor in condition 4, the vapor enters the condenser where it is condensed to a liquid at some temperature t_3. After the condenser, the liquid enters an expansion valve, which separates the high- and low-pressure regions and passes through the valve in a throttling process with $h_1 = h_2$. The refrigerant then enters the evaporator (or freezing compartment) where it boils because it is receiving heat from the refrigerator and its contents. The vapor from the evaporator enters the compressor and the cycle starts over.

The heart of any refrigeration system is the compressor. While the types of compressors used are similar to those used for air or other gases, the positive-displacement reciprocating compressor is the unit most widely used in industrial vapor compression refrigeration installations. Centrifugal and gear-type positive displacement compressors are also used. The gear-type shows good volumetric efficiencies, but the centrifugal compressors are usually inefficient in smaller sizes, and they are used when the size of a reciprocating unit would be excessively large.

Figure 8.9 shows a typical vertical reciprocating compressor for refrigerant compression. It is a two-cylinder, single-acting type with safety head construction. The safety head construction is used in large compressors where there is danger of operation with wet compression or danger of operation with

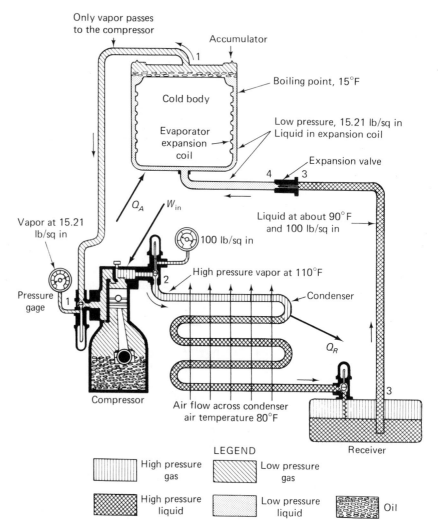

Only vapor passes to the compressor

Accumulator

1

Boiling point, 15°F

Cold body

Evaporator expansion coil

Low pressure, 15.21 lb/sq in
Liquid in expansion coil

Expansion valve

4   3

Q_A W_{in}

Liquid at about 90°F and 100 lb/sq in

Vapor at 15.21 lb/sq in

100 lb/sq in

High pressure vapor at 110°F

2

Condenser

Pressure gage

1

Q_R

Compressor

Air flow across condenser air temperature 80°F

3

Receiver

LEGEND

| | High pressure gas | | Low pressure gas |
| | High pressure liquid | | Low pressure liquid | | Oil |

Figure 8.8 Diagrammatic layout of a refrigerating system (From *Theory and Practice of Heat Engines* by V. M. Faires, Macmillan, Inc., New York, 1948, p. 360, with permission)

foreign material in the cylinder. The safety head is basically a second head placed at the end of the cylinder and held in position by heavy helical springs. If wet refrigerant or foreign material enters the cylinder space, the movement of the safety head relieves any excessive pressure buildup in the cylinder. The vapor from the evaporator is drawn into the crankcase and then passes upward through the suction valves mounted in the piston crown. Compressed vapor is forced past the discharge valves mounted in the safety head assembly. Multiple suction and discharge valves provide larger flow areas than for single valves and are often used to minimize the inevitable drop of pressure occurring at these valves. Reciprocating and rotary positive-displacement compressors in forms other than that shown are used in small domestic refrigerators (capacities in fractions of a ton). Multicylinder reciprocating compressors with V and W cylinder arrangements are commonly used for the range of capacities between 3 and 200 tons.

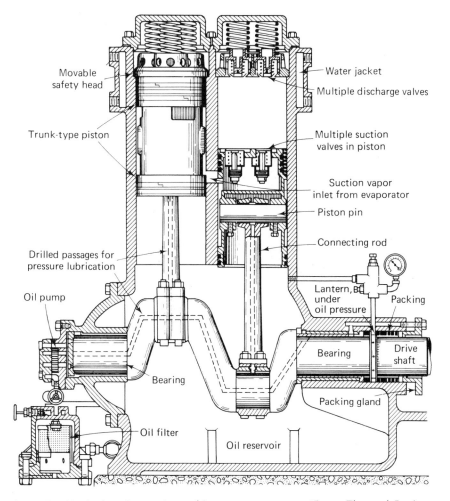

Figure 8.9 Vertical reciprocating refrigerant compressor (From *Thermal Engineering* by C. C. Dillio and E. P. Nye, International Textbook Co., Scranton, Pa., 1959, p. 438, with permission)

Figure 8.10 shows a large two-stage centrifugal compressor. Units of this type are used in large-capacity systems above 75 tons of refrigeration. This unit

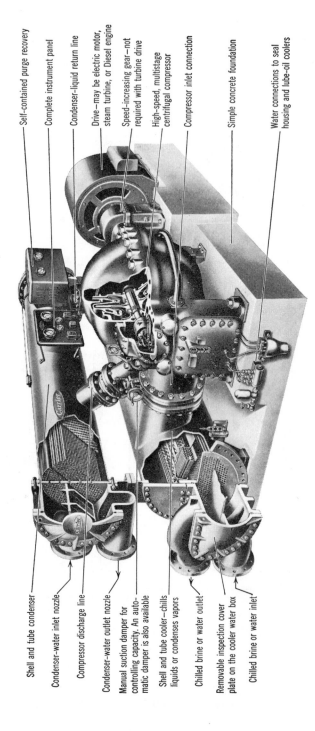

Self-contained purge recovery

Complete instrument panel

Condenser-liquid return line

Drive—may be electric motor, steam turbine, or Diesel engine

Speed-increasing gear—not required with turbine drive

High-speed, multistage centrifugal compressor

Compressor inlet connection

Simple concrete foundation

Water connections to seal housing and lube-oil coolers

Shell and tube condenser

Condenser-water inlet nozzle

Compressor discharge line

Condenser-water outlet nozzle

Manual suction damper for controlling capacity. An automatic damper is also available

Shell and tube cooler—chills liquids or condenses vapors

Chilled brine or water outlet

Removable inspection cover plate on the cooler water box

Chilled brine or water inlet

Figure 8.10 Centrifugal refrigeration machine (From *Fundamentals of Classical Thermodynamics* by G. J. Van Wylen and R. E. Sonntag, John Wiley & Sons, Inc., New York, 1965, p. 10, with permission)

(Fig. 8.10) is used in an air-conditioning system, where brine is cooled and then circulated to provide cooling as needed. The condenser, which is water cooled, is shown in the upper portion of the figure, and the tube-type evaporator used for cooling the brine is shown in the lower left portion of the unit. Single-unit machines of the type shown in Fig. 8.10 have been built in capacities from 75 tons up to 5000 tons.

Figure 8.11 shows two 5000-ton centrifugal chillers recently installed at Houston Natural Gas Company plant servicing the Texas Medical Center in Houston, Texas.

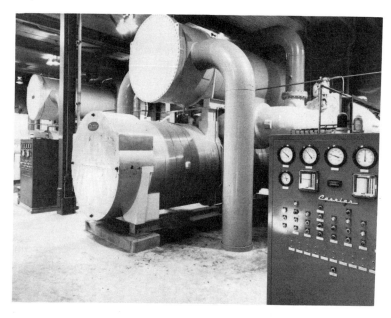

Figure 8.11 Two 5000-ton centrifugal chillers (Courtesy of Carrier Corp.)

The evaporator is another component of the refrigeration system that has to be considered. Many types of evaporators are used, depending upon the specific application. The direct expansion cooling coil shown in Fig. 8.12 is fed just enough refrigerant by the expansion valve so that all the liquid is converted to vapor before the refrigerant reaches the outlet connection of the evaporator. This type of evaporator is widely used for air-conditioning ducts. The plate-type evaporator has continuous loops of steel tubing contained between evacuated plates.

Many considerations enter into the choice of refrigerant for a given application. Some of the refrigerants that are used commercially are ammonia, butane, CO_2, carrene, Freon, methyl chloride, sulfur dioxide, and propane. Based upon the thermodynamics of the vapor-compression cycle that we have studied thus far, the following properties are desirable in a refrigerant.

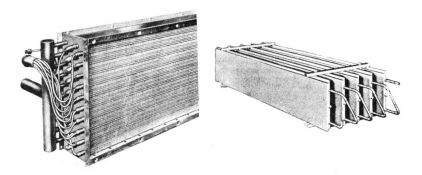

Figure 8.12 Evaporators (Reprinted with permission from *Power, The Engineer's Reference Library*, copyright by McGraw-Hill, Inc., New York)

1 The heat of vaporization of the refrigerant should be high. The higher h_{fg}, the greater the refrigerating effect per pound of fluid circulated.

2 The specific heat of the liquid should be low. The lower the specific heat of the liquid, the less heat it will pick up for a given change in temperature during either throttling or in flow through the piping, and consequently the greater the refrigerating effect per pound of refrigerant.

3 The specific volume of the refrigerant should be low to minimize the work required per pound of refrigerant circulated.

4 The critical temperature of the refrigerant should be higher than the condensing pressure to prevent excessive power consumption.

In addition to the foregoing, it is necessary to consider items of toxicity, corrosiveness, dielectric strength for a hermetically sealed system, viscosity, thermal conductivity, explosiveness, effect on foods, stability, inertness, and cost. No one refrigerant has been found to meet all these requirements. Of the many possible refrigerants, ammonia, Freon, brine, methyl chloride, and sulfur dioxide are the most common. A brief dissertation of each of these refrigerants is given in the following paragraphs.*

Air. Air was one of the earliest refrigerants and was widely used even as late as World War I wherever a completely nontoxic medium was needed. Although air is free of cost and completely safe, its low coefficient of performance makes it unable to compete with the present-day nontoxic refrigerants. Only where

---

*Extracted from *Refrigeration and Air Conditioning*, 2nd Ed., by R. C. Jordan and G. B. Priester, Prentice-Hall, Inc., Englewood Cliffs, N.J., 1956, pp. 81–87, with permission.

operating efficiency is secondary, as in aircraft refrigeration, does air find any modern application as a refrigerant.

Ammonia. Ammonia is one of the oldest and most widely used of all refrigerants. It is highly toxic and flammable. It has a boiling point of $-28.0°F$ and a liquid specific gravity of 0.684 at atmospheric pressure. Its greatest application has been in large industrial and commercial reciprocating compression systems where high toxicity is secondary. For industrial application it has been found valuable because of its low volumetric displacement, low cost, low weight of liquid circulated per ton of refrigeration, and high efficiency. However, in recent years there has been some decrease in the volume of new installations using ammonia. It is also widely used as the refrigerant in absorption systems.

Carbon Dioxide. Carbon dioxide, a colorless and odorless gas, is heavier than air. It has a boiling point of $-109.3°F$ and a liquid specific gravity of 1.56 at atmospheric pressure. It is nontoxic and nonflammable but has extremely high operating pressures. Because of the high horsepower requirements per ton of refrigeration and the high operating pressures, it has received only limited usage. In former years it was selected for marine refrigeration, for theater air-conditioning systems, and for hotel and institutional refrigeration instead of ammonia because it is nontoxic. The Freon group has largely supplanted it for these applications. At the present time its use is limited primarily to the manufacture of dry ice (solid carbon dioxide). The cycle efficiency can be improved by the use of two-stage compression, and when applied in this manner carbonic refrigeration has received some usage. It has also been used for very low temperature work by adapting it to a binary or cascade cycle, in which the efficiency is improved by using carbon dioxide in the low-temperature stage and ammonia or some other refrigerant in the high-temperature stage.

Freon and Genetron Refrigerants. In 1928, Charles Kettering and Thomas Migley, Jr., instigated research to find a nontoxic, nonflammable refrigerant. These efforts culminated in the development of a series of fluorinated hydrocarbons, commonly known by the trade names Freon and Genetron. They are probably the most important group of refrigerants in use today. The commonest of these are trichloromonofluoromethane (Freon-11, Genetron-11), CCl_3F; dichlorodifluoromethane (Freon-12, Genetron-12), CCl_2F_2; monochlorotrifluoromethane (Freon 13), $CClF_3$; tetrafluoromethane (Freon-14), CF_4; $CHCl_2F$; monochlorodifluoromethane (Freon-22, Genetron-141), $CHClF_2$; trichlorotrifluoroethane (Freon-113), $CCl_2F—CClF_2$; and dichlorotetrafluoroethane (Freon-114), $C_2Cl_2F_4$. They are almost universally referred to by their trade names. Freon-11 or Genetron-11 has a boiling point of $74.7°F$;

Freon-12 or Genetron-12, $-21.6°F$; Freon-13, $-114.5°F$; Freon-14, $-198.2°F$; Freon-22 or Genetron-141, $-41.4°F$; Freon-113, $117.6°F$; and Freon-114, $38.4°F$. The entire group is clear and water-white in color and has a somewhat ethereal odor similar to that of carbon tetrachloride. They are all nonflammable and for all practical purposes nontoxic. Freon-11, or Genetron-11, is widely used for centrifugal refrigeration. In this field it has almost completely supplanted dichloroethylene and methylene chloride. Freon-12, or Genetron-12, the most widely used of the group, is generally applied to reciprocating compressors. It has received its widest use in air-conditioning applications where nontoxic, nonflammable refrigerants are required. Freon-114 has been applied by several manufacturers to rotary compressors in domestic refrigerators and has also been used experimentally for absorption refrigeration. Freon-22, or Genetron-141, has been developed for reciprocating compressor applications below $-20°F$, and Freon-13 and Freon-14 are intended for extremely low temperature range. Freon-22, however, may receive wide application in higher-temperature installations in the future if increased volume of production will permit a lowering of cost. Its favorable characteristics may allow it to compete successfully with ammonia and possibly with Freon-12 for general refrigeration purposes.

Methyl Chloride. Methyl chloride, CH_3Cl, is a colorless liquid with a faint, sweet, nonirritating odor. Methyl chloride was introduced about 1920 in the United States for refrigeration purposes and is now widely used. It replaced ammonia and carbon dioxide for many new installations in the 1920s and early 1930s and was widely used during World War II as a substitute for Freon, then unavailable. Its use, however, appears to be definitely on the decline. It has a boiling point of $-10.6°F$ and a liquid specific gravity of 1.002 at atmospheric pressure. It is to a certain degree both flammable and toxic. Methyl chloride has been used in domestic units with both reciprocating and rotary compressors and in commercial units with reciprocating compressors up to approximately 10-ton capacity.

Sulfur Dioxide. Sulfur dioxide, SO_2, a colorless gas or liquid, is extremely toxic and has a pungent irritating odor. It is nonexplosive and nonflammable, and has a boiling point of $13.8°F$ and a liquid specific gravity of 1.36. It is at present one of the most prevalent of all refrigerants in domestic systems, primarily because of the large number of sulfur dioxide domestic units built since the 1930s. It has been applied to both reciprocating and rotary compressors. With such applications the volume of refrigerant charge is small, and there is little danger of fatal concentrations resulting through refrigerant leakage. Sulfur dioxide has also been used to a considerable extent in small-tonnage commercial machines. However, the volume of new units using sulfur dioxide as a refrigerant is small.

Water Vapor. Water vapor, H_2O, is the cheapest and probably the safest of all refrigerants. However, because of its high freezing temperature of 32°F, it is limited in application to high-temperature refrigeration. Its application has been to steam-jet refrigeration and to centrifugal compression refrigeration. It is, of course, nontoxic, nonflammable, and nonexplosive. Because of its high-temperature limitations and its complete safety, it has been used principally for comfortable air-conditioning applications and to some extent for water cooling.

Hydrocarbon Refrigerants. Many of the hydrocarbons are used as refrigerants in industrial installations, where they are frequently available at low cost. These include butane (C_4H_{10}), isobutane (C_4H_{10}), propane (C_3H_8), propylene (C_3H_6), ethane (C_2H_6), and ethylene (C_2H_4). However, they are all highly flammable and explosive, and therefore their use has been limited principally to the chemical and refining industries, where similar hazards already exist. They all possess satisfactory thermodynamic properties.

Several of the hydrocarbons, including propane, ethane, and ethylene, exhibit promise for use as refrigerants at −100°F or lower. Ethylene has a saturation temperature of −176.8°F at a pressure of 6.75 psia and makes an excellent refrigerant when used in a cascade system with an auxiliary cycle.

Isobutane was used by one manufacturer of domestic refrigeration in a rotary compressor until 1933, but it has no such application at the present time. Propane has received limited use as both the motive fuel and the refrigerant in a refrigerated truck unit. Such a cycle is termed transitory, the propane first passing through the evaporator and then to the engine.

Halogenated Hydrocarbons and Other Refrigerants. Chemical compounds formed from methane (CH_4) and ethane (C_2H_6) by the substitution of chlorine, fluorine, or bromine for part of their hydrogen content are termed halogenated hydrocarbons. Many refrigerants, including methyl chloride and the Freon and Genetron groups, are included in this class. Some of the others are described below.

Dichlorethylene (Dielene). $C_2H_2Cl_2$ is a colorless liquid with a boiling point of 118.0°F and a liquid specific gravity of 1.27. It has a strong, nonirritating odor similar to that of chloroform and is to a limited extent both toxic and explosive. Its principal application has been in centrifugal compression systems, in which it received limited usage.

Ethyl chloride. C_2H_5Cl is a colorless liquid with a boiling point of 54.5°F. It is to a certain degree both toxic and flammable, and is similar in many respects to methyl chloride but with lower operating pressures. It is not used in refrigerating equipment at the present time, but has in the past been selected for both rotary and reciprocating compressors.

TABLE 8.1

PHYSICAL AND THERMAL PROPERTIES OF
COMMON REFRIGERANTS

REFRIGERANT	Chemical Formula	Boiling Point, °F	Freezing Point, °F	CRITICAL POINT Temperature, °F	Pressure, lb per sq in. abs.	Specific Gravity of Liquid at Atmos. Press.	Specific Heat of Liquid Ave. 5°F to 86°F
Ammonia	NH_3	−28.0	−107.9	271.4	1657.0	0.684	1.12
Azeotropic mixture Freon-12 and unsymmetrical difluoroethane (Carrene-7)	78.3% F-12 26.2% G-100	−28.0	−254.0	221.1	631.0	—	—
Bromotrifluoromethane (Kulene-131)	CF_3Br	−73.6	−226.0	153.5	587.0	—	0.19
Carbon dioxide	CO_2	−109.3	−69.0	87.8	1069.9	1.560	0.77
Dichlorodifluoromethane (Freon-12, Genetron-12)	CCl_2F_2	−21.6	−252.0	233.6	596.9	1.480	0.23
Ethylene	C_2H_4	−155.0	−272.0	48.8	731.8	—	—
Isobutane	C_4H_{10}	−10.3	−229.0	272.7	537.0	0.549	0.62
Methyl chloride	CH_2Cl	−10.8	−144.0	289.4	968.7	1.002	0.38
Methylene chloride (Carrene-1)	CH_2Cl_2	105.2	−142.0	480.0	670.0	1.291	0.33
Monochlorodifluoromethane (Freon-22, Genetron-141)	$CHClF_2$	−41.4	−256.0	204.8	716.0	1.411	0.30
Sulfur dioxide	SO_2	14.0	−103.9	314.8	1141.5	1.357	0.34
Trichloromonofluoromethane (Freon-11, Genetron-11)	CCl_3F	74.7	−168.0	388.4	635.0	1.468	0.21
Trichlorotrifluoroethane (Freon-113)	$CCl_2F\text{-}CClF_2$	117.6	−31.0	417.4	495.0	1.559	0.21
Water	H_2O	212.0	32.0	706.1	3226.0	1.000	1.00

Methylene chloride. CH_2Cl_2 is a clear, water-white liquid with a sweet, nonirritating odor similar to that of chloroform. It has a boiling point of 103.6°F and a liquid specific gravity of 1.291. It is nonflammable and nonexplosive and is toxic only at comparatively high concentrations.

Methylene chloride is used by several manufacturers in domestic rotary compressors and has found some use commercially for absorption refrigeration because of its low toxicity and absence of fire hazard. It has been used successfully in centrifugal compressors but has been supplanted in recent years by Freon-11 (Genetron-11).

Bromotrifluoromethane. (Kulene-131). CF_3Br is a nontoxic, nonflammable, noncorrosive, halogenated hydrocarbon particularly suitable for low-temperature refrigeration. It is nicely adapted to use in a two-stage cascade system in the lower stage with an evaporator temperature of about $-75°F$. Under such conditions the evaporator pressure is approximately atmospheric and the compressor displacement desirably low.

Table 8.1 summarizes the physical and the thermal properties of the refrigerants discussed in the previous paragraphs of this chapter.

In the actual cycle there are deviations from the ideal cycle due to compression inefficiencies, pressure drops in piping, temperature differences between the elements interchanging heat, and so on. Since heat is transferred in both the condenser and evaporator of the vapor compression system, temperature differences exist between these units and the medium they are transferring heat to. In the case of the evaporator, the coils must be at a lower temperature than the region being cooled. The temperature difference for the evaporator usually is of the order of 5°F, while in the condenser the refrigeration fluid is of the order of 10°F higher than the coolant fluid. However, among these effects, those usually considered are the inefficiency in the compression part of the cycle and pressure differences in long piping systems. The other effects are usually considered to be either too difficult to analyze generally or small enough that they can be safely ignored. The following example will serve to illustrate some of these considerations.

ILLUSTRATIVE PROBLEM 8.4

A Freon-12 vapor-compression refrigeration system has a compressor of 80 percent adiabatic efficiency. At inlet to the compressor, the refrigerant has a pressure of 5.3 psia and 40°F superheat; at discharge from the compressor the pressure is 100 psia.

Saturated liquid Freon at 100 psia leaves the condenser and passes through an expansion valve into the evaporator coils. The condenser is supplied with cooling water, which enters at 60° and leaves at 70°F. For a plant capacity of 5 tons, find the following:

1 The horsepower required to drive the compressor if it has a mechanical efficiency of 100 percent.

2 The required capacity in gallons per minute of the cooling water to the pump.

Solution

A *Ts* diagram for this problem is shown in Fig. 8.13. This problem will require both the tables and *ph* chart for Freon 12 given in Appendix 3.

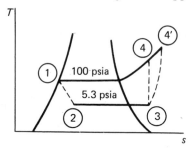

Figure 8.13 Illustrative Problem 8.4

1 By definition, the efficiency of the compressor is the ratio of the ideal compression work to actual compression work. Based on the points on Fig. 8.13,

$$\eta = \frac{h_4 - h_3}{h'_4 - h_3}$$

There is close correspondence between 5.3 psia and $-60°F$ for saturated conditions. Therefore, state ③ is a superheated vapor at 5.3 psia and approximately $-20°F$, since the problem states that state ③ has a 40° superheat. Interpolation in the Freon tables in Appendix III yields

$$T = -20°F$$

p	h	s
7.5	75.719	0.18371
5.3	75.886	0.18985
5.0	75.990	0.19069

$h_3 = 75.886 \text{ Btu/lb}$

At 100 psia and $s = 0.18985$

t	s	h
170°F	0.18996	100.571
169.6°F	0.18985	100.5
160°F	0.18726	98.884

$h_4 = 100.5$ Btu/lb

The weight of refrigerant is given by

$$\frac{200(\text{tons})}{h_3 - h_1} = \frac{200 \times 5}{75.886 - h_1}$$

In the saturated tables, h_1 is

p	h
101.86	26.832
100 psia	26.542
98.87	26.365

$$\frac{\text{weight flow}}{\text{min}} = \frac{200(5)}{75.886 - h_1} = \frac{200(5)}{75.886 - 26.542} = 20.3 \text{ lb/min}$$

$$\text{work of compression} = 20.3(h_4' - h_3)$$

where

$$h_4' - h_3 = \frac{h_4 - h_3}{\eta} = \frac{100.5 - 75.886}{0.8} = 30.7 \text{ Btu/lb}$$

Therefore,

$$\text{work} = \frac{20.3 \times 30.7 \times 778}{33,000} = 14.7 \text{ hp}$$

2 Assuming a specific heat of the water as unity,

$$\dot{m} = \frac{20.3(h_4' - h_1)}{(70 - 60)}$$

From part 1,

$$h_4' - h_3 = 30.7$$

$$h_4' = 30.7 + 75.886$$

$$= 106.59 \text{ Btu/lb}$$

Therefore,

$$\dot{m} = \frac{20.3 \times 106.59}{70 - 60}$$

$$= 216 \text{ lb/min of cooling water}$$

$$= 25.9 \text{ gal/min}$$

The student will note the effort involved in obtaining this answer when working directly from tables. Just as the Mollier chart simplifies calculations of power cycles, problems in refrigeration are simplified considerably by use of a modified Mollier chart. Such a chart uses pressure–enthalpy coordinates and usually has other curves of entropy and temperature on it. Figure 8.14 shows a skeleton chart using *ph* coordinates of a refrigerant. The ordinate, pressure, is usually plotted on a logarithmic scale for convenience. In the superheat region, lines of constant volume, constant entropy, and constant temperature are displayed. Shown by dashed lines is an ideal simple vapor-compression cycle with end states corresponding to the events shown on the simplified schematic diagram of Fig. 8.6. The following problem will serve to illustrate the use of the *ph* diagram, as well as the savings obtainable in both time and effort by using this modified Mollier chart.

ILLUSTRATIVE PROBLEM 8.5

Solve Illustrative Problem 8.4 using the *ph* chart for Freon-12 in Appendix III.

Solution

1 From the Appendix, reading the *ph* diagram directly,

$$h_3 = 76.2 \text{ Btu/lb}$$

$$h_4 = 100.5 \text{ Btu/lb}$$

$$\text{work of compression} = \frac{100.5 - 76.2}{0.8} = 30.4 \text{ Btu/lb}$$

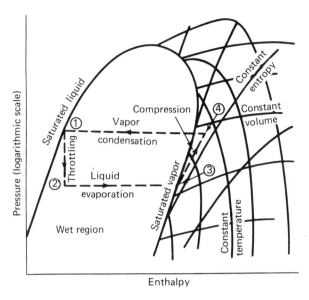

Figure 8.14 Pressure–enthalpy diagram

The enthalpy of saturated liquid at 100 psia is given as 26.1 Btu/lb. Proceeding as before

$$\frac{\text{weight flow}}{\text{min}} = \frac{200(5)}{76.2-26.1} = 20 \text{ lb/min}$$

$$\text{total ideal work of compression} = \frac{20 \times 30.4 \times 778}{33,000} = 14.3 \text{ hp}$$

2

$$h'_4 = 76.2 + 30.4 = 106.8 \text{ Btu/lb}$$

$$\dot{m} = \frac{20 \times 106.8}{70-60} = 214 \text{ lb/min} \quad \text{or} \quad 25.6 \text{ gal/min}$$

The accuracy afforded by the diagram is sufficient for engineering applications.

8.4b Gas Cycle Refrigeration

Just as it was possible to reverse the Carnot and Rankine cycles to obtain a refrigerating effect, it should be possible to reverse any cycle to obtain a similar effect. Among the many gas cycles that have been proposed as prototypes for practical engines, the reversed Brayton cycle has been used to produce refrigeration. The earliest mechanical refrigeration system used air as the refrigerant due to its availability and safety. However, due to its high operating costs and low coefficient of performance, it has largely become obsolete. However, with the introduction of high-speed aircraft and missiles, lightweight high-refrigeration-capacity systems are required to cause a minimum reduction in payload. For example, a jet fighter traveling at 600 mph requires a refrigeration system having a capacity of 10 to 20 tons. In passenger aircraft, solar radiation, the occupants, electrical and mechanical equipment all cause the heating of cabin air. In addition, the adiabatic stagnation of the air relative to the moving airplane (see Chapter 5) can cause temperature increases of the air of approximately 65°F at a relative air speed of 600 mph. Also, all modern aircraft operate with pressurized cabins, which requires compression of outside air to nearly atmospheric pressure, and in the process the temperature of the compressed air increases. The gas cycle refrigeration system using air as the refrigerant has become generally used for this application due to the small size and weight of the components, which is of prime importance. The power to operate the system is of secondary importance in this application. In addition, the power source used for the air cycle aircraft refrigeration system is the same as is used for pressurization of the cabin. Since pressurization is not needed at sea level but refrigeration is, and at high altitudes pressurization is required but less refrigeration is needed, it is found that the power requirement for the combined pressurization and cooling is approximately constant.

Figure 8.15 shows an aircraft refrigeration unit, and Fig. 8.16 shows the schematic diagram for this unit. In this unit, high pressure bleed air, previously compressed by the jet engine compressor, passes into a surface-type heat exchanger. Using relatively cool air from outside of the airplane as the coolant, the compressor bleed air temperature is lowered, in this case from 415° to 172°F. The cooled bleed air enters the turbine where it expands while producing shaft work to drive the centrifugal fan. The cooled, expanded air now at 25°F is mixed with compressor bleed air automatically (using a temperature control valve), and the tempered air is ducted to the cabin.

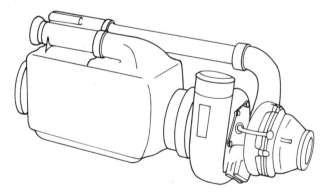

Figure 8.15 Aircraft refrigeration unit (From *Thermal Engineering* by C. C. Dillio and E. P. Nye, International Textbook Co., Scranton, Pa., 1959, pp. 428, 429, with permission)

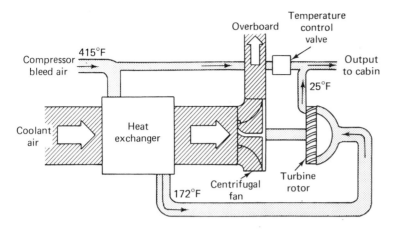

Figure 8.16 Schematic of an aircraft refrigeration unit (From *Thermal Engineering* by C. C. Dillio and E. P. Nye, International Textbook Co., Scranton, Pa., 1959, pp. 428, 429, with permission)

Let us now consider the reversed Brayton cycle shown schematically in Fig. 8.17. This cycle is a closed cycle in that the working fluid (air) is continuously recycled. As shown in Fig. 8.17, the cycle consists of an expander (turbine), a compressor (centrifugal fan), and two heat exchangers. Figure 8.18 shows the *pv* and *Ts* diagram for the cycle shown in Fig. 8.17 with corresponding points (①, ②, ③, and ④) noted on each of these figures. As noted in Chapter 7, the Brayton cycle consists of two isentropic and two constant pressure (isopiestic or isobaric) portions.

Consider that a single charge of working fluid is in the device and that the cycle starts from the condition denoted as ① in Figs. 8.17 and 8.18. At this

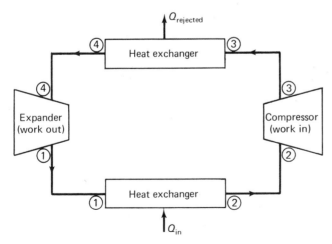

Figure 8.17 Schematic of simple closed cycle Brayton cycle.

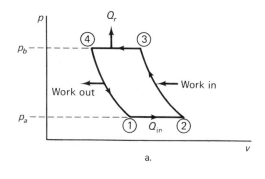

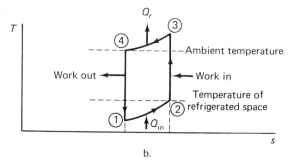

Figure 8.18 *Ts* and *pv* diagram for reversed Brayton cycle

point the gas must be colder than the room (or second fluid) that is to be cooled. It flows at constant pressure through the required piping and absorbs heat from the area to be cooled. During this part of the cycle the temperature of the cooled area will be greater than T_2. After being heated, the gas is compressed isentropically along path ② to ③. In general, T_3 will be greater than room temperature (or local cooling water temperature), and the gas is therefore capable of being cooled in the next part of the path. This is accomplished at constant pressure (③ to ④), in which T_4 is always greater than the temperature of available coolant. Finally, the gas is cooled to state ① by an isentropic expansion during which work is removed from the system. There is one basic point, however, that causes this cycle to deviate from the previously considered vapor cycle. The vapor cycle employs a throttling process to reduce the temperature of the working fluid. The same effect could be achieved by expanding the liquid in an engine, but this engine is not practical and would be prohibitively expensive. It will be recalled that a throttling process is carried out at constant enthalpy. For an ideal gas a throttling process is carried out at constant temperature and is therefore incapable of lowering the temperature for the required refrigerating effect. Even in real gases the throttling process does not provide much of a refrigerating effect. To obtain this effect when gas is used as the refrigerant, it is necessary to create the required low temperature level by letting the refrigerant do work by expanding in some form of engine.

Each of the nonflow processes constituting this gas cycle can be evaluated from the considerations given in Chapter 5. Thus, from the definition of COP and assuming an ideal gas with constant specific heat,

$$\text{COP}_{\text{Brayton}} = \frac{\text{heat removed}}{\text{net work required}} = \frac{c_p(T_2 - T_1)}{{}_2W_3 - {}_4W_1} \quad (8.13)$$

The denominator of Eq. (8.13) represents the net area behind the ③ to ② and ④ to ① curves. Since all elements of the cycle are reversible, it follows that the net work of the cycle must equal the difference of the heat rejected by the cycle to the heat into the cycle. Therefore,

$$\text{COP}_{\text{Brayton}} = \frac{c_p(T_2 - T_1)}{c_p(T_3 - T_4) - c_p(T_2 - T_1)} = \frac{1}{\dfrac{T_3 - T_4}{T_2 - T_1} - 1}$$

$$(8.14a)$$

In terms of pressure,

$$\text{COP}_{\text{Brayton}} = \frac{1}{\left[(p_b/p_a)^{(k-1)/k} - 1\right]} \quad (8.14b)$$

Also

$$\text{COP}_{\text{Brayton}} = \frac{T_1}{T_4 - T_1} = \frac{T_2}{T_3 - T_2} \quad (8.14c)$$

By comparing the foregoing relations with a reversed Carnot cycle operating between the same limits, it will be noted that the index of performance (COP) of the reversed Brayton cycle is less than that of the Carnot cycle. The fundamental difference between the Brayton and Carnot cycles is that the Brayton does not operate at constant heat rejection and constant heat absorption temperatures, whereas the Carnot does.

Since it may be of interest to know the work of the compressor and the turbine, it is necessary only to note that each of these processes represents a steady-flow isentropic process; thus

$$\text{work of compressor per pound} = c_p(T_3 - T_2) \quad (8.15a)$$

$$\text{work of expander per pound} = c_p(T_4 - T_1) \quad (8.15b)$$

By proper substitution of the path equation, pv^k, these equations can be put into terms of pressures.

ILLUSTRATIVE PROBLEM 8.6

An ideal gas refrigeration cycle is operated so that the upper temperature of the cycle is 150°F, the lowest temperature of the cycle is −100°F, and the COP is 2.5. Determine the work of the expander, the work of the compressor, and the net work of the cycle per pound of air. Also determine the air flow required per ton of refrigeration. Take $c_p = 0.24$ Btu/lb°F.

Solution

From Eq. (8.14),

$$2.5 = \frac{T_1}{T_4 - T_1}, \qquad 2.5(T_4 - T_1) = T_1, \qquad T_1 = 360°R$$

Therefore,

$$T_4 = \frac{3.5}{2.5}(T_1) = \frac{3.5}{2.5}(360) = 504°R \quad (44°F)$$

Also

$$2.5 = \frac{T_2}{T_3 - T_2}, \qquad 2.5(150 + 460 - T_2) = T_2$$

$$T_2 = 436°R \, (-24°F)$$

The work of the expander is

$$c_p(T_4 - T_1) = 0.24(504 - 360) = 34.6 \text{ Btu/lb of air}$$

The work of the compressor is

$$c_p(T_3 - T_2) = 0.24(610 - 436) = 41.8 \text{ Btu/lb of air}$$

The net work required by the cycle is

$$41.8 - 34.6 = 7.2 \text{ Btu/lb} \quad \text{(work in)}$$

Per ton of refrigeration, the required air flow is

$$\frac{200}{c_p(T_2 - T_1)} = \frac{200}{0.24(436 - 360)} = 10.96 \text{ lb/min per ton}$$

In an actual cycle the $COP_{Brayton}$ would be much lower because of the irreversible effects in each part of the cycle.

The air cycle described earlier for aircraft use is an example of an open cycle in which the working fluid is not caused to continually recycle; instead it is continuously discharged, and a fresh air charge is continuously introduced into the cycle at the entering conditions of the cycle. Figure 8.19 shows a simple open air cycle used for refrigeration. The student should compare this cycle to the aircraft refrigeration cycle described earlier.

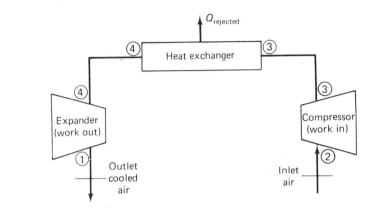

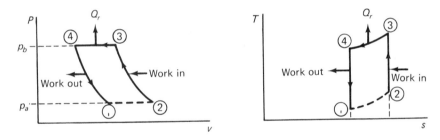

Figure 8.19 Open Brayton refrigeration cycle

In addition to the simple Brayton refrigeration cycle, two other versions of this cycle are also used. The first of these is known as the bootstrap system. In this system, as shown in Fig. 8.20, there are two heat exchangers with cooling air provided by the ram pressure of the aircraft forcing outside air through the exchangers. Air bled from the gas turbine engine compressor is first cooled in the initial heat exchanger, further compressed by the secondary compressor, then cooled further in the secondary heat exchanger, and finally expanded in the cooling turbine and delivered to the cabin of the airplane. The work delivered by the cooling turbine is used to drive the secondary compressor. The bootstrap system has the disadvantage that the airplane must be in flight to obtain the required ram air. To overcome this, a fan is provided to pull air over the secondary heat exchanger, giving a system having the features of both the simple and bootstrap system.

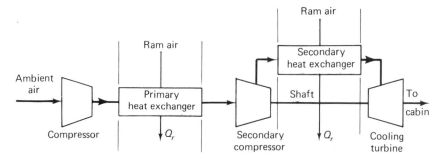

Figure 8.20 Bootstrap system

The second version of the reversed Brayton cycle that is used is the regenerative system. This system is used when the discharge temperature of the simple cycle is too high, as may be the case for very high speed aircraft. In this cycle, as shown in Fig. 8.21, some of the turbine discharge air is diverted back to cool the air entering the turbine. This serves to cool the air entering the turbine to a temperature lower than that which would be obtained by using only ambient air.

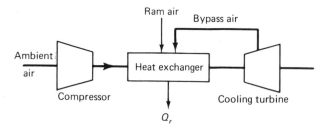

Figure 8.21 Regenerative system

8.4c Absorption Refrigeration Cycle

One of the fundamental concepts of thermodynamics is the equivalence of various forms of energy. A good portion of this study has been devoted to the concept that heat and work are forms of energy in transition. The absorption refrigeration cycle takes advantage of this concept by essentially replacing the vapor-compression pump compressor of the simple vapor compression cycle with an "equivalent" heat source. In practice, this cycle leads to certain complications in "plumbing", and it is usual to find that the vapor compression system has a higher index of performance (COP) than the absorption system.

Figure 8.22 shows a simple absorption system in which the pump compressor of the vapor-compression system (shown dashed for reference on Fig. 8.22) has been replaced by an absorber, a pump, and a vapor generator, while the rest of the cycle is the same as the simple vapor compression cycle.

The most common absorption refrigeration cycle is one using ammonia as the refrigerant. In terms of the cycle shown in Fig. 8.22, the ammonia solution

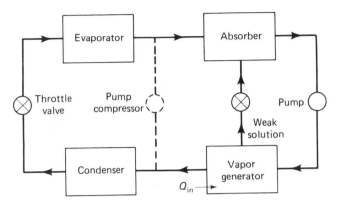

Figure 8.22 Simple absorption refrigeration cycle

in the vapor generator is heated to create ammonia vapor. The ammonia vapor liberated in the vapor generator proceeds along the indicated path to the condenser and then goes through the conventional part of the cycle. After leaving the evaporator, the ammonia enters the absorber. The weak solution in the vapor generator is mixed with the ammonia in the absorber, where the weak solution absorbs the ammonia and the resulting strong solution is pumped to the generator. In this cycle the work of the circulating pump is very small for a given refrigerating effect, since the pump is pumping a liquid that has a small specific volume. To reduce the steam and cooling water requirements of the simple absorption system, a regenerative heat exchanger is placed between the absorber and generator as shown in Fig. 8.23. The purpose of this heat exchanger is to transfer heat from the hot, weak solution to the cool, strong solution. A typical commercial absorption system is shown in Fig. 8.24.

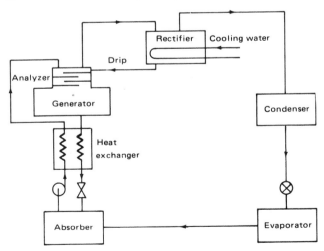

Figure 8.23 Simple regenerative absorption refrigeration cycle (From *Refrigeration and Air Conditioning* by W. F. Stoecker, McGraw-Hill Book Co., Inc., New York, 1958, with permission)

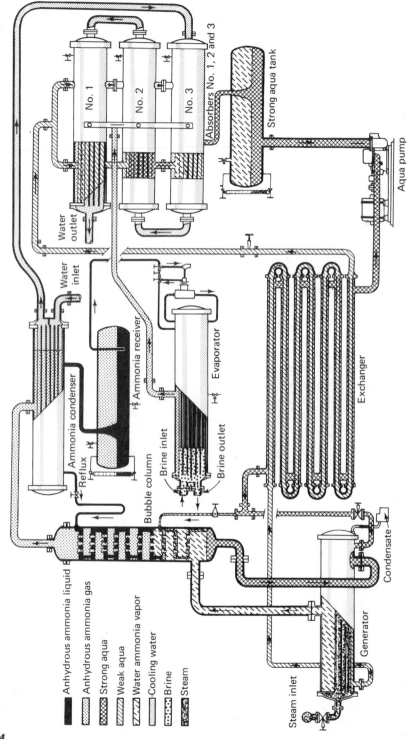

Figure 8.24 Typical commercial absorption flow diagram (From *Refrigeration and Air Conditioning*, 2nd Ed., by R. C. Jordan and G. B. Priester, Prentice-Hall, Inc. Englewood Cliffs, N.J., 1956, p. 372, with permission)

Absorbers No. 1, 2 and 3

No. 1

No. 2

No. 3

Strong aqua tank

Aqua pump

Water outlet

Water inlet

Ammonia condenser

Reflux

Bubble column

Ammonia receiver

Evaporator

Brine inlet

Brine outlet

Exchanger

Generator

Steam inlet

Condensate

Anhydrous ammonia liquid
Anhydrous ammonia gas
Strong aqua
Weak aqua
Water ammonia vapor
Cooling water
Brine
Steam

A domestic absorption-type refrigerator is shown (simplified) in Fig. 8.25. Three fluids are used in this unit: ammonia as the refrigerant, water as the absorber, and hydrogen to maintain the total system pressure. In the generator, heat from a gas flame drives off the ammonia vapor, and the vapor carrying entrained liquid droplets flows to the separator. The separator serves to separate the liquid and vapor, with the vapor going to the condenser while the liquid drains into the absorber. The vapor is condensed in the condenser, and the condensate flows to the evaporator where it receives heat and vaporizes.

In the absorber, the weak solution from the evaporator absorbs water vapor from the evaporator, and the mixture returns by gravity to the generator where the cycle recommences. Circulation within the system takes place due to the vapor-lift pump in which the density of the ammonia–ammonia vapor mixture is less than the density of the liquid in the absorber–generator lines. In the evaporator and absorber, hydrogen maintains the total pressure equal to the pressure of the ammonia and water in the condenser and generator. In the evaporator the ammonia is evaporated at a low temperature due to its low

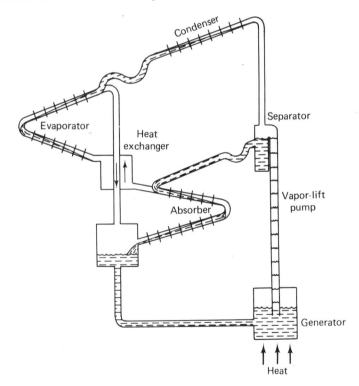

Figure 8.25 Simple Electrolux absorption system (From *Refrigeration and Air Conditioning* by W. F. Stoecker, McGraw-Hill Book Co., Inc., New York, 1958, p. 178, with permission)

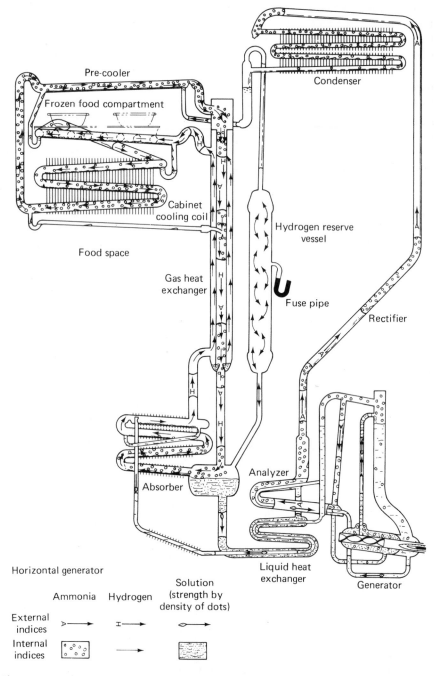

Pre-cooler

Frozen food compartment

Condenser

Cabinet cooling coil

Hydrogen reserve vessel

Food space

Gas heat exchanger

Fuse pipe

Rectifier

Analyzer

Absorber

Liquid heat exchanger

Generator

Horizontal generator

	Ammonia	Hydrogen	Solution (strength by density of dots)
External indices			
Internal indices			

Figure 8.26 Absorption refrigerator cycle (From *Refrigeration and Air Conditioning*, 2nd Ed., by R. C. Jordan and G. B. Priester, Prentice-Hall, Inc., Englewood Cliffs, N.J., 1956, p. 379, with permission)

vapor pressure, while in the condenser, where there is no hydrogen, condensation occurs at a temperature high enough to reject heat to the atmosphere. U bend traps after the separator and condenser are used to maintain the seals which prevent hydrogen escape from the low side of the system.

Figure 8.26 shows an actual cycle in which several refinements have been made to the simple cycle of Fig. 8.25. A liquid heat exchanger is used for the weak solution going to the absorber and the strong solution going to the generator. The analyzer and rectifier are added to remove the water vapor that may have formed in the generator. Thus only ammonia vapor goes to the condenser. The condenser and evaporator each consist of two sections, thus permitting the condenser to extend below the top of the evaporator to segregate the freezing portion of the evaporator and to also provide additional surface. A reserve hydrogen vessel has been added to give constant efficiency under variable room temperatures.

A recent development uses lithium bromide salt and water, with the water acting as the refrigerant. The boiling point of the salt, a solid at ordinary temperatures, is so high it behaves like a nonvolatile substance. Thus there is no vaporization of the absorbent in the generator and no carryover of the absorbent vapor to the condenser. The characteristics of the absorption cycle limit its usefulness to places where sources of heat and cooling water are plentiful and cheap.

Figure 8.27 shows an absorption refrigeration machine that uses steam or hot liquid with lithium bromide absorbent. This unit is typical of modern design, which has eliminated the earlier collection of tanks, pipes, and coils. Its

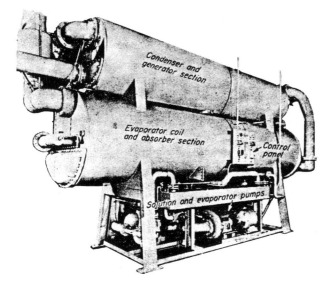

Figure 8.27 Absorption refrigeration unit (Reprinted with permission from *Power, The Engineer's Reference Library,* copyright by McGraw-Hill, Inc., New York)

condenser and generator are in a single vessel, and the evaporator and absorber are in the other vessel. Both are supported by the same set of legs with solution and evaporator pumps underneath them.

8.4d Vacuum Refrigeration Cycle

To understand the physical processes involved in this refrigeration cycle, let us start with a simple experiment. Take a flask half filled with water, say at 70°F, and place it under a bell jar which can be evacuated. The partial pressure of the water vapor in the air in the flask will correspond to its initial temperature. As the pressure in the bell jar is lowered, no change can be seen in the flask. For all practical purposes, only the air is evacuated and the water stays essentially isothermal. As the bell jar pressure reaches the saturation pressure (approximately 19 mm Hg abs), the water will appear to "boil" violently. Actually, the violent agitation of the water is due to the air that was absorbed in the water *outgassing*. Once this violent motion has subsided, the continued pumping will lower the pressure below the initial saturation value. As this occurs, water vapor will be drawn off the surface of the liquid, and the temperature of the remaining fluid will be lowered until it corresponds to the pressure existing in the bell jar. The lowering of the temperature is caused by the decrease in internal energy of the remaining liquid necessitated by the energy required to vaporize some of the liquid at the lower pressure. During the period from the time the outgassing ceases until approximately 4.5 mm Hg abs is reached, the water will be still and no visual change will be observed. At approximately 4.5 mm Hg abs the surface of the water will quite suddenly become coated with a layer of ice. Thus by lowering the pressure it has been possible to lower the temperature of the liquid below its surroundings. In this case a change of phase from liquid to solid has been achieved.

A schematic of a steam-jet refrigeration system in which water is used as the refrigerant is shown in Fig. 8.28. In this system a steam ejector is used to establish and maintain the required vacuum, which causes a portion of the water to vaporize and cool the rest of the remaining water. The steam-jet ejector is used as the vacuum pump, drawing off both vaporized water and any entrained air, compressing them to a higher pressure. The compressed vapor and steam are then condensed. This condenser requires considerably more cooling water than the condenser for a conventional mechanical compression system, since it must remove the heat of the power steam as well as that liberated from the chilled water.

When the steam-jet ejector system is used, it is common to utilize low-pressure plant steam for reasons of economy. It is necessary to provide a condenser on the steam jet as well as an air ejector to take care of outgassed air and any air that may leak into the subatmospheric parts of the system. The operation of the steam-jet ejector system is simple and does not require moving parts, but the jet is a poor compressor and requires large amounts of steam.

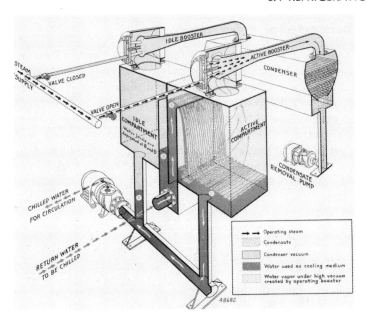

Figure 8.28 Steam-jet refrigeration system

We can analyze the refrigeration process in the simple vacuum refrigeration system by referring to Fig. 8.29. Since this is a steady flow system, water is continuously supplied and withdrawn with the difference in the mass of water vapor going to the pumping system. Writing the mass balance for this system yields

$$\dot{m}_1 = \dot{m}_2 + \dot{m}_3 \qquad (8.16)$$

and

$$\dot{m}_1 h_1 = \dot{m}_2 h_2 + \dot{m}_3 h_3 \qquad (8.17)$$

The refrigerating effect (or heat removed from the system) can be obtained from the vapor as $\dot{m}_3(h_3 - h_1)$ or from the liquid as $\dot{m}_2(h_1 - h_2)$.

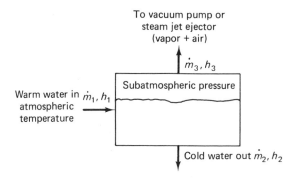

Figure 8.29 Analysis of vacuum refrigeration system

8.4e Thermoelectric Refrigerator

In 1822, Thomas J. Seebeck found that an electromotive force is generated between the junctions of dissimilar metals at different temperatures. This is the basis of the thermocouple as a temperature-measuring device (discussed in some detail in Chapter 1). For metals, the electromotive force is of the order of microvolts per degree of temperature difference, but recent advances in semi-conductor materials have produced materials having much larger voltage outputs per degree of temperature difference. While such systems are relatively inefficient direct converters of heat to electricity, they are reliable and have no moving parts. Figure 8.30a shows a schematic of a thermoelectric converter.

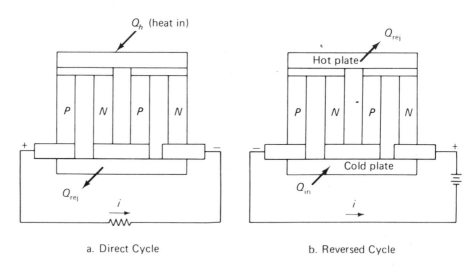

a. Direct Cycle   b. Reversed Cycle

Figure 8.30 Thermoelectric converters

In 1834, Jean Peltier found that, when a current flows around a loop of two dissimilar metals, one end warms up while the other end cools. In effect, the thermoelectric converter has been reversed in a manner similar to the reversal of a power cycle to obtain a refrigeration cycle. Thus, if one junction (the hot one) is kept in the ambient surroundings while the other (the cold one) is kept in the refrigerated space, and a potential is applied as shown schematically in Fig. 8.30b, heat will be transferred from the space to be refrigerated to the cold junction, while the hot junction will reject heat to the surroundings as its temperature will rise above ambient temperature.

At present, the thermoelectric refrigerator cannot compete with the more conventional refrigeration systems. However, in such space-limited applications as the removal of heat from electronic devices and assemblies, the thermoelectric refrigerator is in commercial use. More commercial applications will become economical as this type of refrigeration effect is developed further.

8.5 THE HEAT PUMP

Thus far we have directed our attention to the heat removed from the region to be cooled and denoted this as the refrigeration effect. If, instead, we consider the energy rejected as heat from the refrigeration cycle, we have a device that has been called the heat pump. To understand the basic principles of operation of this device, let us once again consider the reversed Carnot cycle shown in Figs. 8.3 (repeated) and 8.4 (repeated). During the process of cooling a given

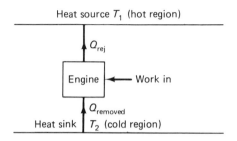

Figure 8.3 Reversed Carnot cycle (repeated)

space, energy (heat) is rejected at some higher temperature. As can be seen from Fig. 8.3 (repeated), the heat rejected is equal to the heat removed from the cold region plus the work into the system. For the heat to be rejected, say as in a household refrigerator, the temperature of the fluid in the cycle must be above the temperature of the surroundings. As shown in Fig. 8.4 (repeated), the total energy rejected is given by the rectangle $A'BCD'$, which is also equal to $T_1(s_2 - s_1)$. The energy (or work) supplied is equal to $(T_1 - T_2)(s_2 - s_1)$. If we now define the performance index for such a system as the ratio of the energy delivered (the heating effect or total energy rejected) to the net work supplied as the coefficient of performance, we have

$$\text{COP}_{\text{Carnot heat pump}} = \frac{T_1(s_2 - s_1)}{(T_1 - T_2)(s_2 - s_1)} = \frac{T_1}{T_1 - T_2} \quad (8.18)$$

Figure 8.4 Reversed Carnot cycle (repeated)

and
$$\text{COP}_{\text{heat pump}} = \left(1 + \text{COP}_{\text{refrig.}}\right)_{\text{Carnot cycle}} \qquad (8.18a)$$

In an actual machine, the necessity for finite temperature differences to transfer the heat, as well as other irreversibilities, will make the actual performance less than the optimum performance of a heat pump.

ILLUSTRATIVE PROBLEM 8.7

Determine the COP as a heat pump for the cycle described in Illustrative Problem 8.1.

Solution

We can solve this problem by using the cycle temperatures, that is, a rejection temperature of 530°R and a cold temperature of 492°R. Thus

$$\text{COP}_{\text{Carnot heat pump}} = \frac{T_1}{(T_1 - T_2)} = \frac{530}{530 - 492} = 13.95$$

The COP can also be obtained from the energy items solved for in Illustrative Problem 8.1. The work was found to be 77.2 Btu/min and the total energy rejection was 1077.2 Btu/min. Therefore, the COP = 1077.2/77.2 = 13.95, as before for the Carnot heat pump.

ILLUSTRATIVE PROBLEM 8.8

If the cycle described in Illustrative Problems 8.1 and 8.7 has its lower temperature reduced to 0°F, determine the work in, the heat rejected, and the COP as a heat pump.

Solution

Let us first consider the cycle as a refrigeration cycle. The COP as a refrigeration cycle is $(0 + 460)/(530 - 460) = 6.57$. The work input would be $1000/6.57 = 152.2$ Btu/min, and the total heat rejection would be $1000 + 152.2 = 1152.2$ Btu/min. The COP as a heat pump is $1152.2/152.2 = 7.57$. As a check, $6.57 + 1 = 7.57$, Eq. (8.18a).

Notice, as a result of Illustrative Problems 8.7 and 8.8, that as the outside temperature decreased from 32° to 0°F, the COP as a heat pump was almost halved, and that the energy delivered to the higher temperature increased by 7 percent while the required work into the system doubled. Thus, when the demand is the greatest as the outside temperature drops, the ability of a given heat pump to meet this demand decreases. In northern latitudes the heat pump is found to be uneconomical if it is used solely for heating, but it can and is used in southern latitudes where there are moderate heating loads and relatively long cooling needs. In such an installation, the same equipment is used for both heating and cooling, and whenever additional heating requirements are needed, electrical resistance elements in the air ducts are used to make up this additional heat requirement. Figure 8.31 shows the operation of the heat pump used for summer cooling and winter heating. Suitable valving is necessary to reverse the path of the refrigerant and to properly operate the system.

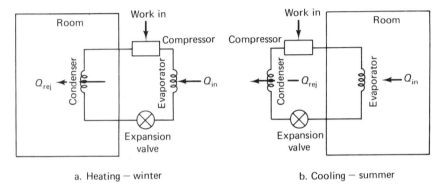

a. Heating — winter   b. Cooling — summer

Figure 8.31 All-year heat pump operation

In Fig. 8.31 the atmosphere is indicated to be the energy source when the heat pump is operated on the heating cycle. Unfortunately, atmospheric air is a variable temperature fluid and, as was noted earlier, as the temperature of the air decreases, requiring a greater heat output, the heat pump is less able to meet this demand. To overcome this problem well water, and the earth itself have been used rather than atmospheric air. If well water is used, it is necessary that the supply be adequate and that the water be returned underground to prevent local water table lowering. When the heated water is returned it should be at some distance from where it is initially taken from the ground to prevent heating of the water source. If coils are buried in the earth, it is necessary to insure good thermal contact between the coil and the earth.

Figure 8.32 shows a package heat pump that is purchased as a complete unit; it is only necessary to connect the unit to a power source and add appropriate ducting to make it operative.

The application of the heat pump to a specific installation or for a specific use is an economic problem. In areas where low cost electricity is available, the heat pump finds applications in the heating and cooling of both homes and industrial buildings. Also, industrial processes often require either heating or cooling, and the heat pump could be used for specific applications. One such application is where cooling of a process fluid is required, and the heat rejected by the heat pump could be used to heat the plant or office space. The heat pump should not be used without a prior thorough investigation of the economics of the proposed installation being made after engineering feasibility has been established.

Figure 8.32 Heat pump

8.6 CLOSURE

Refrigeration is accepted as part of the daily life style of most industrialized nations. Its use for food preservation, comfort, and process control has become an indispensable part of our technology. The basic understanding of this process is found in our study of the reversed Carnot cycle, which serves to establish the limiting performance factors for refrigeration cycles. The practical achievement of commercial refrigeration is found in the reversed Rankine cycle (vapor compression), the reversed Brayton cycle (air refrigeration), and in the use of the absorption process and vacuum refrigeration process. While it is impossible to cover all the practical problems and hardware associated with these refrigeration systems, an attempt has been made to cover some of the more important aspects of each system. For the interested student, it is suggested that the references at the end of this chapter be consulted, as well as the publications of the American Society of Heating, Refrigeration, and Air Conditioning Engineers (ASHRAE), for further details and information on specific system variables.

REFERENCES

1 *Fundamentals of Classical Thermodynamics* by G. J. Van Wylen and R. E. Sonntag, John Wiley & Sons, Inc., New York, 1965.

2 *Engineering Thermodynamics* by W. C. Reynolds and H. C. Perkins, McGraw-Hill Book Co., New York, 1970.

3 *Principles of Engineering Thermodynamics*, 2nd Ed., by P. J. Kiefer, G. F. Kinney, and M. C. Stuart, John Wiley & Sons, Inc., New York, 1954.

4 *Heat and Thermodynamics*, 4th Ed., by M. W. Zemansky, McGraw-Hill Book Co., New York, 1957.

5 *Thermodynamics*, 2nd Ed., by F. P. Durham, Prentice-Hall, Inc., Englewood Cliffs, N.J., 1959.

6 *Air Conditioning and Refrigeration* by W. H. Severns and J. K. Fellows, John Wiley & Sons, Inc., New York, 1958.

7 *Chemical Engineering Thermodynamics* by B. F. Dodge, McGraw-Hill Book Co., New York, 1944.

8 *Refrigeration and Air Conditioning*, 2nd Ed., by R. C. Jordon and G. B. Priester, Prentice-Hall, Inc., Englewood Cliffs, N.J., 1956.

9 *Thermodynamics* by J. H. Keenan, John Wiley & Sons, Inc., New York, 1941.

10 *Elementary Applied Thermodynamics* by Irving Granet, John Wiley & Sons, Inc., New York, 1965.

11 *Thermal Engineering* by C. C. Dillio and E. P. Nye, International Textbook Co., Scranton, Pa., 1959.

12 *Refrigeration and Air Conditioning* by W. F. Stoecker, McGraw-Hill Book Co., New York, 1958.

13 *Theory and Practice of Heat Engines* by V. M. Faires, Macmillan, Inc., New York, 1948.

14 *Elements of Applied Energy* by F. T. Morse, Litton Educational Publishing, Inc., New York, 1947.

15 *Thermal Engineering* by H. L. Solberg, O. C. Cromer, and H. R. Spalding, John Wiley & Sons, Inc., New York, 1960.

16 *Thermodynamics* by J. P. Holman, McGraw-Hill Book Co., New York, 1969.

17 *The Engineers Reference Library—Power*, McGraw-Hill Book Co., New York.

PROBLEMS

8.1 A Carnot refrigeration cycle takes heat from water at 33°F and discards it to a room at 72°F. If the refrigeration effect is equal to 8 tons of refrigeration, (a) how much heat is discarded to the room? (b) How much work is required? (c) How much heat is removed from the water?

8.2 Determine the horsepower required for a Carnot refrigeration machine if its capacity is rated at 8 tons of refrigeration while operating between 10° and 110°F.

8.3 If the cycle in Problem 8.3 was rated for 8 tons of equivalent heating when operating as a heat pump, determine the power required.

8.4 If Illustrative Problem 8.3 had been a Carnot cycle operating between the same temperature limits, determine items (a), (b), and (c) required by this problem. Compare the results.

8.5 The device described in Illustrative Problem 8.2 is operated as a heat pump. Determine the maximum COP and the power input for the continuous supply of 1 ton of refrigeration.

8.6 Derive the expression

$$\text{COP}_{\text{heat pump}} = \left(1 + \text{COP}_{\text{refrig.}}\right)_{\text{Carnot cycle}}$$

8.7 A reversed Carnot cycle is used for building heating. Assuming that 25,000 Btu/min is required to keep the building at 72°F when the outside air temperature is 40°F, determine the power required and the COP for the cycle as a heat pump.

8.8 A plant is proposed in which a heat pump will provide the heat in the winter. It is estimated that the peak heating load will correspond to 50,000 Btu/hr. A well will be installed which can supply water with a constant temperature of 45°F. For comfort it is decided that the heated air will not exceed 85°F. If the cycle is operated as a Carnot heat pump, determine (a) the Carnot heat pump COP and (b) the compressor work.(c) If an actual cycle achieves 80 percent of the Carnot COP, determine the compressor work.

8.9 A refrigerator operating between 0° and 100°F removes 1000 Btu/min. If the COP is three-fourths of a Carnot refrigerator operating between the same temperatures, determine the work input and heat rejected by the actual cycle and the Carnot cycle.

8.10 A dry compression refrigeration cycle using ammonia as the working fluid operates between 80° and 10°F. Determine the ideal COP for this cycle. Use the ammonia tables in Appendix III.

8.11 Solve Problem 8.10 using the *ph* diagram for ammonia given in Appendix III.

8.12 If the compressor efficiency in Problem 8.10 is 80 percent, determine the COP of the cycle.

8.13 Compute the number of pounds of ammonia that must be circulated per minute in a 15-ton refrigerating system operating between pressures of 15 and 140 psia, with the ammonia entering the expansion valve at saturation temperature and leaving the evaporator as dry saturated vapor.

8.14 A vapor-compression system uses Freon-12 as refrigerant. The vapor in the evaporator is at −10°F and in the condenser it is at 100°F. When the vapor leaves the evaporator, it is as a dry saturated vapor, and it enters the expansion valve as saturated liquid. Determine the refrigerating effect per pound of Freon circulated.

8.15 A 10-ton vapor-compression refrigeration system uses Freon-12 as refrigerant. The vapor in the evaporator is at $-20°F$ and leaves as dry saturated vapor. The high side pressure is 180 psia, with Freon-12 entering the expansion valve as a saturated liquid. Compute the Freon-12 flow.

8.16 An ideal gas refrigeration cycle is operated so that the gas is expanded from 150 to 15 psia. Assuming that the ratio of specific heats (k) is 1.4 and the upper temperature of the cycle is 200°F, determine the COP and the temperature before the compression part of the cycle.

8.17 If the upper temperature of a Brayton refrigeration cycle is 180°F when the lowest temperature is $-80°F$, and the COP is 2.7, determine the air flow per ton of refrigeration. $c_p = 0.24$ Btu/lb°F.

8.18 A vacuum refrigeration system cools incoming water at 80°F to 50°F. Determine the mass of water vapor that must be removed per pound of entering water.

8.19 A vacuum refrigeration cycle is operated at 0.12166 psia in the vacuum chamber. If the incoming water is at 70°F, determine per pound of incoming water (a) pounds of cooled water, (b) pounds of vapor drawn off, and (c) refrigerating effect.

8.20 Solve Problem 8.19, if there is a heat leak into the system equal to 10 Btu/lb of incoming water.

chapter **9**

heat transfer

9.1 INTRODUCTION

In the earlier chapters of this book we considered heat to be energy in transition, and there has been only one reference to the mechanisms that must exist for this type of energy transport. This limitation that was found was from the second law of thermodynamics in the Clausius axiom. "Heat, cannot, of itself, pass from a lower to a higher temperature." Thus for heat transfer to occur we can state that a temperature difference must exist between the bodies, with heat flowing from the body at the higher temperature to the body at the lower temperature. For the purposes of this book, we shall only consider steady state heat transfer in the system being considered. The condition for steady state is that the temperatures in the system shall be independent of time and, as a consequence, the rate of heat transfer out of the system must equal the rate of heat transfer to the system.

The mechanisms of heat transfer that we shall consider in this chapter are conduction, convection, and radiation. In any industrial application it is possible to encounter more than one of these mechanisms occurring simultaneously, and it is necessary to consider them in combination when designing or analyzing heat-transfer equipment. The formal categorization of heat transfer into three separate and distinct mechanisms is a somewhat arbitrary but useful approach to complex technical problems. The usefulness of this approach will become apparent as our study progresses.

Figure 9.1 shows a modern steam generator in which specialized heat transfer surfaces are used to achieve high efficiencies. Waterwalls within the unit receive their heat by radiation from the combustion of the fuel. This heat is conducted through the steel tubes comprising the waterwalls and thence transferred to the water–steam mixture in the tubes. The superheater can use both radiation or convection heat transfer from the hot furnace gases to superheat the steam in the tubes. Thus, in the convection superheater, the flow of hot gas over the tubes causes heat to be transferred to the tubes, where it is then conducted through the metal wall and eventually is exchanged to the steam within the tubes. In the convection section, heat is transferred by the somewhat cooler gas to the tubing to vaporize water in the tubes. Additional convection heat transfer surface is provided in the economizer and air heater to extract more heat from the now cooler combustion gases to heat the entering feedwater and the incoming combustion air.

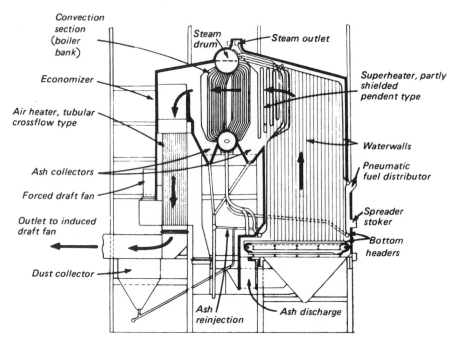

Figure 9.1 Modern steam generator (Reprinted with permission from *Power*, special report "Steam Generation," copyright by McGraw-Hill, Inc., New York, June 1964)

9.2 CONDUCTION

Consider the experiment shown in Fig. 9.2, which consists of a uniform bar of cross-sectional area A perfectly insulated on all sides except at the ends; that is, heat can only flow in the x direction. When one end of the bar is maintained at t_1 and the other at t_2, Q Btu/hr will be transferred steadily from station ① to

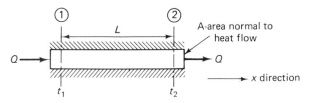

Figure 9.2 Conduction heat transfer

station ②. If the cross-sectional area of the bar is doubled while all other conditions are kept constant, it will be found that $2Q$ is now being transferred. In other words, the rate at which heat is being transferred is directly proportional to the cross-sectional area of the bar normal to the direction of heat flow. Returning to the original bar, we now make the temperature difference $(t_1 - t_2)$ twice its original value, and again we find the rate of heat transfer to be $2Q$; we therefore conclude that the heat transfer rate is directly proportional to the temperature difference between the ends of the bar. Finally, returning to the original conditions, we now make the bar twice as long $(2L)$, and this time we find only half the amount of heat is being transferred, leading to the conclusion that the rate of heat transfer is inversely proportional to the length of the bar. If we combine all these events into a mathematical statement, we have

$$Q \propto \frac{A(t_1 - t_2)}{L} \qquad (9.1)$$

or

$$Q = \frac{-kA(t_2 - t_1)}{L} \qquad (9.2)$$

where the proportionality constant, k, is a property of the material called the thermal conductivity. The negative sign has been included in Eq. (9.2) to indicate a positive heat flow in the increasing x direction, which is the direction of decreasing temperature. The conductivity, k, is usually found to be a function of temperature, but for moderate temperatures and temperature differences it can be taken to be a constant. If we now rewrite Eq. (9.2) in more general terms for one-dimensional conduction, we have

$$Q = \frac{-kA(\Delta t)}{\Delta x} \qquad (9.3)$$

Equation (9.3) is called Fourier's law of heat conduction in one dimension in honor of the noted French physicist, Joseph Fourier. In this equation the heat transfer rate Q is expressed in usual English engineering units as Btu/hr, the normal area A is expressed in square feet, the temperature difference Δt is in °F and the length Δx is in feet, giving us k in units of Btu/(hr)(sq ft)(°F/ft). This unit of k is often written as Btu/(hr ft °F). The nomenclature of Eq. (9.3) is shown in Fig. 9.3. Table 9.1 gives the thermal conductivities of some solids at room temperature, and Fig. 9.4 shows the variation of thermal conductivity as a function of temperature for many materials. A table of the thermal conductivity of some building and insulating equipment is given in Appendix 3. In SI units k is $W/m \cdot {}^\circ C$ or $J/s \cdot m \cdot {}^\circ C$.

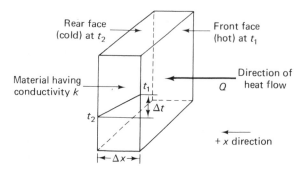

Figure 9.3 Nomenclature for Equation (9.3)

TABLE 9.1*
THERMAL CONDUCTIVITIES OF SOLIDS AT
TEMPERATURES NEAR 100°F

MATERIAL	*CONDUCTIVITY BTU/HR FT°F*	*CONDUCTIVITY W/M·°C*
Cotton wool	0.01	0.017
Corkboard	0.025	0.043
Mineral wool	0.026	0.045
Balsa	0.040	0.069
Asbestos fiber	0.044	0.076
White pine	0.065	0.112
Fir	0.090	0.156
Gypsum plaster	0.30	0.519
Common brick	0.40	0.692
Concrete (average house construction)	0.80	1.385
Porcelain	0.95	1.644
Mild steel	26	45.0
Wrought iron	34.5	59.7
Yellow brass	52	90.0
Aluminum	118	204.2
Copper	220	381.0
Silver	242	419.0

Note: 1 Btu/h·ft·F = 1.7307 W/m·°C.

*Reprinted with permission from Thermodynamics, 2nd Ed., by F. P. Durham, Prentice-Hall, Inc., Englewood Cliffs, N.J., 1959, p. 278.

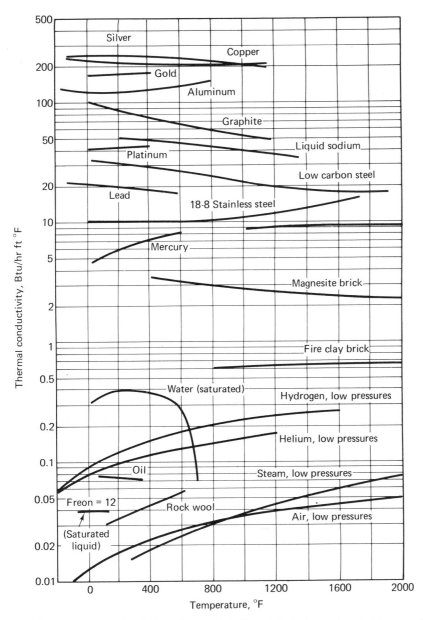

Figure 9.4 Thermal conductivity of material (Reprinted from *Heat, Mass and Momentum Transfer* by W. M. Rohscnow and H. Y. Choi, Prentice-Hall, Inc., Englewood Cliffs, N.J., 1961, p. 508, with permission)

The foregoing developments have been based upon observable events in a hypothetical experiment. The conduction of heat can also be visualized as occurring as the transfer of energy by more active molecules at a higher temperature colliding with less active molecules at a lower temperature. Gases have longer molecular spacings than liquids and consistently exhibit much lower thermal conductivities than liquids. Due to the complex structure of solids, some have high values of k while others have low values of k. However, for pure crystalline metals which are good electrical conductors, there is a large number of free electrons in the lattice structure that makes them also good thermal conductors. Table 9.2 gives the order of magnitude of the thermal conductivity k for various classes of materials, which may be used for rough estimates of conduction heat transfer.

TABLE 9.2*

ORDER OF MAGNITUDE OF k FOR VARIOUS CLASSES OF MATERIAL

MATERIAL	k Btu/hr ft°F
Gases	0.005–0.02
Insulating materials	0.014–0.10
Wood	0.04–0.10
Liquids (nonmetallic)	0.05–0.40
Brick, concrete, stone, plaster	0.2–2.0
Refractory materials	0.50–10.0
Metals and alloys	10–240

*Reprinted with permission from Introduction to Heat Transfer, 3rd Ed., by A. I. Brown and S. M. Marco, McGraw-Hill Book Co., New York, 1958, p. 24.

ILLUSTRATIVE PROBLEM 9.1

A common brick wall 6 in. thick has one face maintained at 150°F and the other face maintained at 80°F. Determine the heat transfer per square foot of wall.

Solution

From Table 9.1, the thermal conductivity of common brick near 100°F is 0.40 Btu/hr ft°F, and the wall is $\frac{6}{12}$ feet thick. Applying Eq. (9.3),

$$\frac{Q}{A} = \frac{-k(\Delta t)}{\Delta x} = \frac{-0.40(80-150)}{6/12} = 56 \text{ Btu/hr ft}^2$$

ILLUSTRATIVE PROBLEM 9.2

A brick wall 150 mm thick has one face maintained at 30°C while the other face is at 70°C. Determine the heat transfer per unit wall area.

Solution

Using k of 0.692 W/m·°C,

$$\frac{Q}{A} = \frac{-k(\Delta t)}{\Delta x} = \frac{-0.692(30-70)}{0.150} = 184.5 \text{ W/m}^2$$

For most cases of conduction heat transfer, it is satisfactory to select a value of k at the mean temperature of the process.

The Fourier equation has a direct analogue in Ohm's law for electrical circuits. This can be seen by rewriting Eq. (9.3) in the following form:

$$Q = \frac{\Delta t}{R_t} \qquad (9.3a)$$

where $R_t = \Delta x / kA$ and is called the thermal resistance. Ohm's law for a direct current resistance can be expressed as

$$i = \frac{\Delta E}{R_e} \qquad (9.4)$$

where ΔE is the potential difference (in volts), R_e is the electrical resistance (in ohms), and i is the current (in amperes). Comparison of Ohm's law and the Fourier equation shows Q to be analogous to i, Δt to correspond to ΔE, and R_t to correspond to R_e. Table 9.3 shows the correspondence between these systems.

TABLE 9.3
THERMAL–ELECTRICAL ANALOGY

QUANTITY	*THERMAL SYSTEM*	*ELECTRICAL SYSTEM*
Potential	Temperature difference, °F	Voltage difference, volts
Flow	Heat transfer, Btu/hr	Current, amperes
Resistance	Resistance, hr °F/Btu	Resistance, ohms

ILLUSTRATIVE PROBLEM 9.3

A simple resistive electrical circuit is to be used to determine the heat transfer through the wall of Illustrative Problem 9.1. If a 9-V battery is available and it is desired to have 1 A correspond to 100 Btu/hr ft², what resistance is needed?

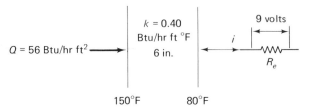

Figure 9.5 Illustrative Problem 9.3

Solution

Referring to Fig. 9.5, we have, for the thermal resistance, $R_t = \Delta x / kA =$ $(6/12)/0.4 \times 1 = 1.25$ hr °F/Btu. If we now take the ratio of Eqs. (9.3a) and (9.4), we have

$$\frac{Q}{i} = \frac{\Delta t / R_t}{\Delta E / R_e}$$

but the problem statement is that $Q/i = 100$ (numerically). Therefore,

$$100 = \frac{\Delta t}{R_t} \bigg/ \frac{\Delta E}{R_e}$$

Solving for R_e,

$$R_e = \frac{100 \, \Delta E R_t}{\Delta t} = \frac{100 \times 9 \times 1.25}{70} = 16.1 \text{ ohms}$$

As a check, $i = \Delta E / R_e = 9/16.1 = 0.559$ A, which when multiplied by 100 should give $Q = 56$ Btu/hr ft². The value of 55.9 is satisfactory.

The analogy between the flow of heat and the flow of electricity is very useful in both visualizing and solving heat transfer problems. The rules applying to electrical circuits can be used to solve thermal circuits that would otherwise be quite formidable. The techniques of solving dc circuits are applicable to solving steady state thermal conduction problems. As an application of this type of technique, let us consider a wall composed of several thermal resistances in series, as shown in Fig. 9.6a and an analogous electrical circuit shown in Fig. 9.6b. It will be recalled that for a series dc circuit the overall resistance (R_{oe}) is the sum of the individual resistances:

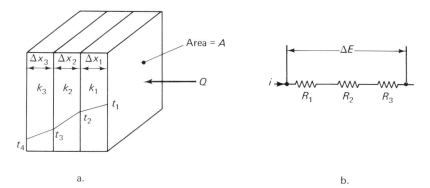

a.   b.

Figure 9.6 Thermal resistances in series

$$R_{oe} = R_1 + R_2 + R_3 \qquad (9.5)$$

Therefore, by analogy, the overall resistance of the thermal circuit (R_{ot}) is

$$R_{ot} = R_1 + R_2 + R_3 = \frac{\Delta x_1}{k_1 A} + \frac{\Delta x_2}{k_2 A} + \frac{\Delta x_3}{k_3 A} \qquad (9.6)$$

ILLUSTRATIVE PROBLEM 9.4

A composite wall consists of 6 in. of ordinary brick $(k=0.4$ Btu/hr ft °F), $\frac{1}{2}$ in. of concrete $(k=0.8$ Btu/hr ft °F), and $\frac{1}{2}$ in. of plaster $(k=0.3$ Btu/hr ft °F). If the inside of the wall is maintained at 70°F when the outside is 30°F, determine the heat transfer per square foot of wall. The overall situation is shown in Fig. 9.7.

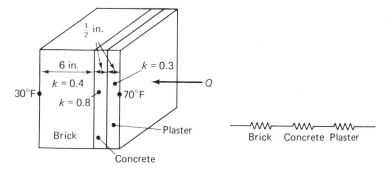

Figure 9.7 Illustrative Problem 9.4

Solution

For brick,

$$R = \frac{\Delta x}{kA} = \frac{6/12}{0.4 \times 1} = 1.25 \frac{\text{hr } ^\circ\text{F}}{\text{Btu}}$$

For concrete,

$$R = \frac{\Delta x}{kA} = \frac{1/2}{12} \Big/ (0.8 \times 1) = 0.052 \frac{\text{hr } ^\circ\text{F}}{\text{Btu}}$$

For plaster,

$$R = \frac{\Delta x}{kA} = \frac{1/2}{12} \Big/ (0.3 \times 1) = 0.139 \frac{\text{hr } ^\circ\text{F}}{\text{Btu}}$$

The overall resistance $R_{ot} = R_1 + R_2 + R_3 = 1.25 + 0.053 + 0.139 = 1.442$ hr°F/Btu, and the heat transfer $Q = (70 - 30)/1.442 = 27.8$ Btu/hr ft² since the area considered is 1 sq ft.

ILLUSTRATIVE PROBLEM 9.5

Calculate the temperature at the brick–concrete and concrete–plaster interfaces for the composite wall of Illustrative Problem 9.4.

Solution

Since each resistance in a series circuit carries the same current (heat flow), it is only necessary to successively apply Ohm's law (Fourier's equation) to each element in turn. Thus

$$Q = \frac{\Delta t}{R} \quad \text{or} \quad \Delta t = RQ \quad \text{with } Q = 27.8 \frac{\text{Btu}}{\text{hr ft}^2}$$

from Illustrative Problem 9.3. Therefore, for the brick,

$$\Delta t = 1.25(27.8) = 34.75 ^\circ\text{F}$$

For the concrete,

$$\Delta t = 0.052(27.8) = 1.45 ^\circ\text{F}$$

For the plaster,

$$\Delta t = 0.139(27.8) = \frac{3.86 ^\circ\text{F}}{40.06 ^\circ\text{F}}$$

Check:

$$\Delta t \text{ (overall)} = 40.06$$

The interface temperatures are

For brick–concrete	$30 + 34.75 = 64.75°F$
For concrete–plaster	$64.75 + 1.45 = 66.20°F$

ILLUSTRATIVE PROBLEM 9.6

If the composite wall of Fig. 9.7 consists of 150 mm of brick ($k = 0.692$ W/m·°C), 12 mm of concrete ($k = 1.385$ W/m·°C) and plaster ($k = 0.519$ W/m·°C) with wall temperatures of 0°C and 20°C, respectively, determine the heat transfer per square metre of wall.

Solution

Proceeding as in Illustrative Problem 9.4, for brick,

$$R = \frac{\Delta x}{kA} = \frac{0.150}{0.692 \times 1} = 0.217 \frac{°C}{W}$$

For concrete,

$$R = \frac{\Delta x}{kA} = \frac{0.012}{1.385 \times 1} = 0.009 \frac{°C}{W}$$

For plaster,

$$R = \frac{\Delta x}{kA} = \frac{0.012}{0.519 \times 1} = 0.023 \frac{°C}{W}$$

The total resistance is the sum of the individual resistances, which equals 0.249 °C/W. The heat transfer is therefore $(20-0)/0.249 = 80.3$ W/m^2.

The electrical analogy, when applied to the case of a composite plane wall with parallel sections, yields a considerable saving and is a distinct aid in visualizing the problem. Consider the wall shown in Fig. 9.8a, which consists of sections side by side. Each wall section has a different area for heat transfer, their conductivities are different, but their thicknesses are equal, and the front faces are kept at t_1 while the back faces are kept at t_2. This type of wall is called a parallel wall, and we shall solve it by using the parallel electrical circuit

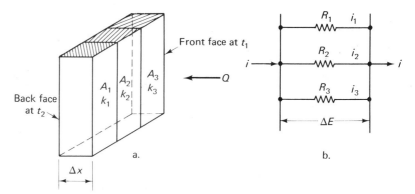

Figure 9.8 Parallel circuits

shown in Fig. 9.8b. For the parallel electrical circuit, the potential difference is the same for all elements and the total current i is the sum of the branch currents. Thus

$$i = i_1 + i_2 + i_3 \qquad (9.7)$$

By analogy for the thermal circuit

$$Q = Q_1 + Q_2 + Q_3 \qquad (9.8)$$

The overall resistance of the parallel electrical circuit is

$$R_{oe} = \frac{1}{(1/R_1) + (1/R_2) + (1/R_3)} \qquad (9.9)$$

which gives us by analogy for the thermal circuit

$$R_{ot} = \frac{1}{\dfrac{1}{(\Delta x / k_1 A_1)} + \dfrac{1}{(\Delta x / k_2 A_2)} + \dfrac{1}{(\Delta x / k_3 A_3)}} \qquad (9.10)$$

ILLUSTRATIVE PROBLEM 9.7

A wall 7 ft high and 6 ft wide is 4 in. thick. Two feet of the wall is made of fir ($k = 0.090$ Btu/hr ft °F), 2 ft is made of pine ($k = 0.065$ Btu/hr ft°F), and the final 2 ft is made of corkboard ($k = 0.025$ Btu/hr ft °F). Determine the heat loss from the wall if one face is maintained at 80°F while the other face is kept at 60°F.

Solution

The problem is essentially the case shown in Fig. 9.8. As the first step in the solution, we shall calculate the individual thermal resistances. Thus

$$R_{\text{fir}} = \frac{\Delta x}{kA} = \frac{4/12}{0.090 \times 7 \times 2} = 0.265 \frac{\text{hr } ^\circ\text{F}}{\text{Btu}}; \quad \frac{1}{R} = 3.774$$

$$R_{\text{pine}} = \frac{\Delta x}{kA} = \frac{4/12}{0.065 \times 7 \times 2} = 0.366 \frac{\text{hr } ^\circ\text{F}}{\text{Btu}}; \quad \frac{1}{R} = 2.732$$

$$R_{\text{corkboard}} = \frac{\Delta x}{kA} = \frac{4/12}{0.025 \times 7 \times 2} = 0.952 \frac{\text{hr } ^\circ\text{F}}{\text{Btu}}; \quad \frac{1}{R} = 1.050$$

$$R_{\text{overall}} = \frac{1}{(1/R_1) + (1/R_2) + (1/R_3)}$$

$$= \frac{1}{3.774 + 2.732 + 1.050}$$

$$= \frac{1}{7.556} = 0.132$$

Therefore,

$$Q = \frac{\Delta t}{R} = \frac{(80 - 60)}{0.132} = 151.5 \frac{\text{Btu}}{\text{hr}}$$

As a check,

$$Q_{\text{fir}} = \frac{\Delta t}{R} = \frac{(80 - 60)}{0.265} = \frac{20}{0.265} = 75.5 \frac{\text{Btu}}{\text{hr}}$$

$$Q_{\text{pine}} = \frac{\Delta t}{R} = \frac{80 - 60}{0.366} = \frac{20}{0.366} = 54.6 \frac{\text{Btu}}{\text{hr}}$$

$$Q_{\text{corkboard}} = \frac{\Delta t}{R} = \frac{80 - 60}{0.952} = \frac{20}{0.952} = 21.0 \frac{\text{Btu}}{\text{hr}}$$

$$Q_{\text{TOTAL}} = Q_1 + Q_2 + Q_3$$

$$= 75.5 + 54.6 + 21.0 = 151.1 \text{ Btu/hr}$$

Thus far we have been concerned with conduction through plane walls whose heat-transfer area remained constant. The conduction of heat through pipes represents a practical problem of considerable interest in which the heat-transfer area is constantly changing. To solve this problem, let us consider a long, uniform hollow cylinder whose outer surface is maintained at a temperature t_o and whose inner surface is maintained at a temperature t_i. As is shown in Fig. 9.9, we will denote the inner radius to be r_i and the outer radius to be r_o and the radius at any portion of the cylinder to be r. The length of cylinder in question will be denoted as L. Let us now apply the Fourier equation to a small cylinder of thickness Δr, located at a radius r from the center. The surface area of this cylinder is $2\pi rL$, and its thickness is Δr. Therefore,

$$Q = \frac{-kA\,\Delta t}{\Delta x} = \frac{-k2\pi rL\,\Delta t}{\Delta r} \qquad (9.11)$$

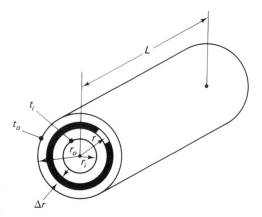

Figure 9.9 Conduction in a hollow cylinder

Rearranging,

$$\frac{Q}{2\pi kL}\left(\frac{\Delta r}{r}\right) = -\Delta t \qquad (9.12)$$

Since the heat transfer Q must go through all such elements, it is a constant and we can rewrite Eq. (9.12) as

$$\frac{Q}{2\pi kL}\sum_{r_i}^{r_o}\frac{\Delta r}{r} = -\sum_{t_i}^{t_o}\Delta t \qquad (9.13)$$

where the symbol Σ is used to denote the summation of the variable between the limits indicated. For the right side of the equation, we immediately note that the sum of all the Δt's is simply the overall temperature difference, and with the negative sign the summation gives us $t_i - t_o$. The summation of $\Delta r/r$ is similar to the summation of $\Delta v/v$ or $\Delta t/t$, which we have already noted yields the natural logarithm (ln) of the argument between its limits. Therefore,

Eq. (9.13) can be summed to yield

$$t_i - t_o = \frac{Q}{2\pi kL} \ln \frac{r_o}{r_i} \qquad (9.14a)$$

or

$$Q = \frac{(t_i - t_o)2\pi kL}{\ln \dfrac{r_o}{r_i}} \frac{Btu}{hr} \qquad (9.14b)$$

and the thermal resistance

$$R_t = \ln \frac{r_o/r_i}{2\pi kL}$$

ILLUSTRATIVE PROBLEM 9.8

A bare steel pipe having an outside diameter of 3.50 in. and an inside diameter of 3.00 in. is 5 ft long. Determine the heat loss from the pipe if the inside temperature is 240°F and its outside temperature is 120°F. Use a k of 26 Btu/hr ft °F for the steel.

Solution

Since the ratio of r_o/r_i is the same as the ratio of the corresponding diameters, we can apply Eq. (9.14b) directly:

$$Q = \frac{2\pi(26)(5)(240 - 120)}{\ln(3.50/3.00)} = 635,860 \frac{Btu}{hr}$$

ILLUSTRATIVE PROBLEM 9.9

A bar steel pipe, with outside diameter of 90 mm and inside diameter of 75 mm, is 2 m long. The outside temperature is 40°C while the inside temperature is 110°C. If k is 45 W/m·°C, determine the heat loss from the pipe.

Solution

Using Eq. (9.14b),

$$Q = \frac{2\pi \times 45 \times 3(110 - 40)}{\ln(90/75)} = 325.7 \times 10^3 \text{ W}$$

The results of Illustrative Problems 9.8 and 9.9 show the extremely large heat loss from a bare pipe. To decrease the loss, it is usual to insulate the pipe with a material having a low thermal conductivity. When this is done we have a situation of two resistances in series, each having variable heat transfer areas. Referring to Fig. 9.10 and applying Eq. (9.14b) to each of the cylinders yields the following: for the inner cylinder,

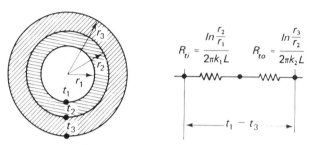

Figure 9.10 Compound cylinder

$$Q = \frac{2\pi k_1 L(t_1 - t_2)}{\ln(r_2/r_1)}; \qquad R_{ti} = \frac{\ln(r_2/r_1)}{2\pi k_1 L} \qquad (9.14c)$$

For the outer cylinder,

$$Q = \frac{2\pi k_2 L}{\ln(r_3/r_2)}(t_3 - t_2); \qquad R_{to} = \frac{\ln(r_3/r_2)}{2\pi k_2 L} \qquad (9.14d)$$

If, at this point, we apply the electrical analogy we can write directly that the overall resistance is the sum of the individual resistances. The same result can be obtained by noting that $t_1 - t_3 = (t_1 - t_2) + (t_2 - t_3)$. Using Eqs. (9.14c) and (9.14d), $t_1 - t_2 = QR_{ti}$, and $t_2 - t_3 = QR_{to}$. Therefore, $t_1 - t_3 = Q(R_{ti} + R_{to})$ or

$$Q = \frac{(t_1 - t_3)2\pi L}{(1/k_1)\ln(r_2/r_1) + (1/k_2)\ln(r_3/r_2)} \qquad (9.15)$$

ILLUSTRATIVE PROBLEM 9.10

If 1 in. of mineral wool ($k = 0.026$ Btu/hr ft °F) insulation is added to the pipe of Illustrative Problem 9.8 and the temperature on the outside of this insulation is found to be 85°F, determine the heat loss.

Solution

Using Eq. (9.15) and the data of Illustrative Problem 9.8,

$$\frac{1}{k_1}\ln\frac{r_2}{r_1} = \frac{1}{k_1}\ln\frac{D_2}{D_1} = \frac{1}{26}\times\ln\left(\frac{3.500}{3.00}\right) = 0.006$$

$$\frac{1}{k_2}\ln\frac{r_3}{r_2} = \frac{1}{k_2}\ln\frac{D_3}{D_2} = \frac{1}{0.026}\ln\left(\frac{5.50}{3.50}\right) = 17.384$$

Therefore,

$$Q = \frac{(240 - 85)2\pi(5)}{0.006 + 17.384} = 280.0 \frac{\text{Btu}}{\text{hr}}$$

Two things are evident from a comparison of Illustrative Problems 9.8 through 9.10. The first is the decrease in heat loss of more than a thousand fold by the addition of a relatively small amount of insulation, and the second is that the resistance of the steel could have been neglected since it was only a minute fraction of the resistance of the insulation.

Before leaving the subject of conduction heat transfer, one topic must be mentioned, thermal contact resistance. When two materials are brought into physical contact and heat flows from one to the other across the interface, it is found that there is a discontinuous and sometimes very large temperature drop at the interface plane, as shown in Fig. 9.11. This temperature drop is attributed to a thermal contact resistance, which can be thought of as being caused by two parallel heat paths at the interface: solid-to-solid conduction at discrete contact points and conduction through air entrapped at the gas interface. Due to the relatively poor thermal conductivity of air (or other gases) as compared to that of metals, the larger part of the joint thermal contact resistance is due to the entrapped air. The prediction of thermal contact resistance is a complex problem that as yet has not been adequately solved, and the student is cautioned that in actual practice allowance must be made for this effect when designing industrial equipment.

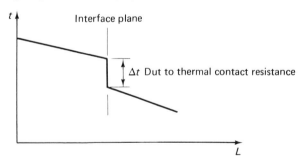

Figure 9.11 Thermal contact resistance

9.3 CONVECTION

Heat transfer by convection from a body involves the motion of a fluid (liquid or gas) relative to the body. If the motion is caused by the differences in density due to the difference in temperature at various locations in the fluid, it is known as natural convection. If the motion of the fluid is caused by an external agent such as a blower or fan, it is called forced convection. Heat transfer from a surface whose temperature is higher than the surrounding fluid occurs in a complex fashion. We can, however, visualize it as occurring in the following sequential order. First, the particles of fluid adjacent to the walls are heated by conduction from the wall, which increases their temperature. These "hot" particles will collide with colder particles, imparting some of their energy to these colder particles. This action will occur due to both particle motion as well as movement of the hotter fluid relative to the colder bulk fluid. To categorize the types of convective heat-transfer mechanisms, it is necessary to briefly discuss the mechanism of flow.

The term *laminar* (or *streamline*) flow is applied to a flow regime in which the flow is smooth and the fluid moves in layers or paths parallel to each other. When a fluid moves in laminar flow over a hotter surface, heat is transferred principally by molecular conduction within the fluid and from layer to layer. This type of convection heat transfer yields low heat-transfer rates. In contrast to laminar flow there is the flow regime known as *turbulent* flow. As the name implies, this type of flow is characterized by eddies that cause mixing of the layers of fluid until the layers are no longer distinguishable. The mixing of the fluid due to this turbulence causes an increase in the heat transfer, and consequently the greater the turbulence, the greater the heat transfer rate.

The basic equation for convection heat transfer is known as Newton's law of cooling and is given by

$$Q = hA(\Delta t) \qquad (9.16)$$

where Q = heat transfer rate (Btu/hr)

A = heat transfer area (ft^2)

Δt = temperature difference between the surface and the bulk of the fluid away from the surface (°F)

h = coefficient of heat transfer, film coefficient, thermal convective conductance, heat transfer coefficient, or film heat transfer factor (Btu/hr ft^2 °F)

By a comparison of Eq. (9.16) to Eq. (9.3a), we can write the thermal resistance for convective heat transfer, R_c, as

$$R_c = \frac{1}{hA} \qquad (9.17)$$

and it is treated in the same manner as we treated the resistance concept in conduction heat transfer. Some typical values of h are given in Table 9.4.

TABLE 9.4*

TYPICAL VALUES OF h Btu/hr ft^2°F

Gases (natural convection)	0.1–5
Flowing gases	2–50
Flowing liquids (nonmetallic)	30–1000
Flowing liquid metals	1000–50000
Boiling liquids	200–50000
Condensing vapors	500–50000

Note: In SI units 1 Btu/h·ft^2 °F = 5.6786 W/m^2·°C.

From Heat, Mass, and Momentum Transfer by W. M. Rohsenow and H. Y. Choi, Prentice-Hall, Inc., Englewood Cliffs, N.J., 1961, p. 102, with permission.

ILLUSTRATIVE PROBLEM 9.11

Assume that the base pipe in Illustrative Problem 9.8 has a heat transfer coefficient on the outside due to natural convection to the surrounding air at 70°F of 0.9 Btu/hr ft^2 °F. Determine the heat transfer from the pipe to the surrounding air.

Solution

The resistance of the pipe is

$$R_{pipe} = \ln \frac{(r_2/r_1)}{2\pi kL} = \ln \frac{(3.50/3.00)}{2\pi(26)5} = 0.00019$$

$$R_{convection} = \frac{1}{hA} = \frac{1}{0.9 \times \pi(3.5)/12 \times 5} = 0.2425$$

$$\text{Total } R = 0.00019 + 0.2425 = 0.243$$

$$Q = \frac{\Delta t}{R} = \frac{240 - 70}{0.243} = 699.6 \frac{\text{Btu}}{\text{hr}}$$

It is interesting to note that the outside film coefficient has acted in a manner similar to an insulator for this case (see Illustrative Problems 9.8 and 9.10), and the resistance of the pipe wall is essentially negligible.

9.3a Natural Convection*

The evaluation of the heat-transfer coefficient h is quite difficult since it usually involves the interaction of complex physical phenomena. As was noted earlier, natural convection heat transfer occurs due to density differences in the fluid caused by a body at a temperature different than the fluid exchanging heat to the fluid. These density differences cause a pumping action of the fluid relative to the body. Using the techniques of dimensional analysis, it can be shown that the parameters involved in natural convection heat transfer can be cast into the form

$$N_u = A(Gr)^a(Pr)^b \qquad (9.18)$$

where

$N_u = $ Nusselt number $ = hL/k$ or hD/k (dimensionless)

$Pr = $ Prandtl number $ = c_p u/k$ (dimensionless)

$Gr = $ Grashof number $ = g\beta(\Delta t)L^3\rho^2/u^2$ (dimensionless)

$A, a, b = $ constants depending on the system under consideration

$\beta = $ coefficient of expansion

$\rho = $ density

$\mu = $ viscosity

$g = $ acceleration of gravity

$D = $ diameter

$L = $ length

$c_p = $ specific heat at constant pressure

At this point it should be noted that the character of the flow process must be considered. The boundary layer of the fluid will be either laminar or turbulent, and this in turn will effect the constants in Eq. (9.18). Based upon experimentally determined values, it is found that when the product (Gr) (Pr) exceeds 10^8 there is an increase in the heat transfer coefficient, indicating a transition from a laminar boundary layer to a turbulent boundary layer.

Equation (9.18) can be recast into the following form for Pr near unity, which is the case for many gases.

$$N_u = C_L(Gr \times Pr)^{1/4} \qquad (9.19)$$

$$N_u = C_T(Gr \times Pr)^{1/3} \qquad (9.20)$$

---

*A portion of this material in this section is from "Natural Convection Heat Transfer Design Aids" by Irving Granet, *Design News*, March, 1972, with permission.

Equation (9.19) applies to laminar flow, and C_L is the coefficient for laminar flow. Equation (9.20) applies to turbulent flow, and C_T is the coefficient for turbulent flow. The evaluation of these equations is, at best, tedious and in some cases necessitates the use of an iterative process to obtain a solution. Fortunately, the properties of air, CO, N_2, and O_2 in the temperature range of 100° to 1500°F vary in such a manner that it is possible to lump all the properties that are individually temperature dependent into a single constant that is essentially temperature invariant to obtain the following simplified forms of Eqs. (9.19) and (9.20).

$$h = C_{L'}\left(\frac{\Delta t}{L}\right)^{1/4} \tag{9.21a}$$

$$h = C_{T'}(\Delta t)^{1/3} \tag{9.21b}$$

Equation (9.21a) applies to laminar flow, and Eq. (9.21b) applies to turbulent flow, Δt is the temperature difference in °F between the surface and the bulk temperature of the gas, L in feet is a characteristic dimension (either a length or a diameter), h is the heat transfer coefficient in Btu/hr ft² °F, and $C_{L'}$ and $C_{T'}$ are the constants for laminar and turbulent flow, respectively.

If the references at the end of this chapter are examined, it will be found that there is as much as 100 percent difference between various authors for values of the coefficients $C_{L'}$ and $C_{T'}$. A consistent set of data for $C_{L'}$ and $C_{T'}$ that yields conservative design values is given in Eqs. (9.22) and (9.23).

Vertical Plates

$$h = 0.29\left(\frac{\Delta t}{L}\right)^{1/4} \qquad \text{for } 10^{-2} < (L^3\Delta t) < 10^3 \atop \text{(laminar)} \tag{9.22}$$

$$h = 0.21(\Delta t)^{1/3} \qquad \text{for } 10^3 < (L^3\Delta t) < 10^6 \atop \text{(turbulent)} \tag{9.23}$$

Horizontal Pipes

Evidence exists to indicate that vertical pipes have higher heat–transfer coefficients than horizontal pipes, but this difference can be considered to be small and the equation given for horizontal pipes can be used for vertical pipes.

$$h = 0.25\left(\frac{\Delta t}{D}\right)^{1/4} \qquad \text{for } 10^{-2} < (D^3\Delta t) < 10^3 \atop \text{(laminar)} \tag{9.24}$$

$$h = 0.18(\Delta t)^{1/3} \qquad \text{for } 10^3 < (D^3\Delta t) < 10^6 \atop \text{(turbulent)} \tag{9.25}$$

Horizontal Square Plates

$$h = 0.27\left(\frac{\Delta t}{L}\right)^{1/4} \qquad \text{for } 1.0 < (L^3 \Delta t) < 20 \atop \text{(laminar, hot side up)} \qquad (9.26)$$

$$h = 0.22(\Delta t)^{1/3} \qquad \text{for } 20 < (L^3 \Delta t) < 30{,}000 \atop \text{(turbulent, hot side up)} \qquad (9.27)$$

$$h = 0.12\left(\frac{\Delta t}{L}\right)^{1/4} \qquad \text{for } 0.3 < (L^3 \Delta t) < 30{,}000 \atop \text{(hot side down)} \qquad (9.28)$$

The foregoing is presented in graphical form in Figs. 9.12 through 9.14. Figure 9.12 is used first to determine whether the character of the flow is

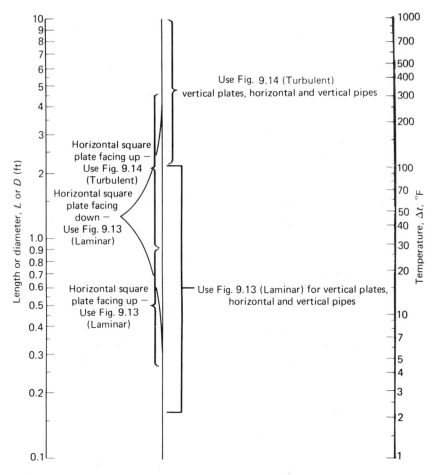

Figure 9.12 Chart for determining character of natural convection process

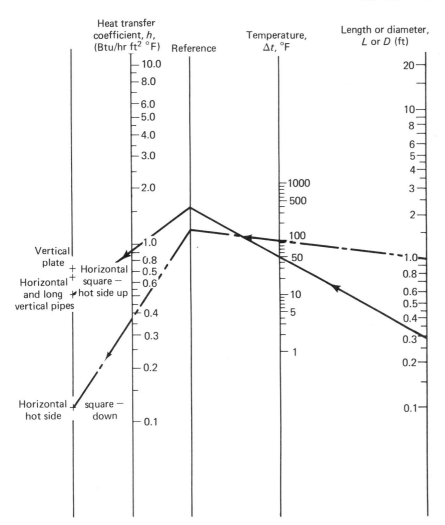

Figure 9.13 Heat-transfer coefficient of air, CO, N_2, and O_2 for natural convection, laminar flow

laminar or turbulent. The necessary data for entering this chart are Δt and L (or D). Having determined the flow character, either Fig. 9.13 or 9.14 is entered. Figure 9.13 is for the laminar region and Fig. 9.14 is for the turbulent region. The use of these charts is illustrated by the following examples.

ILLUSTRATIVE PROBLEM 9.12

Determine the heat-transfer coefficient from a horizontal square plate with hot side facing down if the plate is one foot by one foot and $\Delta t = 100°F$.

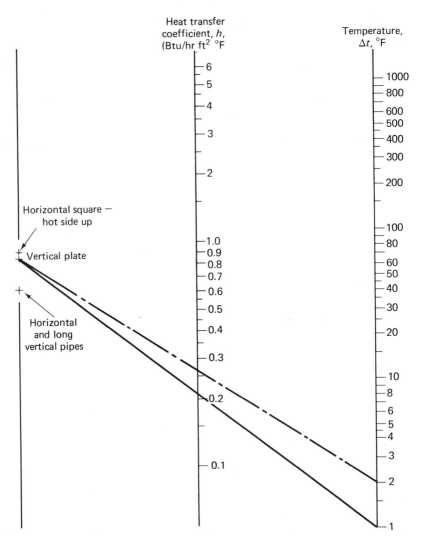

Figure 9.14 Heat-transfer coefficient of air, CO, N_2, and O_2 for natural convection, turbulent flow

Solution

From Fig. 9.12, the flow is found to be laminar and Fig. 9.13 is to be used. Entering Fig. 9.13 at $L = 1$ ft and $\Delta t = 100°F$, and connecting the reference scale to the point marked horizontal square—hot side down, yields $h = 0.38$ Btu/hr ft^2 °F.

ILLUSTRATIVE PROBLEM 9.13

Determine the heat-transfer coefficient for a vertical plate if it is 10 ft high and $\Delta t = 2°F$.

Solution

From Fig. 9.12, the flow is found to be turbulent. Entering Fig. 9.14 at $\Delta t = 2$ and the point for a vertical plate yields $h = 0.26$ Btu/hr ft^2 °F.

ILLUSTRATIVE PROBLEM 9.14

A bare 3.50-in. outside diameter pipe has an outside temperature of 120°F and is in a room at 70°F. Determine the heat loss from a section of 5 ft long (see Illustrative Problem 9.11) due to convection.

Solution

From Fig. 9.12 at $\Delta t = 50°F$, $D = 3.5/12 = 0.292$ ft, the flow is laminar and Fig. 9.13 is to be used. From Fig. 9.13, $h = 0.9$ Btu/hr ft^2 °F, $Q = hA \Delta t = 0.9 \times \pi(3.5)/12 \times 5(120 - 70) = 206.2$ Btu/hr.

ILLUSTRATIVE PROBLEM 9.15

A vertical wooden wall 8 ft high $\times$ 7 ft wide $\times$ 3 in. thick ($k = 0.07$ Btu/hr ft °F) has warm air on one side at 80°F and cold air at 50°F on the other side. Determine the heat transfer through the wall and the wall temperature.

Solution

This problem cannot be solved directly since the individual film resistances are functions of unknown temperature differences. Therefore, as a first approximation, let us assume that h for both sides of the wall can be taken as $\frac{1}{2}$. The wall resistance is $\Delta x / kA$, which for 1 ft^2 is $(3/12)/0.07 = 3.57$. The overall series resistance is therefore $1/(1/2) + 1/(1/2) + 3.57 = 7.57$. Using 7.57, we can now obtain Q and the individual temperature differences. $Q = (80 - 50)/7.57 = 3.96$ Btu/hr ft^2, and Δt through the "hot" air film is $3.96/(1/2) = 7.92°F$; through the wall the Δt is $3.57 \times 3.96 = 14.1°F$, and through the "cold" air film Δt is also $3.96/(1/2) = 7.92°F$. With these temperature differences, we can now enter Figs. 9.12 and 9.14 to verify our approximation. From Fig. 9.14 we find $h = 0.42$ Btu/hr ft^2 °F. Using $h = 0.42$, we have for the overall resistance $(1/0.42) + (1/0.42) + 3.57 = 8.33$. $Q = (80 - 50)/8.33 = 3.6$ Btu/hr ft^2. Δt through both air films is $3.6/0.42 = 8.57°F$ (say 8.6°F), and through the wall, $\Delta t = 3.6 \times 3.57 =$

12.8°F. Entering Fig. 9.14 we find that h stays essentially 0.42, and our solution is that the heat flow is 3.6 Btu/hr ft², the "hot" side of the wall is at $80 - 8.6$°F or 71.4°F, and the "cold" side is at $50 + 8.6$°F $= 58.6$°F and the temperature drop in the wall is $71.4 - 58.6 = 12.8$°F, which checks our wall Δt calculation.

9.3b Forced Convection

Forced convection flow can be either laminar or turbulent, inside tubes or outside tubes, and involve changes of phase such as when a fluid is being boiled. Figure 9.15 shows a modern chemical plant where all these events occur. Due to the complexity and the number of cases that would have to be studied to cover this topic, we shall limit ourselves to the situation where we

Figure 9.15 Large, modern chemical plant, which utilizes large tubular heat exchangers with specialized flow patterns to produce ethylene oxide and ethylene glycol (Courtesy of Foster Wheeler Corp.)

have a liquid or gas flowing inside a tube in turbulent flow. For this condition the heat transfer coefficient can be calculated from the following type of equation:

$$N_u = C(Pr)^a (Re)^b \qquad (9.29a)$$

where the nomenclature is the same as for Eq. (9.18); that is a, b, and C are constants, N_u is the Nusselt number, Pr is the Prandtl number, and Re is the Reynolds number, which is $DV\rho/\mu$ or DG/μ, where G is the mass flow rate per square foot of flow area, $\dot{m}/A$. It is to be remembered that these "numbers" are dimensionless groups, and consistent units must be used throughout. The form of Eq. (9.29a) that is most generally used for turbulent flow (the Reynolds

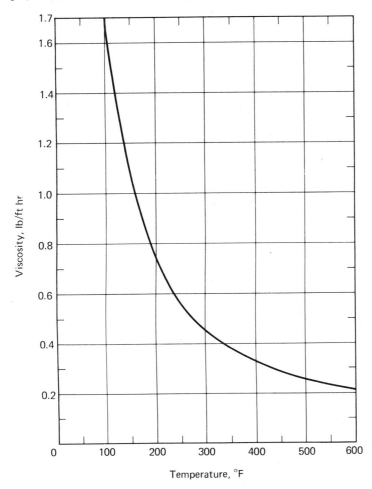

Figure 9.16 Viscosity of saturated water (From W. H. McAdams, *Heat Transmission*, 3rd Ed., McGraw-Hill Book Co., New York, 1954, p. 484)

number must be greater than 2100) is

$$\frac{hD}{k} = 0.023\left(\frac{C_p\mu}{k}\right)^{1/3}\left(\frac{DV\rho}{\mu}\right)^{0.8} \qquad (9.29b)$$

with the properties of specific heat, viscosity, and thermal conductivity evaluated at the bulk temperature of the fluid. To facilitate the use of this equation for water and air flowing turbulently in tubes, Figs. 9.16 through 9.20 have been developed.* Figures 9.16 and 9.17 give the viscosity of water and air and are used to check the Reynolds number to insure that the flow is turbulent. Figures 9.18 and 9.19 yield the "basic" heat-transfer coefficient h_1 as a function of the weight flow $W/1000$, where W is in pounds per hour. Finally, Fig. 9.20 is a correction factor for the variation of the inside diameter from 1 in. The desired heat transfer coefficient h is then simply equal to $F \times h_1$.

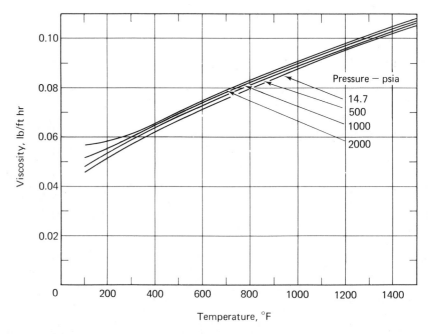

Figure 9.17 Viscosity of dry air

ILLUSTRATIVE PROBLEM 9.16

Water flows in a tube that has a 1-in. outside diameter and a 0.065-in. wall (ID = 0.87 in.). If 20 lb/min of water at 400°F is flowing, calculate the heat

*See "Heat Transfer to Subsaturated Water, Dry Air and Hydrogen in Turbulent Flow Inside a Tube" by Irving Granet, *Journal of the American Society of Naval Engineers*, Nov. 1957, pp. 787–794.

transfer coefficient on the inside of the tube. Figure 9.21 shows a high-tempera-ture forced circulation hot-water generator of this type.

Solution

The first step is to check the Reynolds number. It will be recalled that the Reynolds number is given by $DV\rho/\mu$ and is dimensionless. Therefore, we can use D, diameter in feet; V, velocity in ft/hr; ρ, density in lb/ft^3, and μ, viscosity in lb/ft hr. Alternately, the Reynolds number is given by DG/μ, where G is the mass flow rate per unit area (lb/hr ft^2). For this problem

$$G = \frac{20 \times 60}{\dfrac{\pi(0.87)^2}{4 \times 144}} = 290{,}680 \text{ lb/hr ft}^2$$

$$\mu = 0.33 \text{ lb/ft hr (from Fig. 9.16.)}$$

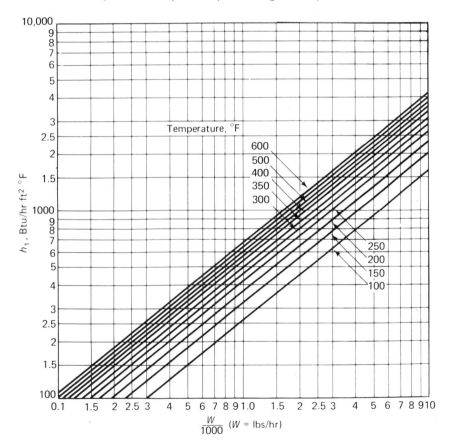

Figure 9.18 Basic heat-transfer coefficient for subsaturated water

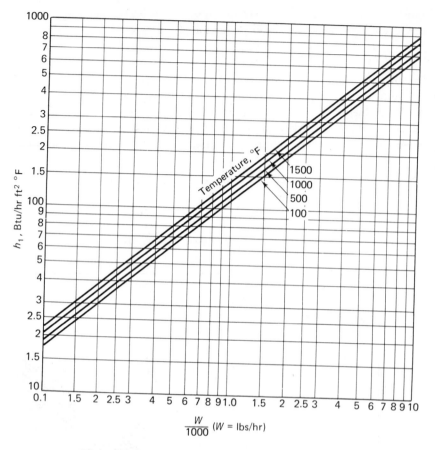

Figure 9.19 Basic heat-transfer coefficient for dry air

Therefore, the Reynolds number is

$$DG/\mu = \frac{(0.87/12) \times 290{,}680}{0.33} = 63{,}860$$

which is well into the turbulent flow regime. The next step is to enter Fig. 9.18 at $W/1000$ of $20 \times 60/1000 = 1.2$ and $400°F$ to obtain $h_1 = 630$. From Fig. 9.20 we obtain $F = 1.25$ for an inside diameter of 0.87 in. The final desired value of h is therefore equal to

$$F \times h_1 = 1.25 \times 630 = 788 \text{ Btu/hr ft}^2 \text{ °F}$$

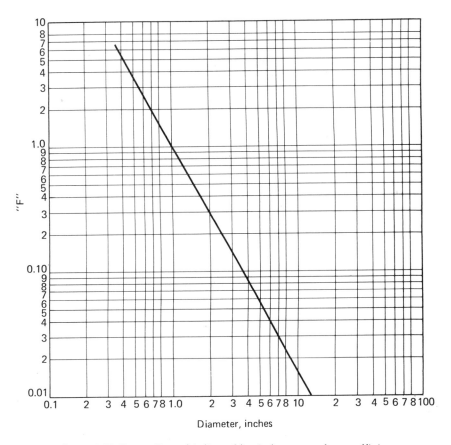

Figure 9.20 Factor F: multiplier of basic heat-transfer coefficient

Figure 9.21 High temperature forced circulation hot water generator: partially assembled unit showing closely spaced tubes covering the walls; water flows inside tubes in circuits having equal pressure drops to insure a hydraulically balanced system (Courtesy of Riley Stoker Corp.)

ILLUSTRATIVE PROBLEM 9.17

If, instead of water, atmospheric pressure air was flowing in the tube of Illustrative Problem 9.16, determine the inside film coefficient.

Solution

We first check the Reynolds number and note that G is the same as for Illustrative Problem 9.16. The viscosity of air at these conditions is obtained from Fig. 9.17 as 0.062 lb/ft hr. The Reynolds number, DG/μ, is therefore

$$\frac{(0.87/12) \times 290{,}680}{0.062} = 339{,}900$$

which places the flow in the turbulent regime. Since $W/1000$ is the same as for Illustrative Problem 9.16 and equals 1.2, we now enter Fig. 9.19 at 1.2 and 400°F to obtain $h_1 = 135$. Since the inside tube diameter is the same as before, $F = 1.25$. Therefore,

$$h = 135 \times 1.25 = 169 \text{ Btu/hr ft}^2 \text{ °F}$$

It is interesting to note that for equal mass flow rates, water yields a heat transfer coefficient almost five times greater than air.

9.4 RADIATION

Radiant heat transfer differs from both conduction and convection in that a medium is not required to transfer the heat. Basically, radiant heat transfer is an electromagnetic phenomena similar to the transmission of light, x-rays, and radio waves, and all bodies radiate heat. A net interchange of heat occurs when the absorption of radiant energy by one body exceeds the energy that it is radiating. A body that absorbs all the radiation that strikes it regardless of the wave length of the radiation is said to be a *black body*. Real bodies reflect as well as absorb thermal radiation, and it is found that brightly polished metals are good reflectors of thermal radiation. The fraction of the incident heat that is reflected is known as the *reflectivity* of the body, the fraction absorbed is known as the *absorptivity*, and the effectiveness of the body as a thermal radiator at a given temperature is known as its *emissivity*. Thus emissivity is also the ratio of the emission of heat at a given temperature to the emission of heat from a black body at the same temperature.

The radiation from a black body can be determined from the Stefan–Boltzmann law, which states that the radiation from a black body is proportional to the fourth power of the absolute temperature of the body. Thus

$$Q_r = 0.173 \times 10^{-8} A T^4 \tag{9.30}$$

TABLE 9.5

RADIATION BETWEEN SOLIDS, FACTORS FOR USE IN EQUATION (9.31)

SURFACES BETWEEN WHICH RADIATION IS BEING INTERCHANGED	AREA A	F_A	F_e
1. Infinite parallel planes.	A_1 or A_2	1	$\dfrac{1}{\dfrac{1}{\varepsilon_1} + \dfrac{1}{\varepsilon_2} - 1}$
2. Completely enclosed body, small compared with enclosing body. (Subscript 1 refers to enclosed body.)	A_1	1	ε_1
3. Completely enclosed body, large compared with enclosing body. (Subscript 1 refers to enclosed body.)	A_1	1	$\dfrac{1}{\dfrac{1}{\varepsilon_1} + \dfrac{1}{\varepsilon_2} - 1}$
4. Intermediate case between 2 and 3. (Incapable of exact treatment except for special shapes.) (Subscript 1 refers to enclosed body.)	A_1	1	$\varepsilon_1 > F_e > \dfrac{1}{\dfrac{1}{\varepsilon_1} + \dfrac{1}{\varepsilon_2} - 1}$
5. Concentric spheres or infinite cylinders, special case of 4. (Subscript 1 refers to enclosed body.)	A_1	1	$\dfrac{1}{\dfrac{1}{\varepsilon_1} + \dfrac{A_1}{A_2}\left(\dfrac{1}{\varepsilon_2} - 1\right)}$*
6. Surface element dA and area A_2. There are various special cases of 6 with results presentable in graphical form. They follow as cases 7, 8, 9.	dA See special cases 7, 8, 9†		$\varepsilon_1\varepsilon_2$

TABLE 9.5
(CONT'D)

SURFACES BETWEEN WHICH RADIATION IS BEING INTERCHANGED	AREA A	F_A	F_ϵ
7. Element dA and rectangular surface above and parallel to it, with one corner of rectangle contained in normal to dA.	dA	See Fig. 9.23	$\epsilon_1\epsilon_2$
8. Element dA and any rectangular surface above and parallel to it. Split rectangle into four having common corner at normal to dA and treat as in case 7.	dA	Sum of F_A's determined for each rectangle as in case 7	$\epsilon_1\epsilon_2$
9. Element dA and circular disk in plane parallel to plane of dA.	dA	Formula below‡	$\epsilon_1\epsilon_2$
10. Two parallel and equal squares or disks of width or diameter D and distance between of L.	A_1 or A_2	Fig. 9.24, curves 1 and 2	$\epsilon_1\epsilon_2$
11. Same as case 10, except planes connected by nonconducting reradiating walls.	A_1 or A_2	Fig. 9.24, curve 3	$\epsilon_1\epsilon_2$
12. Two equal rectangles in parallel planes directly opposite each other and distance L between.	A_1 or A_2	$F_A'F_A''$§	$\epsilon_1\epsilon_2$ or $\dfrac{1}{\dfrac{1}{\epsilon_1}+\dfrac{1}{\epsilon_2}-1}$

TABLE 9.5
(CONT'D)

SURFACES BETWEEN WHICH RADIATION IS BEING INTERCHANGED	AREA A	F_A	F_ϵ
13. Two rectangles with common sides, in perpendicular planes.	A_1 or A_2	Fig. 9.25	$\epsilon_1 \epsilon_2$
14. Radiation from a plane to a tube bank (1 or 2 rows) above and parallel to the plane.	A_1 or A_2	Fig. 9.26	$\epsilon_1 \epsilon_2$

From Introduction to Heat Transfer, 3rd Ed., by A. I. Brown and S. M. Marco, McGraw-Hill Book Co., New York, 1952, with permission.

This form results from assumption of completely diffuse reflection. If reflection is completely specular (mirrorlike), then $F_\epsilon = 1/[(1/\epsilon_1 + 1/\epsilon_2) - 1]$.

A complete treatment of this subject, including formulas for special complicated cases and the description of a mechanical device for solving problems in radiation, is given by H. C. Hottel in Mech. Eng., 52 (7), 699 (July 1930).

Case 9, R = radius of disk + distance between planes; x = distance from dA to normal through center of disk + distance between planes.

$$F_A = \frac{1}{2}\left\{ 1 - \frac{x^2 + 1 - R^2}{\sqrt{x^2 + 2(1 - R^2)x^2 + (1 + R^2)^2}} \right\}$$

§ $F'_A = F_A$ for squares equivalent to short side of rectangle (Fig. 9.24 curve 2)
$F''_A = F_A$ for squares equivalent to long side of rectangle (Fig. 9.24, curve 2)
$F_\epsilon = \epsilon_1 \epsilon_2$ if the areas are small compared with L
$F_\epsilon = 1/[(1/\epsilon_1 + 1/\epsilon_2) - 1]$ if the areas are large compared with L

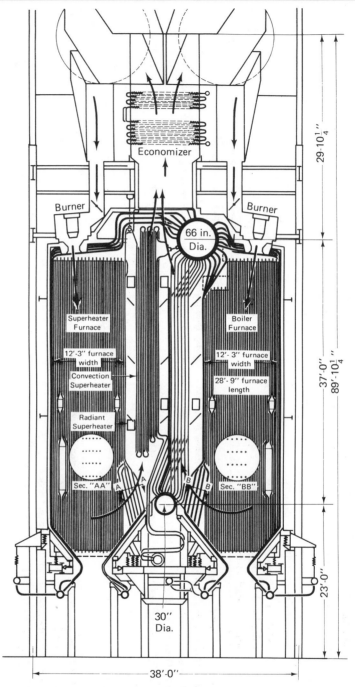

Figure 9.22 Large central station twin furnace unit: in this unit steam generation is largely by radiation in the boiler furnace, and a large portion of the superheating is done by radiation in the superheating furnace (Courtesy of Foster-Wheeler Corp.)

where Q_r is the radiant heat transfer in Btu/hr, A is the radiating area in sq ft, and T is the absolute temperature in °R. The net interchange of heat by radiation between two bodies at different temperatures can be written as

$$Q_r = \sigma F_e F_A A (T_1^4 - T_2^4) \qquad (9.31)$$

where

σ = Stefan–Boltzmann constant = 0.173×10^{-8}

  (in SI, 5.669×10^{-8})

F_e = emissivity factor to allow for the departure of the surfaces interchanging heat from complete blackness; F_e is a function of the surface emissivities and configurations

F_A = geometric factor to allow for the average solid angle through which one surface "sees" the other

A = area in square feet (in SI, m^2)

T_1, T_2 = absolute temperatures, °R (in SI, Kelvin)

Figure 9.22 shows a twin furnace unit where radiation plays a large role in the generation and superheating of steam.

Table 9.5 and Figs. 9.23 through 9.26 give the required values of F_e and F_A for most cases of practical interest. To evaluate F_e, it is necessary to know the emissivities (ε) of the surfaces involved. A table of emissivity of various surfaces is given in Appendix III. In general, highly polished metals have low emissivities; the emissivity of most materials increases with temperature; most nonmetals have high emissivities; and the emissivity of a given surface will have wide variations depending on the conditions of the surface.

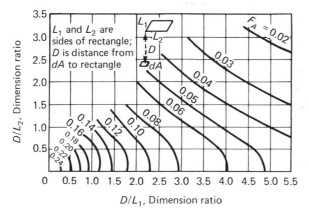

Figure 9.23 Radiation between surface element and rectangle above and parallel to it

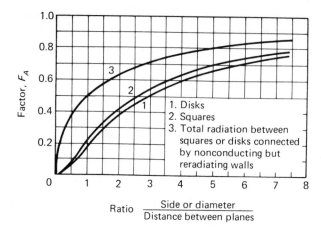

Figure 9.24 Direct radiation between equal disks or squares in parallel planes directly opposed

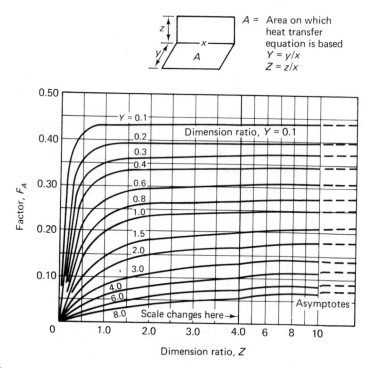

Figure 9.25 Radiation between adjacent rectangles in perpendicular planes

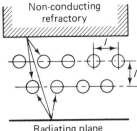

Non-conducting refractory

Radiating plane

Ordinate is fraction of heat radiated from the plane to an infinite number of rows of tubes or to a plane replacing the tubes

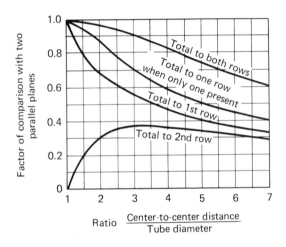

Figure 9.26 Radiation from a plane to one or two rows of tubes above and parallel to the plane

---

ILLUSTRATIVE PROBLEM 9.18

A bare steel pipe having a 3.50 in. outside diameter runs through a room whose walls are at 70°F. Determine the heat loss by radiation from 5 ft of the pipe if its outside temperature is 120°F.

Solution

From Table 9.5, case 2, $F_A = 1$, A is area of pipe, and F_e is the emissivity of the steel pipe. From Appendix III, for oxidized steel $e = 0.79$. Therefore,

$$Q = 0.173 \times 10^{-8} \times 0.79 \times 1 \times \frac{\pi(3.5)}{12}$$

$$\times 5\left[(120+460)^4 - (70+460)^4\right] = 214.5 \text{ Btu/hr}$$

It should be noted that Eq. (9.31) contains a $(T_1^4 - T_2^4)$ term, and not a $(T_1 - T_2)^4$ term, a very common mistake.

In many situations where both radiation and convection occur simultaneously from a body, it is desirable to evaluate a combined heat-transfer coefficient for the process. To arrive at a heat-transfer coefficient for radiation, we will equate Eqs. (9.16) and (9.31) as follows:

$$Q_r = h_r(T_1 - T_2)A = \sigma F_e F_A A(T_1^4 - T_2^4) \qquad (9.32)$$

and

$$h_r = \left[\frac{\sigma F_e F_A (T_1^4 - T_2^4)}{(T_1 - T_2)} \right] \qquad (9.33)$$

which can be rewritten as

$$h_r = F_e F_A \left[\frac{\sigma(T_1^4 - T_2^4)}{(T_1 - T_2)} \right] = F_e F_A h_r' \qquad (9.34)$$

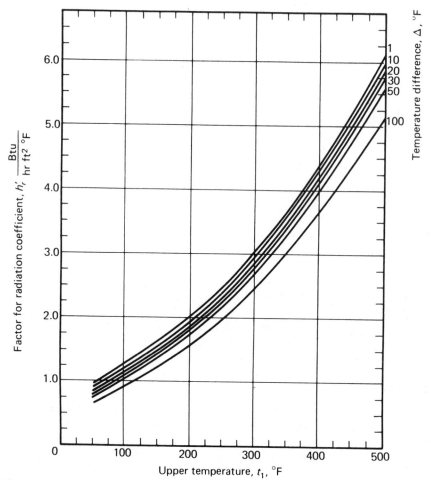

Figure 9.27 Factor for radiation coefficient (From the "Coefficient of Radiant Heat Transfer" by Irving Granet, *Design News*, Sept. 1970)

For small temperature differences the term in brackets, h_r', has been evaluated and plotted in terms of the upper temperature t_1 in degrees Fahrenheit and the temperature difference Δ degrees Fahrenheit between the two bodies in Fig. 9.27.

ILLUSTRATIVE PROBLEM 9.19

Determine the radiation heat-transfer coefficient for the pipe of Illustrative Problem 9.18.

Solution

The upper temperature is given as $120°F$ and the temperature difference Δ is $120 - 70 = 50°F$. Using Fig. 9.27, $h_r' = 1.18$ and $h_r = F_e F_A h_r' = 1 \times 0.79 \times 1.18 = 0.93$. As a check, using the results of Illustrative Problem 9.18,

$$h_r = \frac{Q}{A\,\Delta t} = \frac{214.5}{(\pi(3.5)/12)\times 5(120-70)} = 0.94 \text{ Btu/hr ft}^2 \text{ °F}$$

ILLUSTRATIVE PROBLEM 9.20

Solve Illustrative Problem 9.14 taking into account both convection and radiation.

Solution

Since the conditions of Illustrative Problem 9.14 are the same as for Illustrative Problems 9.18 and 9.19, we can solve this problem in two ways to obtain a check. Thus, adding the results of these problems yields $Q_{\text{TOTAL}} = 206.2 + 214.5 = 420.7$ Btu/hr. We can also approach this solution by obtaining a combined radiation and convection heat-transfer coefficient. Thus $h_{\text{combined}} = 0.9 + 0.94 = 1.84$. $Q_{\text{TOTAL}} = 1.84(\pi \times 3.5/12)5 \times (120 - 70) = 421.5$ Btu/hr. This procedure of obtaining combined or overall heat transfer coefficients will be discussed further in the next section of this chapter.

9.5 HEAT EXCHANGERS

When heat is transferred from one fluid to another in an industrial process without mixing, the fluids are separated and the heat transfer takes place in an apparatus known as a heat exchanger. A heat exchanger can be of varied shape and size and is usually designed to perform a specific function. The steam-generation plant uses heat exchangers as condensers, economizers, air heaters,

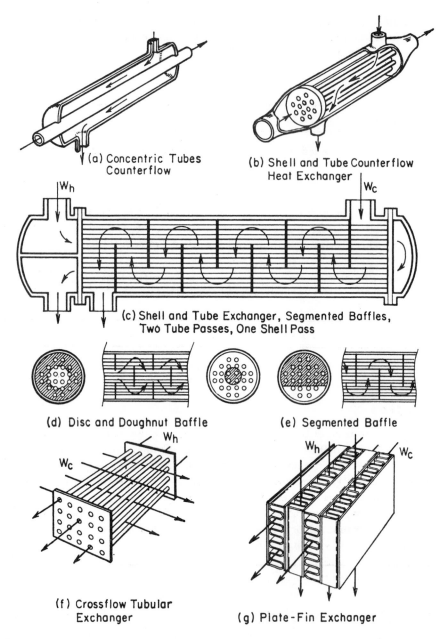

(a) Concentric Tubes Counterflow

(b) Shell and Tube Counterflow Heat Exchanger

(c) Shell and Tube Exchanger, Segmented Baffles, Two Tube Passes, One Shell Pass

(d) Disc and Doughnut Baffle

(e) Segmented Baffle

(f) Crossflow Tubular Exchanger

(g) Plate-Fin Exchanger

Figure 9.28 Representative types of heat exchangers (From *Heat, Mass and Momentum Transfer* by W. M. Rohsenow and H. Y. Choi, Prentice-Hall, Inc., Englewood Cliffs, N.J., 1961, with permission)

feedwater heaters, reheaters, and so on. It is common to designate heat exchangers by their geometric shape and the relative directions of flow of the heat-transfer fluids. For example, Fig. 9.28a shows a concentric tube (or double pipe) unit in which the fluids would be said to be flowing parallel to each other, and the unit would be called a parallel-flow double-pipe unit. Other common types are shown in the remainder of Fig. 9.28. Because of the extensive use of the shell and tube type of heat exchanger, a standard nomenclature has evolved for the parts of this class of unit. This nomenclature is shown in Fig. 9.29.

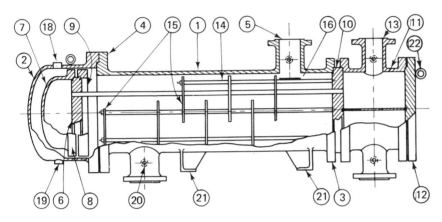

Nomenclature

1. Shell	9. Floating head backing device	16. Impingement baffle
2. Shell cover	10. Stationary tubesheet	17. Longitudinal baffle
3. Shell channel end flange	11. Channel	18. Vent connection
4. Shell cover end flange	12. Channel cover	19. Drain connection
5. Shell nozzle	13. Channel nozzle	20. Test connection
6. Floating tubesheet	14. Tie rods and spacers	21. Support saddles
7. Floating head	15. Transverse baffles or support	22. Lifting ring
8. Floating head flange	plates	

Figure 9.29 Single pass shell and tube heat exchangers (Used with permission from Standards of Tubular Exchanger Manufacturers Association.)

The problem of calculating the heat transfer in these units differs from our previous discussion in that the temperature of one or both of the fluids varies continuously as the fluids proceed through the heat exchanger. This can be seen in Fig. 9.30, where the fluid temperatures have been plotted as a function of the heat transfer surface for the most common cases of parallel flow, counterflow, and for one fluid at constant temperature. The subscript h is used to denote the hot fluid, and the subscript c denotes the cold fluid. The sub-subscript $①$ is used to denote the temperature at the entry of a fluid to the heat exchanger, and $②$ denotes the temperature of the fluid at the exit of the heat exchanger. The direction of flow of each fluid through the exchanger is shown by the arrowheads on the temperature curves. The largest temperature difference between the fluids in the unit (at either inlet or outlet) is designated as θ_A, and the least temperature difference between the fluids (at either inlet or outlet) is designated as θ_B.

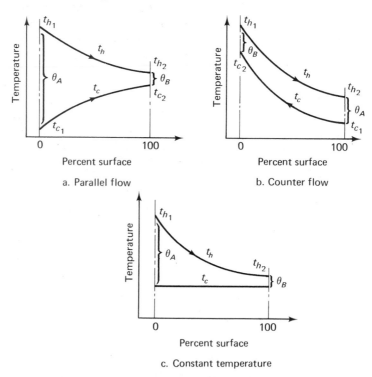

Figure 9.30 Fluid temperatures in heat exchangers

Newton's law of cooling [Eq. (9.16)] can be written for the heat exchangers as

$$Q = UA(\Delta t)_m \qquad (9.35)$$

where U is the overall conductance or overall heat-transfer coefficient having the same physical units as the convection coefficient h, Btu/hr ft^2 °F; A is the heat transfer surface in square feet; and $(\Delta t)_m$ is an appropriate mean temperature difference. The overall coefficient of heat transfer, U, in Eq. (9.35) is not usually constant for all locations in the heat exchanger, and its local value is a function of the local fluid temperatures. However, it is usual practice to evaluate the individual heat-transfer coefficients based upon the arithmetic average fluid temperatures. By analogy to convection, we have $1/UA =$ resistance. The concept of the overall heat-transfer coefficient is best illustrated by Illustrative Problems 9.21 and 9.22.

ILLUSTRATIVE PROBLEM 9.21

Determine the overall heat-transfer coefficient for the composite wall of Illustrative Problem 9.4 if h on the hot side is 0.9 Btu/hr ft^2 °F and h on the cold side is 1.5 Btu/hr ft^2 °F. The temperatures given are to be the respective air temperatures (see Fig. 9.7, repeated here).

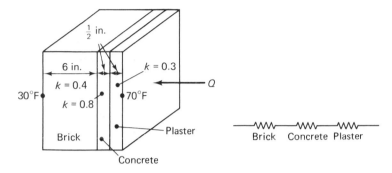

Figure 9.7 Illustrative Problem 9.4

Solution

For a plane wall the areas are all the same, and if we use 1 ft^2 of wall surface as the reference area,

$$\text{brick resistance} = \frac{\Delta x}{kA} = \frac{6/12}{0.4 \times 1} = 1.25$$

$$\text{concrete resistance} = \frac{\Delta x}{kA} = \frac{\frac{1}{2}/12}{0.8 \times 1} = 0.052$$

$$\text{plaster resistance} = \frac{\Delta x}{kA} = \frac{\frac{1}{2}/12}{0.3 \times 1} = 0.139$$

$$\text{``hot film'' resistance} = \frac{1}{hA} = \frac{1}{0.9 \times 1} = 1.11$$

$$\text{``cold film'' resistance} = \frac{1}{hA} = \frac{1}{1.5 \times 1} = 0.67$$

$$\text{total resistance} = \qquad 3.22$$

The overall conductance (or overall heat-transfer coefficient) $U = 1/(\text{overall resistance}) = 1/3.22 = 0.31$ Btu/hr ft^2. In Illustrative Problem 9.18 the solution is straightforward since the heat transfer area is constant for all the series resistances.

ILLUSTRATIVE PROBLEM 9.22

A steel pipe, $k = 26$ Btu/hr ft °F, having an outside diameter of 3.5 in., an inside diameter of 3.00 in., and 5 ft long, is covered with 1 in. of mineral wool, $k = 0.026$ Btu/hr ft °F. If the film coefficient on the inside of the pipe is 45 Btu/hr ft² °F and on the outside it is 0.9 Btu/hr ft² °F, determine the overall heat-transfer coefficient. (See Fig. 9.31 and also Illustrative Problems 9.8 and 9.10.)

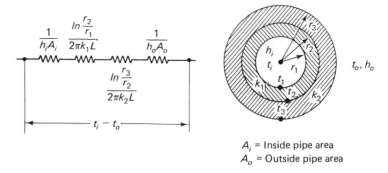

A_i = Inside pipe area
A_o = Outside pipe area

Figure 9.31 Illustrative Problem 9.22

Solution

Since the same amount of heat traverses each of the paths, we can write

$$Q = Q_i = A_i h_i (t_i - t_1) = 2\pi r_1 L h_i (t_i - t_1)$$

$$= \frac{2\pi k_1 L}{\ln(r_2/r_1)} (t_1 - t_2)$$

$$= \frac{2\pi k_2 L}{\ln(r_3/r_2)} (t_2 - t_3)$$

$$= A_o h_o (t_3 - t_o) = 2\pi r_3 L h_o (t_o - t_3)$$

Solving for the temperature differences and adding them yields

$$Q = \frac{t_i - t_o}{\dfrac{1}{2\pi r_1 L h_i} + \dfrac{\ln(r_2/r_1)}{2\pi k_1 L} + \dfrac{\ln(r_3/r_2)}{2\pi k_2 L} + \dfrac{1}{2\pi r_3 L h_o}} \qquad (a)$$

While this equation looks formidable, we can simplify it and interpret it in terms of items previously discussed in this chapter. Thus

$$Q = \frac{(t_i - t_o)2\pi L}{\dfrac{1}{h_i r_1} + \dfrac{\ln(r_2/r_1)}{k_1} + \dfrac{\ln(r_3/r_2)}{k_2} + \dfrac{1}{h_o r_3}} \qquad (b)$$

Let us now define U_o as the overall heat transfer coefficient based upon the outside pipe surface A_o as

$$Q = U_o A_o (t_i - t_o) \qquad (c)$$

If we multiply the numerator and denominator of Eq. (b) by r_3, we obtain

$$Q = \frac{(t_i - t_o)2\pi L r_3}{\dfrac{r_3}{h_i r_1} + \dfrac{r_3}{k_1}\ln\dfrac{r_2}{r_1} + \dfrac{r_3}{k_2}\ln\dfrac{r_3}{r_2} + \dfrac{r_3}{h_o r_3}} \qquad (d)$$

Comparison of Eqs. (c) and (d) yields

$$U_o = \frac{1}{\dfrac{1}{h_i \dfrac{r_1}{r_3}} + \dfrac{r_3}{k_1}\ln\dfrac{r_2}{r_1} + \dfrac{r_3}{k_2}\ln\dfrac{r_3}{r_2} + \dfrac{1}{h_o}} \qquad (e)$$

Note that U_o is the overall heat transfer coefficient based upon the outside tube surface. If we had multiplied Eq. (b) by r_1/r_1 we would obtain the overall heat-transfer coefficient U_i based upon the inside surface as

$$U_i = \frac{1}{\dfrac{1}{h_i} + \dfrac{r_1}{k_1}\ln\dfrac{r_2}{r_1} + \dfrac{r_1}{k_2}\ln\dfrac{r_3}{r_2} + \dfrac{1}{h_o \dfrac{r_3}{r_1}}} \qquad (f)$$

In effect we have required $U_o A_o = U_i A_i$. When discussing an overall heat transfer coefficient the reference area must be given. Proceeding with the numerical problem

$$\frac{1}{h_i} = \frac{1}{45} = 0.02222$$

$$\frac{r_1}{k_1}\ln\frac{r_2}{r_1} = \frac{3.00}{2} \Big/ (26 \times 12)\ln\left(\frac{3.50}{3.00}\right) = 0.00074$$

$$\frac{r_1}{k_2}\ln\frac{r_3}{r_2} = \frac{3.00}{2} \Big/ (0.026 \times 12)\ln\left(\frac{5.50}{3.50}\right) = 2.1730$$

$$\frac{1}{h_0(r_3/r_1)} = \frac{1}{0.9(5.50/3.00)} = \underline{0.6061}$$

$$\sum = 2.8021$$

Therefore,

$$U_i = \frac{1}{2.8021} = 0.357\ \frac{\text{Btu}}{\text{hr ft}^2\ {}^\circ\text{F}} \quad \text{(of inside area)}$$

Since $U_o A_o = U_i A_i$, $U_o = 0.357 \times A_i/A_o = 0.357 D_1/D_3 = 0.357(3.00/5.50) = 0.195$ Btu/(hr ft^2 °F) (of outside area).

Some typical values of overall heat transfer coefficients are given in Table 9.6 that are useful in making preliminary design calculation.

If it is assumed that:

1 U is constant over the entire heat exchanger.
2 Both fluid flows are steady, that is, constant with time.
3 The specific heat of each fluid is constant over the entire heat exchanger.
4 Heat losses are negligible,

then $(\Delta t)_m$ in Eq. (9.35) is given for parallel flow, counterflow, and constant temperature exchangers as

$$(\Delta t)_m = \frac{\theta_A - \theta_B}{\ln(\theta_A/\theta_B)} \qquad (9.36)$$

where θ_A is the greatest temperature difference between the fluids (at either inlet or outlet) and θ_B is the least temperature difference between the fluids (at

TABLE 9.6*
APPROXIMATE OVERALL COEFFICIENTS FOR
PRELIMINARY ESTIMATES

DUTY	OVERALL COEFFICIENT (Btu/hr sq ft° F)
Steam to water	
Instantaneous heater	400–600
Storage-tank heater	175–300
Steam to oil	
Heavy fuel	10–30
Light fuel	30–60
Light petroleum distillate	50–200
Steam to aqueous solutions	100–600
Steam to gases	5–50
Water to compressed air	10–30
Water to water, jacket water coolers	150–275
Water to lubricating oil	20–60
Water to condensing oil vapors	40–100
Water to condensing alcohol	45–120
Water to condensing Freon-12	80–150
Water to condensing ammonia	150–250
Water to organic solvents, alcohol	50–150
Water to boiling Freon-12	50–150
Water to gasoline	60–90
Water to gas, oil, or distillate	35–60
Water to brine	100–200
Light organics to light organics	40–75
Medium organics to medium organics	20–60
Heavy organics to heavy organics	10–40
Heavy organics to light organics	10–60
Crude oil to gas oil	30–55

Note: $1 \ Btu/hr \cdot ft^2 \cdot °F = 5.6786 \ W/m^2 \cdot °C.$

* *Reproduced from Principles of Heat Transfer by F. Kreith, International Textbook Co., Scranton, Pa., 1958, p. 463, with permission.*

either inlet or outlet). Thus $(\Delta t)_m$ is known as the logarithmic mean temperature difference. Since heat losses are assumed to be negligible, the heat transferred from the hot fluid must equal that received by the cold fluid. Therefore,

$$\dot{m}_c (c_p)_c (t_{c2} - t_{c1}) = \dot{m}_h (c_p)_h (t_{h1} - t_{h2}) \qquad (9.37)$$

ILLUSTRATIVE PROBLEM 9.23

A counterflow heat exchanger is used to cool a flow of 400 lb/min of lubricating oil. Hot oil enters at 215°F and leaves at 125°F. The specific heat of the oil is 0.85 Btu/lb °F, and the overall coefficient of heat transfer of the unit is 40 Btu/hr ft² °F (of outside tube surface). Water enters the unit at 60°F and leaves at 90°F. Determine the outside tube surface required.

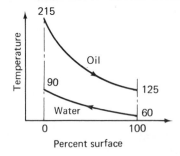

Figure 9.32 Illustrative Problem 9.20

Solution

From Fig. 9.32, $\theta_A = 215 - 90 = 125$°F and $\theta_B = 125 - 60 = 65$°F. Therefore,

$$(\Delta t)_m = \frac{\theta_A - \theta_B}{\ln(\theta_A/\theta_B)} = \frac{(125 - 65)}{\ln(125/65)} = 92°F$$

From the oil data, the heat transfer $Q = \dot{m}c_p(\Delta t) = 400 \times 60 \times 0.85(215 - 125) = 1,836,000$ Btu/hr, and from the heat-transfer equation, $Q = UA(\Delta t)_m = 1,836,000 = 40 \times A \times 92$. Therefore, $A = 499$ ft² of outside surface required.

ILLUSTRATIVE PROBLEM 9.24

If the heat exchanger in Illustrative Problem 9.23 is operated in parallel flow, determine the outside tube surface required.

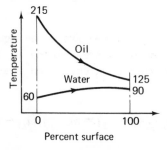

Figure 9.33 Illustrative Problem 9.24

Solution

From Fig. 9.33, $\theta_A = 215 - 60 = 155°F$ and $\theta_B = 125 - 90 = 35°F$. Therefore,

$$(\Delta t)_m = \frac{\theta_A - \theta_B}{\ln(\theta_A/\theta_B)} = \frac{155 - 35}{\ln(155/35)} = 80.5°F$$

Since all other conditions are the same, $Q = 1,836,000$ Btu/hr.

$$1,836,000 = 40 \times A \times 80.5$$

Therefore, $A = 570$ ft^2 of outside surface required.

From the results of Illustrative Problems 9.23 and 9.24, we note that operation of a heat exchanger in parallel flow requires more surface for the same terminal temperatures than for a unit operated in counterflow. This conclusion is general, since $(\Delta t)_m$ between the same terminal temperature limits is always greater for counterflow than for parallel flow. Thus, where a choice exists, it is preferable to operate a unit in counterflow since this type of operation will give the minimum surface requirements. Another advantage of counterflow is that it is possible to raise the exit temperature of the cooling fluid more closely to the inlet temperature of the hot fluid.

After a period of operation it is found that heat exchangers cannot transfer as much heat as when they are first started up clean. This is due to a buildup of scale, dirt, or oxide films and is known as *fouling*. This effect is taken into account in heat-exchanger design by introducing series resistances known as fouling factors in the design calculations. Table 9.7 gives typical values of fouling factors for various fluids.

TABLE 9.7
TYPICAL FOULING FACTORS*

TYPES OF FLUID	*FOULING RESISTANCE* (hr °F sq ft/Btu)
Sea water below 125°F	0.0005
Sea water above 125°F	0.001
Treated boiler feedwater above 125°F	0.001
East River water below 125°F	0.002–0.003
Fuel oil	0.005
Quenching oil	0.004
Alcohol vapors	0.0005
Steam, non-oil-bearing	0.0005
Industrial air	0.002
Refrigerating liquid	0.001

Note: Dividing the values by 5.6786 will yield m^2·°C/W.

Reproduced with permission from Principles of Heat Transfer by F. Kreith, International Textbook Co., Inc., Scranton, Pa., 1958, p. 461.

ILLUSTRATIVE PROBLEM 9.25

Using Table 9.7 for the appropriate fouling factors, calculate the surface required for Illustrative Problem 9.23.

Solution

For the oil side, a resistance (fouling factor) of 0.005 hr °F sq ft/Btu can be used, and for the water side, a fouling factor of 0.001 hr °F sq ft/Btu can be used. Due to the approximate nature of these resistances, we shall not correct them for inside or outside reference areas, and we will assume that they can be used directly with the value of U of 40 Btu/hr ft² °F. The overall resistance and overall heat-transfer coefficient are obtained as

$$
\begin{array}{lr}
\text{oil, } R = & 0.005 \\
\text{water, } R = & 0.001 \\
\text{clean unit, } R = 1/40 & 0.025 \\
\hline
R_{\text{overall}} = & 0.031
\end{array}
$$

$$
U_{\text{overall}} = \frac{1}{0.031} = 32.3 \; \frac{\text{Btu}}{\text{hr ft}^2 \; °\text{F}}
$$

Since all other parameters are the same, the surface required will vary inversely as U. Therefore, $A = 400 \times 40/32.3 = 618$ sq ft or an increase in surface required of approximately 24 percent due to fouling. This obviously represents an important consideration in the design of industrial equipment.

9.6 CLOSURE

The general subject of heat transfer is a vast field that encompasses many technical disciplines. In an introductory chapter such as this, it has only been possible to briefly cover some of the basic topics of interest. A large portion of the material in this field has been based upon empirical test data in the past, and in the recent decades great strides have been made in developing analytical and numerical procedures for the calculation of many heat-transfer problems. As an example, work done in conjunction with the space program has included fundamental and applied studies in such diverse areas as radiation heat transfer to space vehicles, ablation, lightweight "super" insulations, heat transfer in high speed flow, transpiration cooling, thermal contact resistances, heat transfer from plasmas, and compact heat exchangers. In more everyday areas we find that the design of furnaces has been placed on a more rational basis, the design of nuclear fuel elements (which includes internal heat sources) has been extensively studied, thermal stress calculations are almost universally carried out by suitable programs on high speed digital computers, and so on. This is a truly fertile field with an almost infinite number of unsolved problems that represents great potential for original work. Mastery of the material in this chapter is a minimum requirement for understanding and evaluating industrial heat power equipment, as well as for more advanced work in heat transfer.

REFERENCES

1 *Thermodynamics*, 2nd Ed., by F. P. Durham, Prentice-Hall, Inc., Englewood Cliffs, N.J., 1959.

2 *Heat Mass and Momentum Transfer* by W. M. Rohsenow and H. Y. Choi, Prentice-Hall, Inc., Englewood Cliffs, N.J., 1961.

3 *Heat Transfer*, 4th Ed., by J. P. Holman, McGraw-Hill Book Co., New York, 1976.

4 *Introduction to Heat Transfer*, 3rd Ed., by A. I. Brown and S. M. Marco, McGraw-Hill Book Co., New York, 1958.

5 *Principles of Heat Transfer* by F. Kreith, International Textbook Co., Scranton, Pa., 1958.

6 *Thermodynamics* by G. F. Babits, Allyn & Bacon, Inc., Boston, 1963.

7 *Fluid Mechanics for Engineering Technology* by Irving Granet, Prentice-Hall, Inc., Englewood Cliffs, N.J., 1971.

8 "Natural Convection Heat Transfer Aids" by Irving Granet, *Design News*, March 20, 1972.

9 "Heat Transfer to Subsaturated Water, Dry Air, and Hydrogen in Turbulent Flow Inside a Tube" by Irving Granet, *Journal of the American Society of Naval Engineers*, November 1957, pp. 787–794.

10 *Heat Transmission*, 3rd Ed., by W. H. McAdams, McGraw-Hill Book Co., New York, 1954.

11 "The Coefficient of Radiant Heat Transfer" by Irving Granet, *Design News*, September 29, 1970.

12 "Heat Transfer Performance Curves" by Irving Granet, *Chemical Engineering*, March 1955, pp. 187–190.

PROBLEMS

Use the data of Table 9.1 and Fig. 9.3 for these problems unless indicated otherwise.

9.1 A common brick wall is 4 in. thick. Determine the rate of heat transfer through the wall if one face is at 95°F while the other is at 32°F.

9.2 Compare the insulating qualities of the wall in Problem 9.1 with that of a wooden white pine wall 2 in. thick.

9.3 Compare the insulating qualities of a conducting air gap $\frac{1}{4}$ in. thick with the brick wall of Problem 9.1.

9.4 A test is conducted to determine the thermal conductivity of a material. If the test specimen is 1 ft by 1 ft and 6 in. thick and steady state surface temperatures are found to be 100° and 92°F, respectively, while 60 Btu/hr is being applied, determine the thermal conductivity of the unknown material.

9.5 A brick wall is 100 mm thick. How much heat is transferred through the wall if one face is held at 40°C while the other is held at 0°C?

9.6 A test is conducted in which the test specimen is 1 m² by 150 mm thick. Steady state temperatures are found to be 35° and 30°C, respectively. If 20 W is applied, determine the thermal conductivity of the material.

9.7 A furnace wall is 12 in. thick and is made of firebrick whose thermal conductivity can be taken to be 0.11 Btu/hr ft °F. If the heat loss is designed not to exceed 100 Btu/hr ft², determine the outside wall temperature if the inside wall temperature is 1400°F.

9.8 A wall is designed to limit the heat transfer through it to 500 W/m². If it is of firebrick whose $k = 0.22$ W/m · °C and it is 500 mm thick, what is the design temperature differential across the wall?

9.9 A composite series wall has an inside surface temperature of 125°F and an outside surface temperature of 52°F. If it consists of 3 in. of mineral wool, $\frac{1}{2}$ in. of plaster on the outside, and $\frac{1}{2}$ in. of corkboard on the inside, determine the heat loss per square foot of wall.

9.10 Determine the interface temperatures in Problem 9.9.

9.11 A so-called "solid brick" construction consists of three courses of common brick each 4 in. thick. Comment on the insulating qualities of this wall when compared to a hollow wall filled with 3 in. of mineral wool.

9.12 A bar of steel 1 in. in diameter and 6 in. long is cut in half and the cut ends are pressed together. If the thermal contact resistance can be thought of as an equivalent air gap of 0.001 in. thick ($k = 0.01$ Btu/hr ft °F), determine the percent increase in resistance to heat transfer from one end of the bar to the other due to the cutting of the bar, that is, [(cut resistance − uncut resistance)/uncut resistance] × 100.

9.13 A wall is to be made of 4-in. common brick, 2 in. of mineral wool, and $\frac{1}{2}$ in. of wallboard ($k = 0.04$ Btu/hr ft °F from Appendix III). Determine the heat transfer from the wall if the inside wall temperature is at 74°F when the outside wall is at 0°F.

9.14 Determine the interface temperature in Problem 9.13.

9.15 A wall consists of 100 mm of mineral wool, 12 mm of plaster, and 12 mm of corkboard. If a temperature difference of 30°C is maintained across the wall, what is the steady state heat transfer?

9.16 If a film coefficient of 1 W/m·°C exists on the inside of the wall in Problem 9.15, and the temperature differential is across the film plus the composite wall, determine the heat transfer.

9.17 A wall, 7 ft by 7 ft, conducts 500 Btu/hr. If there is a film coefficient on the inside of the wall of 1 Btu/hr ft^2 °F, and the wall has a resistance equal to 1 in. of mineral wool, determine the temperature drop across each resistance.

9.18 A composite wall consists of $\frac{1}{2}$ in. of plaster and 2 in. of fir. If the hot-side air is at 105°F, the cold side air is at 10°F, the hot-side film coefficient is 2 Btu/hr ft^2 °F, and the cold side film coefficient is 4 Btu/hr ft^2 °F, determine the heat transfer per square foot of wall.

9.19 Determine the temperature drops through each resistance in Problem 9.18.

9.20 What is the heat loss from a bare steel pipe ($k = 45$ W/m·°C) whose inside temperature is 100°C and whose outer temperature is 10°C. The inside diameter of the pipe is 25 mm and the outside diameter is 40 mm. Its length is 2 m.

9.21 A steel pipe having a $4\frac{1}{2}$-in. OD is insulated with a molded pipe covering of diatomaceous earth ($k = 0.036$ Btu/hr ft °F) $1\frac{1}{2}$ in. thick. Thermocouples embedded in the insulation read 212°F on the inside and 130°F on the outside. Find the heat loss per foot length of pipe.

9.22 Determine the heat loss from 50 ft of $3\frac{1}{2}$ in. OD pipe covered with 1-in. insulation ($k = 0.03$ Btu/hr ft °F) if the inner temperature of the insulation is 350°F and the outer temperature is 100°F.

9.23 A large steel pipe having an 8 in. OD carries superheated steam. If the inside insulation temperature is 800°F and the pipe is insulated with 3 in. of molded pipe covering ($k = 0.036$ Btu/hr ft °F), determine the heat loss per foot of pipe if the outside insulation temperature does not exceed 140°F.

9.24 If the steel pipe in Problem 9.23 has a wall thickness of $\frac{1}{2}$ in. and $k_{steel} = 26$ Btu/hr ft °F, determine the heat loss per foot of pipe. Assume the inside of the pipe is at 800°F and the outside of the insulation remains at 140°F. Compare the results with Problem 9.23.

9.25 If the pipe in Problem 9.23 has an outside heat transfer coefficient of 2.5 Btu/hr ft^2 °F, and the room temperature is 140°F, determine the heat loss per foot of pipe. Neglect the steel wall resistance.

9.26 A bare horizontal pipe with 6 in. OD has its outer surface at 140°F in a room whose air temperature is 65°F. Determine the natural convection heat-transfer coefficient on the outside of the pipe.

9.27 If, instead of a pipe, the surface in Problem 9.26 was a 1 ft by 1 ft square plate with the hot side facing up, determine the convection heat-transfer coefficient.

9.28 Determine the heat loss to the room by convection if the pipe in Problem 9.26 is 10 ft long.

9.29 If the hot surface of the plate in Problem 9.27 faces down, determine the convection heat transfer coefficient.

9.30 Atmospheric air flows in a 1 in. ID tube at the rate of 0.2 lb/sec. If the average air temperature is 150°F, determine the film coefficient on the inside of the tube.

9.31 If water flows in a 1 in. ID tube at the rate of 1 lb/sec, determine the film coefficient on the inside of the tube. The average water temperature is 150°F.

9.32 Air flows in a 1.5 in. ID tube at the rate of 0.4 lb/sec and has an average temperature of 500°F. If the air is at atmospheric pressure, determine the heat transfer coefficient on the inside of the tube.

9.33 Water having an average temperature of 200°F flows in a 2 in. ID pipe at the rate of 1.5 lb/sec. Determine the heat-transfer coefficient on the inside of the pipe.

9.34 Calculate the rate of heat radiation from a black body per square foot of radiating area if the temperature of the body is 1000°, 100°, and 0°F.

9.35 A $3\frac{1}{2}$ in. OD oxidized iron pipe whose outer temperature is 175°F passes through a room at 75°F. If $\epsilon_{pipe} = 0.8$, determine h_r, the radiation heat-transfer coefficient.

9.36 If, in Problem 9.34, there is a convection heat transfer coefficient of 1.5 Btu/hr ft² °F on the outside of the pipe, determine the combined heat-transfer coefficient and the heat loss per foot of pipe.

9.37 A body whose emissivity is 0.9 is placed in a large room whose walls are at 20°C. If the body is at 250°C, determine the heat radiated to the walls per square metre of body surface. Assume that the body is small compared to the dimensions of the room.

9.38 Calculate the radiant heat interchange between two square plates having 1-ft sides if they are separated by $\frac{1}{2}$ ft. Assume one square has an emissivity of 0.8 while the other has an emissivity of 0.6. The hotter surface is at 1000°F and the colder surface is at 100°F.

9.39 A tube is made of steel and has a thermal conductivity of 26 Btu/hr ft °F; on one side the film coefficient is 500 Btu/hr ft² °F, while on the other side the film coefficient is 250 Btu/hr ft² °F. Determine the overall heat transfer coefficient if the tube is $\frac{1}{4}$ in. thick.

9.40 A condenser has condensed steam on its shell side at 81.7°F. If the cooling water enters at 60°F and leaves at 70°F, determine the logarithmic mean temperature difference in the unit.

9.41 If the overall heat transfer coefficient in Problem 9.40 is 1000 Btu/hr ft^2 °F of outside tube surface, determine the heat transfer per square foot of exchanger outside tube surface.

9.42 A counterflow heat exchanger cools oil from 175° to 125°F. The cooling water enters at 65°F and leaves at 85°F. Calculate the logarithmic mean temperature difference in the unit.

9.43 If the heat exchanger in Problem 9.42 is operated as a parallel flow unit, determine the logarithmic mean temperature difference.

9.44 A counterflow heat exchanger operates with oil cooled from 90° to 50°C. The cooling water enters at 15°C and leaves at 25°C. If the overall heat transfer coefficient based on the outside tube surface is 200 W/m^2·°C, determine the heat transfer per square metre of outside tube surface.

9.45 If the heat exchanger in Problem 9.44 is operated as a parallel flow unit, determine the heat transfer.

9.46 A condenser operates with steam condensing on the shell side at 27°C. Cooling water enters at 5°C and leaves at 10°C. If the overall heat transfer coefficient is 5000 W/m^2·°C based on the outside tube surface, determine the heat transfer per square metre of outside tube surface.

9.47 A nuclear steam generator boils water (makes steam) at 500°F on the shell side of a steam generator. Water enters the tubes at 570°F and leaves at 525°F. Determine the logarithmic mean temperature difference.

9.48 A heat exchanger is used to transfer 1×10^6 Btu/hr. At inlet the temperature difference between fluids is 75°F and at outlet the temperature difference is 35°F. Determine the surface required if the overall heat transfer coefficient is 175 Btu/hr ft^2 °F, based on the outside area of the tubes.

9.49 How much heat is being exchanged in a heat exchanger having an overall heat-transfer coefficient of 60 Btu/hr ft^2 °F based on the outside area of the tubes, 625 sq ft of outside tube area, and temperature differences between fluids at inlet of 62°F and at outlet of 36°F.

9.50 A shell and tube heat exchanger has a film coefficient on the inside of the tube of 100 Btu/hr ft^2 °F, a steel tube wall thickness of 0.105 in., ($k = 26$ Btu/hr ft °F), a tube OD of $\frac{3}{4}$ in., and a film coefficient on the shell side (outside of tube) of 50 Btu/hr ft^2 °F. Determine the overall film coefficient based upon the inside area of the tube.

9.51 Determine the overall film coefficient of the unit in Problem 9.50 based upon the outside area of the tube.

9.52 A counter flow heat exchanger is used to cool 2000 lb/hr of oil from 150°

to 100°F. Assume c_p of oil to be 0.5 Btu/lb °F. Water ($c_p = 1$ Btu/lb °F) enters at 55°F and leaves at 75°F. U, based on the outside area of the tubes, is 30 Btu/hr ft^2 °F. Determine the area required.

9.53 A shell and tube heat exchanger is used to condense steam on the shell side at 81.7°F. Cooling water enters the tubes at 60°F and leaves at 70°F. The tubes have a 1 in. OD, a 0.902 in. ID, and a conductivity of 63 Btu/hr ft °F. The film coefficient on the inside of the tubes is 1200 Btu/hr ft^2 °F and on the outside, 950 Btu/hr ft^2 °F. If the unit extracts 766×10^6 Btu/hr, determine the outside tube area.

appendix 1

appendix of thermodynamic terms

The following is intended to provide the student with a convenient word list for reference. It is not a complete glossary, and the definitions have been kept as brief as possible, consistent with accuracy.

Absolute humidity
> Weight of water vapor per pound of dry air in an air–water vapor mixture. *See also* Specific humidity.

Absolute pressure
> Pressure measured relative to a perfect vacuum.

Adiabatic process
> A process during which no energy as heat enters or leaves a system undergoing the specified state change.

Avogadro's law
> Equal volumes of gases at the same temperature and pressure contain the same number of particles.

British thermal unit
> Defined as 778.169 ft lb.

Carnot cycle
> A reversible cycle consisting of two isothermal and two isentropic

processes.

Coefficient of performance

Ratio of the heat removed in a refrigeration process to the work input.

Compression ratio

Ratio of the total volume in a cylinder at the beginning of the compression part of the cycle to that at the end of the compression cycle.

Continuity equation

An equation expressing the conservation of mass in a steady-flow system.

Critical point

A limiting state of a fluid in which the density of saturated liquid equals the density of saturated vapor. Also, the latent heat of vaporization is at zero at this point.

Critical pressure

The pressure of a fluid at the critical point.

Critical pressure ratio

The ratio of the pressure at the minimum area in a converging–diverging nozzle to the inlet pressure. The velocity at this section of the nozzle is sonic under certain conditions.

Critical temperature

The temperature of a fluid at the critical point.

Cycle

A series of thermodynamic processes during which the working fluid can be made to undergo changes involving energy transitions and is subsequently returned to its original state.

Cycles

Brayton
Carnot
Diesel
Otto
Rankine
Regenerative
Reheat
Reheat regenerative
Stirling

Degrees of superheat

Temperature excess of vapor over the saturation temperature at a given pressure.

Density

Mass per unit volume.

Dew-point temperature

Temperature that a gas–vapor mixture must reach at constant total mixture pressure to condense the vapor.

Discharge coefficient

Ratio of the actual mass flow from a nozzle to the ideally calculated mass flow rate.

Dry-bulb temperature

The temperature of a mixture of air and water vapor.

Dry compression

The compression of a vapor in a vapor–liquid vapor–compression refrigeration cycle.

Dryness

See Quality

Energy

The capacity for performing work (sometimes expressed as the capacity to produce an effect).

Enthalpy

The sum of internal energy and pv/J.

Entropy

A property of a substance. Since it is a property it depends only on the end states of a process and not the path of the process.

Equation of state

A thermodynamic relation giving the functional dependence of the properties of the substance with each other.

Expansion ratio

Ratio of the total volume at the end of the expansion process of a cycle to the volume in the cylinder at the beginning of the process.

Flow work

The product of pressure and specific volume of a fluid in a given state in a flow process.

Gage pressure

Pressure above local atmospheric pressure.

Gas Tables

Gas Tables by J. H. Keenan and J. Kaye, John Wiley & Sons, Inc., New York, 1948.

Grain

1/7000th of a pound.

Gravimetric

By weight.

Heat pump

A reversed heat cycle in which work is the input and heat is rejected to a sink at a higher temperature than the source.

Heat rate

Energy as heat required per horsepower-hour or kilowatt-hour.

Humidity ratio

See Specific humidity.

Ideal gas

See Perfect gas.

Isentropic process

A process carried out reversibly without energy interchange as heat. Also a process carried out with no entropy change.

Isobaric

See Isopiestic.

Isometric process

A process carried out at constant volume.

Isopiestic process

A process carried out at constant pressure.

Isothermal process

A process carried out at constant temperature.

Kelvin temperature

Degrees Celsius (Centigrade) plus 273.16.

Latent heat of vaporization

The energy required to produce saturated vapor from saturated liquid at constant pressure per unit mass of fluid.

Law of corresponding states

All gases having the same reduced properties are at the same state.

Mach number

Ratio of the velocity at a point in a fluid to the velocity of sound at that point at a given instant of time.

Mass

A quantity of matter; also an index of the inertia of a body.

Micron

10^{-3} mm Hg.

Mollier diagram

An enthalpy–entropy or enthalpy–pressure chart showing the thermodynamic properties of a fluid.

Perfect gas

A hypothetical gas obeying the relation $pv = RT$.

Phase

A phase is any physically and chemically homogeneous quantity of matter.

Polytropic process

A nonadiabatic reversible process characterized by the equation of state, $pv^{n} = $ constant.

Pressure

Normal force per unit area.

Property

An observable characteristic of state which is determined by the state and, in turn, aids in determining the state of a fluid. It is not dependent on the path or means of attaining the state.

Psychrometry

The study of air–water vapor mixtures.

Quality

Weight fraction of a vapor–liquid mixture.

Rankine temperature

Degrees Fahrenheit plus 459.69.

Refrigerant

Working fluid in a reversed heat cycle.

Relative humidity

Ratio of the partial pressure of vapor to the saturation pressure of the vapor at the same temperature in an air–water vapor mixture.

Reversible process

A process by which a fluid is made to undergo a change of state and by traversing the path in exactly the reverse of the original path is returned to its original state, and all associated systems are similarly returned to their original states.

Saturation

That state of a fluid or vapor in which the vapor and liquid states coexist in equilibrium in any proportion. Saturation temperature and saturation pressure refer, respectively, to the properties in the saturation state.

Shaft work

Energy in mechanical or other form delivered from a system. Heat energy is not included in this term.

Specific heat

Ratio of energy transferred as heat per unit mass of working fluid to the corresponding temperature change of the fluid.

Specific humidity

Ratio of the weight of vapor to the weight of gas in a unit volume of an air–water vapor mixture.

Specific volume

Reciprocal of density.

State

The condition of a system fixing the energy stored in the system and identified by the properties of the system.

Steam Tables

Steam Tables by J. H. Keenan, F. G. Keyes, P. G. Hill, and J. G. Moore, John Wiley & Sons, Inc., New York, 1969.

Subcooled liquid

A liquid at a temperature less than that corresponding to the pressure of the system.

Superheated vapor

A vapor whose temperature is greater than the saturation temperature corresponding to the pressure.

System

A grouping of matter taken in any convenient or arbitrary manner.

Thermal efficiency

Ratio of shaft work out of a system to the heat energy into the system.

Throttling

An irreversible adiabatic steady-flow process in which the fluid is caused to flow through an obstruction in a pipe with a resulting drop in pressure.

Ton of refrigeration

Equivalent to the removal of 200 Btu/min as heat from a system.

Torr

One torr is identically equal to the pressure exerted by 1 mm Hg when the density of Hg is 13.6 g/cm^3.

Type efficiency

Ratio of the ideal thermal efficiency of a cycle to that of a Carnot cycle operating between the same temperature limits.

Velocity coefficient

Ratio of the actual velocity to the velocity calculated from ideal conditions.

Wet-bulb temperature

The equilibrium temperature registered by a thermometer wetted by a wick in a stream of an air–water vapor mixture. Also the temperature at which water, by evaporating into air, can bring the air to saturation adiabatically at the same temperature.

Wet compression

The compression of a vapor–liquid refrigerant to saturation conditions in a vapor–compression refrigeration cycle.

Wet mixture

A mixture of vapor and liquid.

Work

The product of force and distance where distance is measured in the direction of the force. A form of energy in transition that is not stored in a system.

appendix 2

answers to even-numbered problems

chapter 1

1.2 -17.8 C; $-12.2°C$, $10°C$
1.4 $R = 1.8$ K; Derivation
1.6 $-130.15°$
1.8 $40°$
1.10 251.52 kla
1.12 24.52 kla
1.14 25 lb/cu ft; 0.04 cu ft/lb
1.16 Derivation
1.18 6.7 ft
1.20 67.72 kla
1.22 10 psia
1.24 $p_A - p_B = -0.0342$ psi
1.26 $p_A - p_B = 0.434$ psi
1.28 $a = g_c$
1.30 979.06 N
1.32 10.198 kg
1.34 61.19 kg
1.36 0.39 lb
1.38 38.32 N

chapter 2

2.2 294.18 J
2.4 5.1 m
2.6 38.9 ft
2.8 600 ft lb/lb; 196.5 ft/sec
2.10 1.02 kg
2.12 0.871 m
2.14 69.3 ft lb
2.16 693.1 kJ/kg
2.18 70 Btu/lb increase
2.20 45 kJ/kg
2.22 -60 kJ/kg
2.24 -8.84 Btu/lb
2.26 166.7 Btu/lb increase; 476.3°F rise
2.28 500 kJ/kg; 695.8°C rise
2.30 $\dfrac{W}{J} = 14.6$ Btu/lb out
2.32 -2.4 Btu/lb

2.34 2.04 ft/sec
2.36 1.8 Mg/hr
2.38 Derivation
2.40 11.6 hp
2.42 61.8 hp in
2.44 100 N·m/kg
2.46 500 Btu/lb;
not necessarily
2.48 $c = 2$ Btu/lb °F
2.50 $c = 0.005$ kJ/kg·K
2.52 176.5 Btu/lb
2.54 758.3 kJ/kg
2.56 50.46 Btu/lb
2.58 79.5 Btu/lb
2.60 211.3 kJ/kg
2.62 4002 fps
2.64 634.4 m/s
2.66 490 Btu/lb
2.68 $q = 240.05$ Btu/lb
into system

chapter 3

3.2 $\eta = 34.2\%$; $\eta = 38.5\%$;
$\eta = 41.1\%$; Lower T_2
3.4 68.2%
3.6 yes
3.8 82.3 Btu/min
3.10 1138.9 W
3.12 58.2%
582 Btu (work);
418 Btu rejected
3.14 256.1°C; 44.6%
3.16 0.41 hp
3.18 0.46 hp
3.20 972.8 Btu/min
3.22 23.7 kW
3.24 0.1 hp
3.26 $\Delta s = 1.8528$ Btu/lb °R
3.28 $\Delta s = 2.186$ Btu/lb °R
3.30 $\Delta s = -0.312$ Btu/lb °R
3.32 $\Delta s = 0.5938$ kJ/kg·K
3.34 $\Delta s = 0.1106$ Btu/lb °R
3.36 $\Delta s = 0.019$ Btu/R

3.38 905°C
3.40 51 Btu/lb; 56 Btu/lb

chapter 4

4.2 at 10 bars
$h_g = 2778.1$ J/g
$s_g = 6.5865$ J/g·K
$V_g = 194.44$ cm^3/g
$u_g = 2583.6$ J/g

at 11 bars
2781.7 J/g
6.5536 J/g·J/g·K
177.53 cm^3/g
2586.4 J/g
4.4 at 350°F
$p = 134.53$ psia
$v_f = 0.017988$ cu ft/lb
$h_f = 321.80$ Btu/lb

at 500°F
680 psia
0.02043 cu ft/lb
487.7 Btu/lb
4.6 $h = 1143.35$ Btu/lb
$s = 1.54694$ Btu/lb R
$u = 1065.41$ Btu/lb
$v = 4.213$ cu ft/lb
4.8 82.3%
4.10 2.9261 cu ft/lb
4.12 11.09 bars
4.14 10.72 lb
4.16 52.78 lb vapor;
1063.4 lb water
4.18 49.21 kg
4.20 $v = 2.004$ cu ft/lb
4.22 2830.2 J/g
4.24 2620.8 J/g
4.26 500.25 Btu/lb;
2.6% error
4.28 $t = 1038.8$°F;
$h = 1541.8$ Btu/lb
4.30 314.0 Btu/lb
4.32 756.44; from chart approx. 755°F

4.34 moisture 7.6%

4.36 moisture 2%

4.38 130 Btu/lb

4.40 1058.06 Btu/lb

4.42 1179.89 Btu/lb

4.44 0.531 Btu/lb°F

4.46 350 Btu/lb

4.48 891.31 Btu/lb

4.50 76.6 Btu/lb

4.52 141.8 Btu/lb

4.54 567, 660 Btu

chapter 5

5.2 163.8 K

5.4 1.190 kg/m^3

5.6 34.9 psig

5.8 830.5 kPa

5.10 277.9 kPa

5.12 $c_p = 0.2967$ Btu/lb °F
$c_v = 0.2283$ Btu/lb °F

5.14 $c_v = 0.34$ Btu/lb °F

5.16 $c_v = 3.1243$ kJ/kg·K

5.18 $c_v = 0.2291$ Btu/lb °F

5.20 41.2 cu ft

5.22 -193.4 kJ/kg (in)

5.24 $\Delta S = 0.0176$ kJ/K

5.26 $\Delta S = 0.2325$ kJ/K

5.28 5.83 cu ft

5.30 96 Btu/lb

5.32 $W/J = 91.1$ Btu/lb
$q = 316.8$ Btu/lb
$\Delta u = 225.7$ Btu/lb

5.34 $q = 64.8$ Btu/lb
$\Delta s = 0.0880$ Btu/lb °R

5.36 $q = 16.9$ Btu/lb
$\Delta s = 0.02777$ Btu/lb °R

5.38 $q = 56.6$ Btu/lb
$\Delta s = 0.07965$ Btu/lb °R

5.40 395.2°R

5.42 395.2°R

5.44 425.5°R

5.46 1.29

5.48 $n = 1.24$

5.50 $n = 1.30$

5.52 $\dfrac{W}{J} = 85.4$ Btu/lb (in)

5.54 $W = 133.6$ kJ/kg in

5.56 $c_p = 0.2503$ Btu/lb °R

5.58 $c_p = 0.226$ Btu/lb °R

5.60 $v = 0.245$ cu ft/lb

5.62 13.3°F

5.64 27.5 psia;
320.8°F

5.66 435°R

chapter 6

6.2 moles $CH_4 = 0.06238$, moles
$O_2 = 0.03125$; $^xCH_4 = 0.666$;
$^xO_2 = 0.334$

6.4 CO, 17.6 psia; N_2, 44.0 psia;
O_2, 7.7 psia; CH_4, 30.7 psia

6.6 2.91 lb

6.8 2850 cu ft

6.10 Volume $= 69.5$ cu ft;
CH_4, 53.4 cu ft;
O_2, 16.1 cu ft;
$p_{CH_4} = 57.6$ psia;
$p_{O_2} = 17.4$ psia;
$^xCH_4 = 0.768$;
$^xO_2 = 0.232$; MW $= 19.73$

6.12 Percent by volume; $O_2 = 63.6\%$;
$CH_4 = 27.3\%$;
$N_2 = 9.1\%$; 300.11 lb;
MW $= 27.3$; $R = 56.6$

6.14 Percent by weight; $N_2 = 28.5\%$
$O_2 = 45.5\%$;
$CH_4 = 26.0\%$;
MW $= 24.62$; $R = 62.8$

6.16 Percent by volume; $O_2 = 37.0\%$;
$N_2 = 14.8\%$;
$CH_4 = 48.1\%$; percent by
weight $-O_2 = 50\%$;
$N_2 = 17.5\%$; $CH_4 = 32.5\%$
MW $= 23.7$; $R = 65.2$

6.18 $t = 89.9°$F, $p = 86.5$ psia

6.20 $c_v = 0.171$ Btu/lb °F

6.22 71°F

6.24 69°F, 0.35 psia, 106 grains/lb dry air

6.26 46% relative humidity,
$p = 0.23$ psia, 57°F

6.28 $\phi = 42\%$, 73°F

6.30 4.9 Btu/lb

6.32 6.6 Btu/lb

6.34 Final dry bulb = 62°F,
final dew point = 59°F,
initial dew point = 54°F

6.36 36%

6.38 $W = 92$ grains/lb,
dew point = 65°F

6.40 Not possible

6.42 64°F dry-bulb, 56% relative humidity,
50 grains/lb

6.44 3380 lb/hr water; 138, 390 lb/hr air

chapter 7

7.2 25.8%

7.4 80%; 200 kJ/k;
800 kJ/hr

7.6 5.2%

7.8 34.9%

7.10 1.79 Btu/lb

7.12 32.9%

7.14 35.4%

7.16 32.8%

7.18 37.4%

7.20 86.8%

7.22 9641 Btu/kW hr

7.24 7.9 lb kW/hr

7.26 15.9 lb/lb

7.28 16.5% moisture

7.30 82.9%

7.32 34.8%

7.34

k	$\eta(\%)$
1.1	16.4
1.2	30.1
1.3	41.6
1.4	51.2

7.36 $\eta = 54.08\%$,
mep = 209 psi

7.38 $\eta = 54.08\%$,
mep = 173.9 psi

7.40 65.5 hp

7.42 70.4%

7.44

ratio	$\eta(\%)$
0.01	68.8
0.04	65.8
0.08	62.5
0.10	61.0

7.46 Derivation

7.48 $p = 1325.8$ psia,
$T = 3839$°R

7.50 37%

7.52 893.17 K

7.54 $\eta = 47.47\%$

7.56 $\eta = 79.7\%$

chapter 8

8.2 8.03 hp

8.4 (a) 4.54 (b) 1321.6 Btu/min
(c) 6000 Btu/min

8.6 Proof

8.8 (a) 13.63 (b) 3668 Btu/hr
(c) 4585 Btu/hr

8.10 5.74

8.12 4.59

8.14 45.1 Btu/lb

8.16 1.08; 343°R

8.18 $\dot{m} = 0.0278$ lb/lb of incoming water

8.20 38.95 Btu/lb

chapter 9

9.2 Fire wall resistance =
3.08 × brick wall

9.4 $k = 3.75$ Btu/hr ft °F

9.6 $k = 0.6 \dfrac{W}{m \cdot C}$

9.8 1136.4°C

9.10 114.3°F; 52.9°F

9.12 43.3%

9.14 65°F, 9.6°F

9.16 $8.51 \dfrac{W}{m^2}$

9.18 34.7 Btu/hr ft²

9.20 108.3 kW

9.22 5213 Btu/hr

9.24 267 Btu/hr ft

9.26 $h = 0.9$ Btu/hr ft^2 °F

9.28 1060 Btu/hr

9.30 85 Btu/hr^2 °F

9.32 74.3 Btu/hr ft^2 °F

9.34 7861 Btu/hr^2 ft^2
170.1 Btu/hr ft^2
77.5 Btu/hr ft^2

9.36 $h = 2.6$ Btu/hr ft^2 °F;
238.2 Btu/hr ft

9.38 1513 Btu/hr ft^2

9.40 16.2°F

9.42 74.0°F

9.44 9.69 kW/m^2

9.46 97 kW/m^2

9.48 108.6 sq ft

9.50 40.5 Btu/hr ft^2 °F

9.52 28.3 sq ft

appendix 3

supplemental tables

TABLE A-1
SATURATION: TEMPERATURE*

Temp. Fahr. t	Press. Lbf. Sq. In. p	Specific Volume		Internal Energy			Enthalpy			Entropy		
		Sat. Liquid v_f	Sat. Vapor v_g	Sat. Liquid u_f	Evap. u_{fg}	Sat. Vapor u_g	Sat. Liquid h_f	Evap. h_{fg}	Sat. Vapor h_g	Sat. Liquid s_f	Evap. s_{fg}	Sat. Vapor s_g
32	.08859	.016022	3305.	.01	1021.2	1021.2	.01	1075.4	1075.4	.00003	2.1870	2.1870
32.018	.08866	.016022	3302.	.00	1021.2	1021.2	.01	1075.4	1075.4	.00000	2.1869	2.1869
35	.09992	.016021	2948.	2.99	1019.2	1022.2	3.00	1073.7	1076.7	.00607	2.1704	2.1764
40	.12166	.016020	2445.	8.02	1015.8	1023.9	8.02	1070.9	1078.9	.01617	2.1430	2.1592
45	.14748	.016021	203.7	13.04	1012.5	1025.5	13.04	1068.1	1081.1	.02618	2.1162	2.1423
50	.17803	.016024	1704.2	18.06	1009.1	1027.2	18.06	1065.2	1083.3	.03607	2.0899	2.1259
60	.2563	.016035	1206.9	28.08	1002.4	1030.4	28.08	1059.6	1087.7	.05555	2.0388	2.0943
70	.3632	.016051	867.7	38.09	995.6	1033.7	38.09	1054.0	1092.0	.07463	1.9896	2.0642
80	.5073	.016073	632.8	48.08	988.9	1037.0	48.09	1048.3	1096.4	.09332	1.9423	2.0356
90	.6988	.016099	467.7	58.07	982.2	1040.2	58.07	1042.7	1100.7	.11165	1.8966	2.0083
100	.9503	.016130	350.0	68.04	975.4	1043.5	68.05	1037.0	1105.0	.12963	1.8526	1.9822
110	1.2763	.016166	265.1	78.02	968.7	1046.7	78.02	1031.3	1109.3	.14730	1.8101	1.9574
120	1.6945	.016205	203.0	87.99	961.9	1049.9	88.00	1025.5	1113.5	.16465	1.7690	1.9336
130	2.225	.016247	157.17	97.97	955.1	1053.0	97.98	1019.8	1117.8	.18172	1.7292	1.9109
140	2.892	.016293	122.88	107.95	948.2	1056.2	107.96	1014.0	1121.9	.19851	1.6907	1.8892
150	3.722	.016343	96.99	117.95	941.3	1059.3	117.96	1008.1	1126.1	.21503	1.6533	1.8684
160	4.745	.016395	77.23	127.94	934.4	1062.3	127.96	1002.2	1130.1	.23130	1.6171	1.8484
170	5.996	.016450	62.02	137.95	927.4	1065.4	137.97	996.2	1134.2	.24732	1.5819	1.8293
180	7.515	.016509	50.20	147.97	920.4	1068.3	147.99	990.2	1138.2	.26311	1.5478	1.8109
190	9.343	.016570	40.95	158.0	913.3	1071.3	158.03	984.1	1142.1	.27866	1.5146	1.7932
200	11.529	.016634	33.63	168.04	906.2	1074.2	168.07	977.9	1145.9	.29400	1.4822	1.7762
210	14.125	.016702	27.82	178.10	898.9	1077.0	178.14	971.6	1149.7	.30913	1.4508	1.7599
220	17.188	.016772	23.15	188.17	891.7	1079.8	188.22	965.3	1153.5	.32406	1.4201	1.7441
230	20.78	.016845	19.386	198.26	884.3	1082.6	198.32	958.8	1157.1	.33880	1.3901	1.7289
240	24.97	.016922	16.327	208.36	876.9	1085.3	208.44	952.3	1160.7	.35335	1.3609	1.7143
250	29.82	.017001	13.826	218.49	869.4	1087.9	218.59	945.6	1164.2	.36772	1.3324	1.7001
260	35.42	.017084	11.768	228.64	861.8	1090.5	228.76	938.8	1167.6	.38193	1.3044	1.6864

TABLE A-1
(CONT'D.)

Temp. Fahr. t	Press. Lbf. Sq. In. p	Specific Volume Sat. Liquid v_f	Specific Volume Sat. Vapor v_g	Internal Energy Sat. Liquid u_f	Internal Energy Evap. u_{fg}	Internal Energy Sat. Vapor u_g	Enthalpy Sat. Liquid h_f	Enthalpy Evap. h_{fg}	Enthalpy Sat. Vapor h_g	Entropy Sat. Liquid s_f	Entropy Evap. s_{fg}	Entropy Sat. Vapor s_g
270	41.85	.017170	10.066	238.82	854.1	1093.0	238.95	932.0	1170.9	.39597	1.2771	1.6731
280	49.18	.017259	8.650	249.02	846.3	1095.4	249.18	924.9	1174.1	.40986	1.2504	1.6602
290	57.53	.017352	7.467	259.25	838.5	1097.7	259.44	917.8	1177.2	.42360	1.2241	1.6477
300	66.98	.017448	6.472	269.52	830.5	1100.0	269.73	910.4	1180.2	.43720	1.1984	1.6356
310	77.64	.017548	5.632	279.81	822.3	1102.1	280.06	903.0	1183.0	.45067	1.1731	1.6238
320	89.60	.017652	4.919	290.14	814.1	1104.2	290.43	895.3	1185.8	.46400	1.1483	1.6123
330	103.00	.017760	4.312	300.51	805.7	1106.2	300.84	887.5	1188.4	.47722	1.1238	1.6010
340	117.93	.017872	3.792	310.91	797.1	1108.0	311.30	879.5	1190.8	.49031	1.0997	1.5901
350	134.53	.017988	3.346	321.35	788.4	1109.8	321.80	871.3	1193.1	.50329	1.0760	1.5793
360	152.92	.018108	2.961	331.84	779.6	1111.4	332.35	862.9	1195.2	.51617	1.0526	1.5688
370	173.23	.018233	2.628	342.37	770.6	1112.9	342.96	854.2	1197.2	.52894	1.0295	1.5585
380	195.60	.018363	2.339	352.95	761.4	1114.3	353.62	845.4	1199.0	.54163	1.0067	1.5483
390	220.2	.018498	2.087	363.58	752.0	1115.6	364.34	836.2	1200.6	.55422	.9841	1.5383
400	247.1	.018638	1.8661	374.27	742.4	1116.6	375.12	826.8	1202.0	.56672	.9617	1.5284
425	325.6	.019014	1.4249	401.24	717.4	1118.6	402.38	802.1	1204.5	.59767	.9066	1.5043
450	422.1	.019433	1.1011	428.6	690.9	1119.2	430.2	775.4	1205.6	.6282	.8523	1.4806
475	539.3	.019901	.8594	456.6	662.6	1119.2	458.5	746.4	1204.9	.6586	.7985	1.4571
500	680.0	.02043	.6761	485.1	632.3	1117.4	487.7	714.8	1202.5	.6888	.7448	1.4335
525	847.1	.02104	.5350	514.5	599.5	1113.9	517.8	680.0	1197.8	.7191	.6906	1.4007
550	1044.0	.02175	.4249	544.9	563.7	1108.6	549.1	641.6	1190.6	.7497	.6354	1.3851
575	1274.0	.02259	.3378	576.5	524.3	1100.8	581.9	598.6	1180.4	.7808	.5785	1.3593
600	1541.0	.02363	.2677	609.9	480.1	1090.0	616.7	549.7	1166.4	.8130	.5187	1.3317
625	1849.7	.02494	.2103	645.7	429.4	1075.1	654.2	492.9	1147.0	.8467	.4544	1.3010
650	2205.	.02673	.16206	685.0	368.7	1053.7	695.9	423.9	1119.8	.8831	.3820	1.2651
675	2616.	.02951	.11952	731.0	289.3	1020.3	745.3	332.9	1078.2	.9252	.2934	1.2186
700	3090.	.03666	.07438	801.7	145.9	947.7	822.7	167.5	990.2	.9902	.1444	1.1346
705.44	3204.	.05053	.05053	872.6	0	872.6	902.5	0	902.5	1.0580	0	1.0580

*Tables A-1 through A-4 are abridged from *Steam Tables—Thermodynamic Properties of Water Including Vapor, Liquid and Solid Phases*, by J. H. Keenan, F. G. Keyes, P. G. Hill, and J. G. Moore, John Wiley & Sons, Inc., New York, 1969, with permission.

TABLE A-2
SATURATION PRESSURES

Press. Lbf/Sq.In. p	Temp. Fahr. t	Specific Volume Sat. Liquid v_f	Specific Volume Sat. Vapor v_g	Internal Energy Sat Liquid u_f	Internal Energy Evap. u_{fg}	Internal Energy Sat. Vapor u_g	Enthalpy Sat. Liquid h_f	Enthalpy Evap. h_{fg}	Enthalpy Sat. Vapor h_g	Entropy Sat. Liquid s_f	Entropy Evap. s_{fg}	Entropy Sat. Vapor s_g
.50	79.56	.016071	641.5	47.64	989.2	1036.9	47.65	1048.6	1096.2	.09250	1.9443	2.0368
1.0	101.70	.016136	333.6	69.74	974.3	1044.0	69.74	1036.0	1105.8	.13266	1.8453	1.9779
1.5	115.65	.016187	227.7	83.65	964.8	1048.5	83.65	1028.0	1111.7	.15714	1.7867	1.9438
2.0	126.04	.016230	173.75	94.02	957.8	1051.8	94.02	1022.1	1116.1	.17499	1.7448	1.9198
3.0	141.43	.016300	118.72	109.38	947.2	1056.6	109.39	1013.1	1122.5	.20089	1.6852	1.8861
4.0	152.93	.016358	90.64	120.88	939.3	1060.2	120.89	1006.4	1127.3	.21983	1.6426	1.8624
5.0	162.21	.016407	73.53	130.15	932.9	1063.0	130.17	1000.9	1131.0	.23486	1.6093	1.8441
7.5	179.91	.016508	50.30	147.88	920.4	1068.3	147.90	990.2	1138.1	.26297	1.5481	1.8110
10	193.19	.016590	38.42	161.20	911.0	1072.2	161.23	982.1	1143.3	.28358	1.5041	1.7877
14.696	211.99	.016715	26.80	180.10	897.5	1077.6	180.15	970.4	1150.5	.31212	1.4446	1.7567
15	213.03	.016723	26.29	181.14	896.8	1077.9	181.19	969.7	1150.8	.31367	1.4414	1.7551
20	227.96	.016830	20.09	196.19	885.8	1082.0	196.26	960.1	1156.4	.33580	1.3962	1.7320
25	240.08	.016922	16.306	208.44	876.9	1085.3	208.52	952.2	1160.7	.35345	1.3607	1.7142
30	250.34	.017004	13.748	218.84	869.2	1088.0	218.93	945.4	1164.3	.36821	1.3314	1.6996
35	259.30	.017078	11.900	227.93	862.4	1090.3	228.04	939.3	1167.4	.38093	1.3064	1.6873
40	267.26	.017146	10.501	236.03	856.2	1092.3	236.16	933.8	1170.0	.39214	1.2845	1.6767
45	274.46	.017209	9.403	243.37	850.7	1094.0	243.51	928.8	1172.3	.40218	1.2651	1.6673
50	281.03	.017269	8.518	250.08	845.5	1095.6	250.24	924.2	1174.4	.41129	1.2476	1.6589
55	287.10	.017325	7.789	256.28	840.8	1097.0	256.46	919.9	1176.3	.41963	1.2317	1.6513
60	292.73	.017378	7.177	262.06	836.3	1098.3	262.25	915.8	1178.0	.42733	1.2170	1.6444
65	298.00	.017429	6.657	267.46	832.1	1099.5	267.67	911.9	1179.6	.43450	1.2035	1.6380
70	302.96	.017478	6.209	272.56	828.1	1100.6	272.79	908.3	1181.0	.44120	1.1909	1.6321
75	307.63	.017524	5.818	277.37	824.3	1101.6	277.61	904.8	1182.4	.44749	1.1790	1.6265
80	312.07	.017570	5.474	281.95	820.6	1102.6	282.21	901.4	1183.6	.45344	1.1679	1.6214
85	316.29	.017613	5.170	286.30	817.1	1103.5	286.58	898.2	1184.8	.45907	1.1574	1.6165
90	320.31	.017655	4.898	290.46	813.8	1104.3	290.76	895.1	1185.9	.46442	1.1475	1.6119
95	324.16	.017696	4.654	294.45	810.6	1105.0	294.76	892.1	1186.9	.46952	1.1380	1.6076
100	327.86	.017736	4.434	298.28	807.5	1105.8	298.61	889.2	1187.8	.47439	1.1290	1.6034
105	331.41	.017775	4.234	301.97	804.5	1106.5	302.31	886.4	1188.7	.47906	1.1204	1.5995
110	334.82	.017813	4.051	305.52	801.6	1107.1	305.88	883.7	1189.6	.48355	1.1122	1.5957
115	338.12	.017850	3.884	308.95	798.8	1107.7	309.33	881.0	1190.4	.48786	1.1042	1.5921
120	341.30	.017886	3.730	312.27	796.0	1108.3	312.67	878.5	1191.1	.49201	1.0966	1.5886
125	344.39	.017922	3.588	315.49	793.3	1108.8	315.90	875.9	1191.8	.49602	1.0893	1.5853

TABLE A-2
(CONT'D.)

Press. Lbf/Sq.In. p	Temp. Fahr. t	Specific Volume Sat. Liquid v_f	Sat. Vapor v_g	Internal Energy Sat. Liquid u_f	Evap. u_{fg}	Sat. Vapor u_g	Enthalpy Sat. Liquid h_f	Evap. h_{fg}	Sat. Vapor h_g	Entropy Sat. Liquid s_f	Evap. s_{fg}	Sat. Vapor s_g
130	347.37	.017957	3.457	318.61	790.7	1109.4	319.04	873.5	1192.5	.49989	1.0822	1.5821
135	350.27	.017991	3.335	321.64	788.2	1109.8	322.08	871.1	1193.2	.50364	1.0754	1.5790
140	353.08	.018024	3.221	324.58	785.7	1110.3	325.05	868.7	1193.8	.50727	1.0688	1.5761
145	355.82	.018057	3.115	327.45	783.3	1110.8	327.93	866.4	1194.4	.51079	1.0624	1.5732
150	358.48	.018089	3.016	330.24	781.0	1111.2	330.75	864.2	1194.9	.51422	1.0562	1.5704
160	363.60	.018152	2.836	335.63	776.4	1112.0	336.16	859.8	1196.0	.52078	1.0443	1.5651
170	368.47	.018214	2.676	340.76	772.0	1112.7	341.33	855.6	1196.9	.52700	1.0330	1.5600
180	373.13	.018273	2.533	345.68	767.7	1113.4	346.29	851.5	1197.8	.53292	1.0223	1.5553
190	377.59	.018331	2.405	350.39	763.6	1114.0	351.04	847.5	1198.6	.53857	1.0122	1.5507
200	381.86	.018387	2.289	354.9	759.6	1114.6	355.6	843.7	1199.3	.5440	1.0025	1.5464
225	391.87	.018523	2.043	365.6	750.2	1115.8	366.3	834.5	1200.8	.5566	.9799	1.5365
250	401.04	.018653	1.8448	375.4	741.4	1116.7	376.2	825.8	1202.1	.5680	.9594	1.5274
275	409.52	.018777	1.6813	384.5	733.0	1117.5	385.4	817.6	1203.1	.5786	.9406	1.5192
300	417.43	.018896	1.5442	393.0	725.1	1118.2	394.1	809.8	1203.9	.5883	.9232	1.5115
350	431.82	.019124	1.3267	408.7	710.3	1119.0	409.9	795.0	1204.9	.6060	.8917	1.4978
400	444.70	.019340	1.1620	422.8	696.7	1119.5	424.2	781.2	1205.5	.6218	.8638	1.4856
450	456.39	.019547	1.0326	435.7	683.9	1119.6	437.4	768.2	1205.6	.6360	.8385	1.4746
500	467.13	.019748	.9283	447.7	671.7	1119.4	449.5	755.8	1205.3	.6490	.8154	1.4645
550	477.07	.019943	.8423	458.9	660.2	1119.1	460.9	743.9	1204.8	.6611	.7941	1.4551
600	486.33	.02013	.7702	469.4	649.1	1118.6	471.7	732.4	1204.1	.6723	.7742	1.4464
700	503.23	.02051	.6558	488.9	628.2	1117.0	491.5	710.5	1202.0	.6927	.7378	1.4305
800	518.36	.02087	.5691	506.6	608.4	1115.0	509.7	689.6	1199.3	.7110	.7050	1.4160
900	532.12	.02123	.5009	523.0	589.6	1112.6	526.6	669.5	1196.0	.7277	.6750	1.4027
1000	544.75	.02159	.4459	538.4	571.5	1109.9	542.4	650.0	1192.4	.7432	.6471	1.3903
1250	572.56	.02250	.3454	573.4	528.3	1101.7	578.6	603.0	1181.6	.7778	.5841	1.3619
1500	596.39	.02346	.2769	605.0	486.9	1091.8	611.5	557.2	1168.7	.8082	.5276	1.3359
1750	617.31	.02450	.2268	634.4	445.9	1080.2	642.3	511.4	1153.7	.8361	.4748	1.3109
2000	649.20	.02565	.18813	662.4	404.2	1066.6	671.9	464.4	1136.3	.8623	.4238	1.2861
2250	652.90	.02698	.15692	689.9	360.7	1050.6	701.1	414.8	1115.9	.8876	.3728	1.2604
2500	668.31	.02860	.13059	717.7	313.4	1031.0	730.9	360.5	1091.4	.9131	.3196	1.2327
2750	682.46	.03077	.10717	747.3	258.6	1005.9	763.0	297.4	1060.4	.9401	.2604	1.2005
3000	695.52	.03431	.08404	783.4	185.4	968.8	802.5	213.0	1015.5	.9732	.1843	1.1575
3203.6	705.44	.05053	.05053	872.6	0	872.6	902.5	0	902.5	1.0580	0	1.0580

TABLE A-3
PROPERTIES OF SUPERHEATED STEAM

p(t Sat.)		Vapor									
		14.696 (211.99)				20 (227.96)				30 (250.34)	
t		v	u	h	s	v	u	h	s	v	u	h	s
Sat.		26.80	1077.6	1150.5	1.7567	20.09	1082.0	1156.4	1.7320	13.748	1088.0	1164.3	1.6996
150		24.10	1054.5	1120.0	1.7090	17.532	1052.0	1116.9	1.6710	11.460	1047.3	1111.0	1.6185
160		24.54	1058.2	1125.0	1.7171	17.870	1056.0	1122.1	1.6795	11.701	1051.6	1116.5	1.6275
170		24.98	1062.0	1129.9	1.7251	18.204	1059.9	1127.2	1.6877	11.938	1055.8	1122.0	1.6364
180		25.42	1065.7	1134.9	1.7328	18.535	1063.8	1132.4	1.6957	12.172	1059.9	1127.5	1.6449
190		25.85	1069.5	1139.8	1.7405	18.864	1067.6	1137.4	1.7036	12.403	1064.0	1132.9	1.6533
200		26.29	1073.2	1144.7	1.7479	19.191	1071.4	1142.5	1.7113	12.631	1068.1	1138.2	1.6615
210		26.72	1076.9	1149.5	1.7553	19.515	1075.2	1147.5	1.7188	12.857	1072.1	1143.5	1.6694
220		27.15	1080.6	1154.4	1.7624	19.837	1079.0	1152.4	1.7262	13.081	1076.1	1148.7	1.6771
230		27.57	1084.2	1159.2	1.7695	20.157	1082.8	1157.4	1.7335	13.303	1080.0	1153.9	1.6847
240		28.00	1087.9	1164.0	1.7764	20.475	1086.5	1162.3	1.7405	13.523	1084.0	1159.0	1.6921
250		28.42	1091.5	1168.8	1.7832	20.79	1090.3	1167.2	1.7475	13.741	1087.9	1164.1	1.6994
260		28.85	1095.2	1173.6	1.7899	21.11	1094.0	1172.1	1.7543	13.958	1091.7	1169.2	1.7064
270		29.27	1098.8	1178.4	1.7965	21.42	1097.7	1177.0	1.7610	14.173	1095.6	1174.2	1.7134
280		29.69	1102.4	1183.1	1.8030	21.73	1101.4	1181.8	1.7676	14.387	1099.4	1179.2	1.7202
290		30.11	1106.0	1187.9	1.8094	22.05	1105.0	1186.6	1.7741	14.600	1103.2	1184.2	1.7269
300		30.52	1109.6	1192.6	1.8157	22.36	1108.7	1191.5	1.7805	14.812	1106.9	1189.2	1.7334
310		30.94	1113.2	1197.4	1.8219	22.67	1112.4	1196.3	1.7868	15.023	1110.7	1194.1	1.7399
320		31.36	1116.8	1202.1	1.8280	22.98	1116.0	1201.0	1.7930	15.233	1114.4	1199.0	1.7462
330		31.77	1120.4	1206.8	1.8340	23.28	1119.7	1205.8	1.7991	15.442	1118.2	1203.9	1.7525
340		32.19	1124.0	1211.6	1.8400	23.59	1123.3	1210.6	1.8051	15.651	1121.9	1208.8	1.7586
350		32.60	1127.6	1216.3	1.8458	23.90	1126.9	1215.4	1.8110	15.859	1125.6	1213.6	1.7646
360		33.02	1131.2	1221.0	1.8516	24.21	1130.6	1220.1	1.8168	16.067	1129.3	1218.5	1.7706
370		33.43	1134.8	1225.7	1.8574	24.51	1134.2	1224.9	1.8226	16.273	1133.0	1223.3	1.7765
380		33.84	1138.4	1230.5	1.8630	24.82	1137.8	1229.7	1.8283	16.480	1136.7	1228.1	1.7822
390		34.26	1142.0	1235.2	1.8686	25.12	1141.4	1234.4	1.8340	16.686	1140.3	1233.0	1.7880
400		34.67	1145.6	1239.9	1.8741	25.43	1145.1	1239.2	1.8395	16.891	1144.0	1237.8	1.7936
420		35.49	1152.8	1249.3	1.8850	26.03	1152.3	1248.7	1.8504	17.301	1151.4	1247.4	1.8047
440		36.31	1160.1	1258.8	1.8956	26.64	1159.6	1258.2	1.8611	17.709	1158.7	1257.0	1.8155
460		37.13	1167.3	1268.3	1.9060	27.25	1166.9	1267.7	1.8716	18.116	1166.1	1266.6	1.8260
480		37.95	1174.6	1277.8	1.9162	27.85	1174.2	1277.2	1.8819	18.523	1173.4	1276.2	1.8364

TABLE A-3
(CONT'D.)

Vapor

p(t Sat.)	14.696 (211.99)				20 (227.96)				30 (250.34)			
t	v	u	h	s	v	u	h	s	v	u	h	s
Sat.	26.80	1077.6	1150.5	1.7567	20.09	1082.0	1156.4	1.7320	13.748	1088.0	1164.3	1.6996
500	38.77	1181.8	1287.3	1.9263	28.46	1181.5	1286.8	1.8919	18.928	1180.8	1285.9	1.8465
520	39.59	1189.1	1296.8	1.9361	29.06	1188.8	1296.3	1.9018	19.333	1188.2	1295.5	1.8564
540	40.41	1196.5	1306.4	1.9457	29.66	1196.1	1305.9	1.9114	19.737	1195.5	1305.1	1.8661
560	41.22	1203.8	1315.9	1.9552	30.26	1203.5	1315.5	1.9210	20.140	1203.0	1314.8	1.8757
580	42.04	1211.2	1325.5	1.9645	30.87	1210.9	1325.2	1.9303	20.543	1210.4	1324.4	1.8851
600	42.86	1218.6	1335.2	1.9737	31.47	1218.4	1334.8	1.9395	20.95	1217.8	1334.1	1.8943
620	43.67	1226.1	1344.8	1.9827	32.07	1225.8	1344.5	1.9485	21.35	1225.3	1343.8	1.9034
640	44.49	1233.5	1354.5	1.9916	32.67	1233.3	1354.2	1.9575	21.75	1232.8	1353.6	1.9123
660	45.30	1241.0	1364.2	2.0004	33.27	1240.8	1363.9	1.9662	22.15	1240.4	1363.3	1.9211
680	46.12	1248.6	1374.0	2.0090	33.87	1248.3	1373.7	1.9749	22.55	1247.9	1373.1	1.9298
700	46.93	1256.1	1383.8	2.0175	34.47	1255.9	1383.5	1.9834	22.95	1255.5	1383.0	1.9384
720	47.75	1263.7	1393.6	2.0259	35.07	1263.5	1393.3	1.9918	23.35	1263.2	1392.8	1.9468
740	48.56	1271.4	1403.4	2.0342	35.66	1271.2	1403.2	2.0001	23.75	1270.8	1402.7	1.9551
760	49.37	1279.0	1413.3	2.0424	36.26	1278.8	1413.0	2.0082	24.15	1278.5	1412.6	1.9633
780	50.19	1286.7	1423.2	2.0504	36.86	1286.5	1423.0	2.0163	24.55	1286.2	1422.5	1.9714
800	51.00	1294.4	1433.1	2.0584	37.46	1294.3	1432.9	2.0243	24.95	1294.0	1432.5	1.9793
850	53.03	1313.9	1458.1	2.0778	38.96	1313.8	1457.9	2.0438	25.95	1313.5	1457.6	1.9988
900	55.07	1333.6	1483.4	2.0967	40.45	1333.5	1483.2	2.0627	26.95	1333.2	1482.8	2.0178
950	57.10	1353.5	1508.8	2.1151	41.94	1353.4	1508.6	2.0810	27.95	1353.2	1508.3	2.0362
1000	59.13	1373.7	1534.5	2.1330	43.44	1373.5	1534.4	2.0989	28.95	1373.3	1534.0	2.0541
1100	63.19	1414.6	1586.4	2.1674	46.42	1414.5	1586.3	2.1334	30.94	1414.3	1586.1	2.0886
1200	67.25	1456.5	1639.3	2.2003	49.41	1456.4	1639.2	2.1663	32.93	1456.2	1639.1	2.1215
1300	71.30	1499.3	1693.2	2.2318	52.39	1499.2	1693.1	2.1978	34.92	1499.1	1692.9	2.1530
1400	75.36	1543.0	1747.9	2.2621	55.37	1542.9	1747.9	2.2281	36.91	1542.8	1747.7	2.1833
1500	79.42	1587.6	1803.6	2.2912	58.35	1587.6	1803.5	2.2572	38.90	1587.5	1803.4	2.2125
1600	83.47	1633.2	1860.2	2.3194	61.33	1633.2	1860.1	2.2854	40.88	1633.1	1860.0	2.2407
1800	91.58	1727.0	1976.1	2.3731	67.29	1727.0	1976.1	2.3391	44.86	1726.9	1976.0	2.2944
2000	99.69	1824.4	2095.5	2.4237	73.25	1824.3	2095.4	2.3897	48.83	1824.2	2095.3	2.3450
2200	107.80	1924.8	2218.0	2.4716	79.21	1924.8	2218.0	2.4376	52.81	1924.7	2217.9	2.3929
2400	115.91	2028.1	2343.4	2.5170	85.17	2028.1	2343.3	2.4830	56.78	2028.0	2343.3	2.4383

TABLE A-3
(CONT'D.)

p (t Sat.) t	40 (267.26)				50 (281.03)				60 (292.73)			
	v	u	h	s	v	u	h	s	v	u	h	s
Sat.	10.501	1092.3	1170.0	1.6767	8.518	1095.6	1174.4	1.6589	7.177	1098.3	1178.0	1.6444
200	9.346	1064.6	1133.8	1.6243	7.370	1060.9	1129.1	1.5940	6.047	1057.1	1124.2	1.5680
210	9.523	1068.8	1139.3	1.6327	7.519	1065.4	1135.0	1.6029	6.178	1061.9	1130.5	1.5774
220	9.699	1073.0	1144.8	1.6409	7.665	1069.9	1140.8	1.6115	6.307	1066.6	1136.6	1.5864
230	9.872	1077.2	1150.3	1.6488	7.810	1074.2	1146.5	1.6198	6.432	1071.2	1142.6	1.5952
240	10.043	1081.3	1155.6	1.6565	7.952	1078.6	1152.1	1.6279	6.556	1075.7	1148.5	1.6036
250	10.212	1085.4	1161.0	1.6641	8.092	1082.8	1157.7	1.6358	6.677	1080.1	1154.3	1.6118
260	10.380	1089.4	1166.2	1.6714	8.231	1087.0	1163.1	1.6434	6.797	1084.5	1160.0	1.6198
270	10.546	1093.4	1171.4	1.6786	8.368	1091.1	1168.5	1.6509	6.915	1088.8	1165.6	1.6275
280	10.711	1097.3	1176.6	1.6857	8.504	1095.2	1173.9	1.6582	7.031	1093.0	1171.1	1.6351
290	10.875	1101.2	1181.7	1.6926	8.639	1099.2	1179.2	1.6653	7.146	1097.2	1176.5	1.6424
300	11.038	1105.1	1186.8	1.6993	8.772	1103.2	1184.4	1.6722	7.260	1101.3	1181.9	1.6496
310	11.200	1109.0	1191.9	1.7059	8.904	1107.2	1189.6	1.6790	7.373	1105.4	1187.3	1.6565
320	11.360	1112.8	1196.9	1.7124	9.036	1111.2	1194.8	1.6857	7.485	1109.5	1192.6	1.6634
330	11.520	1116.6	1201.9	1.7188	9.166	1115.1	1199.9	1.6922	7.596	1113.5	1197.8	1.6700
340	11.680	1120.4	-1206.9	1.7251	9.296	1119.0	1205.0	1.6986	7.706	1117.4	1203.0	1.6766
350	11.838	1124.2	1211.8	1.7312	9.425	1122.8	1210.0	1.7049	7.815	1121.4	1208.2	1.6830
360	11.996	1128.0	1216.8	1.7373	9.553	1126.7	1215.1	1.7110	7.924	1125.3	1213.3	1.6893
370	12.153	1131.7	1221.7	1.7432	9.681	1130.5	1220.1	1.7171	8.032	1129.2	1218.4	1.6955
380	12.310	1135.5	1226.6	1.7491	9.808	1134.3	1225.0	1.7231	8.139	1133.1	1223.5	1.7015
390	12.467	1139.2	1231.5	1.7549	9.935	1138.1	1230.0	1.7290	8.246	1136.9	1228.5	1.7075
400	12.623	1143.0	1236.4	1.7606	10.061	1141.9	1235.0	1.7348	8.353	1140.8	1233.5	1.7134
420	12.933	1150.4	1246.1	1.7718	10.312	1149.4	1244.8	1.7461	8.565	1148.4	1243.5	1.7249
440	13.243	1157.8	1255.8	1.7828	10.562	1156.9	1254.6	1.7572	8.775	1156.0	1253.4	1.7360
460	13.551	1165.2	1265.5	1.7934	10.811	1164.4	1264.4	1.7679	8.984	1163.6	1263.3	1.7469
480	13.858	1172.7	1275.2	1.8038	11.059	1171.9	1274.2	1.7784	9.192	1171.1	1273.2	1.7575
500	14.164	1180.1	1284.9	1.8140	11.305	1179.4	1284.0	1.7887	9.399	1178.6	1283.0	1.7678
520	14.469	1187.5	1294.6	1.8240	11.551	1186.8	1293.7	1.7988	9.606	1186.2	1292.8	1.7780
540	14.774	1194.9	1304.3	1.8338	11.796	1194.3	1303.5	1.8086	9.811	1193.7	1302.6	1.7879
560	15.078	1202.4	1314.0	1.8434	12.041	1201.8	1313.2	1.8183	10.016	1201.2	1312.4	1.7976
580	15.382	1209.9	1323.7	1.8529	12.285	1209.3	1323.0	1.8277	10.221	1208.8	1322.2	1.8071

TABLE A-3
(CONT'D.)

p (t Sat.)		40 (267.26)				50 (281.03)				60 (292.73)			
t		v	u	h	s	v	u	h	s	v	u	h	s
Sat.		10.501	1092.3	1170.0	1.6767	8.518	1095.6	1174.4	1.6589	7.177	1098.3	1178.0	1.6444
600		15.685	1217.3	1333.4	1.8621	12.529	1216.8	1332.8	1.8371	10.425	1216.3	1332.1	1.8165
620		15.988	1224.8	1343.2	1.8713	12.772	1224.4	1342.5	1.8462	10.628	1223.9	1341.9	1.8257
640		16.291	1232.4	1353.0	1.8802	13.015	1231.9	1352.4	1.8552	10.832	1231.5	1351.7	1.8347
660		16.593	1239.9	1362.8	1.8891	13.258	1239.5	1362.2	1.8641	11.035	1239.1	1361.6	1.8436
680		16.895	1247.5	1372.6	1.8977	13.500	1247.1	1372.0	1.8728	11.237	1246.7	1371.5	1.8523
700		17.196	1255.1	1382.4	1.9063	13.742	1254.8	1381.9	1.8814	11.440	1254.4	1381.4	1.8609
720		17.498	1262.8	1392.3	1.9147	13.984	1262.4	1391.8	1.8898	11.642	1262.0	1391.3	1.8694
740		17.799	1270.5	1402.2	1.9231	14.226	1270.1	1401.7	1.8982	11.844	1269.7	1401.2	1.8778
760		18.100	1278.2	1412.1	1.9313	14.467	1277.8	1411.7	1.9064	12.045	1277.5	1411.2	1.8860
780		18.401	1285.9	1422.1	1.9394	14.708	1285.6	1421.7	1.9145	12.247	1285.2	1421.2	1.8942
800		18.701	1293.7	1432.1	1.9474	14.949	1293.3	1431.7	1.9225	12.448	1293.0	1431.2	1.9022
850		19.452	1313.2	1457.2	1.9669	15.551	1312.9	1456.8	1.9421	12.951	1312.7	1456.4	1.9218
900		20.202	1333.0	1482.5	1.9859	16.152	1332.7	1482.2	1.9611	13.452	1332.5	1481.8	1.9408
950		20.951	1352.9	1508.0	2.0043	16.753	1352.7	1507.7	1.9796	13.954	1352.5	1507.4	1.9593
1000		21.700	1373.1	1533.8	2.0223	17.352	1372.9	1533.5	1.9975	14.454	1372.7	1533.2	1.9773
1100		23.20	1414.2	1585.9	2.0568	18.551	1414.0	1585.6	2.0321	15.454	1413.8	1585.4	2.0119
1200		24.69	1456.1	1638.9	2.0897	19.747	1456.0	1638.7	2.0650	16.452	1455.8	1638.5	2.0448
1300		26.18	1498.9	1692.8	2.1212	20.943	1498.8	1692.6	2.0966	17.449	1498.7	1692.4	2.0764
1400		27.68	1542.7	1747.6	2.1515	22.138	1542.6	1747.4	2.1269	18.445	1542.5	1747.3	2.1067
1500		29.17	1587.4	1803.3	2.1807	23.332	1587.3	1803.2	2.1561	19.441	1587.2	1803.0	2.1359
1600		30.66	1633.0	1859.9	2.2089	24.53	1632.9	1859.8	2.1843	20.44	1632.8	1859.7	2.1641
1800		33.64	1726.9	1975.9	2.2626	26.91	1726.8	1975.8	2.2380	22.43	1726.7	1975.7	2.2179
2000		36.62	1824.2	2095.3	2.3132	29.30	1824.1	2095.2	2.2886	24.41	1824.0	2095.1	2.2685
2200		39.61	1924.7	2217.8	2.3611	31.68	1924.6	2217.8	2.3365	26.40	1924.5	2217.7	2.3164
2400		42.59	2028.0	2343.2	2.4066	34.07	2027.9	2343.1	2.3820	28.39	2027.8	2343.1	2.3618

TABLE A-3
(CONT'D.)

t	200 (381.86) v	u	h	s	300 (417.43) v	u	h	s	350 (431.82) v	u	h	s	400 (444.70) v	u	h	s
Sat.	2.289	1114.6	1199.3	1.5464	1.5442	1118.2	1203.9	1.5115	1.3267	1119.0	1204.9	1.4978	1.1620	1119.5	1205.5	1.4856
400	2.361	1123.5	1210.8	1.5600	*1.4915*	*1108.2*	*1191.0*	*1.4967*								
410	2.399	1128.2	1217.0	1.5672	*1.5221*	*1114.0*	*1198.5*	*1.5054*								
420	2.437	1132.9	1223.1	1.5741	1.5517	1119.6	1205.7	1.5136	*1.2950*	*1112.0*	*1195.9*	*1.4875*				
430	2.475	1137.5	1229.1	1.5809	1.5805	1125.0	1212.7	1.5216	*1.3219*	*1117.9*	*1203.6*	*1.4962*	*1.1257*	*1110.3*	*1193.6*	*1.4723*
440	2.511	1142.0	1234.9	1.5874	1.6086	1130.3	1219.6	1.5292	1.3480	1123.7	1211.0	1.5045	*1.1506*	*1116.6*	*1201.7*	*1.4814*
450	2.548	1146.4	1240.7	1.5938	1.6361	1135.4	1226.2	1.5365	1.3733	1129.2	1218.2	1.5125	1.1745	1122.6	1209.6	1.4901
460	2.584	1150.8	1246.5	1.6001	1.6630	1140.4	1232.7	1.5436	1.3979	1134.6	1225.2	1.5201	1.1977	1128.5	1217.1	1.4984
470	2.619	1155.2	1252.1	1.6062	1.6894	1145.3	1239.1	1.5505	1.4220	1139.9	1232.0	1.5275	1.2202	1134.1	1224.4	1.5063
480	2.654	1159.5	1257.7	1.6122	1.7154	1150.1	1245.3	1.5572	1.4455	1145.0	1238.6	1.5346	1.2421	1139.6	1231.5	1.5139
490	2.689	1163.7	1263.3	1.6181	1.7410	1154.8	1251.5	1.5637	1.4686	1150.0	1245.1	1.5415	1.2634	1144.9	1238.4	1.5212
500	2.724	1168.0	1268.8	1.6239	1.7662	1159.5	1257.5	1.5701	1.4913	1154.9	1251.5	1.5482	1.2843	1150.1	1245.2	1.5282
510	2.758	1172.2	1274.2	1.6295	1.7910	1164.1	1263.5	1.5763	1.5136	1159.7	1257.8	1.5546	1.3048	1155.2	1251.8	1.5351
520	2.792	1176.3	1279.7	1.6351	1.8156	1168.6	1269.4	1.5823	1.5356	1164.5	1263.9	1.5610	1.3249	1160.2	1258.2	1.5417
530	2.826	1180.5	1285.0	1.6405	1.8399	1173.1	1275.2	1.5882	1.5572	1169.1	1270.0	1.5671	1.3447	1165.0	1264.6	1.5481
540	2.860	1184.6	1290.4	1.6459	1.8640	1177.5	1281.0	1.5940	1.5786	1173.7	1276.0	1.5731	1.3642	1169.8	1270.8	1.5544
550	2.893	1188.7	1295.7	1.6512	1.8878	1181.9	1286.7	1.5997	1.5998	1178.3	1281.9	1.5790	1.3833	1174.6	1277.0	1.5605
560	2.926	1192.7	1301.0	1.6565	1.9114	1186.2	1292.3	1.6052	1.6207	1182.8	1287.7	1.5848	1.4023	1179.2	1283.0	1.5665
570	2.960	1196.8	1306.3	1.6616	1.9348	1190.5	1297.9	1.6107	1.6414	1187.2	1293.5	1.5904	1.4210	1183.8	1289.0	1.5723
580	2.993	1200.8	1311.6	1.6667	1.9580	1194.8	1303.5	1.6161	1.6619	1191.6	1299.3	1.5960	1.4395	1188.4	1294.9	1.5781
590	3.025	1204.9	1316.8	1.6717	1.9811	1199.0	1309.0	1.6214	1.6823	1196.0	1304.9	1.6014	1.4579	1192.9	1300.8	1.5837
600	3.058	1208.9	1322.1	1.6767	2.004	1203.2	1314.5	1.6266	1.7025	1200.3	1310.6	1.6068	1.4760	1197.3	1306.6	1.5892
620	3.123	1216.9	1332.5	1.6864	2.049	1211.6	1325.4	1.6368	1.7424	1208.9	1321.8	1.6172	1.5118	1206.1	1318.0	1.5999
640	3.188	1224.9	1342.9	1.6959	2.094	1220.0	1336.2	1.6467	1.7818	1217.4	1332.8	1.6274	1.5471	1214.8	1329.3	1.6103
660	3.252	1232.8	1353.2	1.7053	2.139	1228.2	1347.0	1.6564	1.8207	1225.8	1343.8	1.6372	1.5819	1223.4	1340.5	1.6203
680	3.316	1240.8	1363.5	1.7144	2.183	1236.4	1357.6	1.6658	1.8593	1234.2	1354.6	1.6469	1.6163	1231.9	1351.6	1.6301
700	3.379	1248.8	1373.8	1.7234	2.227	1244.6	1368.3	1.6751	1.8975	1242.5	1365.4	1.6562	1.6503	1240.4	1362.5	1.6397
720	3.442	1256.7	1384.1	1.7322	2.270	1252.8	1378.9	1.6841	1.9354	1250.8	1376.2	1.6654	1.6840	1248.8	1373.4	1.6490
740	3.505	1264.7	1394.4	1.7408	2.314	1261.0	1389.4	1.6930	1.9731	1259.1	1386.9	1.6744	1.7175	1257.2	1384.3	1.6581
760	3.568	1272.7	1404.7	1.7493	2.357	1269.1	1400.0	1.7017	2.0104	1267.3	1397.5	1.6832	1.7506	1265.5	1395.1	1.6670
780	3.631	1280.6	1415.0	1.7577	2.400	1277.3	1410.5	1.7103	2.0476	1275.6	1408.2	1.6919	1.7836	1273.8	1405.9	1.6758

TABLE A-3
(CONT'D.)

p(t Sat.)	200 (381.86)				300 (417.43)				350 (431.82)				400 (444.70)			
t	v	u	h	s	v	u	h	s	v	u	h	s	v	u	h	s
Sat.	2.289	1114.6	1199.3	1.5464	1.5442	1118.2	1203.9	1.5115	1.3267	1119.0	1204.9	1.4978	1.1620	1119.5	1205.5	1.4856
800	3.693	1288.6	1425.3	1.7660	2.442	1285.4	1421.0	1.7187	2.085	1283.8	1418.8	1.7004	1.8163	1282.1	1416.6	1.6844
820	3.755	1296.6	1435.6	1.7741	2.485	1293.6	1431.5	1.7270	2.121	1292.0	1429.4	1.7088	1.8489	1290.5	1427.3	1.6928
840	3.818	1304.7	1446.0	1.7821	2.527	1301.7	1442.0	1.7351	2.158	1300.3	1440.0	1.7170	1.8813	1298.8	1438.0	1.7011
860	3.879	1312.7	1456.3	1.7900	2.569	1309.9	1452.5	1.7432	2.194	1308.5	1450.6	1.7251	1.9135	1307.1	1448.7	1.7093
880	3.941	1320.8	1466.7	1.7978	2.611	1318.1	1463.1	1.7511	2.231	1316.7	1461.2	1.7331	1.9456	1315.4	1459.4	1.7173
900	4.003	1328.9	1477.1	1.8055	2.653	1326.3	1473.6	1.7589	2.267	1325.0	1471.8	1.7409	1.9776	1323.7	1470.1	1.7252
920	4.064	1337.0	1487.5	1.8131	2.695	1334.5	1484.1	1.7666	2.303	1333.3	1482.5	1.7487	2.0094	1332.0	1480.8	1.7330
940	4.126	1345.2	1497.9	1.8206	2.736	1342.8	1494.7	1.7742	2.339	1341.6	1493.1	1.7563	2.0411	1340.4	1491.5	1.7407
960	4.187	1353.3	1508.3	1.8280	2.778	1351.1	1505.3	1.7817	2.375	1349.9	1503.7	1.7639	2.0727	1348.7	1502.2	1.7483
980	4.249	1361.6	1518.8	1.8353	2.819	1359.3	1515.8	1.7891	2.411	1358.2	1514.4	1.7713	2.1043	1357.1	1512.9	1.7558
1000	4.310	1369.8	1529.3	1.8425	2.860	1367.7	1526.5	1.7964	2.446	1366.6	1525.0	1.7787	2.136	1365.5	1523.6	1.7632
1020	4.371	1378.0	1539.8	1.8497	2.902	1376.0	1537.1	1.8036	2.482	1375.0	1535.7	1.7859	2.167	1373.9	1534.3	1.7705
1040	4.432	1386.3	1550.3	1.8568	2.943	1384.4	1547.7	1.8108	2.517	1383.4	1546.4	1.7931	2.198	1382.4	1545.1	1.7777
1060	4.493	1394.6	1560.9	1.8638	2.984	1392.7	1558.4	1.8178	2.553	1391.8	1557.1	1.8002	2.229	1390.8	1555.9	1.7849
1080	4.554	1403.0	1571.5	1.8707	3.025	1401.2	1569.1	1.8248	2.588	1400.2	1567.9	1.8072	2.261	1399.3	1566.6	1.7919
1100	4.615	1411.4	1582.2	1.8776	3.066	1409.6	1579.8	1.8317	2.624	1408.7	1578.6	1.8142	2.292	1407.8	1577.4	1.7989
1200	4.918	1453.7	1635.7	1.9109	3.270	1452.2	1633.8	1.8653	2.799	1451.5	1632.8	1.8478	2.446	1450.7	1631.8	1.8327
1300	5.220	1496.9	1690.1	1.9427	3.473	1495.6	1688.4	1.8973	2.974	1495.0	1687.6	1.8799	2.599	1494.3	1686.8	1.8648
1400	5.521	1540.9	1745.3	1.9732	3.675	1539.8	1743.8	1.9279	3.148	1539.3	1743.1	1.9106	2.752	1538.7	1742.4	1.8956
1500	5.822	1585.8	1801.3	2.0025	3.877	1584.8	1800.0	1.9573	3.321	1584.3	1799.4	1.9401	2.904	1583.8	1798.8	1.9251
1600	6.123	1631.6	1858.2	2.0308	4.078	1630.7	1857.0	1.9857	3.494	1630.2	1856.5	1.9685	3.055	1629.8	1855.9	1.9535
1800	6.722	1725.6	1974.4	2.0847	4.479	1724.9	1973.5	2.0396	3.838	1724.5	1973.1	2.0225	3.357	1724.1	1972.6	2.0076
2000	7.321	1823.0	2094.0	2.1354	4.879	1822.3	2093.2	2.0904	4.182	1822.0	2092.8	2.0733	3.658	1821.6	2092.4	2.0584
2200	7.920	1923.6	2216.7	2.1833	5.280	1922.9	2216.0	2.1384	4.525	1922.5	2215.6	2.1212	3.959	1922.2	2215.2	2.1064
2400	8.518	2026.8	2342.1	2.2288	5.679	2026.1	2341.4	2.1838	4.868	2025.8	2341.1	2.1667	4.260	2025.4	2340.8	2.1519

TABLE A-3
(CONT'D.)

t	450(456.39) v	u	h	s	500(467.13) v	u	h	s	550(477.07) v	u	h	s	600(486.33) v	u	h	s
Sat.	1.0326	1119.6	1205.6	1.4746	.9283	1119.4	1205.3	1.4645	.8423	1119.1	1204.8	1.4551	.7702	1118.6	1204.1	1.4464
450	*1.0183*	*1115.5*	*1200.3*	*1.4687*												
460	1.0405	1121.8	1208.5	1.4777	*.9133*	*1114.7*	*1199.2*	*1.4578*								
470	1.0620	1128.0	1216.4	1.4863	.9342	1121.3	1207.8	1.4671	*.8283*	*1114.1*	*1198.4*	*1.4483*				
480	1.0828	1133.8	1224.0	1.4944	.9543	1127.7	1216.0	1.4759	.8480	1121.1	1207.4	1.4579	*.7582*	*1113.9*	*1198.1*	*1.4401*
490	1.1029	1139.5	1231.4	1.5022	.9736	1133.8	1223.9	1.4843	.8669	1127.7	1215.9	1.4669	.7769	1121.1	1207.4	1.4500
500	1.1226	1145.1	1238.5	1.5097	.9924	1139.7	1231.5	1.4923	.8850	1134.0	1224.1	1.4755	.7947	1128.0	1216.2	1.4592
510	1.1417	1150.4	1245.5	1.5170	1.0106	1145.4	1238.9	1.4999	.9056	1140.1	1232.0	1.4836	.8118	1134.5	1224.6	1.4679
520	1.1605	1155.7	1252.3	1.5239	1.0283	1150.9	1246.1	1.5073	.9196	1146.0	1239.6	1.4914	.8283	1140.7	1232.7	1.4762
530	1.1788	1160.8	1258.9	1.5307	1.0456	1156.3	1253.1	1.5144	.9361	1151.7	1246.9	1.4989	.8443	1146.8	1240.5	1.4841
540	1.1969	1165.8	1265.5	1.5372	1.0625	1161.6	1259.9	1.5212	.9522	1157.2	1254.1	1.5061	.8598	1152.6	1248.0	1.4917
550	1.2146	1170.7	1271.9	1.5436	1.0792	1166.7	1266.6	1.5279	.9679	1162.6	1261.1	1.5131	.8749	1158.2	1255.4	1.4990
560	1.2320	1175.6	1278.2	1.5498	1.0955	1171.8	1273.1	1.5343	.9834	1167.8	1267.9	1.5198	.8896	1163.7	1262.5	1.5060
570	1.2492	1180.3	1284.4	1.5559	1.1115	1176.7	1279.5	1.5406	.9985	1173.0	1274.6	1.5263	.9040	1169.1	1269.5	1.5128
580	1.2662	1185.0	1290.5	1.5618	1.1273	1181.6	1285.9	1.5467	1.0133	1178.0	1281.1	1.5327	.9181	1174.3	1276.3	1.5194
590	1.2830	1189.7	1296.5	1.5675	1.1429	1186.4	1292.1	1.5527	1.0280	1183.0	1287.6	1.5388	.9320	1179.5	1282.9	1.5253
600	1.2996	1194.3	1302.5	1.5732	1.1583	1191.1	1298.3	1.5585	1.0424	1187.9	1293.9	1.5448	.9456	1184.5	1289.5	1.5320
610	1.3160	1198.8	1308.4	1.5788	1.1735	1195.8	1304.3	1.5642	1.0566	1192.7	1300.2	1.5507	.9590	1189.5	1295.9	1.5381
620	1.3323	1203.3	1314.2	1.5842	1.1885	1200.4	1310.4	1.5698	1.0706	1197.4	1306.4	1.5565	.9722	1194.4	1302.3	1.5440
630	1.3484	1207.8	1320.0	1.5896	1.2033	1205.0	1316.3	1.5753	1.0845	1202.1	1312.5	1.5621	.9853	1199.2	1308.6	1.5497
640	1.3644	1212.2	1325.8	1.5948	1.2181	1209.5	1322.2	1.5807	1.0982	1206.7	1318.5	1.5676	.9982	1203.9	1314.8	1.5554
650	1.3803	1216.6	1331.5	1.6000	1.2327	1214.0	1328.0	1.5860	1.1118	1211.3	1324.5	1.5730	1.0109	1208.6	1320.9	1.5609
660	1.3960	1221.0	1337.2	1.6051	1.2472	1218.4	1333.8	1.5912	1.1252	1215.9	1330.4	1.5783	1.0235	1213.3	1326.9	1.5664
670	1.4116	1225.3	1342.9	1.6101	1.2615	1222.9	1339.6	1.5963	1.1386	1220.4	1336.3	1.5836	1.0360	1217.9	1332.9	1.5717
680	1.4272	1229.6	1348.5	1.6151	1.2758	1227.3	1345.3	1.6014	1.1518	1224.9	1342.1	1.5887	1.0483	1222.5	1338.9	1.5769
690	1.4426	1233.9	1354.1	1.6199	1.2899	1231.7	1351.0	1.6063	1.1649	1229.4	1347.9	1.5938	1.0606	1227.0	1344.8	1.5821
700	1.4580	1238.2	1359.6	1.6248	1.3040	1236.0	1356.7	1.6112	1.1779	1233.8	1353.7	1.5987	1.0727	1231.5	1350.6	1.5872
720	1.4884	1246.7	1370.7	1.6342	1.3319	1244.7	1367.9	1.6208	1.2037	1242.6	1365.1	1.6085	1.0968	1240.4	1362.2	1.5971
740	1.5186	1255.2	1381.7	1.6435	1.3594	1253.3	1379.1	1.6302	1.2291	1251.3	1376.4	1.6180	1.1205	1249.3	1373.7	1.6067
760	1.5485	1263.7	1392.6	1.6525	1.3867	1261.8	1390.1	1.6394	1.2543	1260.0	1387.6	1.6273	1.1439	1258.1	1385.1	1.6161
780	1.5782	1272.1	1403.5	1.6614	1.4138	1270.3	1401.1	1.6483	1.2793	1268.6	1398.8	1.6364	1.1671	1266.8	1396.3	1.6253

p(t Sat.)

TABLE A-3
(CONT'D.)

p(t Sat.)

t	450(456.39) v	u	h	s	500(467.13) v	u	h	s	550(477.07) v	u	h	s	600(486.33) v	u	h	s
Sat.	1.0326	1119.6	1205.6	1.4746	.9283	1119.4	1205.3	1.4645	.8423	1119.1	1204.8	1.4551	.7702	1118.6	1204.1	1.4464
800	1.6077	1280.5	1414.4	1.6701	1.4407	1278.8	1412.1	1.6571	1.3040	1277.1	1409.8	1.6452	1.1900	1275.4	1407.6	1.6343
820	1.6369	1288.9	1425.2	1.6786	1.4673	1287.3	1423.0	1.6657	1.3285	1285.7	1420.9	1.6539	1.2128	1284.1	1418.7	1.6430
840	1.6660	1297.3	1436.0	1.6870	1.4938	1295.7	1433.9	1.6742	1.3528	1294.2	1431.9	1.6625	1.2353	1292.7	1429.8	1.6517
860	1.6950	1305.6	1446.8	1.6952	1.5201	1304.2	1444.8	1.6825	1.3770	1302.7	1442.9	1.6708	1.2577	1301.2	1440.9	1.6601
880	1.7238	1314.0	1457.5	1.7033	1.5463	1312.6	1455.7	1.6906	1.4010	1311.2	1453.8	1.6791	1.2800	1309.8	1451.9	1.6684
900	1.7524	1322.4	1468.3	1.7113	1.5723	1321.0	1466.5	1.6987	1.4249	1319.7	1464.7	1.6872	1.3021	1318.4	1462.9	1.6766
920	1.7810	1330.8	1479.1	1.7191	1.5982	1329.5	1477.4	1.7066	1.4487	1328.2	1475.6	1.6951	1.3240	1326.9	1473.9	1.6846
940	1.8094	1339.2	1489.8	1.7269	1.6240	1337.9	1488.2	1.7144	1.4723	1336.7	1486.6	1.7030	1.3459	1335.5	1484.9	1.6925
960	1.8377	1347.6	1500.6	1.7345	1.6497	1346.4	1499.0	1.7221	1.4958	1345.2	1497.5	1.7107	1.3676	1344.0	1495.9	1.7003
980	1.8660	1356.0	1511.4	1.7420	1.6753	1354.9	1509.9	1.7296	1.5193	1353.7	1508.4	1.7183	1.3893	1352.6	1506.8	1.7079
1000	1.8941	1364.4	1522.2	1.7495	1.7008	1363.3	1520.7	1.7371	1.5426	1362.3	1519.3	1.7259	1.4108	1361.2	1517.8	1.7155
1020	1.9221	1372.9	1533.0	1.7568	1.7262	1371.8	1531.6	1.7445	1.5659	1370.8	1530.2	1.7333	1.4322	1369.7	1528.8	1.7230
1040	1.9501	1381.4	1543.8	1.7641	1.7515	1380.4	1542.4	1.7518	1.5890	1379.3	1541.1	1.7406	1.4536	1378.3	1539.7	1.7303
1060	1.9780	1389.9	1554.6	1.7712	1.7768	1388.9	1553.3	1.7590	1.6121	1387.9	1552.0	1.7478	1.4749	1386.9	1550.7	1.7376
1080	2.0058	1398.4	1565.4	1.7783	1.8020	1397.4	1564.2	1.7661	1.6352	1396.5	1562.9	1.7550	1.4961	1395.6	1561.7	1.7448
1100	2.034	1406.9	1576.3	1.7853	1.8271	1406.0	1575.1	1.7731	1.6581	1405.1	1573.9	1.7620	1.5173	1404.2	1572.7	1.7519
1150	2.103	1428.4	1603.5	1.8025	1.8896	1427.5	1602.4	1.7904	1.7152	1426.7	1601.3	1.7793	1.5699	1425.9	1600.2	1.7692
1200	2.172	1450.0	1630.8	1.8192	1.9518	1449.2	1629.8	1.8072	1.7720	1448.5	1628.8	1.7962	1.6222	1447.7	1627.8	1.7861
1250	2.240	1471.8	1658.3	1.8355	2.0137	1471.1	1657.4	1.8235	1.8285	1470.3	1656.5	1.8126	1.6742	1469.6	1655.5	1.8026
1300	2.308	1493.7	1685.9	1.8515	2.075	1493.1	1685.1	1.8395	1.8848	1492.4	1684.2	1.8286	1.7260	1491.7	1683.4	1.8186
1350	2.376	1515.8	1713.7	1.8670	2.137	1515.2	1712.9	1.8551	1.9409	1514.6	1712.2	1.8443	1.7775	1514.0	1711.4	1.8343
1400	2.444	1538.1	1741.7	1.8823	2.198	1537.6	1741.0	1.8704	1.9967	1537.0	1740.2	1.8596	1.8289	1536.5	1739.5	1.8497
1450	2.512	1560.6	1769.8	1.8972	2.259	1560.1	1769.2	1.8853	2.0525	1559.6	1768.5	1.8746	1.8801	1559.1	1767.8	1.8647
1500	2.580	1583.3	1798.2	1.9119	2.320	1582.8	1797.5	1.9000	2.1080	1582.3	1796.9	1.8892	1.9312	1581.9	1796.3	1.8794
1600	2.715	1629.3	1855.4	1.9403	2.442	1628.9	1854.8	1.9285	2.219	1628.4	1854.3	1.9178	2.033	1628.0	1853.7	1.9080
1800	2.983	1723.7	1972.1	1.9944	2.684	1723.3	1971.7	1.9827	2.440	1722.9	1971.2	1.9720	2.236	1722.6	1970.8	1.9622
2000	3.251	1821.3	2092.0	2.0453	2.926	1820.9	2091.6	2.0335	2.660	1820.6	2091.2	2.0229	2.438	1820.2	2090.8	2.0131
2200	3.519	1921.8	2214.9	2.0933	3.167	1921.5	2214.5	2.0815	2.879	1921.1	2214.2	2.0709	2.639	1920.8	2213.8	2.0612
2400	3.787	2025.1	2340.4	2.1388	3.408	2024.7	2340.1	2.1270	3.098	2024.4	2339.7	2.1164	2.840	2024.0	2339.4	2.1067

TABLE A-3
(CONT'D.)

p(t Sat)	800(518.36)				1000(544.75)			
t	v	u	h	s	v	u	h	s
Sat	.5691	1115.0	1199.3	1.4160	.4459	1109.9	1192.4	1.3903
500								
510	.5554	1107.9	1190.1	1.4066				
520	.5717	1116.4	1201.0	1.4178				
530	.5870	1124.3	1211.2	1.4282				
540	.6015	1131.8	1220.8	1.4378	.4389	1105.2	1186.4	1.3844
550	.6154	1138.8	1229.9	1.4469	.4534	1114.8	1198.7	1.3966
560	.6287	1145.6	1238.6	1.4555	.4669	1123.6	1210.0	1.4077
570	.6415	1152.0	1247.0	1.4637	.4795	1131.7	1220.5	1.4179
580	.6539	1158.3	1255.1	1.4714	.4915	1139.4	1230.4	1.4275
590	.6659	1164.3	1262.9	1.4789	.5030	1146.7	1239.8	1.4365
600	.6776	1170.1	1270.4	1.4861	.5140	1153.7	1248.8	1.4450
610	.6890	1175.8	1277.8	1.4930	.5245	1160.3	1257.4	1.4531
620	.7002	1181.3	1285.0	1.4997	.5348	1166.7	1265.7	1.4609
630	.7111	1186.7	1292.0	1.5062	.5447	1172.9	1273.7	1.4682
640	.7218	1192.0	1298.9	1.5125	.5543	1178.9	1281.5	1.4754
650	.7324	1197.2	1305.6	1.5186	.5637	1184.7	1289.1	1.4822
660	.7428	1202.3	1312.3	1.5245	.5730	1190.4	1296.5	1.4889
670	.7530	1207.4	1318.8	1.5304	.5820	1196.0	1303.7	1.4953
680	.7631	1212.3	1325.3	1.5361	.5908	1201.4	1310.8	1.5015
690	.7730	1217.2	1331.7	1.5416	.5995	1206.8	1317.7	1.5076
700	.7829	1222.1	1338.0	1.5471	.6080	1212.0	1324.6	1.5135
720	.8023	1231.6	1350.4	1.5577	.6247	1222.3	1337.9	1.5249
740	.8212	1241.0	1362.6	1.5680	.6410	1232.3	1350.9	1.5359
760	.8399	1250.3	1374.6	1.5779	.6569	1242.1	1363.7	1.5464
780	.8583	1259.4	1386.5	1.5875	.6725	1251.7	1376.2	1.5566
800	.8764	1268.5	1398.2	1.5969	.6878	1261.2	1388.5	1.5664
820	.8943	1277.4	1409.8	1.6061	.7028	1270.6	1400.6	1.5760
840	.9120	1286.4	1421.4	1.6150	.7176	1279.9	1412.7	1.5853
860	.9295	1295.2	1432.8	1.6238	.7323	1289.1	1424.6	1.5944
880	.9468	1304.1	1444.2	1.6324	.7467	1298.2	1436.4	1.6033
900	.9640	1312.9	1455.6	1.6408	.7610	1307.3	1448.1	1.6120
920	.9811	1321.7	1466.9	1.6490	.7752	1316.3	1459.7	1.6205
940	.9980	1330.4	1478.2	1.6572	.7892	1325.3	1471.3	1.6288
960	1.0149	1339.2	1489.4	1.6651	.8031	1334.3	1482.9	1.6370
980	1.0316	1348.0	1500.7	1.6730	.8169	1343.2	1494.4	1.6451
1000	1.0482	1356.7	1511.9	1.6807	.8305	1352.2	1505.9	1.6530
1020	1.0647	1365.5	1523.1	1.6883	.8441	1361.1	1517.3	1.6608
1040	1.0812	1374.2	1534.3	1.6959	.8576	1370.0	1528.7	1.6684
1060	1.0975	1383.0	1545.5	1.7033	.8710	1378.9	1540.1	1.6760
1080	1.1138	1391.7	1556.6	1.7106	.8844	1387.9	1551.5	1.6834
1100	1.1300	1400.5	1567.8	1.7178	.8976	1396.8	1562.9	1.6908
1120	1.1462	1409.3	1579.0	1.7249	.9108	1405.7	1574.3	1.6980
1140	1.1623	1418.1	1590.2	1.7319	.9240	1414.6	1585.6	1.7052
1160	1.1783	1426.9	1601.4	1.7389	.9370	1423.6	1597.0	1.7122
1180	1.1943	1435.8	1612.6	1.7458	.9500	1432.5	1608.3	1.7192
1200	1.2102	1444.6	1623.8	1.7526	.9630	1441.5	1619.7	1.7261
1220	1.2261	1453.5	1635.0	1.7593	.9759	1450.4	1631.0	1.7329
1240	1.2420	1462.3	1646.2	1.7659	.9888	1459.4	1642.4	1.7396
1260	1.2578	1471.3	1657.4	1.7725	1.0016	1468.4	1653.8	1.7462
1280	1.2735	1480.2	1668.7	1.7790	1.0144	1477.4	1665.1	1.7528
1300	1.2892	1489.1	1680.0	1.7854	1.0272	1486.5	1676.5	1.7593
1350	1.3284	1511.6	1708.2	1.8013	1.0589	1509.1	1705.1	1.7753
1400	1.3674	1534.2	1736.6	1.8167	1.0905	1531.9	1733.7	1.7909
1450	1.4062	1556.9	1765.1	1.8319	1.1218	1554.8	1762.4	1.8061
1500	1.4448	1579.9	1793.7	1.8467	1.1531	1577.8	1791.2	1.8210
1600	1.5218	1626.2	1851.5	1.8754	1.2152	1624.4	1849.3	1.8499
1800	1.6749	1721.0	1969.0	1.9298	1.3384	1719.5	1967.2	1.9046
2000	1.8271	1818.8	2089.3	1.9808	1.4608	1817.4	2087.7	1.9557
2200	1.9789	1919.4	2212.4	2.0290	1.5828	1918.1	2211.0	2.0038
2400	2.1305	2022.7	2338.1	2.0745	1.7046	2021.3	2336.7	2.0494

TABLE A-4
PROPERTIES OF COMPRESSED LIQUID.

p(t Sat.)	Liquid	0				500(467.13)				1000(544.75)			
t	v	v	u	h	s	v	u	h	s	v	u	h	s
Sat.						.019748	447.70	449.53	.64904	.021591	538.39	542.38	.74320
32	.016022		0.01	0.01	.00003	.015994	.00	1.49	.00000	.015967	.03	2.99	.00005
50	.016024		18.06	18.06	.03607	.015998	18.02	19.50	.03599	.015972	17.99	20.94	.03592
100	.016130		68.05	68.05	.12963	.016106	67.87	69.36	.12932	.016082	67.70	70.68	.12901
150	.016344		117.95	117.95	.21504	.016318	117.66	119.17	.21457	.016293	117.38	120.40	.21410
200	.016635		168.05	168.05	.29402	.016608	167.65	169.19	.29341	.016580	167.26	170.32	.29281
250	.017003		218.52	218.52	.36777	.016972	217.99	219.56	.36702	.016941	217.47	220.61	.36628
300	.017453		269.61	269.61	.43732	.017416	268.92	270.53	.43641	.017379	268.24	271.46	.43352
350	.018000		321.59	321.59	.50359	.017954	320.71	322.37	.50249	.017909	319.83	323.15	.50140
400	.018668		374.85	374.85	.56740	.018608	373.68	375.40	.56604	.018550	372.55	375.98	.56472
450	.019503		429.96	429.96	.62970	.019420	428.40	430.19	.63798	.019340	426.89	430.47	.62632
500	.02060		488.1	488.1	.6919	.02048	485.9	487.8	.6896	.02036	483.8	487.5	.6874
510	.02087		500.3	500.3	.7046	.02073	497.9	499.8	.7021	.02060	495.6	499.4	.6997
520	.02116		512.7	512.7	.7173	.02100	510.1	512.0	.7146	.02086	507.6	511.5	.7121
530	.02148		525.5	525.5	.7303	.02130	522.6	524.5	.7273	.02114	519.9	523.8	.7245
540	.02182		538.6	538.6	.7434	.02162	535.3	537.3	.7402	.02144	532.4	536.3	.7372
550	.02221		552.1	552.1	.7569	.02198	548.4	550.5	.7532	.02177	545.1	549.2	.7499
560	.02265		566.1	566.1	.7707	.02237	562.0	564.0	.7666	.02213	558.3	562.4	.7630
570	.02315		580.8	580.8	.7851	.02281	576.0	578.1	.7804	.02253	571.8	576.0	.7763
580						.02332	590.8	592.9	.7946	.02298	585.9	590.1	.7899
590						.02392	606.4	608.6	.8096	.02349	600.6	604.9	.8041
600										.02409	616.2	620.6	.8189
610										.02482	632.9	637.5	.8348

p	4000				18,000				20,000			
t	v	u	h	s	v	u	h	s	v	u	h	s
32	.015807	.10	11.80	.00005	.015188	0.54	50.05	-.00372	.015116	-.65	55.30	-.00446
50	.015821	17.36	29.47	.03534	.015227	16.32	67.04	.03021	.015154	16.14	72.23	.02936
100	.015942	66.72	78.52	.12714	.015372	62.83	114.03	.11817	.015298	62.37	118.99	.11688
150	.016150	115.77	127.73	.21136	.015572	109.64	161.51	.19941	.015497	108.91	166.26	.19778
200	.016425	165.02	177.18	.28931	.015813	156.62	209.29	.27474	.015736	155.62	213.86	.27281
250	.016765	214.52	226.93	.36200	.016096	203.57	257.19	.34472	.016015	202.28	261.55	.34250
300	.017174	264.43	277.15	.43038	.016422	250.58	305.28	.41021	.016333	248.96	309.41	.40766
350	017659	314.98	328.05	.49526	.016791	297.80	353.73	.47197	.016693	295.83	357.61	.46911
400	.018235	366.35	379.85	.55734	.017207	345.32	402.63	.53057	.017096	342.97	406.24	.52738
450	.018924	418.83	432.84	.61725	.017669	393.15	452.00	.58639	.017541	390.39	455.31	.58286
500	.019766	472.9	487.5	.6758	.018183	441.3	501.9	.6397	.018031	438.1	504.8	.6358
520	.020161	495.2	510.1	.6990	.018404	460.6	521.9	.6605	.018242	457.2	524.7	.6564
540	.020600	517.9	533.1	.7223	.018636	480.0	542.1	.6808	.018461	476.4	544.7	.6766
560	.021091	541.2	556.8	.7457	.018879	499.5	562.4	.7009	.018689	495.6	564.8	.6965
580	.021648	565.2	581.2	.7694	.019134	519.0	582.8	.7207	.018928	514.9	585.0	.7160
600	.02229	590.0	606.5	.7936	.01940	538.7	603.3	.7403	.01918	534.3	605.2	.7354
620	.02304	616.0	633.0	.8183	.01968	558.4	623.9	.7596	.01944	553.7	625.6	.7544
640	.02394	643.3	661.1	.8441	.01998	578.2	644.8	.7787	.01972	573.2	646.1	.7732
660	.02506	672.7	691.2	.8712	.02030	598.1	665.7	.7976	.02001	592.7	666.8	.7918
680	.02653	704.9	724.5	.9007	.02064	618.2	686.9	.8163	.02031	612.4	687.6	.8102
700	.02867	742.1	763.4	.9345	.02099	638.4	708.3	.8349	.02063	632.1	708.5	.8285
710	.03026	764.3	786.7	.9545	.02118	648.5	719.1	.8442	.02080	642.1	719.1	.8375

TABLE A-5

THERMAL CONDUCTIVITIES OF SOME BUILDING AND INSULATING MATERIALS*

$[k = \text{Btu/hr ft}^2 \ ^\circ\text{F/ft}]$

Material	Apparent density ρ, lb/cu ft at room temperature	$^\circ F$	k
Aerogel, silica, opacified	8.5	248	0.013
		554	0.026
Asbestos-cement boards	120	68	0.43
Asbestos sheets	55.5	124	0.096
Asbestos slate	112	32	0.087
	112	140	0.114
Aluminum foil, 7 air spaces per 2.5 in.	0.2	100	0.025
		351	0.038
Asphalt	132	68	0.43
Bricks:			
Alumina (92-99% Al_2O_3 by weight) fused	......	801	1.8
Alumina (64-65% Al_2O_3 by weight)	......	2399	2.7
(See also Bricks, fire clay)	115	1472	0.62
Building brickwork	......	68	0.4
Carbon	96.7	......	3.0
Chrome brick (32% Cr_2O_3 by weight)	200	392	0.67
	200	1202	0.85
	200	2399	1.0
Diatomaceous earth, molded and fired	38	399	0.14
	38	1600	0.18
Diatomaceous earth, high burn, large pores	37	392	0.13
	37	1832	0.34
Fire clay, Missouri	......	392	0.58
		1112	0.85
		1832	0.95
		2552	1.02
Kaolin insulating brick	27	932	0.15
	27	2102	0.26
Kaolin insulating firebrick	19	392	0.050
	19	1400	0.113
Magnesite (86.8% MgO, 6.3% Fe_2O_3, 3% CaO, 2.6% SiO_2 by weight)	158	399	2.2
	158	1202	1.6
	158	2192	1.1
Calcium carbonate, natural	162	86	1.3
White marble	......	......	1.7
Chalk	96		0.4
Calcium sulfate ($4H_2O$), artificial	84.6	104	0.22
Plaster, artificial	132	167	0.43
Building	77.9	77	0.25
Cardboard, corrugated	......	......	0.037
Celluloid	87.3	86	0.12
Charcoal flakes	11.9	176	0.043
	15	176	0.051
Coke, petroleum	......	212	3.4
		932	2.9
Coke, powdered	......	32-212	0.11
Concrete, cinder	......	......	0.20
1:4 dry	......	......	0.44
Stone	......	......	0.54
Cotton wool	5	86	0.024
Cork board	10	86	0.025
Cork, ground	9.4	86	0.025
Diatomaceous earth powder, coarse	20.0	100	0.036
	20.0	1600	0.082
Fine	17.2	399	0.040
	17.2	1600	0.074
Molded pipe covering	26.0	399	0.051
	26.0	1600	0.088

*From *Thermodynamics* by G. F. Babits, Allyn & Bacon, Inc., Boston, 1963, pp. 231–234, with permission.

TABLE A-5
(CONT'D.)

Material	Apparent density ρ, lb/cu ft at room temperature	°F	k
Dolomite	167	122	1.0
Ebonite	......	......	0.10
Enamel, Silicate	38	......	0.5-0.75
Felt, wool	20.6	86	0.03
Fiber insulating board	14.8	70	0.028
Glass	......	......	0.2-0.73
Borosilicate type	139	86-167	0.63
Soda glass	......	......	0.3-0.44
Window glass	......	......	0.3-0.61
Granite	......	......	1.0-2.3
Graphite, longitudinal	......	68	95
Gypsum, molded and dry	78	68	0.25
Hair felt, perpendicular to fibers	17	86	0.021
Ice	57.5	32	1.3
Kapok	0.88	68	0.020
Lampblack	10	104	0.038
Leather sole	62.4	......	0.092
Limestone (15.3 vol. %H_2O)	103	75	0.54
Magnesia, powdered	49.7	117	0.35
Magnesia, light carbonate	19	70	0.034
Magnesium oxide, compressed	49.9	68	0.32
Marble	......	......	1.2-1.7
Mica, perpendicular to planes	......	122	0.25
Mineral wool	9.4	86	0.0225
	19.7	86	0.024
Paper	......	......	0.075
Paraffin wax	......	32	0.14
Porcelain	......	392	0.88
Portland cement (see Concrete)	......	194	0.17
Pumice stone	......	70-151	0.14
Pyroxylin plastics	......	......	0.075
Rubber, hard	74.8	32	0.087
Para	......	70	0.109
Soft	......	70	0.075-0.092
Sand, dry	94.6	68	0.19
Sandstone	140	104	1.06
Sawdust	12	70	0.03
Slag, blast furnace	......	75-261	0.064
Slag wool	12	86	0.022
Slate	......	201	0.86
Snow	34.7	32	0.27
Sulphur, monoclinic	......	212	0.09-0.097
Rhombic	......	70	0.16
Wallboard, insulating type	14.8	70	0.028
Wallboard, stiff pasteboard	43	86	0.04
Wood shavings	8.8	86	0.034
Wood, across grain			
Balsa	7-8	86	0.025-0.03
Oak	51.5	59	0.12
Maple	44.7	122	0.11
Pine, white	34.0	59	0.087
Teak	40.0	59	0.10
White fir	28.1	140	0.062
Wood, parallel to grain			
Pine	34.4	70	0.20
Wool, animal	6.9	86	0.021

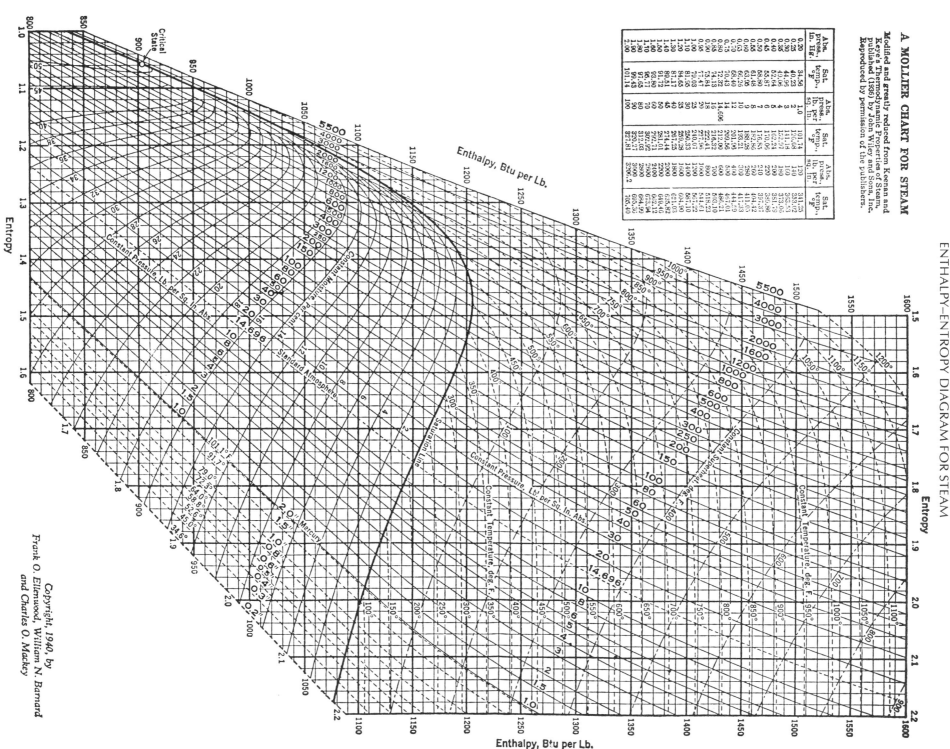

A MOLLIER CHART FOR STEAM

Modified and greatly reduced from Keenan and Keye's *Thermodynamic Properties of Steam*, published (1936) by John Wiley and Sons, Inc. Reproduced by permission of the publishers.

TABLE A-6

ENTHALPY–ENTROPY DIAGRAM FOR STEAM

Enthalpy, Btu per Lb.

Enthalpy, B†u per Lb.

Entropy

Entropy

x

Abs. press., in. Hg.	Sat. temp., F	Abs. press., lb. per sq. in.	Sat. temp., F	Abs. press., lb. per sq. in.	Sat. temp., F
0.20	34.56	1.0	101.74	120	341.25
0.25	40.23	2	126.08	110	333.02
0.30	44.96	3	141.48	160	363.53
0.35	49.06	4	152.97	180	373.06
0.40	52.64	5	162.24	200	381.79
0.45	55.87	6	170.06	220	389.86
0.50	58.80	7	176.85	240	397.37
0.55	61.48	8	182.86	260	404.42
0.60	63.95	9	188.28	280	411.05
0.65	66.26	10	193.21	300	417.33
0.70	68.40	12	201.96	350	431.72
0.75	70.43	14	209.56	400	444.59
0.80	72.32	14.696	212.00	450	456.28
0.85	74.13	16	216.32	500	467.01
0.90	75.84	18	222.41	600	486.21
0.95	77.47	20	227.96	700	503.10
1.00	79.03	25	240.07	800	518.23
1.10	81.96	30	250.33	900	531.98
1.20	84.65	35	259.28	1000	544.61
1.30	87.17	40	267.25	1200	567.22
1.40	89.51	45	274.44	1400	587.10
1.50	91.72	50	281.01	1600	604.90
1.60	93.80	60	292.71	1800	621.03
1.70	95.77	70	302.92	2000	635.82
1.80	97.65	80	312.03	2200	649.46
1.90	99.43	90	320.27	2500	668.13
2.00	101.14	100	327.81	2900	694.99
				3000	695.40
				3206.2	705.40

x

TABLE A-7
AMMONIA: PROPERTIES OF LIQUID AND SATURATED VAPOR[†]

Temp.	Pressure		Volume	Density	Enthaply from −40°F			Entropy from −40°F	
°F	Abs. lb/in.²	Gage lb/in.²	Vapor ft³/lb	Liquid lb/ft³	Liquid Btu/lb	Vapor Btu/lb	Latent Btu/lb	Liquid Btu/lb °F	Vapor Btu/lb °F
t	p	p_d	v_g	$1/v_f$	h_f	h_g	h_{fg}	s_f	s_g
−100	1.24	*27.4	182.90	45.51	−61.5	571.4	632.9	−0.1579	1.6025
− 90	1.86	*26.1	124.28	45.12	−51.4	575.9	627.3	−0.1309	1.5667
− 80	2.74	*24.3	86.54	44.73	−41.3	580.1	621.4	−0.1036	1.5336
− 70	3.94	*21.9	61.65	44.32	−31.1	584.4	615.5	−0.0771	1.5026
− 65	4.69	*20.4	52.34	44.11	−26.0	586.6	612.6	−0.0642	1.4833
− 60	5.55	*18.6	44.73	43.91	−20.9	588.8	609.7	−0.0514	1.4747
− 55	6.54	*16.6	38.38	43.70	−15.7	591.0	606.7	−0.0382	1.4614
− 50	7.67	*14.3	33.08	43.49	−10.5	593.2	603.7	−0.0254	1.4487
− 45	8.95	*11.7	28.62	43.28	− 5.3	595.7	600.7	−0.0128	1.4363
− 40	10.41	*8.7	24.86	43.08	0.0	597.6	597.6	0.0000	1.4242
− 38	11.04	*7.4	23.53	42.99	2.1	598.3	596.2	.0051	.4193
− 36	11.71	*6.1	22.27	42.90	4.3	599.1	594.8	.0101	.4144
− 34	12.41	*4.7	21.10	42.82	6.4	599.9	593.5	.0151	.4096
− 32	13.14	*3.2	20.00	42.73	8.5	600.6	592.1	.0201	.4048
− 30	13.90	*1.6	18.97	42.65	10.7	601.4	590.7	0.0250	1.4001
− 28	14.71	0.0	18.00	42.57	12.8	602.1	589.3	.0300	.3955
− 26	15.55	0.8	17.09	42.48	14.9	602.8	587.9	.0350	.3909
− 24	16.42	1.7	16.24	42.40	17.1	603.6	586.5	.0399	.3863
− 22	17.34	2.6	15.43	42.31	19.2	604.3	585.1	.0448	.3818
− 20	18.30	3.6	14.68	42.22	21.4	605.0	583.6	0.0497	1.3774
− 18	19.30	4.6	13.97	43.13	23.5	605.7	582.2	.0545	.3729
− 16	20.34	5.6	13.29	42.04	25.6	606.4	580.8	.0594	.3686
− 14	21.43	6.7	12.66	41.96	27.8	607.1	579.3	.0642	.3643
− 12	22.56	7.9	12.06	41.87	30.0	607.8	577.8	.0690	.3600
− 10	23.74	9.0	11.50	41.78	32.1	608.5	576.4	0.0738	1.3558
− 8	24.97	10.3	10.97	41.69	34.3	609.2	574.9	.0786	.3516
− 6	26.26	11.6	10.47	41.60	36.4	609.8	573.4	.0833	.3474
− 4	27.59	12.9	9.991	41.52	38.6	610.5	571.9	.0880	.3433
− 2	28.98	14.3	9.541	41.43	40.7	611.1	570.4	.0928	.3393
0	30.42	15.7	9.116	41.34	42.9	611.8	568.9	0.0975	1.3352
2	31.92	17.2	8.714	41.25	45.1	612.4	567.3	.1022	.3312
4	33.47	18.8	8.333	41.16	47.2	613.0	565.8	.1069	.3273
6	35.09	20.4	7.971	41.07	49.4	613.6	564.2	.1115	.3234
8	36.77	22.1	7.629	40.98	51.6	614.3	562.7	.1162	.3195
10	38.51	23.8	7.304	40.89	53.8	614.9	561.1	0.1208	1.3157
12	40.31	25.6	6.996	40.80	56.0	615.5	559.5	.1254	.3118
14	42.18	27.5	6.703	40.71	58.2	616.1	557.9	.1300	.3081
16	44.12	29.4	6.425	40.61	60.3	616.6	556.3	.1346	.3043
18	46.13	31.4	6.161	40.52	62.5	617.2	554.7	.1392	.3006
20	48.21	33.5	5.910	40.43	64.7	617.8	553.1	0.1437	1.2969
22	50.36	35.7	5.671	40.34	66.9	618.3	551.4	.1483	.2933
24	52.59	37.9	5.443	40.25	69.1	618.9	549.8	.1528	.2897
26	54.90	40.2	5.227	40.15	71.3	619.4	548.1	.1573	.2861
28	57.28	42.6	5.021	40.06	73.5	619.9	546.4	.1618	.2825
30	59.74	45.0	4.825	39.96	75.7	620.5	544.8	0.1663	1.2790
32	62.29	47.6	4.637	39.86	77.9	621.0	543.1	.1708	.2755
34	64.91	50.2	4.459	39.77	80.1	621.5	541.4	.1753	.2721
36	67.63	52.9	4.289	39.67	82.3	622.0	539.7	.1797	.2686
38	70.43	55.7	4.126	39.50	84.6	622.5	537.9	.1841	.2652

[†] *Abstracted, by permission, from "Tables of Thermodynamic Properties of Ammonia," U.S. Department of Commerce, Bureau of Standards Circular No. 142, 1945.*

*Inches of mercury below one atmosphere.

TABLE A-7
(CONT'D.)[†]

Temp.	Pressure		Volume	Density	Enthalpy from −40°F			Entropy from −40°F	
°F	Abs. lb/in²	Gage lb/in²	Vapor ft³/lb	Liquid lb/ft³	Liquid Btu/lb	Vapor Btu/lb	Latent Btu/lb	Liquid Btu/lb °F	Vapor Btu/lb °F
t	*p*	*p_d*	*v_g*	*1/v_f*	*h_f*	*h_g*	*h_fg*	*s_f*	*s_g*
40	73.32	58.6	3.971	39.49	86.8	623.0	536.2	0.1885	1.2618
42	76.31	61.6	3.823	39.39	89.0	623.4	534.4	.1930	.2585
44	79.38	64.7	3.682	39.29	91.2	623.9	532.7	.1974	.2552
46	82.55	67.9	3.547	39.19	93.5	624.4	530.9	.2018	.2519
48	85.82	71.1	3.418	39.10	95.7	624.8	529.1	.2062	.2486
50	89.19	74.5	3.294	39.00	97.9	625.2	527.3	0.2105	1.2453
52	92.66	78.0	3.176	38.90	100.2	625.7	525.5	.2149	.2421
54	96.23	81.5	3.063	38.80	102.4	626.1	523.7	.2192	.2389
56	99.91	85.2	2.954	38.70	104.7	626.5	521.8	.2236	.2357
58	103.7	89.0	2.851	38.60	106.9	626.9	520.0	.2279	.2325
60	107.6	92.9	2.751	38.50	109.2	627.3	518.1	0.2322	1.2294
62	111.6	96.9	2.656	38.40	111.5	627.7	516.2	.2365	.2262
64	115.7	101.0	2.565	38.30	113.7	628.0	514.3	.2408	.2231
66	120.0	105.3	2.477	38.20	116.0	628.4	512.4	.2451	.2201
68	124.3	109.6	2.393	38.10	118.3	628.8	510.5	.2494	.2170
70	128.8	114.1	2.312	38.00	120.5	629.1	508.6	0.2537	1.2140
72	133.4	118.7	2.235	37.90	122.8	629.4	506.6	.2579	.2110
74	138.1	123.4	2.161	37.79	125.1	629.8	504.7	.2622	.2080
76	143.0	128.3	2.089	37.69	127.4	630.1	502.7	.2664	.2050
78	147.9	133.2	2.021	37.58	129.7	630.4	500.7	.2706	.2020
80	153.0	138.3	1.955	37.48	132.0	630.7	498.7	0.2749	1.1991
82	158.3	143.6	1.892	37.37	134.3	631.0	496.7	.2791	.1962
84	163.7	149.0	1.831	37.26	136.6	631.3	494.7	.2833	.1933
86	169.2	154.5	1.772	37.16	138.9	631.5	492.6	.2875	.1904
88	174.8	160.1	1.716	37.05	141.2	631.8	490.6	.2917	.1875
90	180.6	165.9	1.661	36.95	143.5	632.0	488.5	0.2958	1.1846
92	186.6	171.9	1.609	36.84	145.8	632.2	486.4	.3000	.1818
94	192.7	178.0	1.559	36.73	148.2	632.5	484.3	.3041	.1789
96	198.9	184.2	1.510	36.62	150.5	632.6	482.1	.3083	.1761
98	205.3	190.6	1.464	36.51	152.9	632.9	480.0	.3125	.1733
100	211.9	197.2	1.419	36.40	155.2	633.0	477.8	0.3166	1.1705
102	218.6	203.9	1.375	36.29	157.6	633.2	475.6	.3207	.1677
104	225.4	210.7	1.334	36.18	159.9	633.4	473.5	.3248	.1649
106	232.5	217.8	1.293	36.06	162.3	633.5	471.2	.3289	.1621
108	239.7	225.0	1.254	35.95	164.6	633.6	469.0	.3330	.1593
110	247.0	232.3	1.217	35.84	167.0	633.7	466.7	0.3372	1.1566
112	254.5	239.8	1.180	35.72	169.4	633.8	464.4	.3413	.1538
114	262.2	247.5	1.145	35.61	171.8	633.9	462.1	.3453	.1510
116	270.1	255.4	1.112	35.49	174.2	634.0	459.8	.3495	.1483
118	278.2	263.5	1.079	35.38	176.6	634.0	457.4	.3535	.1455
120	286.4	271.7	1.047	35.26	179.0	634.0	455.0	0.3576	1.1427
122	294.8	280.1	1.017	35.14	181.4	634.0	452.6	.3618	.1400
124	303.4	288.7	0.987	35.02	183.9	634.0	450.1	.3659	.1372

[†] *From Refrigeration and Air Conditioning, 2nd Ed., by R. C. Jordan and G. B. Priester, Prentice-Hall, Inc., Englewood Cliffs, N.J., 1956.*

TABLE A-8
AMMONIA: PROPERTIES OF SUPERHEATED VAPOR*

Absolute Pressure in lb/in.² (Saturation Temperature in italics)

Temp. °F	5 −63.11			10 −41.34			15 −27.29			20 −16.64		
t	v	h	s	v	h	s	v	h	s	v	h	s
Sat.	49.31	588.3	1.4857	25.81	597.1	1.4276	17.67	602.4	1.3938	13.50	606.2	1.3700
−50	51.05	595.2	1.5025									
−40	52.36	600.3	.5149									
−30	53.67	605.4	.5269	26.58	603.2	1.4420						
−20	54.97	610.4	.5385	27.26	608.5	.4542	18.01	606.4	1.4031			
−10	56.26	615.4	.5498	27.92	613.7	.4659	18.47	611.9	.4154	13.74	610.0	1.3784
0	57.55	620.4	1.5608	28.58	618.9	1.4773	18.92	617.2	1.4272	14.09	615.5	1.3907
10	58.84	625.4	.5716	29.24	624.0	.4884	19.37	622.5	.4386	14.44	621.0	.4025
20	60.12	630.4	.5821	29.90	629.1	.4992	19.82	627.8	.4497	14.78	626.4	.4138
30	61.41	635.4	.5925	30.55	634.2	.5097	20.26	633.0	.4604	15.11	631.7	.4248
40	62.69	640.4	.6026	31.20	639.3	.5200	20.70	638.2	.4709	15.45	637.0	.4356
50	63.96	645.5	1.6125	31.85	644.4	1.5301	21.14	643.4	1.4812	15.78	642.3	1.4460
60	65.24	650.5	.6223	32.49	649.5	.5400	21.58	648.5	.4912	16.12	647.5	.4562
70	66.51	655.5	.6319	33.14	654.6	.5497	22.01	653.7	.5011	16.45	652.8	.4662
80	67.79	660.6	.6413	33.78	659.7	.5593	22.44	658.9	.5108	16.78	658.0	.4760
90	69.06	665.6	.6506	34.42	664.8	.5687	22.88	664.0	.5203	17.10	663.2	.4856
100	70.33	670.7	1.6598	35.07	670.0	1.5779	23.31	669.2	1.5296	17.43	668.5	1.4950
110	71.60	675.8	.6689	35.71	675.1	.5870	23.74	674.4	.5388	17.76	673.7	.5042
120	72.87	680.9	.6778	36.35	680.3	.5960	24.17	679.6	.5478	18.08	678.9	.5133
130	74.14	686.1	.6865	36.99	685.4	.6049	24.60	684.8	.5567	18.41	684.2	.5223
140	75.41	691.2	.6952	37.62	690.6	.6136	25.03	690.0	.5655	18.73	689.4	.5312
150	76.68	696.4	1.7038	38.26	695.8	1.6222	25.46	695.3	1.5742	19.05	694.7	1.5399
160	77.95	701.6	.7122	38.90	701.1	.6307	25.88	700.5	.5827	19.37	700.0	.5485
170	79.21	706.8	.7206	39.54	706.3	.6391	26.31	705.8	.5911	19.70	705.3	.5569
180	80.48	712.1	.7289	40.17	711.6	.6474	26.74	711.1	.5995	20.02	710.6	.5653
190	.....			40.81	716.9	.6556	27.16	716.4	.6077	20.34	715.9	.5736
200	.....			41.45	722.2	1.6637	27.59	721.7	1.6158	20.66	721.2	1.5817
220	.....			.....			28.44	732.4	.6318	21.30	732.0	.5978
240	.....			.....			.....			21.94	742.8	.6135

Temp. °F	25 −7.96			30 −0.57			35 5.89			40 11.66		
Sat.	10.96	609.1	1.3515	9.236	611.6	1.3364	7.991	613.6	1.3230	7.047	615.4	1.3125
0	11.19	613.8	1.3616									
10	11.47	619.4	.3738	9.492	617.8	1.3497	8.078	616.1	1.3289			
20	11.75	625.0	.3855	9.731	623.5	.3618	8.287	622.0	.3413	7.203	620.4	1.3231
30	12.03	630.4	.3967	9.966	629.1	.3733	8.493	627.7	.3532	7.387	626.3	.3353
40	12.30	635.8	.4077	10.20	634.6	.3845	8.695	633.4	.3646	7.568	632.1	.3470
50	12.57	641.2	1.4183	10.43	640.1	1.3953	8.895	638.9	1.3756	7.746	637.8	1.3583
60	12.84	646.5	.4287	10.65	645.5	.4059	9.093	644.4	.3863	7.922	643.4	.3692
70	13.11	651.8	.4388	10.88	650.9	.4161	9.289	649.9	.3967	8.096	648.9	.3797
80	13.37	657.1	.4487	11.10	656.2	.4261	9.484	655.3	.4069	8.268	654.4	.3900
90	13.64	662.4	.4584	11.33	661.6	.4359	9.677	660.7	.4168	8.439	659.9	.4000
100	13.90	667.7	1.4679	11.55	666.9	1.4456	9.869	666.1	1.4265	8.609	665.3	1.4098
110	14.17	673.0	.4772	11.77	672.2	.4550	10.06	671.5	.4360	8.777	670.7	.4194
120	14.43	678.2	.4864	11.99	677.5	.4642	10.25	676.8	.4453	8.945	676.1	.4288
130	14.69	683.5	.4954	12.21	682.9	.4733	10.44	682.2	.4545	9.112	681.5	.4381
140	14.95	688.8	.5043	12.43	688.2	.4823	10.63	687.6	.4635	9.278	686.9	.4471
150	15.21	694.1	1.5131	12.65	693.5	1.4911	10.82	692.9	1.4724	9.444	692.3	1.4561
160	15.47	699.4	.5217	12.87	698.8	.4998	11.00	698.3	.4811	9.609	697.7	.4648
170	15.73	704.7	.5303	13.08	704.2	.5083	11.19	703.7	.4897	9.774	703.1	.4735
180	15.99	710.1	.5387	13.30	709.6	.5168	11.38	709.1	.4982	9.938	708.5	.4820
190	16.25	715.4	.5470	13.52	714.9	.5251	11.56	714.5	.5066	10.10	714.0	.4904
200	16.50	720.8	1.5552	13.73	720.3	1.5334	11.75	719.9	1.5148	10.27	719.4	1.4987
220	17.02	731.6	.5713	14.16	731.1	.5495	12.12	730.7	.5311	10.59	730.3	.5150
240	17.53	742.5	.5870	14.59	742.0	.5653	12.49	741.7	.5469	10.92	741.3	.5309
260	18.04	753.4	.6025	15.02	753.0	.5808	12.86	752.7	.5624	11.24	752.3	.5465
280	.....			15.45	764.1	.5960	13.23	763.7	.5776	11.56	763.4	.5617
300	.....			.....			.....			11.88	774.6	1.5766

*Abstracted, by permission, from "Tables of Thermodynamic Properties of Ammonia," U.S. Department of Commerce, Bureau of Standards Circular No. 142, 1945. From Refrigeration and Air Conditioning, 2nd Ed., by R. C. Jordan and G. B. Priester, Prentice-Hall, Inc., Englewood Cliffs, N.J., 1956.

TABLE A-8
(CONT'D.)

Absolute Pressure in lb/in.² (Saturation Temperature in italics)

Temp. °F	50 *21.67*			60 *30.21*			70 *37.70*			80 *44.40*		
t	*v*	*h*	*s*	*v*	*h*	*s*	*v*	*h*	*s*	*v*	*h*	*s*
Sat.	*5.710*	*618.2*	*1.2939*	*4.805*	*620.5*	*1.2787*	*4.151*	*622.4*	*1.2658*	*3.655*	*624.0*	*1.2545*
30	5.838	623.4	1.3046									
40	5.988	629.5	.3169	4.933	626.8	1.2913	4.177	623.9	1.2688			
50	6.135	635.4	1.3286	5.060	632.9	1.3035	4.290	630.4	1.2816	3.712	627.7	1.2619
60	6.280	641.2	.3399	5.184	639.0	.3152	4.401	636.6	.2937	3.812	634.3	.2745
70	6.423	646.9	.3508	5.307	644.9	.3265	4.509	642.7	.3054	3.909	640.6	.2866
80	6.564	652.6	.3613	5.428	650.7	.3373	4.615	648.7	.3166	4.005	646.7	.2981
90	6.704	658.2	.3716	5.547	656.4	.3479	4.719	654.6	.3274	4.098	652.8	.3092
100	6.843	663.7	1.3816	5.665	662.1	1.3581	4.822	660.4	1.3378	4.190	658.7	1.3199
110	6.980	669.2	.3914	5.781	667.7	.3681	4.924	666.1	.3480	4.281	664.6	.3303
120	7.117	674.7	.4009	5.897	673.3	.3778	5.025	671.8	.3579	4.371	670.4	.3404
130	7.252	680.2	.4103	6.012	678.9	.3873	5.125	677.5	.3676	4.460	676.1	.3502
140	7.387	685.7	.4195	6.126	684.4	.3966	5.224	683.1	.3770	4.548	681.8	.3598
150	7.521	691.1	1.4286	6.239	689.9	1.4058	5.323	688.7	1.3863	4.635	687.5	1.3692
160	7.655	696.6	.4374	6.352	695.5	.4148	5.420	694.3	.3954	4.722	693.2	.3784
170	7.788	702.1	.4462	6.464	701.0	.4236	5.518	699.9	.4043	4.808	698.8	.3874
180	7.921	707.5	.4548	6.576	706.5	.4323	5.615	705.5	.4131	4.893	704.4	.3963
190	8.053	713.0	.4633	6.687	712.0	.4409	5.711	711.0	.4217	4.978	710.0	.4050
200	8.185	718.5	1.4716	6.798	717.5	1.4493	5.807	716.6	1.4302	5.063	715.6	1.4136
210	8.317	724.0	.4799	6.909	723.1	.4576	5.902	722.2	.4386	5.147	721.3	.4220
220	8.448	729.4	.4880	7.019	728.6	.4658	5.998	727.7	.4469	5.231	726.9	.4304
240	8.710	740.5	.5040	7.238	739.7	.4819	6.187	738.9	.4631	5.398	738.1	.4467
260	8.970	751.6	.5197	7.457	750.9	.4976	6.376	750.1	.4789	5.565	749.4	.4626
280	9.230	762.7	1.5350	7.675	762.1	1.5130	6.563	761.4	1.4943	5.730	760.7	1.4781
300	9.489	774.0	.5500	7.892	773.3	.5281	6.750	772.7	.5095	5.894	772.1	.4933

Temp. °F	90 *50.47*			100 *56.05*			120 *66.02*			140 *74.79*		
Sat.	*3.266*	*625.3*	*1.2445*	*2.952*	*626.5*	*1.2356*	*2.476*	*628.4*	*1.2201*	*2.132*	*629.9*	*1.2068*
50												
60	3.353	631.8	1.2571	2.985	629.3	1.2409						
70	3.442	638.3	.2695	3.068	636.0	.2539	2.505	631.3	1.2255			
80	3.529	644.7	.2814	3.149	642.6	.2661	2.576	638.3	.2386	2.166	633.8	1.2140
90	3.614	650.9	.2928	3.227	649.0	.2778	2.645	645.0	.2510	2.228	640.9	.2272
100	3.698	657.0	1.3038	3.304	655.2	1.2891	2.712	651.6	1.2628	2.288	647.8	1.2396
110	3.780	663.0	.3144	3.380	661.3	.2999	2.778	658.0	.2741	2.347	654.5	.2515
120	3.862	668.9	.3247	3.454	667.3	.3104	2.842	664.2	.2850	2.404	661.1	.2628
130	3.942	674.7	.3347	3.527	673.3	.3206	2.905	670.4	.2956	2.460	667.4	.2738
140	4.021	680.5	.3444	3.600	679.2	.3305	2.967	676.5	.3058	2.515	673.7	.2843
150	4.100	686.3	1.3539	3.672	685.0	1.3401	3.029	682.5	1.3157	2.569	679.9	1.2945
160	4.178	692.0	.3633	3.743	690.8	.3495	3.089	688.4	.3254	2.622	686.0	.3045
170	4.255	697.7	.3724	3.813	696.6	.3588	3.149	694.3	.3348	2.675	692.0	.3141
180	4.332	703.4	.3813	3.883	702.3	.3678	3.209	700.2	.3441	2.727	698.0	.3236
190	4.408	709.0	.3901	3.952	708.0	.3767	3.268	706.0	.3531	2.779	704.0	.3328
200	4.484	714.7	1.3988	4.021	713.7	1.3854	3.326	711.8	1.3620	2.830	709.9	1.3418
210	4.560	720.4	.4073	4.090	719.4	.3940	3.385	717.6	.3707	2.880	715.8	.3507
220	4.635	726.0	.4157	4.158	725.1	.4024	3.442	723.4	.3793	2.931	721.6	.3594
230	4.710	731.7	.4239	4.226	730.8	.4108	3.500	729.2	.3877	2.981	727.5	.3679
240	4.785	737.3	.4321	4.294	736.5	.4190	3.557	734.9	.3960	3.030	733.3	.3763
250	4.859	743.0	1.4401	4.361	742.2	1.4271	3.614	740.7	1.4042	3.080	739.2	1.3846
260	4.933	748.7	.4481	4.428	747.9	.4350	3.671	746.5	.4123	3.129	745.0	.3928
280	5.081	760.0	.4637	4.562	759.4	.4507	3.783	758.0	.4281	3.227	756.7	.4088
300	5.228	771.5	.4789	4.695	770.8	.4660	3.895	769.6	.4435	3.323	768.3	.4243

TABLE A-8
(CONT'D.)

Absolute Pressure in lb/in.² (Saturation Temperatures in italics)

Temp. °F	160 *82.64*			180 *89.78*			200 *96.34*			220 *102.42*		
t	v	h	s	v	h	s	v	h	s	v	h	s
Sat.	1.872	631.1	1.1952	1.667	632.0	1.1850	1.502	632.7	1.1756	1.367	633.2	1.1671
90	1.914	636.6	1.2055	1.668	632.2	1.1853						
100	1.969	643.9	1.2186	1.720	639.9	1.1992	1.567	643.4	1.1947	1.400	639.4	1.1781
110	2.023	651.0	.2311	1.770	647.3	.2123	1.612	650.9	.2077	1.443	647.3	.1917
120	2.075	657.8	.2429	1.818	654.4	.2247	1.656	658.1	.2200	1.485	654.8	.2045
130	2.125	664.4	.2542	1.865	661.3	.2364	1.698	665.0	.2317	1.525	662.0	.2167
140	2.175	670.9	.2652	1.910	668.0	.2477						
150	2.224	677.2	1.2757	1.955	674.6	1.2586	1.740	671.8	1.2429	1.564	669.0	1.2281
160	2.272	683.5	.2859	1.999	681.0	.2691	1.780	678.4	.2537	1.601	675.8	.2394
170	2.319	689.7	.2958	2.042	687.3	.2792	1.820	684.9	.2641	1.638	682.5	.2501
180	2.365	695.8	.3054	2.084	693.6	.2891	1.859	691.3	.2742	1.675	689.1	.2604
190	2.411	701.9	.3148	2.126	699.8	.2987	1.897	697.7	.2840	1.710	695.5	.2704
200	2.457	707.9	1.3240	2.167	705.9	1.3081	1.935	703.9	1.2935	1.745	701.9	1.2801
210	2.502	713.9	.3331	2.208	712.0	.3172	1.972	710.1	.3029	1.780	708.2	.2896
220	2.547	719.9	.3419	2.248	718.1	.3262	2.009	716.3	.3120	1.814	714.4	.2989
230	2.591	725.8	.3506	2.288	724.1	.3350	2.046	722.4	.3209	1.848	720.6	.3079
240	2.635	731.7	.3591	2.328	730.1	.3436	2.082	728.4	.3296	1.881	726.8	.3168
250	2.679	737.6	1.3675	2.367	736.1	1.3521	2.118	734.5	1.3382	1.914	732.9	1.3255
260	2.723	743.5	.3757	2.407	742.0	.3605	2.154	740.5	.3467	1.947	739.0	.3340
270	2.766	749.4	.3838	2.446	748.0	.3687	2.189	746.5	.3550	1.980	745.1	.3424
280	2.809	755.3	.3919	2.484	753.9	.3768	2.225	752.5	.3631	2.012	751.1	.3507
290	2.852	761.2	.3998	2.523	759.9	.3847	2.260	758.5	.3712	2.044	757.2	.3588
300	2.895	767.1	1.4076	2.561	765.8	1.3926	2.295	764.5	1.3791	2.076	763.2	1.3668
320	2.980	778.9	.4229	2.637	777.7	.4081	2.364	776.5	.3947	2.140	775.3	.3825
340	3.064	790.7	.4379	2.713	789.6	.4231	2.432	788.5	.4099	2.203	787.4	.3978
360	.....	.....	.....	.....	.....	.....	2.500	800.5	.4247	2.265	799.5	.4127
380	.....	.....	.....	.....	.....	.....	2.568	812.5	.4392	2.327	811.6	.4273

Temp. °F	240 *108.09*			260 *113.42*			280 *118.45*			300 *123.21*		
Sat.	1.253	633.6	1.1592	1.155	633.9	1.1518	1.072	634.0	1.1449	0.999	634.0	1.1383
110	1.261	635.3	1.1621									
120	1.302	643.5	.1764	1.182	639.5	1.1617	1.078	635.4	1.1473			
130	1.342	651.3	.1898	1.220	647.8	.1757	1.115	644.0	.1621	1.023	640.1	1.1487
140	1.380	658.8	.2025	1.257	655.6	.1889	1.151	652.2	.1759	1.058	648.7	.1632
150	1.416	666.1	1.2145	1.292	663.1	1.2014	1.184	660.1	1.1888	1.091	656.9	1.1767
160	1.452	673.1	.2259	1.326	670.4	.2132	1.217	667.6	.2011	1.123	664.7	.1894
170	1.487	680.0	.2369	1.359	677.5	.2246	1.249	674.9	.2127	1.153	672.2	.2014
180	1.521	686.7	.2475	1.391	684.4	.2354	1.279	681.9	.2239	1.183	679.5	.2129
190	1.554	693.3	.2577	1.422	691.1	.2458	1.309	688.9	.2346	1.211	686.5	.2239
200	1.587	699.8	1.2677	1.453	697.7	1.2560	1.339	695.6	1.2449	1.239	693.5	1.2344
210	1.619	706.2	.2773	1.484	704.3	.2658	1.367	702.3	.2550	1.267	700.3	.2447
220	1.651	712.6	.2867	1.514	710.7	.2754	1.396	708.8	.2647	1.294	706.9	.2546
230	1.683	718.9	.2959	1.543	717.1	.2847	1.424	715.3	.2742	1.320	713.5	.2642
240	1.714	725.1	.3049	1.572	723.4	.2938	1.451	721.8	.2834	1.346	720.0	.2736
250	1.745	731.3	1.3137	1.601	729.7	1.3027	1.478	728.1	1.2924	1.372	726.5	1.2827
260	1.775	737.5	.3224	1.630	736.0	.3115	1.505	734.4	.3013	1.397	732.9	.2917
270	1.805	743.6	.3308	1.658	742.2	.3200	1.532	740.7	.3099	1.422	739.2	.3004
280	1.835	749.8	.3392	1.686	748.4	.3284	1.558	747.0	.3184	1.447	745.5	.3090
290	1.865	755.9	.3474	1.714	754.5	.3367	1.584	753.2	.3268	1.472	751.8	.3175
300	1.895	762.0	1.3554	1.741	760.7	1.3449	1.610	759.4	1.3350	1.496	758.1	1.3257
320	1.954	774.1	.3712	1.796	772.9	.3608	1.661	771.7	.3511	1.544	770.5	.3419
340	2.012	786.3	.3866	1.850	785.2	.3763	1.712	784.0	.3667	1.592	782.9	.3576
360	2.069	798.4	.4016	1.904	797.4	.3914	1.762	796.3	.3819	1.639	795.3	.3729
380	2.126	810.6	.4163	1.957	809.6	.4062	1.811	808.7	.3967	1.686	807.7	.3878
400	.....	.....	.....	2.009	821.9	1.4206	1.861	821.0	1.4112	1.732	820.1	1.4024

TABLE A-9
PRESSURE–ENTHALPY DIAGRAM FOR AMMONIA

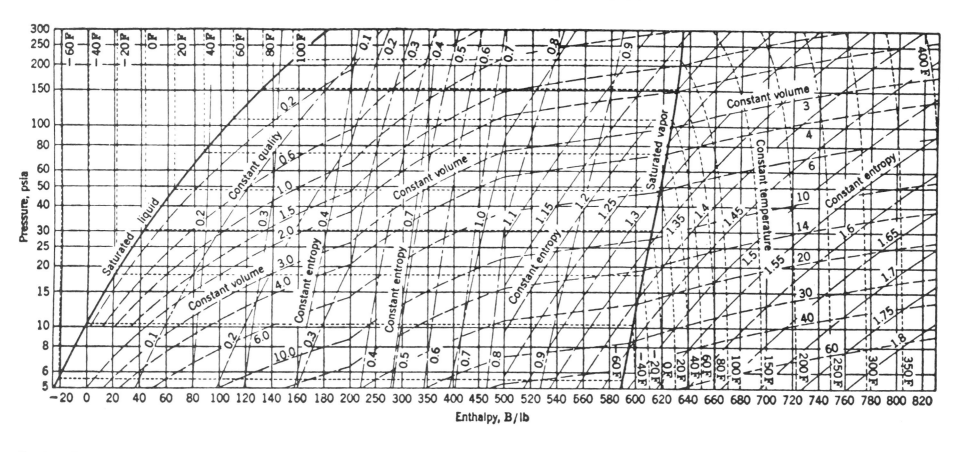

Data from "Tables of Thermodynamic Properties of Ammonia," Bureau of Standards, U.S. Department of Commerce.

TABLE A-10

DICHLORODIFLUOROMETHANE (FREON-12): PROPERTIES OF LIQUID AND SATURATED VAPOR‡

Temp.	Pressure		Volume		Density		Enthalpy from −40°F			Entropy from −40°F	
°F	Abs. lb/in²	Gage lb/in²	Liquid ft³/lb	Vapor ft³/lb	Liquid lb/ft³	Vapor lb/ft³	Liquid Btu/lb	Latent Btu/lb	Vapor Btu/lb	Liquid Btu/lb°F	Vapor Btu/lb°F
t	p	p_d	v_f	v_g	$1/v_f$	$1/v_g$	h_f	h_{fg}	h_g	s_f	s_g
−152	0.13799	29.64024*	0.0095673	197.58	104.52	0.0050614	−23.106	83.734	60.628	−0.063944	0.20818
−150	.15359	29.60849*	.0095822	178.65	104.36	.0055976	−22.697	83.534	60.837	−0.062619	.20711
−145	.19933	29.51537*	.0096198	139.83	103.95	.0071517	−21.674	83.039	61.365	−0.059344	.20452
−140	.25623	29.39951*	.0096579	110.46	103.54	.0090533	−20.652	82.548	61.896	−0.056123	.20208
−135	.32641	29.25663*	.0096966	88.023	103.13	.011361	−19.631	82.061	62.430	−0.052952	.19978
−130	.41224	29.08186*	.0097359	70.730	102.71	.014138	−18.609	81.577	62.968	−0.049830	.19760
−125	0.51641	28.86978*	0.0097758	57.283	102.29	0.017457	−17.587	81.096	63.509	−0.046754	0.19554
−120	.64190	28.61429*	.0098163	46.741	101.87	.021395	−16.565	80.617	64.052	−0.043723	.19359
−115	.79200	28.30869*	.0098574	38.410	101.45	.026035	−15.541	80.139	64.598	−0.040734	.19176
−110	.97034	27.94558*	.0098992	31.777	101.02	.031470	−14.518	79.663	65.145	−0.037786	.19002
−105	1.1809	27.5169*	.0099416	26.458	100.59	.037796	−13.492	79.188	65.696	−0.034877	.18838
−100	1.4280	27.0138*	.0099847	22.164	100.15	0.045119	−12.466	78.714	66.248	−0.032005	0.18683
−95	1.7163	26.4268*	.010029	18.674	99.715	.053550	−11.438	78.239	66.801	−0.029169	.18536
−90	2.0509	25.7456*	.010073	15.821	99.274	.063207	−10.409	77.764	67.355	−0.026367	.18398
−85	2.4371	24.9593*	.010118	13.474	98.830	.074216	−9.3782	77.289	67.911	−0.023599	.18267
−80	2.8807	24.0560*	.010164	11.533	98.382	.086708	−8.3451	76.812	68.467	−0.020862	.18143
−75	3.3879	23.0234*	0.010211	9.9184	97.930	0.10082	−7.3101	76.333	69.023	−0.018156	0.18027
−70	3.9651	21.8482*	.010259	8.5687	97.475	.11670	−6.2730	75.853	69.580	−0.015481	.17916
−65	4.6193	20.5164*	.010308	7.4347	97.016	.13451	−5.2336	75.371	70.137	=0.012834	.17812
−60	5.3575	19.0133*	.010357	6.4774	96.553	.15438	−4.1919	74.885	70.693	−0.010214	.17714
−55	6.1874	17.3237*	.010407	5.6656	96.086	.17650	−3.1477	74.397	71.249	−0.007622	.17621
−50	7.1168	15.4313*	0.010459	4.9742	95.616	0.20104	−2.1011	73.906	71.805	−0.005056	0.17533
−45	8.1540	13.3196*	.010511	4.3828	95.141	.22816	−1.0519	73.411	72.359	−0.002516	.17451
−40	9.3076	10.9709*	0.010564	3.8750	94.661	0.25806	0	72.913	72.913	0	0.17373
−38	9.8035	9.9611*	.010568	3.6922	94.469	.27084	0.4215	72.712	73.134	0.001000	.17343
−36	10.320	8.909*	.010607	3.5198	94.275	.28411	.8434	72.511	73.354	.001995	.17313
−34	10.558	7.814*	.010629	3.3571	94.081	.29788	1.2659	72.309	73.575	.002988	.17285
−32	11.417	6.675*	.010651	3.2035	93.886	.31216	1.6887	72.106	73.795	.003976	.17257
−30	11.999	5.490*	0.010674	3.0585	93.690	0.32696	2.1120	71.903	74.015	0.004361	0.17229
−28	12.604	4.259*	.010696	2.9214	93.493	0.34231	2.5358	71.698	74.234	.005942	.17203
−26	13.233	2.979*	.010719	2.7917	93.296	.35820	2.9601	71.494	74.454	.006919	.17177
−24	13.886	1.649*	.010741	2.6691	93.098	.37466	3.3848	71.288	74.673	.007894	.17151
−22	14.564	0.270*	.010764	2.5529	92.899	.39171	3.8100	71.081	74.891	.008864	.17126
−20	15.267	0.571	0.010787	2.4429	92.699	0.40934	4.2357	70.874	75.110	0.009831	0.17102
−18	15.996	1.300	.010811	2.3387	92.499	.42758	4.6618	70.666	75.328	.010795	.17078
−16	16.753	2.057	.010834	2.2399	92.298	.44645	5.0885	70.456	75.545	.011755	.17055
−14	17.536	2.840	.010858	2.1461	92.096	.46595	5.5157	70.246	75.762	.012712	.17032
−12	18.348	3.652	.010882	2.0572	91.893	.48611	5.9434	70.036	75.979	.013666	.17010
−10	19.189	4.493	0.010906	1.9727	91.689	0.50693	6.3716	69.824	76.196	0.014617	0.16989
−8	20.059	5.363	.010931	1.8924	91.485	.52843	6.8003	69.611	76.411	.015564	.16967
−6	20.960	6.264	.010955	1.8161	91.280	.55063	7.2296	69.397	76.627	.016508	.16947
−4	21.891	7.195	.010980	1.7436	91.074	.57354	7.6594	69.183	76.842	.017449	.16927
−2	22.854	8.158	.011005	1.6745	90.867	.59718	8.0898	68.967	77.057	.018388	.16907
0	23.849	9.153	0.011030	1.6089	90.659	0.62156	8.5207	68.750	77.271	0.019323	0.16888
2	24.878	10.182	.011056	1.5463	90.450	.64670	8.9522	68.533	77.485	.020255	.16869
4	25.939	11.243	.011082	1.4867	90.240	.67263	9.3843	68.314	77.698	.021184	.16851
5†	26.483	11.787	.011094	1.4580	90.135	.68588	9.6005	68.204	77.805	.021647	.16842
6	27.036	12.340	.011107	1.4299	90.030	.69934	9.8169	68.094	77.911	.022110	.16833
8	28.167	13.471	.011134	1.3758	89.818	.72687	10.250	67.873	78.123	.023033	.16815
10	29.335	14.639	0.011160	1.3241	89.606	0.75523	10.684	67.651	78.335	0.023954	0.16798
12	30.539	15.843	.011187	1.2748	89.392	.78443	11.118	67.428	78.546	.024871	.16782
14	31.780	17.084	.011214	1.2278	89.178	.81449	11.554	67.203	78.757	.025786	.16765
16	33.060	18.364	.011241	1.1828	88.962	.84544	11.989	66.977	78.966	.026699	.16750
18	34.378	19.682	.011268	1.1399	88.746	.87729	12.426	66.750	79.176	.027608	.16734
20	35.736	21.040	0.011296	1.0988	88.529	0.91006	12.863	66.522	79.385	0.028515	0.16719
22	37.135	22.439	.011324	1.0596	88.310	.94377	13.300	66.293	79.593	.029420	.16704
24	38.574	23.878	.011352	1.0220	88.091	.97843	13.739	66.061	79.800	.030322	.16690
26	40.056	25.360	.011380	0.98612	87.870	1.0141	14.178	65.829	80.007	.031221	.16676
28	41.580	26.884	.011409	.95173	87.649	1.0507	14.618	65.596	80.214	.032118	.16662

From Refrigeration and Air Conditioning, 2nd Ed., by R. C. Jordan and G. B. Priester, Prentice-Hall, Inc., Englewood Cliffs, N.J., 1956.

†*Standard ton temperature.*

*Inches of mercury below one atmosphere.

‡ *Courtesy E. I. DuPont de Nemours and Co.*

TABLE A-10
(CONT'D.)

Temp.	Pressure		Volume		Density		Enthalpy from −40°F			Entropy from −40°F	
°F	Abs. lb/in²	Gage lb/in²	Liquid ft³/lb	Vapor ft³/lb	Liquid lb/ft³	Vapor lb/ft³	Liquid Btu/lb	Latent Btu/lb	Vapor Btu/lb	Liquid Btu/lb°F	Vapor Btu/lb°F
t	p	pd	v_f	v_g	$1/v_f$	$1/v_g$	h_f	h_{fg}	h_g	s_f	s_g
30	43.148	28.452	0.011438	0.91880	87.426	1.0884	15.058	65.361	80.419	0.033013	.16648
32	44.760	30.064	.011468	.88725	87.202	1.1271	15.500	65.124	80.624	.033905	.16635
34	46.417	31.721	.011497	.85702	86.977	1.1668	15.942	64.886	80.828	.034796	.16622
36	48.120	33.424	.011527	.82803	86.751	1.2077	16.384	64.647	81.031	.035683	.16610
38	49.870	35.174	.011557	.80023	86.524	1.2496	16.828	64.406	81.234	.036569	.16598
40	51.667	36.971	.011588	0.77357	86.296	1.2927	17.273	64.163	81.436	0.037453	0.16586
42	53.513	38.817	.011619	.74798	86.066	1.3369	17.718	63.919	81.637	.038334	.16574
44	55.407	40.711	.011650	.72341	85.836	1.3823	18.164	63.673	81.837	.039213	.16562
46	57.352	42.656	.011682	.69982	85.604	1.4289	18.611	63.426	82.037	.040091	.16551
48	59.347	44.651	.011714	.67715	85.371	1.4768	19.059	63.177	82.236	.040966	.16540
50	61.394	46.698	0.011746	0.65537	85.136	1.5258	19.507	62.926	82.433	0.041839	0.16530
52	63.494	48.798	.011779	.63444	84.900	1.5762	19.957	62.673	82.630	.042711	.16519
54	65.646	50.950	.011811	.61431	84.663	1.6278	20.408	62.418	82.826	.043581	.16509
56	67.853	53.157	.011845	.59495	84.425	1.6808	20.859	62.162	83.021	.044449	.16499
58	70.115	55.419	.011879	.57632	84.185	1.7352	21.312	61.903	83.215	.045316	.16489
60	72.433	57.737	0.011913	0.55839	83.944	1.7909	21.766	61.643	83.409	0.046180	0.16479
62	74.807	60.111	.011947	.54112	83.701	1.8480	22.221	61.380	83.601	.047044	.16470
64	77.239	62.543	.011982	.52450	83.457	1.9066	22.676	61.116	83.792	.047905	.16460
66	79.729	65.033	.012017	.50848	83.212	1.9666	23.133	60.849	83.982	.048765	.16451
68	82.279	67.583	.012053	.49305	82.965	2.0282	23.591	60.580	84.171	.049624	.16442
70	84.888	70.192	0.012089	0.47818	82.717	2.0913	24.050	60.309	84.359	0.050482	0.16434
72	87.559	72.863	.012126	.46383	82.467	2.1559	24.511	60.035	84.546	.051338	.16425
74	90.292	75.596	.012163	.45000	82.215	2.2222	24.973	59.759	84.732	.052193	.16417
76	93.087	78.391	.012201	.43666	81.962	2.2901	25.435	59.481	84.916	.053047	.16408
78	95.946	81.250	.012239	.42378	81.707	2.3597	25.899	59.201	85.100	.053900	.16400
80	98.870	84.174	0.012277	0.41135	81.450	2.4310	26.365	58.917	85.282	0.054751	0.16392
82	101.86	87.16	.012316	.39935	81.192	2.5041	26.832	58.631	85.463	.055602	.16384
84	104.92	90.22	.012356	.38776	80.932	2.5789	27.300	58.343	85.643	.056452	.16376
86†	108.04	93.34	.012396	.37657	80.671	2.6556	27.769	58.052	85.821	.057301	.16368
88	111.23	96.53	.012437	.36575	80.407	2.7341	28.241	57.757	85.998	.058149	.16360
90	114.49	99.79	0.012478	0.35529	80.142	2.8146	28.713	57.461	86.174	0.058997	0.16353
92	117.82	103.12	.012520	.34518	79.874	2.8970	29.187	57.161	86.348	.059844	.16345
94	121.22	106.52	.012562	.33540	79.605	2.9815	29.663	56.858	86.521	.060690	.16338
96	124.70	110.00	.012605	.32594	79.334	3.0680	30.140	56.551	86.691	.061536	.16330
98	128.24	113.54	.012649	.31679	79.061	3.1566	30.619	56.242	86.861	.062381	.16323
100	131.86	117.16	0.012693	0.30794	78.785	3.2474	31.100	55.929	87.029	0.063227	0.16315
102	135.56	120.86	.012738	.29937	78.508	3.3404	31.583	55.613	87.196	.064072	.16308
104	139.33	124.63	.012783	.29106	78.228	3.4357	32.067	55.293	87.360	.064916	.16301
106	143.18	128.48	.012829	.28303	77.946	3.5333	32.553	54.970	87.523	.065761	.16293
108	147.11	132.41	.012876	.27524	77.662	3.6332	33.041	54.643	87.684	.066606	.16286
110	151.11	136.41	0.012924	0.26769	77.376	3.7357	33.531	54.313	87.844	0.067451	0.16279
112	155.19	140.49	.012972	.26037	77.087	3.8406	34.023	53.978	88.001	.068296	.16271
114	159.36	144.66	.013022	.25328	76.795	3.9482	34.517	53.639	88.156	.069141	.16264
116	163.61	148.91	.013072	.24641	76.501	4.0584	35.014	53.296	88.310	.069987	.16256
118	167.94	153.24	.013123	.23974	76.205	4.1713	35.512	52.949	88.461	.070833	.16249
120	172.35	157.65	0.013174	0.23326	75.906	4.2870	36.013	52.597	88.610	0.071680	0.16241
122	176.85	162.15	.013227	.22698	75.604	4.4056	36.516	52.241	88.757	.072528	.16234
124	181.43	166.73	.013280	.22089	75.299	4.5272	37.021	51.881	88.902	.073376	.16226
126	186.10	171.40	.013335	.21497	74.991	4.6518	37.529	51.515	89.044	.074225	.16218
128	190.86	176.16	.013390	.20922	74.680	4.7796	38.040	51.144	89.184	.075075	.16210
130	195.71	181.01	0.013447	0.20364	75.367	4.9107	38.553	50.768	89.321	0.075927	0.16202
132	200.64	185.94	.013504	.19821	74.050	5.0451	39.069	50.387	89.456	.076779	.16194
134	205.67	190.97	.013563	.19294	73.729	5.1829	39.588	50.000	89.588	.077633	.16185
136	210.79	196.09	.013623	.18782	73.406	5.3244	40.110	49.608	89.718	.078489	.16177
138	216.01	201.31	.013684	.18283	73.079	5.4695	40.634	49.210	89.844	.079346	.16168
140	221.32	206.62	0.013746	0.17799	72.748	5.6184	41.162	48.805	89.967	0.080205	0.16159
142	226.72	212.02	.013810	.17327	72.413	5.7713	41.693	48.394	90.087	.081065	.16150
144	232.22	217.52	.013874	.16868	72.075	5.9283	42.227	47.977	90.204	.081928	.16140
146	237.82	223.12	.013941	.16422	71.732	6.0895	42.765	47.553	90.318	.082794	.16130
148	243.51	228.81	.014008	.15987	71.386	6.2551	43.306	47.122	90.428	.083661	.16120

†*Standard ton temperature.*

TABLE A-11

DICHLORODIFLUOROMETHANE (FREON-12): PROPERTIES OF SUPERHEATED VAPOR*

Temp. °F	Abs. Pressure 0.14 lb/in.² Gage Pressure 29.64 in. vac. (Sat. Temp. −151.7°F)			Abs. Pressure 0.20 lb/in.² Gage Pressure 29.51 in. vac. (Sat. Temp. −144.9°F)			Abs. Pressure 0.40 lb/in.² Gage Pressure 29.11 in. vac. (Sat. Temp. −130.7°F)			Abs. Pressure 0.60 lb/in.² Gage Pressure 28.70 in. vac. (Sat. Temp. −121.6°F)		
t	v	h	s	v	h	s	v	h	s	v	h	s
Sat.	(194.91)	(60.666)	(0.20804)	(59.38)	(61.572)	(0.20449)	(72.756)	(62.897)	(0.19788)	(49.786)	(63.881)	(0.19419)
−150	196.01	60.840	0.20864									
−140	202.37	61.916	.21205	141.58	61.906	0.20617						
−130	208.73	63.012	.21543	146.04	63.002	.20955	72.903	62.970	0.19810			
−120	215.09	64.127	.21876	150.50	64.118	.21288	75.139	64.088	.20144	50.020	64.058	0.19472
−110	221.44	65.261	.22205	154.95	65.253	.21618	77.374	65.225	.20474	51.515	65.197	.19802
−100	227.80	66.414	0.22530	159.40	66.406	0.21943	79.607	66.381	0.20799	53.009	66.355	0.20128
−90	234.15	67.585	.22851	163.85	67.578	.22264	81.839	67.554	.21121	54.502	67.530	.20451
−80	240.50	68.774	.23169	168.30	68.768	.22582	84.070	68.746	.21439	55.993	68.723	.20769
−70	246.85	69.981	.23482	172.75	69.975	.22896	86.299	69.954	.21753	57.483	69.934	.21084
−60	253.20	71.206	.23793	177.19	71.200	.23206	88.527	71.181	.22064	58.972	71.161	.21395
−50	259.54	72.447	0.24099	181.64	72.442	0.23513	90.755	72.424	0.22371	60.460	72.406	0.21702
−40	265.89	73.706	.24403	186.09	73.701	.23816	92.982	73.684	.22675	61.947	73.667	.22006
−30	272.23	74.980	.24703	190.53	74.976	.24117	95.207	74.960	.22976	63.433	74.944	.22307
−20	278.58	76.271	.25000	194.97	76.267	.24414	97.433	76.252	.23273	64.919	76.238	.22605
−10	284.92	77.578	.25294	199.42	77.574	.24708	99.657	77.560	.23567	66.404	77.546	.22899
0	291.27	78.901	0.25585	203.86	78.897	0.24998	101.88	78.884	0.23858	67.889	78.871	0.23190
10	297.61	80.239	.25873	208.30	80.235	.25286	104.11	80.223	.24146	69.373	80.210	.23479
20	303.95	81.591	.26158	212.74	81.588	.25571	106.33	81.576	.24431	70.857	81.565	.23764
30	310.30	82.959	.26440	217.18	82.955	.25854	108.55	82.945	.24714	72.340	82.934	.24046
40	316.64	84.341	.26719	221.62	84.338	.26133	110.77	84.327	.24993	73.823	84.317	.24326
50	322.98	85.737	0.26996	226.07	85.734	0.26410	113.00	85.724	0.25270	75.306	85.714	0.24603
60	329.32	87.147	.27270	230.51	87.144	.26684	115.22	87.135	.25544	76.789	87.126	.24877
70	335.66	88.570	.27541	234.95	88.567	.26955	117.44	88.559	.25816	78.271	88.550	.25149
80	342.01	90.007	.27810	239.39	90.004	.27224	119.66	89.996	.26084	79.753	89.988	.25417
90	348.35	91.457	.28076	243.82	91.454	.27490	121.88	91.447	.26351	81.235	91.439	.25684
100	354.69	92.920	0.28340	248.26	92.917	0.27754	124.10	92.910	0.26614	82.716	92.902	0.25948
110	361.03	94.395	.28601	252.70	94.393	.28015	126.32	94.386	.26876	84.197	94.378	.26209
120	367.37	95.882	.28860	257.14	95.880	.28274	128.54	95.874	.27135	85.679	95.867	.26468
130	373.71	97.382	.29116	261.58	97.380	.28530	130.77	97.374	.27391	87.160	97.367	.26725
140	380.05	98.893	.29370	266.02	98.891	.28784	132.99	98.885	.27645	88.641	98.879	.26979

From *Refrigeration and Air Conditioning*, 2nd Ed., by R. C. Jordan and G. B. Priester, Prentice-Hall, Inc., Englewood Cliffs, N.J., 1956.

*Courtesy E. I. DuPont de Nemours and Co.

585

TABLE A-11
(CONT'D.)

Temp. °F	Abs. Pressure 0.80 lb/in.² Gage Pressure 28.29 in. vac. (Sat. Temp. −114.8°F)			Abs. Pressure 1.00 lb/in. Gage Pressure 27.88 in. vac. (Sat. Temp. −109.3°F)			Abs. Pressure 2.0 lb/in.² Gage Pressure 25.85 in. vac. (Sat. Temp. −90.7°F)			Abs. Pressure 3.0 lb/in.² Gage Pressure 23.81 in. vac. (Sat. Temp. −78.8°F)		
t	v	h	s	v	h	s	v	h	s	v	h	s
Sat.	(38.051)	(64.624)	(0.19167)	(30.896)	(65.229)	(0.18977)	(16.195)	(67.276)	(0.18417)	(11.106)	(68.604)	(0.18114)
−110	38.586	65.170	0.19324	......	......	......	......	......	......	......	......	......
−100	39.710	66.329	0.19651	31.730	66.303	0.19279	......	......	......	......	......	......
−90	40.833	67.506	.19974	32.631	67.482	.19602	16.228	67.361	0.18440	......	......	......
−80	41.954	68.701	.20292	33.531	68.679	.19922	16.684	68.567	.18762	......	......	......
−70	43.074	69.913	.20608	34.429	69.892	.20237	17.139	69.788	.19079	11.375	69.683	0.18394
−60	44.194	71.142	.20919	35.327	71.123	.20549	17.593	71.026	.19393	11.681	70.928	.18709
−50	45.312	72.388	0.21227	36.223	72.370	0.20857	18.046	72.279	0.19703	11.986	72.188	0.19021
−40	46.429	73.650	.21531	37.119	73.633	.21162	18.498	73.549	.20009	12.290	73.463	.19328
−30	47.546	74.928	.21832	38.014	74.913	.21463	18.949	74.819	.20311	12.594	74.754	.19632
−20	48.662	76.223	.22130	38.908	76.208	.21761	19.400	76.134	.20611	12.897	76.059	.19932
−10	49.778	77.533	.22424	39.802	77.519	.22056	19.850	77.449	.20906	13.199	77.379	.20229
0	50.893	78.858	0.22716	40.695	78.845	0.22347	20.299	78.780	0.21199	13.500	78.714	0.20523
10	52.007	80.198	0.23004	41.587	80.186	.22636	20.748	80.125	.21488	13.802	80.063	.20813
20	53.121	81.553	.23290	42.480	81.542	.22922	21.197	81.484	.21775	14.102	81.426	.21100
30	54.235	82.923	.23572	43.372	82.912	.23204	21.645	82.858	.22058	14.403	82.803	.21384
40	55.348	84.307	.23852	44.263	84.297	.23484	22.093	84.245	.22339	14.703	84.194	.21665
50	56.461	85.705	0.24129	45.154	85.695	0.23761	22.540	85.646	0.22616	15.002	85.598	0.21944
60	57.574	87.116	.24403	46.045	87.107	.24036	22.988	87.061	.22891	15.302	87.015	.22219
70	58.686	88.541	.24675	46.936	88.533	.24307	23.435	88.489	.23163	15.601	88.445	.22492
80	59.799	89.980	.24944	47.826	89.971	.24576	23.881	89.930	.23433	15.900	89.889	.22762
90	60.911	91.431	.25210	48.716	91.423	.24843	24.328	91.384	.23700	16.198	91.345	.23029
100	62.023	92.895	0.25474	49.606	92.887	0.25107	24.774	92.850	0.23964	16.497	92.813	0.23293
110	63.134	94.371	.25736	50.496	94.364	.25368	25.220	94.329	.24226	16.795	94.293	.23556
120	64.246	95.860	.25995	51.386	95.853	.25628	25.666	95.819	.24485	17.093	95.785	.23815
130	65.357	97.361	.26251	52.275	97.354	.25884	26.112	97.322	.24742	17.391	97.289	.24073
140	66.468	98.873	.26506	53.165	98.867	.26139	26.558	98.836	.24997	17.689	98.805	.24327
150	67.579	100.397	0.26758	54.054	100.391	0.26391	27.003	100.361	0.25249	17.987	100.332	0.24580
160	68.690	101.932	.27007	54.943	101.926	.26640	27.449	101.898	.25499	18.284	101.869	.24830
170	69.801	103.478	.27255	55.832	103.472	.26888	27.894	103.445	.25747	18.582	103.418	.25078
180	70.912	105.035	.27500	56.721	105.030	.27133	28.340	105.002	.25992	18.879	104.977	.25324
190	......	......	......	......	......	......	28.785	106.572	.26236	19.176	106.547	.25567
200	......	......	......	......	......	......	29.230	108.151	0.26477	19.473	108.127	0.25808

TABLE A-11

(CONT'D.)

Temp. °F t	Abs. Pressure 5.0 lb/in.² Gage Pressure 19.74 in. vac. (Sat. Temp. −62.4°F)			Abs. Pressure 7.5 lb/in.² Gage Pressure 14.65 in. vac. (Sat. Temp. −48.1°F)			Abs. Pressure 10.0 lb/in.² Gage Pressure 9.56 in. vac. (Sat. Temp. −37.2°F)			Abs. Pressure 15 lb/in.² Gage Pressure 0.3 lb/in.² (Sat. Temp. −20.8°F)		
	v (6.9069)	h (70.438)	s (0.17769)	v (4.7374)	h (72.017)	s (0.17601)	v (3.6246)	h (75.219)	s (0.17331)	v (2.4856)	h (75.208)	s (0.17111)
Sat.	6.9509	70.729	0.17834	......	......	(0.17601)	......	(75.219)	(0.17331)	......	(75.208)	(0.17111)
−60	7.1378	72.003	0.18149	......	......	......	......	......	......	......	......	......
−40	7.3239	73.291	.18459	4.8401	73.073	0.17755	......	......	......	......	......	......
−30	7.5092	74.593	.18766	4.9664	74.390	.18065	3.6945	74.183	0.17557	......	......	......
−20	7.6938	75.909	.19069	5.0919	75.719	.18371	3.7906	75.526	.17866	2.4885	75.131	0.17134
−10	7.8777	77.239	.19368	5.2169	77.061	.18673	3.8861	76.880	.18171	2.5546	76.512	.17445
0	8.0611	78.582	0.19663	5.3412	78.415	0.18971	3.9809	78.246	0.18471	2.6201	77.902	0.17751
10	8.2441	79.939	.19955	5.4650	79.782	.19265	4.0753	79.624	.18768	2.6850	79.302	.18052
20	8.4265	81.309	.20244	5.5884	81.162	.19556	4.1691	81.014	.19061	2.7494	80.712	.18349
30	8.6086	82.693	.20529	5.7114	82.555	.19843	4.2626	82.415	.19350	2.8134	82.131	.18642
40	8.7903	84.090	.20812	5.8340	83.959	.20127	4.3556	83.828	.19635	2.8770	83.561	.18931
50	8.9717	85.500	0.21091	5.9562	85.377	0.20408	4.4484	85.252	0.19918	2.9402	85.001	0.19216
60	9.1528	86.922	.21367	6.0782	86.806	.20685	4.5408	86.689	.20197	3.0031	86.451	.19498
70	9.3336	88.358	.21641	6.1999	88.247	.20960	4.6329	88.136	.20473	3.0657	87.912	.19776
80	9.5142	89.806	.21912	6.3213	89.701	.21232	4.7248	89.596	.20746	3.1281	89.383	.20051
90	9.6945	91.266	.22180	6.4425	91.166	.21501	4.8165	91.067	.21016	3.1902	90.865	.20324
100	9.8747	92.738	0.22445	6.5636	92.643	0.21767	4.9079	92.548	0.21283	3.2521	92.357	0.20593
110	10.055	94.222	.22708	6.6844	94.132	.22031	4.9992	94.042	.21547	3.3139	93.860	.20859
120	10.234	95.717	.22968	6.8051	95.632	.22292	5.0903	95.546	.21809	3.3754	95.373	.21122
130	10.414	97.224	.23226	6.9256	97.143	.22550	5.1812	97.061	.22068	3.4368	96.896	.21382
140	10.594	98.743	.23481	7.0439	98.665	.22806	5.2720	98.586	.22325	3.4981	98.429	.21640
150	10.773	100.272	0.23734	7.1662	100.198	0.23060	5.3627	100.123	0.22579	3.5592	99.972	0.21895
160	10.952	101.812	.23985	7.2863	101.741	.23311	5.4533	101.669	.22830	3.6202	101.525	.22148
170	11.131	103.363	.24233	7.4063	103.295	.23560	5.5437	103.226	.23080	3.6811	103.088	.22398
180	11.311	104.925	.24479	7.5262	104.859	.23806	5.6341	104.793	.23326	3.7419	104.661	.22646
190	11.489	106.497	.24723	7.6461	106.434	.24050	5.7243	106.370	.23571	3.8025	106.243	.22891
200	11.668	108.079	0.24964	7.7658	108.018	0.24292	5.8145	107.957	0.23813	3.8632	107.835	0.23135
210	1.847	109.670	.25204	7.8855	109.612	.24532	5.9046	109.553	.24054	3.9237	109.436	.23375
220	12.026	111.272	.25441	8.0051	111.215	.24770	5.9946	111.159	.24291	3.9841	111.046	.23614
230	12.205	112.883	.25677	8.1246	112.828	.25005	6.0846	112.774	.24527	4.0445	112.665	.23850
240	......	......	......	8.2441	114.451	.25239	6.1745	114.398	.24761	4.1049	114.292	.24085
250	......	......	......	......	......	......	6.2643	116.031	0.24993	4.1651	115.929	0.24317

TABLE A-11
(CONT'D.)

Temp. °F (t)	Abs. Pressure 20 lb/in.² Gage Pressure 5.3 lb/in.² (Sat. Temp. −8.1°F)			Abs. Pressure 26 lb/in.² Gage Pressure 11.3 lb/in.² (Sat. Temp. 4.1°F)			Abs. Pressure 32 lb/in.² Gage Pressure 17.3 lb/in.² (Sat. Temp. 14.4°F)			Abs. Pressure 40 lb/in.² Gage Pressure 25.3 lb/in.² (Sat. Temp. 25.9°F)		
	v	h	s	v	h	s	v	h	s	v	h	s
Sat.	(1.8977)	(76.597)	(0.16969)	(1.4856)	(77.710)	(0.16860)	(1.2198)	(78.798)	(0.16763)	(0.98743)	(80.000)	(0.16676)
0	1.9390	77.550	0.17222	.....	.....	.....	.....	.....	.....	.....	.....	.....
10	1.9893	78.973	.17528	1.5071	78.566	0.17033	.....	.....	.....	.....	.....	.....
20	2.0391	80.403	.17829	1.5468	80.024	.17340	1.2387	79.634	0.16939	.....	.....	.....
30	2.0884	81.842	.18126	1.5861	81.487	.17642	1.2717	81.123	.17246	0.99865	80.622	0.16804
40	2.1373	83.289	.18419	1.6248	82.956	.17939	1.3042	82.616	.17548	1.0258	82.148	.17112
50	2.1858	84.745	0.18707	1.6632	84.432	0.18232	1.3363	84.113	0.17845	1.0526	83.676	0.17415
60	2.2340	86.210	.18992	1.7013	85.916	.18520	1.3681	85.616	.18137	1.0789	85.206	.17712
70	2.2819	87.684	.19273	1.7390	87.407	.18804	1.3995	87.124	.18424	1.1049	86.739	.18005
80	2.3295	89.168	.19550	1.7765	88.906	.19084	1.4306	88.639	.18707	1.1306	88.277	.18292
90	2.3769	90.661	.19824	1.8137	90.413	.19361	1.4615	90.161	.18987	1.1560	89.819	.18575
100	2.4241	92.164	0.20095	1.8507	91.929	0.19634	1.4921	91.690	0.19263	1.1812	91.367	0.18854
110	2.4711	93.676	.20363	1.8874	93.453	.19904	1.5225	93.227	.19535	1.2061	92.920	.19129
120	2.5179	95.198	.20628	1.9240	94.986	.20171	1.5528	94.771	.19803	1.2309	94.480	.19401
130	2.5645	96.729	.20890	1.9605	96.527	.20435	1.5828	96.323	.20069	1.2554	96.047	.19669
140	2.6110	98.270	.21149	1.9967	98.078	.20695	1.6127	97.883	.20331	1.2798	97.620	.19933
150	2.6573	99.820	0.21405	2.0329	99.637	0.20953	1.6425	99.451	0.20590	1.3041	99.200	0.20195
160	2.7036	101.380	.21659	2.0689	101.204	.21208	1.6721	101.027	.20847	1.3282	100.788	.20453
170	2.7497	102.949	.21910	2.1048	102.781	.21461	1.7017	102.611	.21100	1.3522	102.383	.20708
180	2.7957	104.528	.22159	2.1406	104.367	.21710	1.7311	104.204	.21351	1.3761	103.985	.20961
190	2.8416	106.115	.22405	2.1763	105.961	.21958	1.7604	105.805	.21600	1.3999	105.595	.21210
200	2.8874	107.712	0.22649	2.2119	107.563	0.22202	1.7896	107.414	0.21845	1.4236	107.212	0.21457
210	2.9332	109.317	.22891	2.2474	109.174	.22445	1.8187	109.031	.22089	1.4472	108.837	.21702
220	2.9789	110.932	.23130	2.2828	110.794	.22685	1.8478	110.656	.22330	1.4707	110.469	.21944
230	3.0245	112.555	.23367	2.3182	112.422	.22923	1.8768	112.289	.22568	1.4942	112.109	.22183
240	3.0700	114.186	.23602	2.3535	114.058	.23158	1.9057	113.930	.22804	1.5176	113.757	.22420
250	3.1155	115.826	0.23835	2.3888	115.703	0.23391	1.9346	115.579	0.23038	1.5409	115.412	0.22655
260	3.1609	117.475	.24065	2.4240	117.355	.23623	1.9634	117.235	.23270	1.5642	117.074	.22888
270	3.2063	119.131	.24294	2.4592	119.016	.23852	1.9922	118.900	.23500	1.5874	118.744	.23118
280	3.2517	120.796	.24520	2.4943	120.684	.24079	2.0209	120.572	.23727	1.6106	120.421	.23347
290	3.2970	122.469	.24745	2.5293	122.360	.24304	2.0495	122.251	.23953	1.6337	122.105	.23573

TABLE A-11
(CONT'D.)

Temp. °F	Abs. Pressure 50 lb/in.² Gage Pressure 35.3 lb/in.² (Sat. Temp. 38.2°F)			Abs. Pressure 60 lb/in.² Gage Pressure 45.3 lb/in.² (Sat. Temp. 48.6°F)			Abs. Pressure 80 lb/in.² Gage Pressure 65.3 lb/in.² (Sat. Temp. 66.2°F)			Abs. Pressure 100 lb/in.² Gage Pressure 85.3 lb/in.² (Sat. Temp. 80.8°F)		
t	v	h	s	v	h	s	v	h	s	v	h	s
sat.	(0.79884)	(81.249)	(0.16697)	(0.67006)	(82.299)	(0.16537)	(0.60680)	(84.003)	(0.16460)	(0.40674)	(85.551)	(0.15889)
40	0.80248	81.540	0.16655	......	......	......	......	......	......	......	......	......
50	0.82502	83.109	0.16966	0.67272	82.518	0.16580	......	......	......	......	......	......
60	.84713	84.676	.17271	.69210	84.126	.16892	0.51269	84.640	0.16571	......	......	......
70	.86886	86.243	.17569	.71105	85.729	.17198	.52795	86.316	.16885	......	......	......
80	.89025	87.811	.17862	.72964	87.330	.17497	.54281	87.981	.17190	0.41876	86.964	0.16685
90	.91134	89.380	.18151	.74790	88.929	.17791						
100	0.93216	90.953	0.18434	0.76588	90.528	0.18079	0.55734	89.640	0.17489	0.43138	88.694	0.16996
110	.95275	92.529	.18713	.78360	92.128	.18362	.57158	91.294	.17782	.44365	90.410	.17300
120	.97313	94.110	.18988	.80110	93.731	.18641	.58556	92.945	.18070	.45562	92.116	.17597
130	.99332	95.695	.19259	.81840	95.336	.18916	.59931	94.594	.18352	.46733	93.814	.17888
140	1.0133	97.286	.19527	.83551	96.945	.19186	.61286	96.242	.18629	.47881	95.507	.18172
150	1.0332	98.882	0.19791	0.85247	98.558	0.19453	0.62623	97.891	0.18902	0.49009	97.197	0.18452
160	1.0529	100.485	.20051	.86928	100.776	.19716	.63943	99.542	.19170	.50118	98.884	.18726
170	1.0725	102.093	.20309	.88596	101.799	.19976	.65250	101.195	.19435	.51212	100.571	.18996
180	1.0920	103.708	.20563	.90252	103.427	.20233	.66543	102.851	.19696	.52291	102.257	.19262
190	1.1114	105.330	.20815	.91896	105.060	.20486	.67824	104.511	.19953	.53358	103.944	.19524
200	1.1307	106.958	0.21064	0.93531	106.700	0.20736	0.69095	106.174	0.20207	0.54413	105.633	0.19782
210	1.1499	108.593	.21310	.95157	108.345	.20984	.70356	107.841	.20458	.55457	107.324	.20036
220	1.1690	110.235	.21553	.96775	109.997	.21229	.71609	109.513	.20706	.56492	109.018	.20287
230	1.1880	111.883	.21794	.98385	111.655	.21471	.72853	111.190	.20951	.57519	110.714	.20535
240	1.2070	113.539	.22032	.99988	113.319	.21710	.74090	112.872	.21193	.58538	112.415	.20780
250	1.2259	115.202	0.22268	1.0159	114.989	0.21947	0.75320	114.559	0.21432	0.59549	114.119	0.21022
260	1.2447	116.871	.22502	1.0318	116.666	.22182	.76544	116.251	.21669	.60554	115.828	.21261
270	1.2636	118.547	.22733	1.0476	118.350	.22414	.77762	117.949	.21903	.61553	117.540	.21497
280	1.2823	120.231	.22962	1.0634	120.039	.22644	.78975	119.652	.22135	.62546	119.258	.21731
290	1.3010	121.921	.23189	1.0792	121.736	.22872	.80183	121.361	.22364	.63534	120.980	.21962
300	1.3197	123.618	0.23414	1.0949	123.438	0.23098	0.81386	123.075	0.22592	0.64518	122.707	0.22191
310	1.3383	125.321	.23637	1.1106	125.147	.23321	.82581	124.795	.22817	.65497	124.439	.22417
320	1.3569	127.032	.23857	1.1262	126.863	.23513	.83781	126.521	.23039	.66472	126.176	.22647
330	1.3754	128.749	.24076	1.1418	128.585	.23762	.84973	128.253	.23260	.67444	127.917	.22863
340				1.1574	130.313	.23980	.86161	129.990	.23479	.68411	129.665	.23083

TABLE A-11
(CONT'D.)

Temp. °F	Abs. Press. 120 lb/in.² Gage Press. 105.3 lb/in.² (Sat. Temp. 93.3°F)			Abs. Press. 140 lb/in.² Gage Press. 125.3 lb/in.² (Sat. Temp. 104.4°F)			Abs. Press. 180 lb/in.² Gage Press. 165.3 lb/in.² (Sat. Temp. 123.4°F)			Abs. Press. 220 lb/in.² Gage Press. 205.3 lb/in.² (Sat. Temp. 139.5°F)		
t	v	h	s	v	h	s	v	h	s	v	h	s
Sat.	(0.35896)	(86.459)	(0.16540)	(0.28964)	(87.589)	(0.16299)	(0.22876)	(88.857)	(0.16228)	(0.17917)	(89.937)	(0.16161)
100	0.34655	87.675	0.16559									
110	.35766	89.466	.16876									
120	.36841	91.237	.17184	0.29548	88.448	0.16486						
130	.37884	92.992	.17484	.30549	90.297	.16808	0.22863	90.179	0.16454			
140	.38901	94.736	.17778	.31513	92.120	.17120	.23710	92.136	.16783	0.17957	90.043	0.16179
150	0.39896	96.471	0.18065	.32445	93.923	.17423						
150				0.33350	95.709	0.17718	0.24519	94.053	0.17100	0.18746	92.156	0.16528
160	.40870	98.199	.18346	.34232	97.483	.18007	.25297	95.940	.17407	.19487	94.203	.16861
170	.41826	99.922	.18622	.35095	99.247	.18289	.26047	97.803	.17705	.20190	96.199	.17181
180	.42766	101.642	.18892	.35939	101.003	.18566	.26775	99.647	.17995	.20861	98.157	.17489
190	.43692	103.359	.19159	.36769	102.754	.18838	.27484	101.475	.18279	.21506	100.084	.17788
200	0.44606	105.076	0.19421	0.37584	104.501	0.19104	0.28176	103.291	0.18556	0.22130	101.986	0.18079
210	.45508	106.792	.19679	.38387	106.245	.19367	.28852	105.098	.18828	.22735	103.869	.18362
220	.46401	108.509	.19934	.39179	107.987	.19625	.29516	106.896	.19095	.23324	105.735	.18638
230	.47284	110.227	.20185	.39961	109.728	.19879	.30168	108.689	.19357	.23900	107.589	.18909
240	.48158	111.948	.20432	.40734	111.470	.20130	.30810	110.478	.19614	.24463	109.432	.19175
250	0.49025	113.670	0.20677	0.41499	113.212	0.20377	0.31442	112.263	0.19868	0.25015	111.267	0.19435
260	.49885	115.396	.20918	.42257	114.956	.20621	.32066	114.046	.20117	.25557	113.095	.19691
270	.50739	117.125	.21157	.43008	116.701	.20862	.32682	115.828	.20363	.26091	114.919	.19942
280	.51587	118.857	.21393	.43753	118.449	.21100	.33292	117.610	.20605	.26617	116.738	.20190
290	.52429	120.593	.21626	.44492	120.199	.21335	.33895	119.392	.20845	.27136	118.555	.20434
300	0.53267	122.333	0.21856	0.45226	121.953	0.21567	0.34492	121.174	0.21081	0.27648	120.369	0.20674
310	.54100	124.077	.22084	.45955	123.709	.21797	.35084	122.958	.21314	.28155	122.183	.20912
320	.54929	125.825	.22310	.46680	125.470	.22024	.35672	124.744	.21545	.28657	123.996	.21146
330	.55754	127.578	.22533	.47400	127.233	.22249	.36255	126.531	.21772	.29153	125.809	.21377
340	.56575	129.335	.22754	.48117	129.001	.22471	.36834	128.321	.21998	.29645	127.623	.21605
350	0.57393	131.097	0.22973	0.48831	130.773	0.22692	0.37409	130.113	0.22220	0.30134	129.438	0.21830
360	.58208	132.863	.23190	.49541	132.548	.22910	.37980	131.909	.22441	.30618	131.255	.22053
370	.59019	134.634	.23405	.50248	134.328	.23125	.38549	133.707	.22659	.31099	133.073	.22274
380	.59829	136.410	.23618	.50953	136.112	.23339	.39114	135.509	.22875	.31576	134.893	.22492
390	.60635	138.191	.23829	.51654	137.901	.23551	.39677	137.314	.23088	.32051	136.715	.22708
400							0.40237	139.122	0.23300	0.32523	138.540	0.22921
410							.40794	140.934	.23509	.32992	140.368	.23133

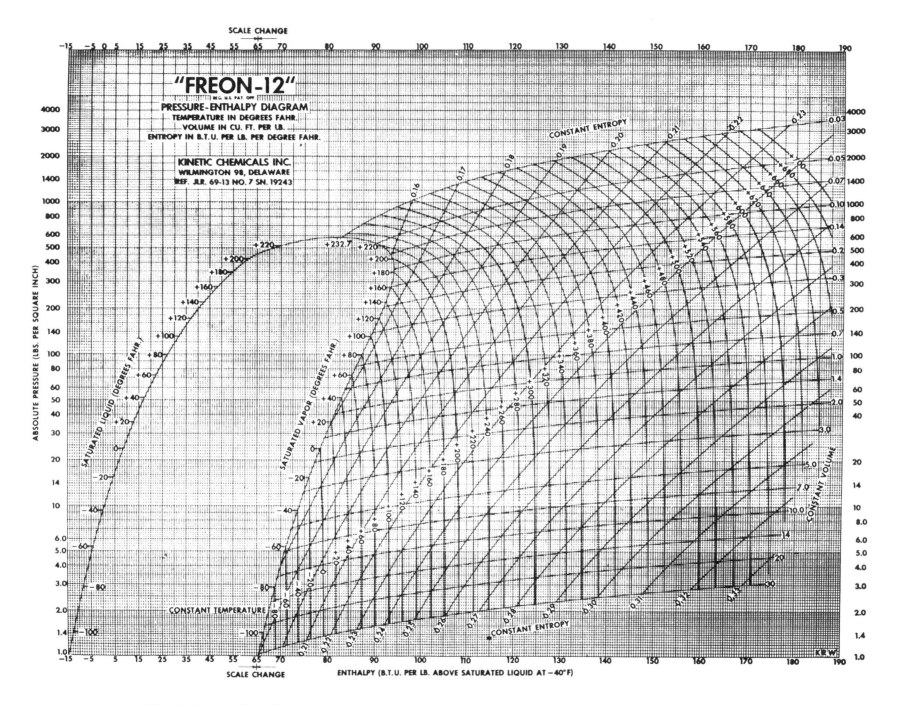

"FREON-12"
PRESSURE-ENTHALPY DIAGRAM
TEMPERATURE IN DEGREES FAHR.
VOLUME IN CU. FT. PER LB.
ENTROPY IN B.T.U. PER LB. PER DEGREE FAHR.

KINETIC CHEMICALS INC.
WILMINGTON 98, DELAWARE
REF. JLR. 69-13 NO. 7 SN. 19243

ENTHALPY (B.T.U. PER LB. ABOVE SATURATED LIQUID AT −40°F)

ABSOLUTE PRESSURE (LBS. PER SQUARE INCH)

From Thermodynamics, 2nd Ed., by F. P. Durham, Prentice-Hall, Inc., Englewood Cliffs, N.J., 1959.

TABLE A-13
GAS-CONSTANT VALUES

Gas	Chemical Formula	Molecular Weight	R ft lb$_f$ $\overline{lb°R}$	c_p Btu $\overline{lb°R}$ at 77°F	c_v Btu $\overline{lb°R}$ at 77°F	k $\dfrac{c_p}{c_v}$
Acetylene............	C_2H_2	26.02	59.39	0.361	0.285	1.27
Air.................	....	28.96	53.36	0.240	0.171	1.40
Ammonia............	NH_3	17.024	90.7	0.52	0.404	1.29
Argon...............	A	39.90	38.73	0.124	0.074	1.68
Butane..............	C_4H_{10}	58.08	26.61	0.406	0.372	1.09
Carbon dioxide.......	CO_2	44.00	35.12	0.201	0.156	1.29
Carbon monoxide......	CO	28.00	55.19	0.248	0.177	1.40
Dodecane............	$C_{12}H_{26}$	170.3	9.074	0.408	0.397	1.03
Ethane..............	C_2H_6	30.05	51.43	0.418	0.352	1.19
Ethylene............	C_2H_4	28.03	55.13	0.360	0.289	1.25
Helium..............	He	4.00	386.33	1.25	0.75	1.67
Hydrogen............	H_2	2.016	766.53	3.416	2.431	1.41
Methane.............	CH_4	16.03	96.40	0.532	0.408	1.30
Nitrogen............	N_2	28.02	55.15	0.248	0.177	1.40
Octane..............	C_8H_{18}	114.14	13.54	0.407	0.390	1.04
Oxygen..............	O_2	32.00	48.29	0.219	0.157	1.39
Propane.............	C_3H_8	44.06	35.07	0.398	0.353	1.13
Sulphur dioxide.......	SO_2	64.07	24.12	0.154	0.123	1.25
Water vapor..........	H_2O	18.01	85.6	0.445	0.335	1.33

TABLE A-14
CRITICAL CONSTANTS*

Substance	Formula	Molecular Weight	Temperature		Pressure		Volume. ft³/lb-mole
			K	°R	atm	lbf/in.²	
Ammonia	NH_3	17.03	405.5	729.8	111.3	1636	1.16
Argon	A	39.944	151	272	48.0	705	1.20
Bromine	Br_2	159.832	584	1052	102	1500	2.17
Carbon dioxide	CO_2	44.01	304.2	547.5	72.9	1071	1.51
Carbon monoxide	CO	28.01	133	240	34.5	507	1.49
Chlorine	Cl_2	70.914	417	751	76.1	1120	1.99
Deuterium (Normal)	D_2	4.00	38.4	69.1	16.4	241	....
Helium	He	4.003	5.3	9.5	2.26	33.2	0.926
Helium³	He	3.00	3.34	6.01	1.15	16.9	....
Hydrogen (Normal)	H_2	2.016	33.3	59.9	12.8	188.1	1.04
Krypton	Kr	83.7	209.4	376.9	54.3	798	1.48
Neon	Ne	20.183	44.5	80.1	26.9	395	0.668
Nitrogen	N_2	28.016	126.2	227.1	33.5	492	1.44
Nitrous oxide	N_2O	44.02	309.7	557.4	71.7	1054	1.54
Oxygen	O_2	32.00	154.8	278.6	50.1	736	1.25
Sulfur dioxide	SO_2	64.06	430.7	775.2	77.8	1143	1.95
Water	H_2O	18.016	647.4	1165.3	218.3	3208	0.90
Xenon	Xe	131.3	289.75	521.55	58.0	852	1.90
Benzene	C_6H_6	78.11	562	1012	48.6	714	4.17
n-Butane	C_4H_{10}	58.120	425.2	765.2	37.5	551	4.08
Carbon tetrachloride	CCl_4	153.84	556.4	1001.5	45.0	661	4.42
Chloroform	$CHCl_3$	119.39	536.6	965.8	54.0	794	3.85
Dichlorodifluoromethane	CCl_2F_2	120.92	384.7	692.4	39.6	582	3.49
Dichlorofluoromethane	$CHCl_2F$	102.93	451.7	813.0	51.0	749	3.16
Ethane	C_2H_5	30.068	305.5	549.8	48.2	708	2.37
Ethylalcohol	C_2H_5OH	46.07	516.0	929.0	63.0	926	2.68
Ethylene	C_2H_4	28.052	282.4	508.3	50.5	742	1.99
n-Hexane	C_6H_{14}	86.172	507.9	914.2	29.9	439	5.89
Methane	CH_4	16.042	191.1	343.9	45.8	673	1.59
Methyl alcohol	CH_3OH	32.04	513.2	923.7	78.5	1154	1.89
Methyl chloride	CH_3Cl	50.49	416.3	749.3	65.9	968	2.29
Propane	C_3H_8	44.094	370.0	665.9	42.0	617	3.20
Propene	C_3H_6	42.078	365.0	656.9	45.6	670	2.90
Propyne	C_3H_4	40.062	401	722	52.8	776	....
Trichlorofluoromethane	CCl_3F	137.38	471.2	848.1	43.2	635	3.97

*From *Fundamentals of Classical Thermodynamics* by G. J. Van Wylen and R. E. Sonntag, John Wiley & Sons, Inc., New York, 1965, p. 579, with permission.

TABLE A-15
THERMODYNAMIC PROPERTIES OF AIR AT LOW PRESSURE*

T, °R	h, Btu/lb	p_r	u, Btu/lb	v_r	ϕ Btu/lb°R
200	47.67	0.04320	33.96	1714.9	0.36303
220	52.46	0.06026	37.38	1352.5	0.38584
240	57.25	0.08165	40.80	1088.8	0.40666
260	62.03	0.10797	44.21	892.0	0.42582
280	66.82	0.13986	47.63	741.6	0.44356
300	71.61	0.17795	51.04	624.5	0.46007
320	76.40	0.22290	54.46	531.8	0.47550
340	81.18	0.27545	57.87	457.2	0.49002
360	85.97	0.3363	61.29	396.6	0.50369
380	90.75	0.4061	64.70	346.6	0.51663
400	95.53	0.4858	68.11	305.0	0.52890
420	100.32	0.5760	71.52	270.1	0.54058
440	105.11	0.6776	74.93	240.6	0.55172
460	109.90	0.7913	78.36	215.33	0.56235
480	114.69	0.9182	81.77	193.65	0.57255
500	119.48	1.0590	85.20	174.90	0.58233
520	124.27	1.2147	88.62	158.58	0.59173
540	129.06	1.3860	92.04	144.32	0.60078
560	133.86	1.5742	95.47	131.78	0.60950
580	138.66	1.7800	98.90	120.70	0.61793
600	143.47	2.005	102.34	110.88	0.62607
620	148.28	2.249	105.78	102.12	0.63395
640	153.09	2.514	109.21	94.30	0.64159
660	157.92	2.801	112.67	87.27	0.64902
680	162.73	3.111	116.12	80.96	0.65621
700	167.56	3.446	119.58	75.25	0.66321
720	172.39	3.806	123.04	70.07	0.67002
740	177.23	4.193	126.51	65.38	0.67665
760	182.08	4.607	129.99	61.10	0.68312
780	186.94	5.051	133.47	57.20	0.68942
800	191.81	5.526	136.97	53.63	0.69558
820	196.69	6.033	140.47	50.35	0.70160
840	201.56	6.573	143.98	47.34	0.70747
860	206.46	7.149	147.50	44.57	0.71323

*Abridged from Table 1 in *Gas Tables* by Joseph H. Keenan and Joseph Kaye, John Wiley & Sons, Inc., New York, 1948.

TABLE A-15
(CONT'D.)

T, °R	h, Btu/lb	p_r	u, Btu/lb	v_r	ϕ Btu/lb°R
880	211.35	7.761	151.02	42.01	0.71886
900	216.26	8.411	154.57	39.64	0.72438
920	221.18	9.102	158.12	37.44	0.72979
940	226.11	9.834	161.68	35.41	0.73509
960	231.06	10.610	165.26	33.52	0.74030
980	236.02	11.430	168.83	31.76	0.74540
1000	240.98	12.298	172.43	30.12	0.75042
1020	245.97	13.215	176.04	28.59	0.75536
1040	250.95	14.182	179.66	27.17	0.76019
1060	255.96	15.203	183.29	25.82	0.76496
1080	260.97	16.278	186.93	24.58	0.76964
1100	265.99	17.413	190.58	23.40	0.77426
1120	271.03	18.604	194.25	22.30	0.77880
1140	276.08	19.858	197.94	21.27	0.78326
1160	281.14	21.18	201.63	20.293	0.78767
1180	286.21	22.56	205.33	19.377	0.79201
1200	291.30	24.01	209.05	18.514	0.79628
1220	296.41	25.53	212.78	17.700	0.80050
1240	301.52	27.13	216.53	16.932	0.80466
1260	306.65	28.80	220.28	16.205	0.80876
1280	311.79	30.55	224.05	15.518	0.81280
1300	316.94	32.39	227.83	14.868	0.81680
1320	322.11	34.31	231.63	14.253	0.82075
1340	327.29	36.31	235.43	13.670	0.82464
1360	332.48	38.41	239.25	13.118	0.82848
1380	337.68	40.59	243.08	12.593	0.83229
1400	342.90	42.88	246.93	12.095	0.83604
1420	348.14	45.26	250.79	11.622	0.83975
1440	353.37	47.75	254.66	11.172	0.84341
1460	358.63	50.34	258.54	10.743	0.84704
1480	363.89	53.04	262.44	10.336	0.85062
1500	369.17	55.86	266.34	9.948	0.85416
1520	374.47	58.78	270.26	9.578	0.85767
1540	379.77	61.83	274.20	9.226	0.86113
1560	385.08	65.00	278.13	8.890	0.86456
1580	390.40	68.30	282.09	8.569	0.86794
1600	395.74	71.73	286.06	8.263	0.87130
1620	401.09	75.29	290.04	7.971	0.87462

TABLE A-15
(CONT'D.)

T, °R	h, Btu/lb	p_r	u, Btu/lb	v_r	ϕ Btu/lb°R
1640	406.45	78.99	294.03	7.691	0.87791
1660	411.82	82.83	298.02	7.424	0.83116
1680	417.20	86.82	302.04	7.168	0.88439
1700	422.59	90.95	306.06	6.924	0.88758
1720	428.00	95.24	310.09	6.690	0.89074
1740	433.41	99.69	314.13	6.465	0.89387
1760	438.83	104.30	318.18	6.251	0.89697
1780	444.26	109.08	322.24	6.045	0.90003
1800	449.71	114.03	326.32	5.847	0.90308
1820	455.17	119.16	330.40	5.658	0.90609
1840	460.63	124.47	334.50	5.476	0.90908
1860	466.12	129.95	338.61	5.302	0.91203
1880	471.60	135.64	342.73	5.134	0.91497
1900	477.09	141.51	346.85	4.974	0.91788
1920	482.60	147.59	350.98	4.819	0.92076
1940	488.12	153.87	355.12	4.670	0.92362
1960	493.64	160.37	359.28	4.527	0.92645
1980	499.17	167.07	363.43	4.390	0.92926
2000	504.71	174.00	367.61	4.258	0.93205
2020	510.26	181.16	371.79	4.130	0.93481
2040	515.82	188.54	375.98	4.008	0.93756
2060	521.39	196.16	380.18	3.890	0.94026
2080	526.97	204.02	384.39	3.777	0.94296
2100	532.55	212.1	388.60	3.667	0.94564
2120	538.15	220.5	392.83	3.561	0.94829
2140	543.74	229.1	397.05	3.460	0.95092
2160	549.35	238.0	401.29	3.362	0.95352
2180	554.97	247.2	405.53	3.267	0.95611
2200	560.59	256.6	409.78	3.176	0.95868
2220	566.23	266.3	414.05	3.088	0.96123
2240	571.86	276.3	418.31	3.003	0.96376
2260	577.51	286.6	422.59	2.921	0.96626
2280	583.16	297.2	426.87	2.841	0.96876
2300	588.82	308.1	431.16	2.765	0.97123
2320	594.49	319.4	435.46	2.691	0.97369
2340	600.16	330.9	439.76	2.619	0.97611
2360	605.84	342.8	444.07	2.550	0.97853
2380	611.53	355.0	448.38	2.483	0.98092
2400	617.22	367.6	452.70	2.419	0.98331

TABLE A-16

PROPERTIES OF SOME GASES AT LOW PRESSURE*

Temp °R	Products of Combustion, 400% Theoretical Air		Products of Combustion, 200% Theoretical Air		Nitrogen		Oxygen	
	$\bar{h}$	$\bar{\phi}$	$\bar{h}$	$\bar{\phi}$	$\bar{h}$	$\bar{\phi}$	$\bar{h}$	$\bar{\phi}$
537	3746.8	46.318	3774.9	46.300	3729.5	45.755	3725.1	48.986
600	4191.9	47.101	4226.3	47.094	4167.9	46.514	4168.3	49.762
700	4901.7	48.195	4947.7	48.207	4864.9	47.588	4879.3	50.858
800	5617.5	49.150	5676.3	49.179	5564.4	48.522	5602.0	51.821
900	6340.3	50.002	6413.0	50.047	6268.1	49.352	6337.9	52.688
1000	7072.1	50.773	7159.8	50.833	6977.9	50.099	7087.5	53.477
1100	7812.9	51.479	7916.4	51.555	7695.0	50.783	7850.4	54.204
1200	8563.4	52.132	8683.6	52.222	8420.0	51.413	8625.8	54.879
1300	9324.1	52.741	9461.7	52.845	9153.9	52.001	9412.9	55.508
1400	10095.0	53.312	10250.7	53.430	9896.9	52.551	10210.4	56.099
1500	10875.6	53.851	11050.2	53.981	10648.9	53.071	11017.1	56.656
1600	11665.6	54.360	11859.6	54.504	11409.7	53.561	11832.5	57.182
1700	12464.3	54.844	12678.6	55.000	12178.9	54.028	12655.6	57.680
1800	13271.7	55.306	13507.0	55.473	12956.3	54.472	13485.8	58.155
1900	14087.2	55.747	14344.1	55.926	13741.6	54.896	14322.1	58.607
2000	14910.3	56.169	15189.3	56.360	14534.4	55.303	15164.0	59.039
2100	15740.5	56.574	16042.4	56.777	15334.0	55.694	16010.9	59.451
2200	16577.1	56.964	16902.5	57.177	16139.8	56.068	16862.6	59.848
2300	17419.8	57.338	17769.3	57.562	16951.2	56.429	17718.8	60.228
2400	18268.0	57.699	18642.1	57.933	17767.9	56.777	18579.2	60.594
2500	19121.4	58.048	19520.7	58.292	18589.5	57.112	19443.4	60.946
2600	19979.7	58.384	20404.6	58.639	19415.8	57.436	20311.4	61.287
2700	20842.8	58.710	21293.8	58.974	20246.4	57.750	21182.9	61.616
2800	21709.8	59.026	22187.5	59.300	21081.1	58.053	22057.8	61.934
2900	22581.4	59.331	23086.0	59.615	21919.5	58.348	22936.1	62.242
3000	23456.6	59.628	23988.5	59.921	22761.5	58.632	23817.7	62.540
3100	24335.5	59.916	24895.3	60.218	23606.8	58.910	24702.5	62.831
3200	25217.8	60.196	25805.6	60.507	24455.0	59.179	25590.5	63.113
3300	26102.9	60.469	26719.2	60.789	25306.0	59.442	26481.6	63.386
3400	26991.4	60.734	27636.4	61.063	26159.7	59.697	27375.9	63.654
3500			28556.8	61.329	27015.9	59.944	28273.3	63.914
3600			29479.9	61.590	27874.4	60.186	29173.9	64.168
3700			30406.0	61.843	28735.1	60.422	30077.5	64.415
3800			31334.8	62.091	29597.9	60.652	30984.1	64.657
3900			32266.2	62.333	30462.8	60.877	31893.6	64.893
4000					31329.4	61.097	32806.1	65.123
4100					32198.0	61.310	33721.6	65.350
4200					33068.1	61.520	34639.9	65.571
4300					33939.9	61.726	35561.1	65.788
4400					34813.1	61.927	36485.0	66.000
4500					35687.8	62.123	37411.8	66.208
4600					36563.8	62.316	38341.4	66.413
4700					37441.1	62.504	39273.6	66.613
4800					38319.5	62.689	40208.6	66.809
4900					39199.1	62.870	41146.1	67.003
5000					40079.8	63.049	42086.3	67.193
5100					40961.6	63.223	43029.1	67.380
5200					41844.4	63.395	43974.3	67.562
5300					42728.3	63.563	44922.2	67.743

*Abridged from Tables 4, 7, 11, 13, 15, 17, 19, and 21 in _Gas Tables_ by Joseph H. Keenan and Joseph Kaye, John Wiley & Sons, Inc., New York, 1948.

$\bar{h}$ = enthalpy, Btu/lb mole

$$\phi = \int_{T=0}^{T} c_{P_0} \frac{dT}{T}, \ Btu/lb \ mole \ °R$$

ϕ is essentially equal to the absolute entropy at 1 atm pressure, Btu/lb mole °R.

TABLE A-16
(CONT'D.)

Temp °R	Water Vapor $\bar{h}$	Water Vapor $\bar{\phi}$	Carbon Dioxide $\bar{h}$	Carbon Dioxide $\bar{\phi}$	Hydrogen $\bar{h}$	Hydrogen $\bar{\phi}$	Carbon Monoxide $\bar{h}$	Carbon Monoxide $\bar{\phi}$
537	4258.3	45.079	4030.2	51.032	3640.3	31.194	3729.5	47.272
600	4764.7	45.970	4600.9	52.038	4075.6	31.959	3168.0	48.044
700	5575.4	47.219	5552.0	53.503	4770.2	33.031	4866.0	49.120
800	6396.9	48.316	6552.9	54.839	5467.1	33.961	5568.2	50.058
900	7230.9	49.298	7597.6	56.070	6165.3	34.784	6276.4	50.892
1000	8078.9	50.191	8682.1	57.212	6864.5	35.520	6992.2	51.646
1100	8942.0	51.013	9802.6	58.281	7564.6	36.188	7716.8	52.337
1200	9820.4	51.777	10955.3	59.283	8265.8	36.798	8450.8	52.976
1300	10714.5	52.494	12136.9	60.229	8968.7	37.360	9194.6	53.571
1400	11624.8	53.168	13344.7	61.124	9673.8	37.883	9948.1	54.129
1500	12551.4	53.808	14576.0	61.974	10381.5	38.372	10711.1	54.655
1600	13494.9	54.418	15829.0	62.783	11092.5	38.830	11483.4	55.154
1700	14455.4	54.999	17101.4	63.555	11807.4	39.264	12264.3	55.628
1800	15433.0	55.559	18391.5	64.292	12526.8	39.675	13053.2	56.078
1900	16427.5	56.097	19697.8	64.999	13250.9	40.067	13849.8	56.509
2000	17439.0	56.617	21018.7	65.676	13980.1	40.441	14653.2	56.922
2100	18466.9	57.119	22352.7	66.327	14714.5	40.799	15463.3	57.317
2200	19510.8	57.605	23699.0	66.953	15454.4	41.143	16279.4	57.696
2300	20570.6	58.077	25056.3	67.557	16199.8	41.475	17101.0	58.062
2400	21645.7	58.535	26424.0	68.139	16950.6	41.794	17927.4	58.414
2500	22735.4	58.980	27801.2	68.702	17707.3	42.104	18758.8	58.754
2600	23839.5	59.414	29187.1	69.245	18469.7	42.403	19594.3	59.081
2700	24957.2	59.837	30581.2	69.771	19237.8	42.692	20434.0	59.398
2800	26088.0	60.248	31982.8	70.282	20011.8	42.973	21277.2	59.705
2900	27231.2	60.650	33391.5	70.776	20791.5	43.247	22123.8	60.002
3000	28386.3	61.043	34806.6	71.255	21576.9	43.514	22973.4	60.290
3100	29552.8	61.426	36227.9	71.722	22367.7	43.773	23826.0	60.569
3200	30730.2	61.801	37654.7	72.175	23164.1	44.026	24681.2	60.841
3300	31918.2	62.167	39086.7	72.616	23965.5	44.273	25539.0	61.105
3400	33116.0	62.526	40523.6	73.045	24771.9	44.513	26399.3	61.362
3500	34323.5	62.876	41965.2	73.462	25582.9	44.748	27261.8	61.612
3600	35540.1	63.221	43411.0	73.870	26398.5	44.978	28126.6	61.855
3700	36765.4	63.557	44860.6	74.267	27218.5	45.203	28993.5	62.093
3800	37998.9	63.887	46314.0	74.655	28042.8	45.423	29862.3	62.325
3900	39240.2	64.210	47771.0	75.033	28871.1	45.638	30732.9	62.551
4000	40489.1	64.528	49231.4	75.404	29703.5	45.849	31605.2	62.772
4100	41745.4	64.839	50695.1	75.765	30539.8	46.056	32479.1	62.988
4200	43008.4	65.144	52162.0	76.119	31379.8	46.257	33354.4	63.198
4300	44278.0	65.444	53632.1	76.464	32223.5	46.456	34231.2	63.405
4400	45553.9	65.738	55105.1	76.803	33070.9	46.651	35109.2	63.607
4500	46835.9	66.028	56581.0	77.135	33921.6	46.842	35988.6	63.805
4600	48123.6	66.312	58059.7	77.460	34775.7	47.030	36869.3	63.998
4700	49416.9	66.591	59541.1	77.779	35633.0	47.215	37751.0	64.188
4800	50715.5	66.866	61024.9	78.091	36493.4	47.396	38633.9	64.374
4900	52019.0	67.135	62511.3	78.398	37356.9	47.574	39517.8	64.556
5000	53327.4	67.401	64000.0	78.698	38223.3	47.749	40402.7	64.735
5100	54640.3	67.662	65490.9	78.994	39092.8	47.921	41288.6	64.910
5200	55957.4	67.918	66984.0	79.284	39965.1	48.090	42175.5	65.082
5300	57278.7	68.172	68479.1	79.569	40840.2	48.257	43063.2	65.252

TABLE A-17
ONE-DIMENSIONAL ISENTROPIC COMPRESSIBLE-FLOW FUNCTIONS FOR AN
IDEAL GAS WITH CONSTANT SPECIFIC HEAT AND MOLECULAR WEIGHT AND $k=1.4$[†]

M	M^*	$\dfrac{A}{A^*}$	$\dfrac{P}{P_o}$	$\dfrac{\rho}{\rho_o}$	$\dfrac{T}{T_o}$
0	0	∞	1.00000	1.00000	1.00000
0.10	0.10943	5.8218	0.99303	0.99502	0.99800
0.20	0.21822	2.9635	0.97250	0.98027	0.99206
0.30	0.32572	2.0351	0.93947	0.95638	0.98232
0.40	0.43133	1.5901	0.89562	0.92428	0.96899
0.50	0.53452	1.3398	0.84302	0.88517	0.95238
0.60	0.63480	1.1882	0.78400	0.84045	0.93284
0.70	0.73179	1.09437	0.72092	0.79158	0.91075
0.80	0.82514	1.03823	0.65602	0.74000	0.88652
0.90	0.91460	1.00886	0.59126	0.68704	0.86058
1.00	1.00000	1.00000	0.52828	0.63394	0.83333
1.10	1.08124	1.00793	0.46835	0.58169	0.80515
1.20	1.1583	1.03044	0.41238	0.53114	0.77640
1.30	1.2311	1.06631	0.36092	0.48291	0.74738
1.40	1.2999	1.1149	0.31424	0.43742	0.71839
1.50	1.3646	1.1762	0.27240	0.39498	0.68965
1.60	1.4254	1.2502	0.23527	0.35573	0.66138
1.70	1.4825	1.3376	0.20259	0.31969	0.63372
1.80	1.5360	1.4390	0.17404	0.28682	0.60680
1.90	1.5861	1.5552	0.14924	0.25699	0.58072
2.00	1.6330	1.6875	0.12780	0.23005	0.55556
2.10	1.6769	1.8369	0.10935	0.20580	0.53135
2.20	1.7179	2.0050	0.09352	0.18405	0.50813
2.30	1.7563	2.1931	0.07997	0.16458	0.48591
2.40	1.7922	2.4031	0.06840	0.14720	0.46468
2.50	1.8258	2.6367	0.05853	0.13169	0.44444
2.60	1.8572	2.8960	0.05012	0.11787	0.42517
2.70	1.8865	3.1830	0.04295	0.10557	0.40684
2.80	1.9140	3.5001	0.03685	0.09462	0.38941
2.90	1.9398	3.8498	0.03165	0.08489	0.37286
3.00	1.9640	4.2346	0.02722	0.07623	0.35714
3.50	2.0642	6.7896	0.01311	0.04523	0.28986
4.00	2.1381	10.719	0.00658	0.02766	0.23810
4.50	2.1936	16.562	0.00346	0.01745	0.19802
5.00	2.2361	25.000	$189(10)^{-5}$	0.01134	0.16667
6.00	2.2953	53.180	$633(10)^{-6}$	0.00519	0.12195
7.00	2.3333	104.143	$242(10)^{-6}$	0.00261	0.09259
8.00	2.3591	190.109	$102(10)^{-6}$	0.00141	0.07246
9.00	2.3772	327.189	$474(10)^{-7}$	0.000815	0.05814
10.00	2.3904	535.938	$236(10)^{-7}$	0.000495	0.04762
∞	2.4495	∞	0	0	0

[†]*Abridged from Table 30 in* Gas Tables *by Joseph H. Keenan and Joseph Kaye, John Wiley & Sons, Inc., New York, 1948.*

TABLE A-18

NORMAL TOTAL EMISSIVITY OF VARIOUS SURFACES*

Surfaces	°F	ε
A. Metals and Their Oxides		
Aluminum:		
Highly polished plate, 98.3% pure	440, 1070	0.039, 0.057
Polished plate	73	0.040
Rough plate	78	0.055
Oxidized at 1110° F	390, 1110	0.11, 0.19
Al-surfaced roofing	110	0.216
Al-treated surfaces, heated at 1110° F:		
Copper	390, 1110	0.18, 0.19
Steel	390, 1110	0.52, 0.57
Brass:		
Highly polished:		
73.2% Cu, 26.7% Zn, by weight	476, 674	0.028, 0.031
62.4% Cu, 36.8% Zn, 0.4% Pb, 0.3% Al, by weight	494, 710	0.0388, 0.037
82.9% Cu, 17.0% Zn, by weight	530	0.030
Hard-rolled, polished, but direction of polishing		
visible	70	0.038
But somewhat attacked	73	0.043
But traces of stearin from polish left on	75	0.053
Polished	100, 600	0.096, 0.096
Rolled plate:		
Natural surface	72	0.06
Rubbed with coarse emery	72	0.20
Dull plate	120, 660	0.22
Oxidized by heating at 1110° F	390, 1110	0.61, 0.59
Chromium:		
See Nickel Alloys for Ni-Cr steels		
Copper:		
Carefully polished electrolytic Cu	176	0.018
Commercial, emeried, polished, but pits remaining	66	0.030
Scraped shiny, but not mirrorlike	72	0.072
Polished	242	0.023
Plate heated at 1110° F	390, 1110	0.57, 0.57
Cuprous oxide	1470, 2010	0.66, 0.54
Plate, heated for a long time, covered with thick		
oxide layer	77	0.78
Molten copper	1970, 2330	0.16, 0.13
Gold:		
Pure, highly polished	440, 1160	0.018, 0.035
Iron and steel:		
Metallic surfaces (or very thin oxide layer):		
Electrolytic iron, highly polished	350, 440	0.052, 0.074
Polished iron	800, 1880	0.144, 0.377
Iron freshly emeried	68	0.242
Cast iron, polished	392	0.21
Wrought iron, highly polished	100, 480	0.28
Cast iron, newly turned	72	0.435
Polished steel casting	1420, 1900	0.52, 0.56
Ground sheet steel	1720, 2010	0.55, 0.61
Smooth sheet iron	1650, 1900	0.55, 0.60
Cast iron, turned on lathe	1620, 1810	0.60, 0.70
Oxidized surfaces:		
Iron plate, pickled, then rusted red	68	0.612
Then completely rusted	67	0.685
Rolled sheet steel	70	0.657
Oxidized iron	212	0.736
Cast iron, oxidized at 1100° F	390, 1110	0.64, 0.78
Steel oxidized at 1100° F	390, 1110	0.79, 0.79
Smooth, oxidized electrolytic iron	260, 980	0.78, 0.82
Iron oxide	930, 2190	0.85, 0.89
Rough ingot iron	1700, 2040	0.87, 0.95

*From _Introduction to Heat Transfer,_ 3rd Ed., by A. I. Brown and S. M. Marco, McGraw-Hill Book Co., New York, 1958, pp. 54–58, with permission.

TABLE A-18

(CONT'D.)

Surfaces	°F	ε
Sheet steel, strong rough oxide layer	75	0.80
Dense shiny oxide layer	75	0.82
Cast plate:		
Smooth	73	0.80
Rough	73	0.82
Cast iron, rough, strongly oxidized	100, 480	0.95
Wrought iron, dull-oxidized	70, 680	0.94
Steel plate, rough	100, 700	0.94, 0.97
High-temperature alloy steels; see Nickel alloys		
Molten metals:		
Molten cast iron	2370, 2550	0.29, 0.29
Molten mild steel	2910, 3270	0.28, 0.28
Lead:		
Pure (99.96%) unoxidized	260, 440	0.057, 0.075
Gray oxidized	75	0.281
Oxidized at 390°F	390	0.63
Mercury, pure clean	32, 212	0.09, 0.12
Molybdenum filament	1340, 4700	0.096, 0.292
Ni-Cu alloy, oxidized at 1110°F	390, 1110	0.41, 0.46
Nickel:		
Electroplated on polished iron, then polished	74	0.045
Technically pure (98.9% Ni by weight, + Mn),		
polished	440, 710	0.07, 0.087
Electroplated on pickled iron, not polished	68	0.11
Wire.....................................	368, 1844	0.096, 0.186
Plate, oxidized by heating at 1110°F	390, 1110	0.37, 0.48
Nickel oxide	1200, 2290	0.59, 0.86
Nickel alloys:		
Cr-Ni alloy	125, 1894	0.64, 0.76
(18-32% Ni, 55-68% Cu, 20% Zn by weight), gray		
oxidized	70	0.262
Alloy steel (8% Ni, 18% Cr); light silvery, rough;		
brown after heating	420, 914	0.44, 0.36
Same, after 24 hr heating at 980°F	420, 980	0.62, 0.73
Alloy (20% Ni, 25% Cr), brown, splotched, oxidized		
from service	420, 980	0.90, 0.97
Alloy (60% Ni, 12% Cr), smooth, black, firm adhesive		
oxide coat from service	520, 1045	0.89, 0.82
Platinum:		
Pure, polished plate	440, 1160	0.054, 0.104
Strip	1700, 2960	0.12, 0.17
Filament	80, 2240	0.036, 0.192
Wire	440, 2510	0.073, 0.182
Silver:		
Polished, pure	440, 1160	0.0198, 0.0324
Polished	100, 700	0.0221, 0.0312
Steel, see Iron		
Tantalum filament	2420, 4580	0.193, 0.31
Tin, bright, tinned iron sheet	76	0.043, 0.064
Tungsten:		
Filament, aged	80, 6000	0.032, 0.35
Filament	6000	0.39
Zinc:		
Commercial, 99.1% pure, polished	440, 620	0.045, 0.053
Oxidized by heating at 750°F	750	0.11
Galvanized sheet iron:		
Fairly bright	82	0.228
Gray, oxidized	75	0.276

B. Refractories, Building Materials, Paints, and Miscellaneous

Asbestos board	74	0.96
Asbestos paper	100, 700	0.93, 0.945
Brick:		
Red, rough, but no gross irregularities	70	0.93
Silica unglazed, rough	1832	0.80

TABLE A-18
(CONT'D.)

Surfaces	°F	ε
Silica, glazed, rough	2012	0.85
Grog brick, glazed	2012	0.75
See Refractory materials, below		
Carbon:		
T-carbon, 0.9% ash	260, 1160	0.81, 0.79
Carbon filament	1900, 2560	0.526
Candle soot	206, 520	0.952
Lampblack:		
Water-glass coating	209, 362	0.959, 0.947
Water-glass coating	260, 440	0.957, 0.952
Thin layer on iron plate	69	0.927
Thick coat	68	0.967
0.003 in. or thicker	100, 700	0.945
Enamel, white, fused on iron	66	0.897
Glass, smooth	72	0.937
Gypsum, 0.02 in. thick or smooth on blackened plate	70	0.903
Marble, light gray, polished	72	0.931
Oak, planed	70	0.895
Oil layers on polished nickel (lubricating oil):		
Polished surface alone	68	0.045
+0.001 in. oil	68	0.27
+0.002 in. oil	68	0.46
+0.005 in. oil	68	0.72
+ ∞	68	0.82
Oil layers on aluminum foil (linseed oil):		
Aluminum foil	212	0.087
+1 coat oil	212	0.561
+2 coats oil	212	0.574
Paints, lacquers, varnishes:		
Snow-white enamel varnish on rough iron plate	73	0.906
Black shiny lacquer, sprayed on iron	76	0.875
Black shiny shellac on tinned iron sheet	70	0.821
Black-matte shellac	170, 295	0.91
Black lacquer	100, 200	0.80, 0.95
Flat black lacquer	100, 200	0.96, 0.98
White lacquer	100, 200	0.80, 0.95
Oil paints, 16 different, all colors	212	0.92, 0.96
Aluminum paints and lacquers:		
10% Al, 22% lacquer body, on rough or smooth surface	212	0.52
26% Al, 27% lacquer body, on rough or smooth surface	212	0.30
Other aluminum paints, varying age and Al content	212	0.27, 0.67
Aluminum lacquer, varnish binder, on rough plate	70	0.39
Aluminum paint, after heating to 620°F	300, 600	0.35
Paper, thin:		
Pasted on tinned iron plate	66	0.924
Pasted on rough iron plate	66	0.929
Pasted on black lacquered plate	66	0.944
Plaster, rough, lime	50, 190	0.91
Porcelain, glazed	72	0.924
Quartz, rough, fused	70	0.932
Refractory materials, 40 different	1110, 1830	
Poor radiators	....	0.65, 0.75
		0.70
Good radiators	....	0.80, 0.85
		0.85, 0.90
Roofing paper	69	0.91
Rubber:		
Hard, glossy plate	74	0.945
Soft, gray, rough (reclaimed)	76	0.859
Serpentine, polished	74	0.900
Water	32, 212	0.95, 0.963

index

Irving Granet is Associate Professor of Mechanical Technology at Queensborough Community College and Associate Professor of Mechanical Engineering Technology at the New York Institute of Technology. A licensed professional engineer, he has also published several books and over 60 technical papers on a variety of engineering topics. Professor Granet is listed in the National Register of Scientific Personnel, American Men of Science, and Who's Who in World Engineering.